Decorative Arts

1850-1950

A Catalogue of the British Museum Collection

Judy Rudoe

Decorative Arts
1850-1950

A Catalogue of the British Museum Collection

PUBLISHED FOR THE TRUSTEES OF THE BRITISH MUSEUM BY
BRITISH MUSEUM PRESS

© 1991 The Trustees of the British Museum
Published by British Museum Press
A division of British Museum Publications Ltd
46 Bloomsbury Street, London WC1B 3QQ

Revised paperback edition 1994

British Library Cataloguing in Publication Data

British Museum
    Decorative arts 1850-1950 : a catalogue
of the British Museum collection.
I. Title   II. Rudoe, Judy
745.074

ISBN 0-7141-0567-8

Designed by Andrew Shoolbred

Printed in Great Britain by
BAS Printers Limited
Over Wallop, Hampshire

Contents

The Trustees of the British Museum
acknowledge with gratitude generous assistance
towards the production of this book from

The Fine Art Society PLC
Nicholas Harris of The Silver & Decorative Arts Gallery
John Jesse Ltd
The Keatley Trust
I. J. Mazure & Company Ltd
Paul Reeves

Preface

The Modern Collection has been built up for the most part by gift and purchase over the past decade. Already by 1978 the Department of Medieval and Later Antiquities possessed some significant material from the period c.1850 onwards, but most of it had arrived by gift, so that it formed a haphazard collection. Among the more interesting of these gifts were a huge Sèvres presentation vase offered by the French government in 1901 (Cat. 80), a group of Bernard Moore flambé wares given by the artist in 1902 (Cat. 199-204), seven pieces of Whitefriars glass presented by the firm in 1923 (Cat. 234, 235a, 237-41) and a group of Martinware bequeathed in 1945 (included within Cat. 158-62). The many other early acquisitions can be found by looking for the year of acquisition, which is the first figure of the registration number.

The arrival in 1978 of the Hull Grundy Gift (of which a separate catalogue has already been published) brought the Museum's collections of jewellery into the twentieth century and gave us works designed by William Burges, Omar Ramsden, Harold Stabler, René Lalique and Tiffany & Co. Already some modern horological material had been acquired. At the same time initiatives had begun in the Departments of Coins and Medals, Prints and Drawings, Ethnography and Oriental Antiquities to extend their collections into the modern period. A curator for the modern collections had been appointed in the Department of Prints and Drawings in 1975. First under the directorship of Sir John Pope-Hennessy, who retired in 1976, and then under his successor, Sir David Wilson, the question was put as to whether the decorative arts should follow suit. In 1979 the Trustees took the decision that the post-medieval collections of the Department of Medieval and Later Antiquities should be actively extended into the twentieth century. As a result a new assistant-keeper post was created, and Mr Michael Collins appointed to it in October. A purchase fund of £15,000 towards the Modern Collection was allocated from the Trustees' central acquisitions fund in the first year, and now stands at £20,000. The Trustees have also contributed additional sums from the central fund in the case of a number of outstanding individual items.

The decision to confine the new collection to the fields of ceramics, glass and metalwork was a corollary of their purpose as an extension of the existing collections. The Department of Medieval and Later Antiquities has never systematically collected sculpture, textiles or furniture, so there was nothing to build on in these areas. In the same way, the question of what modern ceramics, glass or metalwork to acquire was also settled by the character of the existing collections. The British Museum's collections of post-medieval decorative arts have a very different emphasis from those of the Victoria and Albert Museum in their concentration on documentary pieces: to take only one example, at the time of the Bernal sale in 1855 the Victoria and Albert Museum acquired maiolica for its design qualities, while the British Museum sought out signed and dated pieces. Thus in building the Modern Collection an effort has been made to find documented pieces by artists and manufacturers, and this on an international basis, both in Europe and America. In this catalogue the emphasis is placed on the documentation for each piece, and particularly since a significant number were included in international exhibitions of the late nineteenth and early twentieth centuries. The decision not to pursue the development of the collection beyond the end of the 1940s also follows from the British Museum's character as a historical collection. In due course the collection will be extended to include later years (indeed the beginnings of such a development have already been made), but always after the lapse of some decades.

By 1982 the collection had already grown sufficiently for a gallery to be converted for its display. By the summer of 1986, when Mr Michael Collins resigned from the service of the Museum, the bulk of the collection catalogued here had already been acquired, and it had already been given its distinctive shape. Mr Collins's book *Towards Post-Modernism: Design since 1851* was published by British Museum Publications in 1987.

The development of the Modern Collection since 1986 has been the responsibility of Miss Judy Rudoe, whose contribution has been major in the field of acquisitions. In 1987 the Trustees felt that the collection was already worthy of a full-scale catalogue and Miss Rudoe has worked to complete the volume in the last two to three years. A glance at the illustrations will immediately pinpoint the strengths of the collection: most striking are the groups of German and American material, much of which is rare outside the country of origin; within the British sphere, the twenty-five pieces designed by Christopher Dresser are outstanding, perhaps the best representation of his work in any public collection and a reflection of Michael Collins's enthusiasm for Dresser's work.

The 336 entries in this catalogue include the acquisitions made between 1979 and the end of 1989, together with a selection of earlier acquisitions that are relevant to its theme. An appendix lists the new acquisitions made in 1990. Certain areas have been omitted. The jewellery in the Hull Grundy Gift has already been described in the catalogue of that collection. Nineteenth-century French porcelain will be included in Miss Aileen Dawson's forthcoming catalogue of the French porcelain in the British Museum, and other nineteenth-century Wedgwood is in her *Masterpieces of Wedgwood in the British Museum*, 1984. Clocks and watches have always been collected by the Museum primarily as exemplifying technical developments, and the Montague Guest collection of badges, passes and tokens hardly falls within any traditional category of the decorative arts. The large collection of Victorian tiles (acquired to complement the outstanding collection of medieval tiles already in the Museum) will be catalogued in a separate publication; a few German tiles have been included here (Cat. 138 and recent acquisitions Cat. 339).

The publication of this catalogue has been timed to coincide with the exhibition in 1991 of twentieth-century acquisitions made by the British Museum during the directorship of Sir David Wilson. The development of these collections in the different Departments of the Museum would not have been possible without his enthusiasm and support, and I therefore hope that he will regard this catalogue as a suitable tribute on the occasion of his retirement.

Neil Stratford
Keeper of the Department of Medieval and Later Antiquities

Preface to the revised paperback edition 1994

The opportunity to reprint this catalogue has allowed a few corrections to be made to the original text. Such corrections will be found on pages 22 (Cat. 27), 29 (Cat. 41-2), 31 (Cat. 50), 36 (Cat. 58), 40 (Cat. 80), 46 (Cat. 101), 67-8 (Cat. 147-50), 75 (Cat. 184) and 82 (Cat. 214). Addenda to the first edition, comprising new information and bibliography to 1993, appears on pages 142-4. Short entries for acquisitions made between 1991 and 1993 (Cat. 362-448) have been added on pages 304-27. The list of Designers and Companies with Entries in the Catalogue (pp. 11-12), the Concordance (pp. 328-30), the Index of Contemporary Exhibitions (p. 331) and the General Index have been revised accordingly.

Introduction

The catalogue is organised alphabetically by designer or manufacturer, regardless of country. A complete list by country is given on pages 11-12. At the end are two indices: of contemporary exhibitions in which the pieces (or related objects) were included, and a general index. All items are illustrated: the plates have been grouped classifying related material together as far as possible in a chronological sequence. All signatures and factory marks on objects are reproduced in catalogue order in a separate group of plates.

The following format has been adopted in the catalogue entries. After the names and dates of the designer (or manufacturer) is given a chronological bibliography of general publications, either monographs or articles, relating to the artist or manufacturer. These are either given in full, or in abbreviated form: in the latter case, the full reference will be found in the general bibliography. No attempt has been made to give a biography when one is readily available in such standard reference books as Simon Jervis, *The Penguin Dictionary of Design and Designers*, London 1984, nor are references to such works given. Nevertheless, when little has been published on artists, or when there is nothing in English, or when what there is is relatively inaccessible, a short account of their careers has been given: so, for example, in the case of Jacob Bang. In entries where the main heading is an artist, literature on the manufacturer involved is given at the end of the entry.

Within each entry an attempt has been made to locate the object in its historical context, and to elucidate the circumstances which gave rise to its creation. Wherever possible, original sources have been checked, and this has allowed a number of mistakes commonly found in recent literature to be corrected. If an item has a provenance from a significant patron or collector, some information about them has been given.

Apart from published modern writing, the information in this catalogue has been derived from three main sources. The first is contemporary periodicals and exhibition catalogues; a list of contemporary periodicals consulted is given in the general bibliography. Many of these and other early publications are extremely scarce, and I am grateful to the British Library, the Victoria and Albert Museum Library, the Metropolitan Museum of Art in New York, the Zentralinstitut für Kunstgeschichte in Munich, the Germanisches Nationalmuseum in Nuremberg, the Bibliothèque des Arts Décoratifs and the Kunstindustrimuseum in Copenhagen for allowing me access to them.

The second source is the surviving archives relating to some of the firms and artists included. Their archivists and custodians have been unfailingly helpful, and I must thank them all here. In Britain, I am indebted to Wendy Evans of the Museum of London (Powell archive), Sharon Gater of the Wedgwood Museum in Barlaston, Rachel Heath of Birmingham Public Library Archives Department, Joan Jones of Royal Doulton (Minton archive), Pamela Robertson of the Hunterian Museum and Art Gallery (Mackintosh collections), S. Thompson of Royal Brierley Crystal, Hilary Wade of the Dorman Museum in Middlesbrough (Linthorpe Pottery) and Rachel Watson of Northampton County Archive (Godwin); in France, Christiane Jolly of the Musée Bouilhet-Christofle, Paris; in Germany, A.M. Ittstein of Schott Glaswerke in Mainz, Frau Kitzing of the Staatliche Majolika-Manufaktur in Karlsruhe, Christine v. Mengden of the Architektursammlung der Technische Universität in Munich (Riemerschmid designs), Stephan Freiherr von Poschinger of the Poschinger'sche Krystallglasfabrik in Frauenau, Doris

Rangnick of the AEG in Berlin, Elizabeth Schmuttermeier of the Museum für angewandte Kunst in Vienna (Wiener Werkstätte archive), Christina Thon of the Berlin Kunstbibliothek (Olbrich Archive), W. Vollmer of the Theresienthal Krystallglas- und Porzellanmanufaktur; in Denmark, Michael von Essen of the Georg Jensen Museum, Mogens Schlüter of Holmegaards Glasvaerker; in Holland, H. Bordewijk of the Gemeentearchief in The Hague (Rozenburg); in the United States, Bertha Stevenson of the Van Briggle Pottery in Colorado Springs, Janet Zapata of the Tiffany Archive in New York.

Thirdly, I have been assisted by many colleagues, collectors and other scholars working in this field. The following curators have shown me items in their care, and helped me with information concerning them: Marc Bascou of the Musée d'Orsay in Paris, Stella Beddoe of the Brighton Museum and Art Gallery, Reinier Baarsen and Gertie van Berge of the Rijksmuseum in Amsterdam, Elisabeth Bornfleth of the former Gewerbemuseum in Nuremberg, Simon Cottle, formerly of Glasgow Museum and Art Gallery, James Draper, Alice Cooney Frelinghuysen, Frances Gruber-Safford, Craig Miller and Jane Adlin of the Metropolitan Museum of Art in New York, Marianne Ertberg of the Kunstindustrimuseum in Copenhagen, Irmela Franzke of the Badisches Landesmuseum in Karlsruhe, Halina Graham of the Cecil Higgins Art Gallery in Bedford, Richard Gray and Lesley Jackson of Manchester City Art Gallery, Florian Hufnagel and Hans Wichmann of the Neue Sammlung in Munich, Michael Koch of the Bayerisches Nationalmuseum in Munich, Randi Nerdinger of the Munich Stadtmuseum, Jean-Luc Olivié and Evelyne Possémé of the Musée des Arts Décoratifs in Paris, Claus Pese and Ursula Peters of the Germanisches Nationalmuseum in Nuremberg, Heike Schröder of the Württembergisches Landesmuseum in Stuttgart, and Matthew Williams of Cardiff Castle.

Many other curators, dealers and collectors have answered my enquiries: Victor Arwas, Audrey Baker, Keith Baker, Roger Billcliffe, Brian Cargin and Chris Morley, J.D. van Dam of the Gemeentelijk Museum het Princessehof in Leeuwarden, Beth Cathers, Anita Ellis of the Cincinnati Art Museum, Fifty/50 Gallery in New York, Charlotte Gere, Denis Galleon and Daniel Morris, Charles Hajdamach and Roger Dodsworth of Broadfield House Glass Museum, Nicholas Harris and Peter Jeffs, Karl Bernd Heppe of the Düsseldorf Stadtmuseum, Widar Halén, Jeanette Hayhurst, Margarete Jarchow, John Jesse and Irina Laski, Rüdiger Joppien of the Museum für Kunst und Gewerbe in Hamburg, Anne Lajoix, Frans Leidelmeijer, Reino Liefkes, Nina Lobanov-Rostovsky, Alfred Löhr of the Bremer Landesmuseum, Neil McCain, Félix Marcilhac, Ivor Mazure, Chantal Meslin-Perrier of the Musée Adrien Dubouché in Limoges, Gillian Naylor, Judy Neiswander (now of the Fogg Art Museum), Barbara Morris, Geoffrey Munn, Ray Notley, Paul Reeves, Helmut Ricke of the Kunstmuseum Düsseldorf, Peter Rose and Albert Gallichan, Reinhard Sänger of the Badisches Landesmuseum in Karlsruhe, Simon Schmidt, John Scott, John Smith, Kenneth Snowman, Gerald Stiebel and Penelope Hunter Stiebel, Christine Thomas of the British Library's Slavonic section, Michael Whiteway, Albrecht Widmann, Eva Zeisel, and G. Zelleke of the Carnegie Museum of Art, Pittsburgh. Many other people who gave help are thanked in individual entries.

I owe special thanks to David Kiehl of the Metropolitan Museum in New York, who has given exceptional help and encouragement, and to Graham Dry and Beate Dry-von Zezschwitz, who read and commented on all the entries for the German material, and gave me large quantities of new information and references.

It goes without saying that work on this catalogue has required the help of many colleagues in the Victoria and Albert Museum, and in particular of Anne Eatwell, Richard Edgcumbe, Jennifer Opie, Eric Turner and Christopher Wilk.

Within the British Museum, I am grateful for the help of many colleagues in my own and other departments of the Museum, who are too numerous to list. The photographs reproduced here were taken by Ivor Kerslake, Christi Graham, Anthony Milton, John Heffron, Peter Stringer and David Agar. The index of marks, monograms and signatures was designed by Jim Farrant. The objects were cleaned and restored by the Metals and Ceramics Conservation sections, whose members gave me much valuable assistance in discussing the techniques used in manufacture. Technical analysis of various items was carried out by Susan La Niece of the Research Laboratory and information from the Museum Archive was supplied by Christopher Date. At British Museum Press the catalogue has been expertly edited and produced by Teresa Francis and Julie Young.

Finally, I have used much material on Copeland, Taxile Doat, Paul Follot, Bernard Moore, Sèvres, Wedgwood and Worcester assembled by Aileen Dawson, who was responsible for acquiring many of these pieces.

Judy Rudoe
October 1990

Designers and Companies with Entries in the Catalogue

References are to catalogue numbers. Nos 362-448 are new acquisitions 1991-93 (pp. 304-27)

The Catalogue

Aalto, Alvar 1898-1976

There is a vast body of literature on Aalto; the selection of recent publications listed below all discuss his glass designs and give further bibliography.

Schildt, G., *Aalto, The Decisive Years*, New York 1986, 136-9
Rubino, L., *Aino e Alvar Aalto: tutto il design*, Rome 1980, 146-51
Alvar Aalto: Furniture and Glass, exhibition catalogue, New York, Museum of Modern Art, 1984, J.S. Johnson

1 Vase [PLATE 122]

Clear glass, mould-blown with polished rim, vertical walls with fluid curves forming a sinuous outline.

MARKS Incised on the base 'ALVAR AALTO'.

Designed in 1936 and made by Iittala Glassworks, Finland. This example (shape no. 3030) is a recent production.

H 30 cm 1982,12-5,1

Aalto's glass designs were all made in response to competitions, firstly, in 1932, when the Karhula and the Iittala Glassworks held a joint competition for new glassware, and then in 1933, when Riihimäki Glassworks invited him to enter a competition for the Milan Triennale of that year. The 1932 designs were not put into production, but the Riihimäki flower, a series of nesting bowls, was highly successful.

This vase is from the series designed for the Karhula-Iittala competition of 1936, held to encourage new models for the 1937 Paris Exhibition. Aalto gave this series the code name 'Eskimoerindens skinnbyxa' (Eskimo girl's leather breeches), but this particular vase is known as the 'Savoy' vase after the Helsinki restaurant for which Aalto designed the interior and furnishings incorporating vases from this series. For an example in pale green of a 1937 'Savoy' vase (shape no. 9750) in the Victoria and Albert Museum, see London 1989b, no. 189. For a recently made version of shape 3030 in dark green, see London 1989b, no. 190, where it is stated that this shape has been in almost continuous production since 1937 and has been made in several other colours.

Aalto was closely involved in the making of the wooden moulds for the original series of vases; for a wooden mould for the 'Savoy' vase from the Karhula Glass Museum, illustrated with sketches by Aalto for free-form vases, Helsinki, see New York 1984, 17-21. Since 1954 cast-iron moulds have been used.

Adamovich, Mikhail Mikhailovich 1884-1947

There is no monograph on Adamovich. For biographical details, see Oxford and London 1984; Lobanov-Rostovsky 1990.

See also Recent Acquisitions, Cat. 337.

2 Plate [COLOUR PLATE XII]

Hard-paste porcelain, painted in overglaze colours. In the centre, a red star and the monogram of the Soviet republic, 'RSFSR', in gold flowers. Within the star, a hammer and a hand-plough. The border painted with emblems of work in matt and burnished gold on a deep blue ground with gold inner border. The emblems symbolise building, engineering, agriculture and fishing and are all embellished with finely executed engraved detail; the detail on the protractor simulates wood grain. The plate is slightly warped in the firing.

MARKS Printed underglaze green mark of the Imperial Porcelain Factory with the cypher of Nicholas II and the date '1898'; hammer, sickle and cogwheel mark of the State Porcelain Factory and the date '1922' painted in overglaze blue; factory number '216/11' in red.

Painted in 1922, after Adamovich's design, at the State Porcelain Factory, Petrograd, on a pre-revolutionary blank.

D 24.3 cm 1990,6-7,1

Adamovich graduated from the Stroganov Arts and Industry School in Moscow in 1907 and worked as a decorative painter in Moscow. He was an artist at the State Porcelain Factory in Leningrad from 1918 to 1919 and again from 1921 to 1923. He later worked at the Volkhov Ceramic Factory near Novgorod (1924-7) and at the Dulevo Ceramic Factory near Moscow (?1927-33). His designs for propaganda porcelain were often in the Constructivist-Futurist style favoured by the artists of the Russian Revolution, but the design on this plate deliberately uses traditional techniques and colours to depict revolutionary subject-matter. Gilding with richly engraved decoration was a speciality of Russian porcelain of the Imperial period, but is here skilfully exploited for the emblems of the Soviet workers.

An early contemporary illustration of a plate with this design is to be found in Gollerbach 1922, opp. p. 8. For other examples of plates with this design, see Moscow 1962, page 21, and Baranova 1983, pl. 128, in the State Ceramic Museum, Kuskovo, Moscow; Oxford and London 1984, no. 7, in a Moscow private collection; Lobanov-Rostovsky 1990, no. 66. Further examples have been sold in recent London auctions.

For further discussion of Adamovich's porcelain designs, see references cited under Chekhonin.

Argy-Rousseau, Joseph-Gabriel 1885-1953

Bloch-Dermant, J. and Delaborde, Y., *Les Pâtes de Verre G. Argy-Rousseau, Catalogue Raisonné*, Paris 1990
See also Boyer 1928; Bloch-Dermant 1983, 267-285 and Schmitt 1989.

3 Pendant
[PLATE 117]

Moulded glass or pâte-de-verre, square shape, a green pine-cone with purple needles, on a clear ground, suspended from a purple silk cord with purple glass bead. Contained in its original retailer's cardboard case labelled 'Liberty, London and Paris'.

MARKS The initials 'GAR' moulded into the design on the front.

Designed by J.-G. Argy-Rousseau for his own firm in 1921 and sold by Liberty & Co. between 1929 and 1932.

W 5.6 cm   1987,7-10,1

Joseph-Gabriel Rousseau studied at the École Nationale de Céramique at Sèvres, together with Jean Cros, son of the *pâte-de-verre* artist Henri Cros, and Constantin Platon-Argyriades (later painter and artist in ceramics and glass). Following his marriage to the latter's sister, Marianne Argyriades, in 1913, Rousseau adopted the first four letters of his wife's name. He first exhibited works in *pâte-de-verre* at the Salon des Artistes Français of 1914, and in 1921 founded his own company, the 'Société des Pâtes de verre', with workshops at 9 rue de Simplon. Argy-Rousseau executed all his own wax models, which were then handed over for serial production to his assistants. Through his partner, Gustav Moser, director of the Paris agency of Ludwig Moser & Sons of Carlsbad, a parallel production of some of Argy-Rousseau's designs was carried out by Moser in Carlsbad. Argy-Rousseau's company was unable to survive the economic crisis of 1929; it was dissolved on 31 December 1931, and the series production of *pâte-de-verre* came to an end. Argy-Rousseau, however, continued to work in his own small studio.

According to the recently published catalogue raisonné of Argy-Rousseau's work, which makes use of surviving archive material, this pendant was first produced in 1921 (Bloch-Dermant and Delaborde 1990, 186, no. 21.01) as 'pendentif pomme de pin'.

It is illustrated in Liberty's Christmas Gift catalogues between 1929 and 1932. It first appears with a cord tassel and either two or three glass beads in *Liberty Gifts 1929-30*, 44, nos 405 and 407, price 10s. 6d. The same design, with no tassel and a single bead, appears in *Liberty Christmas Gifts 1930-1931*, 41, no. 407, price 8s. 6d. and in *Liberty Christmas Gifts 1931-1932*, 39, no. 339, 2¼ in (5.7 cm) across, price 7s. 6d. The colours illustrated include a brown cone on green, a blue-green cone on yellow-brown and a rust cone on brown. They are described simply as 'French glass' with no mention of the designer, in keeping with Liberty's practice of maintaining the anonymity of all designers and manufacturers.

For other examples of the pine-cone pendant, see Sotheby's, New York, 8-9 June 1988, lots 184-5. Further pendants of the early 1920s, including a cicada design also sold by Liberty's,

are illustrated by Bloch-Dermant 1983, 274; this account also describes Argy-Rousseau's *pâte-de-verre* technique.

Ashbee, Charles Robert 1863-1942

Crawford, A., *C.R. Ashbee: Architect, Designer and Romantic Socialist*, London 1985 (with further bibliography, list of Ashbee's own works and details of primary sources)
For Ashbee's works of particular relevance to the items catalogued here, see Ashbee, C.R., *Craftsmanship in Competitive Industry*, London 1908; *Modern English Silverwork*, London 1909 (new edn 1974 with introductions by S. Bury and A. Crawford). See also Bury, S., 'An Arts and Crafts Experiment: the silverwork of C.R. Ashbee', *Victoria and Albert Museum Bulletin*, Vol. III, no. 1, January 1967, 18-25.

4 Butter knife
[PLATE 66]

Silver, with openwork cage handle formed of thick silver wires twisted together and enclosing a silver ball set on a central rod. The junction of handle and blade is ornamented with beading, as is the end of the handle, which is set with a cabochon chrysoprase.

MARKS Stamped on the blade with London hallmarks and date-letter for 1900 and maker's mark 'CRA' in a shield for Charles Robert Ashbee.

Designed c.1897-1900 and made by the Guild of Handicraft, London, in 1900.

L 13cm   1981,6-7,1

Most of Ashbee's designs for metalwork were executed by the Guild of Handicraft, which he established in 1888, initially in London and then in Chipping Campden, Gloucestershire from 1902 to 1907. The Guild worked mainly in base metal before about 1896, when silverwares were first exhibited at the Arts & Crafts Society exhibition of that year. Wirework was already a prominent feature of Ashbee's designs and the characteristic twisting of wires to form a handle seems to have appeared from about 1897 (see *The Studio* 9, 1897, 130 and *Art Journal*, 1897, 337). Silver balls were also introduced at about this time.

The mark that appears on this butter knife was entered by Ashbee at Goldsmiths' Hall on 29 January 1896. After the Guild's registration as a limited company, Ashbee entered a second mark, which appears on Cat. 5, in December 1898. Both marks were used around 1900 and there seems to be no significance in the use of one or the other, though it has been suggested that pieces made after 1898 which bear the 'CRA' mark were perhaps farmed out to other makers (Bury 1967, 6).

This piece was made during the peak years of the Guild's production of silverwares, around 1900-1; production dropped with the move to Chipping Campden in 1902 and picked up again in 1903. This and Cat. 5 illustrate the wide range of small-wares in production; at this period the Guild produced an almost complete range of tablewares that could match the range of commercial firms, but the competition from the trade and in particular from Liberty's 'Cymric' range introduced in 1901 (see Cat. 133) was one of the causes of the Guild's eventual demise.

This design is illustrated in a catalogue of the Guild's silverwares of c.1905-6 (in the V & A Library); it sold for £1 7s. 6d. (*Guild of Handicraft Ltd. Silversmiths and jewellers by appointment to her Majesty the Queen*, 37). The catalogue records the Guild's two London shops at 16A Brook Street and 67A New Bond Street. For a variant of this butter knife, also date-stamped

1900, but with the maker's mark of the Guild of Handicraft, see Naylor 1971, pl. 83.

After the liquidation of the Guild in 1908, the metal workshop was continued by George Hart (see Cat. 121).

5 Spoon
[PLATE 66]

Silver, hammered bowl tapering to a faceted stem with openwork finial formed of five applied scrolls, the top set with a cabochon chrysoprase.

MARKS Stamped on reverse of stem with London hallmarks and date-letter for 1905 and maker's mark 'G of H Ltd' for the Guild of Handicraft.

Designed before 1902 and made by the Guild of Handicraft, Chipping Campden, Gloucestershire, in 1905.

L 19cm   1980,7-7,1

For an identical spoon exhibited at the Turin Exhibition of 1902, see DK & D XI, 1902-3, 217. This design is illustrated in a catalogue of the Guild's silverwares of 1905-6, 38 (see Cat. 4), price £1 1s. Spoons with bowls of the same shape but with plainer finials sold for 17s. 6d. and 15s.

Bang, Jacob Eiler 1900-65

There is no monograph on Bang. A summary of the relevant biographical details given in the following Danish publications is included below.

Koch-Jensen, P. and Schultz, S., Holmegaards Glasvaerk 1825-1950, Copenhagen n.d. (c.1950)

Lassen, E. and Schlüter, M., Dansk Glas 1925-1985, Copenhagen 1987 (first published in 1975 as Dansk Glas 1925-1975)

6-8 Carafe, stoppered decanter and goblet
[PLATE 121]

Mould-blown glass, the carafe in pale violet, the decanter and goblet in smoky topaz. The goblet stem and stopper to the decanter have the same pattern of five grooves. The goblet bowl is optically blown.

MARKS None.

Designed in 1928 as part of the 'Viol' service and made by Holmegaards Glasvaerk, Naestved, Denmark, between 1928 and c.1935.

6 Carafe: H 17.6cm 1988,1-6,1
7 Decanter: H. 26.5cm (with stopper) 1988,1-6,2
8 Goblet: H 15cm 1988,1-6,3

Bang trained as an architect and worked with the silversmith Kay Fisker until 1925, when he supervised the setting up of the Danish pavilion at the Paris Exhibition. As a result Holmegaard's director, K. Riis-Hansen, invited Bang to design for Holmegaard, alongside Orla Juul Nielsen, the factory's first artist-designer. Bang's first prototypes were shown in the spring and summer of 1928, initially at Aarhus and then at the trade fair in Fredericia, as part of a series of exhibitions throughout Denmark, organised by the two Danish applied arts societies (Foreniging for Kunsthaandvaerk and Anvendt Kunst) to promote Danish manufactures. Bang also designed the displays and was awarded the newly created annual medal for the applied arts. The prototypes were then put into production in June 1928, as the 'Kunstglasservice Viol', a fifty-four-piece service of everyday table glass without ornament. It was strongly influenced by similar tableware designed from 1919 by Simon Gate and Edward Hald at Orrefors, Sweden.

The carafe, decanter and goblet are all from the 'Viol' service; the carafe was no. 23, the decanter no. 31 (with smaller and larger size), the goblet no. 16. Initially this service was produced in the 'viol' colour illustrated by the carafe; in December 1928 three more colours were introduced: 'nefrit' (green), pink and flint. 'Smoke' (smoky topaz) was introduced in May 1929. For items from the 'Viol' service, see Die Schaulade, 6 Jahrgang, Heft 10, August 1930, 658-60; Koch-Jensen and Schultz, 107; Lassen and Schlüter, pls 31-37. The coloured 'Viol' glasses went out of production in about 1935, but the flint glasses, with or without a gold rim, were produced until about 1954. For other pieces from the 'Viol' service, see Leipzig 1989, no. 398 a-c.

Bang wrote several articles on his glass designs and the problems of designing for industry for the journal of the Foreniging for Kunsthaandvaerk, Nyt Tidsskrift for Kunstindustrie, beginning in August 1928. Bang's overriding concern to design practical everyday wares which were also easy to produce is demonstrated by his 'functional programme', a series of sketches contrasting old and new models (Koch-Jensen and Schultz, 92-3). Bang used smooth contours instead of sharp edges, to minimize wear to the wooden moulds, and so that the shapes could be formed with regularity by the average glass-blower, thereby avoiding the rejection of faulty pieces. It is interesting to note in Bang's own explanation of his aims in the design of the 100-piece 'Primula' service that he objected to his glass being promoted as 'Art Glass'; he also disliked the then fashionable coloured glass, hoping for a time when clear glass would be seen as 'modern' (Die Schaulade, 7 Jahrgang, Heft 6, April 1931, 379-80, reprinted from Nyt Tidsskrift for Kunstindustrie).

During the 1930s Bang also designed ornamental wares with cut, engraved, moulded or applied decoration; both these and his undecorated wares were illustrated regularly in The Studio and were sold in London by the Royal Copenhagen Porcelain Company. Bang left Holmegaard in 1941 and later worked for Kastrup Glasvaerk until his death in 1965.

I am grateful to Mogens Schlüter of Holmegaards Glasvaerker for supplying precise details of dates of design and production for this group and Cat. 9-10.

9 Vase
[PLATE 121]

Mould-blown smoky topaz glass.

MARKS None.

Designed c.1928 and made by Holmegaards Glasvaerk, Naestved, Denmark, between 1928 and c.1939.

H 25.6cm 1988,1-6,4

For a vase of this shape, see Lassen and Schlüter, pl. 27, where it is dated 1928-30; see also The Studio 113, April 1937, 206 and The Studio Yearbook of Decorative Art 1938, 114.

10 Jug
[PLATE 121]

Mould-blown smoky topaz glass.

MARKS None.

Designed in 1928 as part of the 'Bo' service and made by Holmegaards Glasvaerk, Naestved, Denmark, between 1928 and c.1935.

H 22.4cm 1988,1-6,5

For pieces from the 'Bo' service with a similar curve at the base, see Lassen and Schlüter, pl. 21. The production number for the jug is 3214.

Behrens, Peter 1869-1940

Hoeber, F., *Peter Behrens*, Munich 1913

Cremers, P.J., *Peter Behrens, Sein Werk von 1909 bis zur Gegenwart*, Essen 1928

Industriekultur, Peter Behrens und die AEG 1907-1914, exhibition catalogue, Buddensieg, T. et al., Berlin, International Design Zentrum, 1978

Peter Behrens und Nürnberg, exhibition catalogue, Nuremberg, Germanisches Nationalmuseum, 1980, ed. P.K. Schuster

Buddensieg, T. and Rogge H., *Industriekultur, Peter Behrens and the AEG 1907-1914*, London and New York, 1984 (first published in German, Munich 1979)

See also Recent Acquisitions, Cat. 338-9.

11 Dessert plate [PLATE 86]

Hard-paste porcelain, with a geometric pattern of intersecting lines stencilled in overglaze deep sea-green on a white ground. The plate is almost flat with barely raised border.

MARKS Printed in overglaze red on the base with the monogram 'PB' in a rectangle for Peter Behrens with 'GESCHÜTZT' below; impressed 'BAUSCHER WEIDEN' in an oval.

Designed in 1901 for Behrens' own house at Darmstadt and made by the Porzellanfabrik Gebrüder Bauscher, Weiden, Oberpfalz, Upper Bavaria.

D 20cm 1981,1-8,1

Behrens trained as a painter and worked in Munich in the 1890s, exhibiting there with the Vereinigte Werkstätten in 1899. In the same year he was invited to join the newly established artists' colony in Darmstadt, where he turned to architecture and interior decoration, designing his own house, complete with furniture and fittings, ceramics, glass and cutlery. The house and its interior formed part of the exhibition held at Darmstadt in 1901. The exhibition title, 'Ein Dokument Deutscher Kunst', had its origins in an address given by Behrens in November 1899 which contained the colony's programme and its intention to create a 'Dokument Deutscher Kunst' of lasting value (see *DK & D*, June 1900, 354 and 370-71). The exhibition was widely perceived as a milestone in German design.

This plate is part of a large dinner, coffee and tea service designed for the dining-room of Behrens' house. The service comprised over one hundred pieces many of which were based on hexagonal forms. The flat shape of the plate is remarkable at this date. For contemporary illustrations of the service *in situ*, see Koch 1902, 36; *DK & D* 9, 1901-2. 171; *Die Kunst* 6, 1901-2, 19. The linear ornament on the plates echoed the pattern on the dining-room ceiling. Behrens' own service was decorated in light grey, to match the colours of his dining room. For examples decorated in light grey, see Nuremberg 1980, no. 64 (in the Kaiser Wilhelm Museum, Krefeld) and Ulmer 1990, cat. no. 5 (in the Museum der Künstlerkolonie, Darmstadt). The decoration was also executed in violet, see Spielmann et al. 1979, no. 99 (a plate in the Museum für Kunst und Gewerbe, Hamburg). For examples with the decoration executed in olive green, see Nuremberg 1980, nos 176-7 (private collection); this large service was part of a complete dowry of household furnishings ordered from Behrens in 1902 by Emilie Reif, the wife of a wealthy Nuremberg businessman, for her daughter.

A porcelain sample plaque, also in a private collection, indicates that three different shades of green were available (Nuremberg 1980, no. 178). The service was exhibited in 1905 in an exhibition of 'Neue Wohnräume-neues Kunstgewerbe' held in the Warenhaus Wertheim, Berlin, The same department store had previously shown Behrens' glasses (see Cat. 13).

The Porzellanfabrik Gebrüder Bauscher, founded in 1881 by August Bauscher (1849-1917), specialised in hotel porcelain and was among the more advanced factories in Germany. August Bauscher had long-standing connections with Darmstadt, having begun his career there, working for the chemical firm of Merck. Wishing to produce porcelain in the currently fashionable 'Jugendstil', he secured the contract for all the porcelain at the artists' colony, including designs by Christiansen, Paul Bürck and Olbrich, for the artists' houses and for the exhibition restaurant. Bauscher's modern-style wares designed by the Darmstadt artists were advertised in *Innen-Dekoration* in January 1902: '*Die Porzellan-Ausstattung für die Villen der Herren Künstler – sowie das Service der Ausstellungs-Restauration wurde von uns geliefert.*' The introduction of new models (as distinct from new patterns on existing shapes) was enormously expensive, but the attaching of artists' names to particular products was a desirable status symbol for many manufacturers. Bauscher later introduced services by Riemerschmid and Curt Stoeving. The Behrens service was produced with two other patterns also designed by Behrens (Nuremberg 1980, nos 65-7; Bauscher 1980, 4; Heller 1982, nos 14-15) and the hexagonal saucer was still in production in 1970 as an ashtray.

For Bauscher, see Bauscher 1980. For further discussion. see Rudoe 1990.

12 Vase [PLATE 85]

Earthenware, cast, bulbous base and tall, flared neck with three handles of triangular section from neck to base. Where the handles join the base, the line of the handle is continued by a relief moulding resembling a stylised leaf. The exterior covered with a purplish-blue glaze which runs over at the top into the interior, glazed white. Hairline crack to one of the handles.

MARKS Printed on the base in brown with the factory mark of the Steingutfabrik & Kunsttöpferei Franz Anton Mehlem, Bonn; impressed number '2779', impressed letter 'H' and faintly impressed circular factory mark.

Designed in 1900-1 and made by the Steingutfabrik & Kunsttöpferei Franz Anton Mehlem, Bonn c.1901.

H 21.4cm, max D 13.3cm 1989,1-2,1

This vase is one of a group of vases designed by Behrens for the exhibition held at the Darmstadt artists' colony in 1901 (see also Cat. 11). Six of these vases, including this model, were illustrated in the book published by Alexander Koch to record the exhibition: *Ein Dokument Deutscher Kunst*, 1902, 388 (the same photograph was used in *DK & D* IX, 1901-2, 190). This vase appears again in the same publication, in a view of the interior of Behrens' house. A further six vases, all different, were illustrated in *Die Kunst* 6, 1901-2, 47. A third illustration was used in *The Studio* 25, October–May 1902, 29, with five additional models, making a total of at least seventeen.

A recent publication on the Mehlem factory illustrates the photograph from Koch's 1902 publication and the photograph from *Die Kunst*; it describes the Behrens vases as now untraceable (Berning, Weisser and Zippelin 1984, 124). Even the seven pieces acquired by the former Gewerbemuseum in Darmstadt from the 1901 exhibition seem to have disappeared; a contemporary illustration of four of these pieces, from *Beilage zum Gewerbeblatt* 3, shows two of the models illustrated in *Die Kunst* and two of the models shown in *The Studio*. For this illustration and a full list of Gewerbemuseum acquisitions, see Weber 1977, 200 and 214. The apparent lack of surviving examples suggests that the vases were not made in large numbers, despite contemporary acclaim. The only other recorded examples of any of the group are a vase of the same model as the British Museum vase, but glazed in red, in the Museum der Künstlerkolonie, Darmstadt (Ulmer 1990, cat. no. 6) and a two-handled vase (shown in Koch's 1902 illustration) with relief floral decoration not designed by Behrens, sold at Galerie Wolfgang Ketterer, Munich, 12 May 1989, lot 273.

Behrens later designed a study for Alexander Koch which was exhibited at the Turin Exhibition of 1902; three of the vases were placed on the mantelpiece. They were probably Behrens' own (Pica 1902-3, 303). For further discussion and reproductions of the contemporary illustrations mentioned above, see Rudoe 1990.

13 Wine glass [PLATE 95]

Clear free-blown glass with a broad gold band below the rim, the gold worn in parts. The gold decoration applied in liquid form, with a stencil, and then burnished by hand.

MARKS None.

Designed in 1902 and made by the Kristallglasfabrik Benedikt von Poschinger, Oberzwieselau, Lower Bavaria, between 1902 and 1925, when the factory closed.

H 18.9 cm, D of base 7.3 cm   1981,11-6,1

This is the white wine glass from a service designed for an exhibition of modern interiors held by the department store, Warenhaus Wertheim, in Berlin in the autumn of 1902. For a contemporary view of the room in which the glasses are set on the dinner table, see Hoeber, 21-2, pl. 16. The complete service included glasses for red and white wine, sparkling wine, liqueur, fruit juice and beer. For further contemporary illustrations of glasses from this service, see *DK & D* VI, 1903, 291, 293 and *Die Kunst* XIII, 1905, 424, where the glasses are described as executed by Benedikt von Poschinger.

Glasses from this service are in a number of museums including the Hessisches Landesmuseum, Darmstadt (Heller 1982, no. 16), the Museum der Künstlerkolonie, Darmstadt (Ulmer 1990, cat. no. 9) the Kunstgewerbemuseum, Zurich (Gysling-Billeter 1975, no. 9), and the Württembergisches Landesmuseum, Stuttgart.

The gold decoration did not stand up well to regular use. Because the gold dust was applied in a liquid solution of volatile oils, the solution eventually wears off and only the gold dust remains. A similar process was used in the decoration of porcelain (see Hanover 1982, 153).

For the firm of B. von Poschinger, see Cat. 257-8. From 1898 this firm commissioned designs for glass from a number of Munich artists, including Behrens, Riemerschmid, and Adelbert Niemeyer.

14 Pair of fish servers; fish knife and fork [PLATE 88]

Silver, with engraved decoration on servers and knife. Both serving-knife and fork are pierced, the knife-blade in the form of a monster fish, the fork with angular prongs. The handles are ornamented with relief teardrop motifs.

MARKS Each piece stamped on the handle with the Copenhagen town mark and date '1916' (servers) and '1917' (knife and fork), the assay master's mark for C.F. Heise, and silver standard mark '830s' with the initials 'BJ', probably for the distributor.

Designed by Behrens in 1903 and made by the firm of Franz Bahner AG, Silberwarenfabrik, Düsseldorf for export to Denmark; dated 1916-17.

14a Serving knife: L 29 cm, max. w of blade 5.2 cm   1988,1-11,1
14b Serving fork: L 23.8 cm, max. w 6.8 cm   1988,1-11,2
14c Knife: L 21.5 cm   1988,1-11,3
14d Fork: L 18.3 cm   1988,1-11,4

These pieces are from a service for meat and fish. For contemporary illustrations of the meat cutlery, see *DK*, 1904-5, 422; for examples in museums in Hanover and Hamburg, see Mosel 1971, no. 9 and Spielmann 1979, no. 101.

There are apparently no contemporary illustrations of Behrens' design for the fish cutlery, but a number of examples survive, showing various modifications. For example, the fish-knife blade was not always engraved (Solingen 1979, no. 8 and Nuremberg 1980, no. 77, from the collection of Giorgio Silzer). Other examples of the knives and forks show a more streamlined design for the blade and prongs: the outward curves and points are absent and there is an additional lozenge motif where the handle begins, as well as engraving on the fork to match that on the knife (Munich 1979, no. 141, private collection). The smoother overall outline suggests that this may be the original Behrens design, whereas the examples with blades and prongs of a more traditional curving shape may be later modifications by the manufacturers. Another possibility is that Behrens designed only the meat cutlery and that the fish cutlery was added by the manufacturers, hence the variations. Further examples of both the fish and meat cutlery in large and small sizes are held by the Hessisches Landesmuseum, Darmstadt (Heppe 1988, no. 254-7), by the Museum der Kunstlerkolonie, Darmstadt (Ulmer 1990, cat. no. 20), and by the Badisches Landesmuseum, Karlsruhe (formerly Silzer collection; see Franzke 1987, no. 253, for a meat fork and a fish knife).

Most of the examples cited above are described as bearing the manufacturer's mark of the firm of Franz Bahner, Düsseldorf, where Behrens was director of the Kunstgewerbeschule from 1903 to 1907. The design appears in the firm's pattern-book (n.d., no. 6200, see Solingen 1979). However, recent research has established that many silver firms acted as wholesalers/distributors and finishers only; these wholesalers often insisted that the goods should be supplied without manufacturer's marks (Bremen 1981, 20; see also van de Velde, Cat. 291). Alternatively, the wholesalers had their own names stamped on goods by the manufacturers (Sänger 1984; see also Olbrich, Cat. 225). Thus examples also occur without Bahner's mark: the pieces in the Museum für Kunst und Gewerbe, Hamburg, bear only German assay marks and the distributor's name, 'G Heisler'.

Bahner had a representative in Denmark from at least 1914; the use of higher 830 silver standard current in Denmark, as distinct from the 800 standard current in Germany, confirms that the British Museum pieces were made for export. According to the *Kleines Export-Handelsbuch* of 1903 (contained within the *Adress- und Handbuch für das deutsche Goldschmiedegewerbe*, Leipzig 1903), foreign wares sold in Denmark were to be stamped with the name of the distributor, not the manufacturer. For another example of German cutlery sold in Denmark, see Cat. 296, by a related Düsseldorf firm.

Anton Bahner took over the firm of Butzen in 1879; his son Franz founded the firm of Franz Bahner in 1895; hollowware was discontinued in 1903 in favour of cutlery. P. Bruckmann, in his 1909 account of silverware manufacture in Germany, noted that Bahner was exceptional in producing high-quality silver cutlery in collaboration with artists (reprinted Bröhan II/2, 1977,511-13). The *Illustrierte Zeitung* of March 1914 also noted Bahner's speciality as the production of silver cutlery in all styles (Sänger 1984, 207). The firm closed before 1967 (see Heppe 1988, 39-41).

During his four-year period as director of the Kunstgewerbe-schule in Düsseldorf, an appointment heavily influenced by the success of his master-classes in Nuremberg (see Cat. 17), Behrens established contact with a number of local industries. Thus the designs of the Kunstgewerbeschule, by both pupils and teachers, were put into production. For discussion of Behrens' activity in Düsseldorf, see Moeller 1984.

15 Electric kettle [PLATE 94]

Brass, octagonal form, the surface cast to imitate a hammered effect, the spout and base plain, with wicker-bound fixed handle attached to circular lugs and wooden knob to lid. The element inside is in the form of a cylindrical bar.

MARKS Stamped on the base with the model number '3690' and '29'.

Designed in 1908-9 and made by AEG (Allgemeine Electricitäts-Gesellschaft), Berlin.

H 20.6cm, W (with spout) 21cm, W of body 15.5cm 1982,10-7,1

Behrens first came into contact with AEG while director of the Kunstgewerbeschule in Düsseldorf; he supplied graphic designs to the company before his appointment in 1907 as the company's architect and artistic adviser, at the request of Emil Rathenau, who had founded the firm in 1883 and was then director. As well as factory buildings, shop-fronts and advertising, Behrens designed a wide range of products for the firm, including three different shapes of electric kettle: oval, bulb-shaped and octagonal. All three models were exhibited at the Behrens exhibition organised by K.E. Osthaus at the Deutsche Museum für Kunst in Handel und Gewerbe, Hagen, in April 1909 (Hagen 1984, 50 and 65). Each shape was available in three different materials (brass, nickel-plated brass and copper-plated brass), in three different surface finishes (plain, spot-hammered and strip-hammered) and in three sizes (0.75, 1.25 and 1.75 l).

For contemporary illustrations of all three shapes with plain surfaces, see *DK & D* 26, 1910, 266. For an advertisement of 1912 for three octagonal kettles in the three different materials, see Buddensieg and Rogge 1984, 428, cat. no. P140. The brass and nickel-plated brass versions are plain, the copper is shown with hammered surface; different model numbers are given for each material and each size. Model no. 3690 in copper (copper-plated brass) with hammered surface held 1.75 litres. For photographs of AEG window displays in Berlin of 1910, showing a

range of electric kettles, see Hoeber, 163-6, pls 185-8 and Cremers, pls 30 and 32. Behrens kettles were also sold through the Deutsche Werkbund, of which he was a founder member in 1907 (*Jahrbuch* 1912, 68).

An example of the bulb-shaped kettle with round handle and strip-hammered surface (i.e. with vertical stripes) may be seen in the Victoria and Albert Museum (M.61 and a.1981), together with a kettle of similar shape with stand and burner (M.45 to b.1970). This was either produced concurrently with the electric version or existed previously. The octagonal shape is so far only known in electric versions. However, it appears to have been produced by other firms for use with stand and burner not designed by Behrens: such an example was sold at Christie's, Amsterdam, 26 October 1989, lot 227 marked 'Gebr.H.Sch'.

For further illustrations and discussions, see Hoeber 107, pls 115-17; Berlin 1978, 55-8, cat. no. P138-40; Buddensieg and Rogge 1984, 426-9, cat. no. P133-41.

16 Electric wall clock [PLATE 94]

Self-starting synchronomous motor, brass case, white face with black twelve-hour numerals and red twenty-four-hour numerals inside.

MARKS On the face, 'Electrochronos AEG'. On the reverse of movement, a metal label with 'TYPE FU', the production number '121729' and model number 'AEG 290408 u 1'.

The face and hands designed by Behrens in 1910 with later modifications; the clock put into production by AEG after 1926.

D 27cm 1982,12-3,4

This is a modification of Behrens' clock-face design of 1910 (see *DK & D* 26, 1910, 266 and *Werkbund Jahrbuch*, 1913, 80, an illustration of the AEG factory showroom). The black twelve-hour numbers and the hands remained virtually unchanged until 1938. However, Behrens' original designs have no red twenty-four-hour numerals and the black twelve-hour numbers are more rounded. For further discussion and illustrations of Behrens' early clock-face designs, see Berlin 1978, cat. no. P154, and Buddensieg and Rogge 1984, cat. no. P106.

According to Abeler 1977, the self-starting synchronomous motor was introduced into AEG's range in 1926. Buddensieg and Rogge (1979/84) refer to AEG's price list of 1931 in which model no. 290408 with 30-mm face cost 55 marks. Reference is also here made to *AEG Mitteilungen* 1928 and 1931, but this appears to be erroneous since the AEG archive has confirmed that the *Mitteilungen* for these years contain no reference to the self-starting synchronomous motor. 'Electrochronos' was produced in large numbers and enjoyed a wide distribution in the 1930s.

Behrens, Nuremberg Master-classes

17 Plate [PLATE 86]

Hard-paste porcelain, glazed white with overglaze stencilled linear decoration in violet blue round the rim.

MARKS Impressed factory mark, the monogram 'HR' in a circle, for Lorenz Hutschenreuther, Selb; printed mark in overglaze red comprising the letters 'NH' and 'BGM' for Nürnberger Handwerkskunst Bayerisches Gewerbemuseum, within a triangular shield, round the outside of the shield: 'BAYR.GEW.MUS' and below, printed mark 'K&A S.' for Krautheim & Adelberg, Selb.

The decoration designed by a member of Behrens' master-classes in applied arts in Nuremberg in 1901 and 1902; the decoration executed by the firm of Krautheim & Adelberg, Selb, on a blank manufactured by L. Hutschenreuther, Selb, Bavaria.

D 24.4 cm, H 4.1 cm   1990,1-8,1   Given by Graham Dry and Beate Dry-v. Zezschwitz

The master-classes ('Meisterkurse') at the Bayerisches Gewerbemuseum in Nuremberg were set up in 1901 by Theodor von Kramer, director of the Bayerisches Gewerbemuseum, as part of the museum's brief to encourage development in all branches of the applied and industrial arts. Nuremberg was not previously a centre of reform; the government was behind the organisation of the classes in an attempt to assist the spread of artists' designs into local factories. Kramer thought highly of Behrens' work for the Darmstadt Exhibition and asked him to direct the first course, which took place from 8 October to 9 November 1901 and was attended by sixteen students. Behrens' second course took place from mid January to mid February 1902. Designs approved by the Bayerisches Gewerbemuseum received the trade mark that appears on this plate and were sold through a specially organised retail outlet in Nuremberg.

The linear decoration on this plate is inspired directly by the motifs that Behrens used in the dining-room of his Darmstadt house, to decorate both the interior itself and the matching porcelain dinner service (see Cat. 11). The decoration was applied to existing Hutschenreuther blanks, which could be obtained relatively cheaply. For another example of a service decorated by Krautheim & Adelberg on a Hutschenreuther blank, see Christiansen, Cat. 38. For Hutschenreuther, see Hohenberg 1989.

For other pieces from the Nuremberg service, see Miami 1988, pl. 108, cat. no. 62; sale catalogue W. Ketterer, Munich, 12 May 1989, lot 274; Dry 1989, 654. For further discussion on the Nuremberg master-classes, see Pese, 1980. Subsequent classes were taken by Richard Riemerschmid, Paul Haustein and Friedrich Adler.

Belkin, Veniamin Pavlovich 1884-1961

There is no monograph on Belkin. For biographical details, see Oxford and London 1984; Vienna 1988.

18 Plate   [PLATE 140]

Hard-paste porcelain, painted in overglaze colours. In the centre, a cluster of factory buildings billowing with smoke from which emerges the slogan 'OCTOBER 1917'. To the right, a classical temple and a red star. Above, a Futurist-style motif of folded red ribbons. Round the rim, a hammer, sickle, axe and carpenter's plane, with the slogan 'The victory of the workers'.

MARKS On the reverse, overglaze painted blue hammer and sickle mark of the State Porcelain Factory and the date '1920'.

The decoration designed in 1919 and painted in 1920, after Belkin's design, at the State Porcelain Factory, Petrograd.

D 23.5 cm   1981,12-8,2

Before the Revolution Belkin had studied in Paris and worked in St Petersburg as a painter and graphic artist. He made designs for the State Porcelain Factory from 1919 to 1921 and later taught at the State art schools and at the Leningrad Academy of Architecture.

This design was created to commemorate the second anniversary of the October Revolution. The classical temple and the red star symbolise the old order giving way to the new Soviet State. Unusually, the blank for this plate was made after the Revolution and does not have the Imperial marks or the turned mouldings found on the backs of many pre-revolutionary plates (see Cat. 2, 34-5, 337, 340-41, 343, 345, 350, 352-3 and 355-6). Another plate with this design, dated 1919 and initialled by the factory artist Alisa Golenkina, is held by the Museum of the Lomonossov Porcelain Factory, Leningrad (Andreeva 1975, 152; Oxford and London 1984, no. 12; Vienna 1988, 159). The State Porcelain Factory was renamed the Lomonossov Porcelain Factory in 1925.

For another frequently illustrated plate by Belkin, 'The Sower', see Gollerbach 1922, 14, Andreeva 1975, 153 and Oxford and London 1984, 42. For further discussion of Russian revolutionary porcelain and bibliography, see Chekhonin, Cat. 35.

Benson, William Arthur Smith 1854-1924

W.A.S. Benson Metalwork, exhibition catalogue, Michael Whiteway in association with Paul Reeves, Haslam & Whiteway, London 1981, with introduction by Michael Collins

In addition to this catalogue there are a number of articles relevant to the items discussed below:

Church, A.H., 'Benson's Lamps', The Portfolio 21, 1890, 19-22

Muthesius, H., 'Benson's elektrische Beleuchtungskörper', Dekorative Kunst 5, 1901, 105-10

Bury, S., 'A craftsman who used the machine: the metalwork of W.A.S. Benson', Country Life CXXVII, 18 March 1965, 624, 627

Rose, P., 'W.A.S. Benson: a Pioneer Designer of Light Fittings', Journal of the Decorative Arts Society 9, 1985, 50-57

For Benson's own writing see: Notes on some of the minor arts, London 1883; 'The Embossing of Metals', English Illustrated Magazine, October 1889, 39–46; 'Metal Work' in Arts & Crafts Essays, London 1899, 68-80; Elements of Handicraft and Design, London 1893; Rudiments of Handicraft, London 1919; Drawing: its History and Uses, London 1925.

W.A.S. Benson trained as an architect with Basil Champneys before turning in 1880 to the design and manufacture of domestic lighting and establishing his own workshops in Fulham for the machine production of metalwork on a large scale. His workshops soon expanded to premises in Chiswick Mall and an even larger factory, the Eyot works, St Peter's Square, Hammersmith, was nearly completed when A.H. Church was writing on Benson in 1890. Benson's first showroom was in Campden Hill Road and in 1887 he moved to 82 New Bond Street. He was a close friend of William Morris, becoming a director of Morris & Company on Morris's death in 1896. Information about Benson's assistants can be gleaned from the detailed listings in the catalogues of the Arts & Crafts Exhibition Society, London, in view of its policy of acknowledging makers as well as designers. Benson exhibited with the Society from its foundation in 1888, when J. Lovegrove is listed as executor. By 1890 Lovegrove, as supervisor of the workshop, was assisted by T. Pinches, J. Taylor and C. Green; J. McVeigh is recorded as a pattern maker (Catalogue of the Third Exhibition) 1890, 178-82, nos 232-51).

By the late 1890s Benson's metalwork was widely admired on the Continent and in America (see *The House Beautiful* v, April 1899). It was exhibited in Bing's Maison de l'Art Nouveau from at least 1896 (*The Studio* VII, 1896, 179), when the Nordenfjeldske Kunstindustrimuseum, Trondheim, purchased a group of nine items (Weisberg 1986, figs 100-105, col. pl. 25). Benson's metalwork was later shown in the Hirschwald Gallery, Berlin (*The Studio* XIII, 1898, 118), at the Paris Exhibition of 1900, the Turin Exhibition of 1902 (*Die Kunst* v, 1901-2, 418) and at the Hohenzollern Kunstgewerbehaus, Berlin, in 1906, as part of an 'English tea-table' (*Velhagen & Klasings Monatsheft* 1905-6, II, March 1906, 119).

It is difficult to date Benson metalwork with any accuracy. A number of items are illustrated in the many articles in contemporary journals of the 1890s and early 1900s, but Benson's earliest surviving catalogues date from about 1897, and there is little information on the firm's early products of the 1880s. The 1896 Trondheim group, which comprises tableware, lamps and hearth furniture, is thus of especial significance. The Trondheim group also includes a rare instance of a registered design, a copper tray registered in 1894 (Wakefield et al. 1961-2, 51-6, figs 53-61). Early in the First World War the factory turned to the manufacture of munitions and never went back to the production of domestic metalwares; the firm closed down in 1920 when Benson retired. Thus, unless a contemporary illustration has been found, most of the items catalogued here have been dated to *c.* 1890-1914.

19 Pair of mantelpiece or piano candlesticks [PLATE 62]

Cast brass with stamped copper drip trays and lathe-turned knops. A weighted sphere at one end enables the candlesticks to stand clear of the mantelpiece.

MARKS Stamped inside each drip tray 'W.A.S.BENSON'.

Designed before 1887 and made in the factory of W.A.S. Benson, London, before 1914.

L 33.3 cm, H 11.2 cm   1982,1-8,2 and 3

A pair of mantelpiece candlesticks of this design are included in a photograph of Benson's Campden Hill Road showroom, which must date from before 1887 (Rose 1985, 53). See also Muthesius 1901, 110, where this candlestick is described as a 'Klavierleuchter'.

In his article of 1890 A.H. Church noted with regret that few of Benson's designs were registered and were therefore prey to the 'countless imitations . . . which meet us at every turn'; he believed the imitations to be of German manufacture. Inferior versions of these candlesticks were indeed made in Germany and bear the mark of the firm of Carl Deffner, Esslingen: the letters 'CDE' between crossed swords (I owe the identification of this mark to Graham Dry; for examples of these candlesticks, see Christie's, South Kensington, 7 September 1990, lot 69).

Church also notes the various methods employed by Benson: 'casting, turning, polishing, plating, bronzing, and lacquering'. He records that brass was used for rigidity and strength, while copper was used for reflecting surfaces, and that 'both metals were protected from corrosion by means of a colourless lacquer; so also are those surfaces which have been plated with silver'. The writer of Benson's obituary notice in *The Times* of 9 July 1924 noted the 'heavy stamping plant, spinning lathes, and shaping tools' in the Hammersmith works, as well as 'a lacquer-

ing department which had benefitted so much from his inventive genius that constant efforts were made by trade rivals to penetrate its secrets' (quoted by W.N. Bruce in the memoir on Benson printed as an introduction to Benson's *Drawing: Its History and Uses*, 1925, xxvi).

20 Wall sconce [PLATE 62]

Copper and brass, with three branches. The leaf-shaped copper wall-plate is hand-beaten with an engraved foliate design and bears three brass candle holders with copper drip trays.

MARKS Stamped on the supports inside each drip tray 'W.A.S BENSON'.

Designed *c.* 1880-90 and made in the factory of W.A.S. Benson, London, before 1914.

H 27.8 cm, W 27.6 cm, D 22.3 cm   1980,10–11,1

A pair of sconces of this design were set above the fireplace in the dining room of Benson's own house, Windleshaw, near Withyham, Sussex (undated archive photograph in the Benson MSS in the Victoria and Albert Museum Library; the same photograph appears in Benson's own book, *Drawing: its History and Uses*, posthumously published in 1925, fig. 48). Wall sconces of different, though related, design, with three branches, are visible in the photograph of the Campden Hill showroom (see previous entry); see also Church 1890. This is a good example of Benson's use of highly polished copper as a reflective surface, both for the wall-plate and the drip trays.

21 Oil lamp [PLATE 62]

Brass, with tall cylindrical glass flame-shield over which the shade is passed. The shade, formed of a flat sheet of brass, scalloped along the lower edge and riveted at its longer side, is hinged to an arm rising from the moulding at the base of the flame and can be adjusted by pulling the chain to direct the light at a particular angle. The feet have leaf-shaped ends.

MARKS Stamped on one of the feet with the Benson shield trade mark and the letter 'B'.

Designed before 1898 and made in the factory of W.A.S. Benson, London, before 1914.

H 53 cm   1982,1-8,1

A version of this design with taller legs and added side supports was illustrated by Walter Crane in *The Bases of Design*, 1898, 77; Crane found the metal shade an improvement on the standard urn-shaped oil lamp design. For a slightly different design, the shade made of overlapping sheets of copper instead of one continuous sheet, see Anscombe and Gere 1978, pl. 69. According to Muthesius, in *Das Englische Haus* of 1904-5, Benson was the first to illumine dining-room tables with light reflected from a shiny metal surface. For contemporary appraisals of Benson's 'rational metal structures, perfectly bare of every kind of adornment' see *The House Beautiful* v, April 1899, 220-22; Muthesius 1901; *Art Journal* 1905, 97-9; Sparrow 1904 and 1909.

Similar lamps were sold by Bing in the 1890s. They were also advertised under the heading 'Benson's Art Metal Designs' by the Army & Navy Stores (see Army & Navy Stores 1907 Price List), though with more traditional opal glass shades. Benson lamps with glass or silk shades continued to be included in the Army & Navy Stores price lists until 1926-7, by which time they were presumably old stock.

22 Coffee-pot and stand with burners [PLATE 63]

Brass, with horn knop to lid and wicker-bound handle. The pot is spun, with stamped lid; the stand is cast and is fitted with three lidded burners.

MARKS The base of the pot stamped with Benson's trade mark: the letters 'WASB' between a mallet flanked by two hammers, within a shield. On either side the letters 'R' and 'S'; the base of the stand stamped 'BENSON'.

Designed c.1890 and made in the factory of W.A.S. Benson, London before 1914.

Coffee-pot: H 23.8 cm. Coffee-pot on stand: H 32.2 cm.
Stand: H 10.5 cm, D 15.2 cm   1980,5-9,1

23 Kettle and stand with burner [PLATE 63]

Electroplate, the kettle with wicker-bound handle ending in decorative 'cartouches' in the eighteenth-century style, the lid with ebonised wood knop. The stand with leaf-shaped rests and paw feet.

MARKS Stamped on the base of the kettle with the Benson trade mark, 'WASB' between a mallet and two hammers within a shield, the letters 'L' and 'I' either side; trade mark also on foot of stand flanked by the letters 'B' and 'V'.

Designed c.1900 and made in the factory of W.A.S. Benson, London, before 1914.

Total H 24.2 cm. Kettle: H 13.4 cm, W 22.5 cm. Stand: H 13.3 cm, W 18.2 cm   1981,1-5,1

It is not certain when Benson began to work in electroplate. However, the detailed listings in the Arts & Crafts Exhibition Society Catalogues give some guidance; Benson's metalwork is usually specified as copper or brass up until 1903, when the first reference to electroplate appears (Arts & Crafts Exhibition Society, *Catalogue of the Seventh Exhibition*, 1903, 149, no. 393, an electroplate teaset).

Most of Benson's kettles are much deeper in form; the shallow, flat shape of this kettle is unusual. For a range of kettles, see London, Haslam & Whiteway, 1981. A number of Benson kettles appear in the Army & Navy Stores 1907 Price List, though unlike the lamps, they are not credited to Benson; they are notably more expensive than other models.

Bogler, Theodor 1897-1968

There is no monograph on Bogler. For biographical details, see Janda 1959; Cologne 1978 and Berlin 1989.

24 Jug [PLATE 132]

Tin-glazed earthenware, the body turned, with flat top, the handle in the form of a raised rectangle and an upward-pointing cylindrical spout through which the jug is filled. Painted in blue and green on a white ground.

MARKS Brush-painted on the base with the monogram 'TB' within the factory mark of the Steingut-Fabriken Velten-Vordamm, Werk Velten.

Designed and made at the Velten works of the Steingut-Fabriken Velten-Vordamm, near Berlin, in 1925-6.

H 12.7 cm, D 13.2 cm   1983,10-8,5

Bogler was a student at the Bauhaus Pottery Workshop in Dornburg from 1920, becoming business manager of the workshop in 1923. His brother-in-law, Otto Lindig, was first a student at and then technical manager of the Bauhaus Pottery Workshop at the same time. From 1925 to 1926 Bogler was artistic director of the Velten works at the Steingut- und Fayence-fabriken Velten-Vordamm, near Berlin, at the invitation of the factory's director, Dr Hermann Harkort. In his two years of work at Velten, Bogler exerted a great influence on the factory's production. After the suicide of his wife in 1925 Bogler converted to Catholicism, and in 1927 became a Benedictine monk, remaining so for the rest of his life. He continued to make ceramics for the Maria Laach monastery and, after the Second World War, for the Karlsruhe Majolika-Manufaktur and the Höhr-Grenzhausen factories.

The painted signature on this piece is that used by Bogler for individual pieces, as distinct from the printed mark for serial production (Cologne 1978, 318). Several variants of this eccentric and impractical model were made at the Velten works: for a similar jug with loop handle instead of a flat handle in the Kunstgewerbemuseum, Cologne, see Cologne 1978, no. 601. Another variant in the Kunstgewerbemuseum, Berlin (Berlin 1972, no. 3) has an extra loop at the side of the body, while the top loop handle is flat instead of round section and placed at right angles to the spout. A third example, closer to the Cologne version, is in the Badisches Landesmuseum, Karlsruhe; this example also has striped decoration (Berlin 1989, no. 242).

For a full discussion of the collaboration between the Bauhaus and Harkort, the proprietor of the Steingut-Fabriken Velten-Vordamm, see Berlin 1989, 202-5 and cat. nos 240ff. For Harkort's own writings on the association of art and industry, see above and Bröhan III, 1985, 553 (which reprints an article of 1922 by Harkort, 'Die Kachel und Töpferkunst'). Hermann Harkort took over the family works at Vordamm in 1908; the new factory at Velten was built in 1913-14; the firm closed down in 1931 (Reineking v. Bock 1979, 312).

Bohemian

25 Goblet [PLATE 8]

Clear glass flashed with amber, free-blown, with facet-cut foot and stem, the bowl wheel-engraved with a scene of stags in a forest.

MARKS None.

Made in Bohemia, in the mid-nineteenth century.

H 23.8 cm   1902,9-14,1 Given by Miss Dollman

Similar goblets with forest hunting scenes, the stems often elaborately cut, were widely popular in the mid-nineteenth century and may have been made as hunting prizes. Goblets of this type are usually attributed to the workshop of August Böhm (1812-90), Meisterdorf or Karl Pfohl (1826-94) in Steinschönau, northern Bohemia (see Rückert 1982, nos 927 and 934, in the Bayerisches Nationalmuseum, Munich).

Brandt, Marianne 1893-1983

There is no monograph on Brandt. For biographical details and quotations from her own writings, see E. Neumann ed., *Bauhaus and Bauhaus people*, New York 1970.

For further discussion of her role in the Bauhaus metal workshop, see: Wingler, H.M., *The Bauhaus*, MIT Press, 1969 (first published in German, Cologne 1962).

26 Tea-infuser [PLATE 131; COLOUR PLATE XV]

Silver, with hemispherical hand-raised body set on a cross-shaped foot, a D-shaped ebony handle and flat lid set off-centre with cylindrical ebony silver-topped knop. The original pierced silver strainer with handle is designed to fit neatly inside the top opening.

MARKS Stamped with German assay marks: a crescent, a crown and '900'.

Designed in 1924 at the Bauhaus Metal Workshop, Weimar, and made either there before 1925 or in Dessau between 1925 and 1929.

H 7.3 cm, D of top 10.6 cm, D of lid 6 cm, W (spout to handle) 16.1 cm. Strainer: H 4 cm, D 5.7 cm   1979, 11-2, 1

Brandt joined the Bauhaus in 1924 and transferred from the Vorkurs to the Metal Workshop in 1924 on the advice of Moholy-Nagy, who directed the Metal Workshop as *Formmeister* from 1923 to 1928. She was the only woman to join the Weimar Metal Workshop and her presence was not immediately accepted, but she succeeded Moholy-Nagy as director of the Workshop at Dessau from 1928 to 1929. Brandt left the Bauhaus to work briefly with Gropius in Berlin and then for the Ruppelwerk metalware factory in Gotha, Thuringia from 1929 to 1932.

The combination of geometric shapes in this tea-infuser is closely related to the Constructivist prints made by Moholy-Nagy at the Bauhaus. The concentration on form rather than decoration was intended to produce designs suitable for industrial production, but early Bauhaus designs such as this were made with little or no experience of designing for industry; this handmade tea-infuser has become famous as a classic Bauhaus object, but it remains in the tradition of costly craft-based metalworking as taught by the *Lehrmeister* (technical instructor), Christian Dell. Brandt herself later wrote of the problems of industrially producing silverware and other tableware (Neumann ed. 1970, 98). For further discussion of these issues, see Naylor 1985.

For a contemporary illustration of this tea-infuser, described as a pot for tea extract with deep strainer, see Gropius 1925, 46; *Die Schaulade*, 6 Jahrgang, Heft 10, July 1926, 216. Apart from the British Museum example, only one other silver example is recorded (sold Christie's, Amsterdam, 26 October 1989, lot 431). In addition, three base-metal examples have been published: a version in brass with silver strainer, in the Bauhaus-Archiv Museum, Berlin (Wingler 1981, no. 193, H 7.5 cm); a version in bronze with nickel-silver foot, spout and handle mounts, silver plating inside and a silver strainer, in the Germanisches Nationalmuseum, Nuremberg (Stuttgart 1975, no. 174, H 8 cm); another bronze version with silver base, spout and handle mount, in the Kunstsammlungen, Weimar, Germany (Brussels 1988, no. 34, H 7.8 cm). These last two examples have a wider knop to the lid which differs from the British Museum example. A similar tea-infuser was included in the Bauhaus Dessau display at the Leipzig Exhibition of 1927 (Leipzig 1928, pl. 11).

In 1924 Brandt also designed a larger teapot, with hinged bow-shaped handle at the top, as part of a six-piece silver tea service (*Die Schaulade*, July 1926, 217); a complete example of this service survives in the Bauhaus-Archiv Museum, Berlin (Wingler 1981, no. 194). The Kunstsammlungen, Weimar has a four-piece service in brass, nickel-silver and silver (Brussels 1988, no. 35), while a silver teapot from this service is in the Museum of Modern Art, New York (Drexler & Daniel 1959,

pl. 37). There was also a second tea-infuser design of spherical shape with semi-circular ebony handle and cross-shaped foot, as on the British Museum infuser (for a bronze example in the Kunstsammlungen, Weimar, see Scheidig 1967, pl. 32).

The tea-infuser was widely praised for its simplicity of form and practicality of construction: the push-on lid placed to the right, away from the spout, so that it did not drip (unlike the usual hinged lids on metal teapots), the wood knop and handle, which were heat-resistant, and the non-drip spout were especially singled out for remark (*Die Schaulade*, July 1926, 222).

Brocard, Philippe-Joseph   d. 1896

There is no monograph on Brocard. For biographical details and further bibliography, see Mundt 1973; Bloch-Dermant 1974, 22-7; Houston 1976, 467; Hilschenz-Mlynek and Ricke 1985, 47-51; Schmitt 1989, 40-49. See also J. Bloch-Dermant, 'Joseph Brocard et la renaissance du verre émaillé après 1860', *L'Estampille*, 1979, no. 111, 44-55; K. Morrison McClinton, 'Brocard and the Islamic Revival', *Connoisseur*, December 1980, 278-81.

27 Mosque lamp [PLATE 21]

Pale-green free-blown bubbly glass, with six applied lugs, gilded and enamelled in blue, red, white, pink, yellow and green. The surface has been gilded all over before the application of the enamels. The pattern is outlined in red and then certain areas filled in with enamels. On the upper register, a band of Arabic outlined in red and filled in with blue enamel; on each side, two armorial roundels in opaque white and red enamel, depicting a mule bearing a ceremonial pack-saddle. The central band of Arabic is outlined in red, but the background is filled in with blue enamel. There are two further armorial roundels on the underside of the bulging centre, interspersed with foliate cartouches in red, white, blue, pink, green and yellow enamel. The green has always misfired and is very pitted. The blue is the most translucent colour; the others are thicker and opaque. The foot has further foliate roundels and an outline pattern of leaves and winged harpies. Both bowl and foot are cracked, probably in the firing.

MARKS Painted in red enamel round the top of the foot 'P Brocard à Paris X^re 1867 Faubourg St Honoré No. 216'.

Designed and made in December 1867 (X = *decem*) in the workshop of P.-J. Brocard, 216 Faubourg St Honoré, Paris.

H 35.6 cm   1902, 11-18, 1   Given by Sir Charles Hercules Read

P.-J. Brocard started his career as a restorer and collector of antiques; fascinated by the Mamluk mosque lamps in the Musée de Cluny, Paris, he began to collect them himself and thus had models close at hand to study. Mosque lamps were luxury objects for hanging in mosques and mausolea and were the most spectacular achievements of enamelled glass from Mamluk Egypt and Syria from the twelfth to the fourteenth centuries. Brocard was among the first to revive Islamic enamelling techniques: vitreous enamels were applied to the surface of the vessel and then fixed by firing so that the enamels fused to the surface. The gilding was applied beneath the enamels in the form of gold leaf or powdered dust and similarly fused to the surface in the firing (for a brief account in English of Islamic enamelled glass, see Pinder-Wilson in London 1976a, 134; for detailed studies, see Schmoranz 1899 and Lamm 1929-30).

It is usually stated that Brocard first exhibited his enamelled glasses at the Paris Exhibition of 1867; this lamp is thus among his earliest documentary pieces. It is copied, though not entirely accurately, from a fourteenth-century mosque lamp then in the Paris collection of Baron Gustave de Rothschild (Lamm 1929, I, pl. 192, no. 6; by that time it was in the Gulbenkian collection in Paris, and it is now in the Gulbenkian Foundation, Lisbon; see *Calouste Gulbenkian Museum, Catalogue*, Lisbon 1982, no. 327). The Rothschild lamp was first illustrated as a colour lithograph in one of the most important French sourcebooks for Islamic art, the *Recueil de dessins pour l'art et l'industrie*, published in Paris in 1859 by E.V. Collinot and A. de Beaumont (pl. 4). Mosque lamps were avidly collected in Paris and elsewhere in Europe during the 1860s. Several examples from a number of different private collections were shown at an exhibition of oriental art held by the Union Centrale des Beaux-Arts, Paris, in 1869; the Rothschild lamp was among them (*Gazette des Beaux-Arts* 1869, II, 340, where it is described with reference to its armorial bearings).

Brocard has either misunderstood or altered elements of the Islamic design: for example, the winged harpies on the foot have no parallels in Mamluk art. When the Brocard lamp is compared with other Islamic mosque lamps in the British Museum, there are some obvious differences: the glass itself is green, rather than clear or pinkish-brown, Brocard's blue enamel is more turquoise in colour, his green enamel is deeper, but the reds are very close. Brocard's enamelling and gilding are uneven and the pattern overall is not well drawn. Nevertheless, Edward Dillon included it in his survey of Saracenic glass as an 'admirably executed imitation', noting that the blue was made with cobalt, instead of lapis, as in Mamluk glass (Dillon 1907, 152). It is an interesting piece because few other documentary mosque lamps by Brocard appear to survive from this early date: for a mosque lamp inscribed on the foot 'Paris 1867' in the Österreichisches Museum für angewandte Kunst, Vienna, see Munich 1972, no. 193.

Brocard's mosque lamps were shown at the International Exhibition in London in 1871 (*Art Journal Illustrated Catalogue*, 1871, 57), at the Vienna Exhibition of 1873 and at the Paris Exhibition of 1878 (*Art Journal Illustrated Catalogue*, 1878, 171, text only). Brocard's later mosque lamps tend to be pastiches rather than direct copies and the enamelling is of better quality. For two small vases in the form of mosque lamps acquired by the Bayerisches Gewerbemuseum, Nuremberg from the Vienna Exhibition of 1873, see Munich 1972, nos 194-5 and Bornfleth 1985, no. 80; in these examples the enamelling is superior to that on the 1867 lamp, but the smaller size may have been easier to execute (the vases are only 13.8cm high). In 1889 the Victoria and Albert Museum purchased a mosque lamp signed and dated 'Brocard Paris 1880' (721-1890, H 23cm) from the Maison Rousseau-Léveillé, Paris; Ernest-Baptiste Léveillé and François Eugène Rousseau, both of whom were glassmakers, opened their shop in the Boulevard Haussmann in 1869, selling their own work and that of others interested in the art of the East. For further mosque lamps by Brocard, in varying sizes, see Polak 1962, pl. 14, a tazza of 1878 in the National Museums of Scotland, Edinburgh; Hilschenz-Mlynek and Ricke 1985, no. 11; Schmitt 1989, nos 10-11, with reference to several others; Leipzig 1989, nos 214-15.

Following his meeting with Émile Gallé in 1878, Brocard's style became freer and more naturalistic, but he continued to make mosque lamps. Curiously, he did not patent his technique until 1891; the patent is published in full in Bloch-Dermant

1974, 26-7. It was necessary for the composition of the enamel colours to be similar to that of the vessel to be decorated so that the colours fused smoothly. In his *Notice sur la production du verre* for the Paris Exhibition of 1884, Gallé admired Brocard's technique and noted that his enamels were not commercially available (quoted in Polak 1967). It should be mentioned that the patent applies only to enamelling methods; it is not certain whether Brocard made his own glass or whether he used blanks supplied by other manufacturers, as in the case of his friend and contemporary E. Rousseau, who decorated blanks made by the firm of Appert Frères of Clichy-la-Garenne (Hilschenz-Mlynek and Ricke 1985, 365).

Brocard's son, Émile, joined the business in 1884 and the company became known as Brocard Fils. P.-J. Brocard died in 1896, but the company continued until 1904 as the Verrerie Brocard. Some idea of the continued popularity of Brocard glass can be gleaned from the interest shown by the New York art dealer, Samuel P. Avery, whose diaries, together with those of his adviser, George Lucas, record purchases of glass from Brocard in Paris between 1873 and 1904 (Morrison McClinton 1980).

Copies of Islamic mosque lamps were also made by Salviati & Company in Murano, Venice, from 1869 (Venice 1982, no. 417), while the French ceramic artist Théodore Deck made earthenware versions which he exhibited at the Paris Exhibition of 1867: the Victoria and Albert Museum acquired a pair of Deck's mosque-lamp vases at the 1867 exhibition; they are also inspired by the same Rothschild lamp as the Brocard example under discussion, but the Arabic inscriptions have been transformed into a floral ground (Philadelphia 1978, no. IV-15; Aslin 1973, no. 25). Both Deck and Brocard would have been familiar with the illustration of the original in the *Recueil de dessins*, but they probably also had direct knowledge of the Rothschild lamp itself. As further evidence of the popularity of the mosque lamp shape, it is worth noting that the enamelled glass vases in the form of mosque lamps were exhibited by the Imperial Glass Manufactory of St Petersburg at the International Exhibition of 1862 in London (Waring 1862, I, pl. 42), while earthenware vases of this form were produced by the Della Robbia Pottery in England around 1900 (e.g. Sotheby's, Chester, 3-5 October 1989, lots 1427-8). The decoration in the latter case is not Islamic.

I am grateful to Michael Rogers for his comments.

Brouwer, Willem Coenraad 1877-1933

E. Ebbinge, *W.C. Brouwer (1877-1933), aarden vaatwerk-tuinaardewerk, bouwaardewerk*, exhibition catalogue, Gemeentelijk Museum Het Princessehof, Leeuwarden, 1980 (catalogue published as no. 97/98, 1980, 1-2, of the Mededelingenblad Nederlandse Vereniging van Vrienden van de Ceramiek, with English summary).

28 Vase [PLATE 79]

Earthenware, red body, hand-thrown, with sgraffito decoration incised through a layer of white slip. The slip glazed deep turquoise, the body and interior glazed green.

MARKS Impressed on the base with the monogram formed of the initials 'WCB' and 'MBB' (Willem Coenraad Brouwer and his wife Margaretha Breedt-Bruyn), contained in a letter 'L' for Leiderdorp, the date code for December 1902 and the model number '37'.

Designed *c.*1900-1 and made by W.C. Brouwer in 1902 in his own factory at Leiderdorp, Holland.

H. 20.7cm   1987,6-11,1

Brouwer trained as a painter in Leiden before turning to ceramics in 1898. His first ceramic exhibition was held in Gouda in February 1899. As a result his pots were shown at het Binnenhuis, the interior design gallery in Amsterdam, at whose suggestion he adopted the monogram of his own and his wife's initials. The mark was used in this form from 1901, when Brouwer moved to Leiderdorp, until 1905, when the word 'HOLLAND' was added (see Ebbinge 1980, 53). For a full account of Brouwer's work, see Ebbinge 1980, where a closely similar vase dated 1900 is illustrated on page 33. Since the British Museum vase bears a low model number it may have been designed during the period 1899-1901, when Brouwer was working in Gouda.

Brouwer exhibited successfully at the international exhibitions in Turin in 1902, Krefeld in 1903, Milan in 1906, Brussels in 1910 etc. The *Studio* report of Brouwer's pottery at the Turin Exhibition described it as 'simple' and 'barbarous . . . but full of a charm of its own . . . Made of coarse clay, varnished in yellow or green, with rudimentary designs cut in relief . . . This pottery has achieved an extraordinary success, but the greater portion of it was purchased before the exhibition opened, by the Director of the Leyden Museum' (vol. 26, 1902, 207). At the exhibition of Dutch applied art in Copenhagen in 1904, the Kunstindustrimuseet acquired a large group of Brouwer's ceramics, including a vase of identical design, bearing the same model number, 37, and glazed in green and brown (Burgers 1972, pl. 24); the shape, however, differs slightly, showing the variations that occurred with hand-thrown models.

Brouwer's use of slip decoration and contrasting glazes to emphasise the pattern shows the influence of both Dutch peasant pottery and of A.W. Finch, the Belgian potter who settled in Finland in 1897. Brouwer's powerful designs, however, were strongly influenced by the play of lines and forms in Maori decoration, notably the '*koru*' motif, resembling a curled tendril. Brouwer had studied the collections of the Ethnographical Museum in Leiden and his combination of geometric forms with the curving Art Nouveau line is highly original.

See also Leidelmeijer and van der Cingel 1983, 80–82.

Burges, William   1827-81

Pullan, R.P. ed., *The Designs of William Burges*, London 1885

Mordaunt Crook, J., *William Burges and the High Victorian Dream*, London 1981

The Strange Genius of William Burges Art-Architect 1827-1881, exhibition catalogue, National Museum of Wales, Cardiff, 1981

See also London 1971 (section D: William Burges) and London 1972 (section B, nos B87–102).

29 Cup and cover   [PLATES 5-6; COLOUR PLATE I]

Maple wood mounted in silver decorated with translucent enamel, the cup and cover formed of turned wood bowls. The lid mounted in silver with a scalloped border above a band of applied scrolls with trefoil terminals; at the top a rosette enamelled in blue, red and green,

surmounted by a raised knop with foliate scrolls, set with a cabochon agate. The bowl mounted with a broad silver rim inscribed in Lombardic script 'WILLIELMUS BURGES ME FIERI FECIT ANNO DM MDCCCLXXVIII' and, at the base, a silver rosette engraved with leaves. The bowl is set on a silver foot enamelled in blue, red and green with four interlaced quatrefoils containing grotesque beasts against a ground decorated with a diaper pattern and butterflies, surmounted by a band of black enamel squares. Inside each half are two enamelled silver medallions. Inside the lid is a camel on a chain, the caparison decorated with a red heart and arrows with the letter 'w' in the field. Inside the bowl is a grotesque winged creature with bearded and capped human head and the signet 'WB' in the centre. Beneath the enamel the silver ground has been engraved with a lozenge pattern incorporating a rosette.

MARKS Each separate piece of silver stamped with full or partial London hallmarks incorporating the date-letter 'B' for 1877-8 or 'C' for 1878-9 (on rim of cover only) and maker's mark 'JB' for Jes Barkentin of Barkentin & Krall. Most of the hallmarks are not visible when the cup is assembled; the cup was dismantled during conservation in 1990 and the marks were recorded as follows:
Rim of base: full hallmarks with date-letter 'B'
Rim of cover: full hallmarks with date-letter 'C'
Enamelled rosette on cover: lion, Sovereign's head, maker's mark
Finial: lion's head and maker's mark
Enamelled disc inside cover: lion, Sovereign's head, maker's mark
Enamelled disc inside base: lion and maker's mark (twice)
Rosette on base: lion, Sovereign's head, maker's mark
Foot: full hallmarks with date-letter 'B'

Designed by Burges for his own use and made by the firm of Barkentin & Krall, London, in 1878.

H 15.4cm, D of bowl 11.9cm   1981,6-3,1

Burges's eclectic inspiration rarely produced objects as restrained and elegant as this cup, which illustrates his interest in French Gothic art, whether thirteenth-century manuscript illumination, from which the grotesques and diaper ground are derived, or fourteenth-century *basse taille* enamelling. The interior enamel medallions are characteristically full of humour – the self-portrait as a medieval man with a grotesque body – and allusions – the chained camel with heart and arrows also alludes to Burges, who often used hearts and arrows in objects designed for himself.

A number of detailed drawings for the cup and its decoration, together with a set of five similar cups that Burges designed for his friends, are preserved among the Burges drawings in the Royal Institute of British Architects, in the volume 'Orfèvrerie Domestique', 15–16. Firstly there is a drawing for the cup in elevation and section, captioned 'Cup for W. Burges', with the enamelled camel medallion inside the lid, the colours as executed (Fig. 4; Orfèvrerie Domestique, 16). On the previous page is a series of drawings of enamelled motifs (Fig. 5): in the centre, a set of four quatrefoils as they appear on Burges's cup, annotated 'this is one set' and 'this set is like used for my cup'. The narrow band of black squares is annotated 'this goes round all the cups'. Below is the design for the butterfly and diaper pattern between each quatrefoil, annotated 'this is common to all'. There follows another set of quatrefoils with different figures. Above are drawings for two circular medallions comparable to those inside the cup, one of which has the same bearded grotesque but with different initials, and four further medallions with initials only, including Burges's own. In each case the names are given below the medallions: A. Rivington, A.C. Bell, H. Curzon, B. Frere and R.W. Edis.

Burges's surviving Estimate Book for 12 August 1875 to 30 March 1881 (in the Victoria and Albert Museum Library, MSS

86,SS.52) confirms that the cup was intended for his own use. Burges recorded details of the work carried out, the contractor, the cost and the client. Under 28 February 1878 is an entry for five silver-gilt cups with enamels made by Hart & Company. The following entry, for 7 March 1878, reads 'I do [ditto] with wood instead of silver bowl, Barkentin, "self", "£9"'. The date-letter 'c' for 1878-9 on the rim of the base of the cup indicates that this part was not completed until after May 1878, since the date-letter was changed in the month of May. The items with date-letter 'B' would have been completed between March and May 1878. The five cups for Burges's friends are probably those listed under 8 February 1878 as 'cups, maple bowl, silver and enamelled with engraved inscriptions, Barkentin, each £10. 10', to which he has added 'if silver bowls instead of maple £12. 10s.'. An annotation of 1 March 1878 reads '5 cups complete in silver for £50'.

This cup was exhibited at the Fine Art Society in 1981 (see London 1981, 18, no. 10); see also Mordaunt Crook 1981, 316, fig. 236.

For Barkentin & Krall, see London 1971, Mordaunt Crook 1981, 212, Cardiff 1981 (section c) and Culme 1987. Jes Barkentin, a metalworker of Danish origin, is recorded in London in the early 1860s and made his name with the silver presentation vase given by the Danish residents in Britain to Princess Alexandra on her wedding in 1863. In 1867 he replaced the firm of John Keith as silversmith to the Ecclesiological Society, with which Burges was closely associated. Barkentin was joined by the German silversmith Carl Christopher Krall c.1873 and the firm continued as Barkentin & Krall until the 1930s.

The Museum also holds a Gothic-style gold pectoral cross and chain designed by Burges, possibly also for his own use; see C. Gere in Gere et al. 1984, cat. no. 1001.

Burton, William 1863-1941

For Pilkington's Tile & Pottery Company, of which William and Joseph Burton were Manager and Assistant Manager, see:
Lomax, A., *Royal Lancastrian Pottery 1900-38*, Bolton, 1957
Cross, A.J., *Pilkington's Royal Lancastrian Pottery and Tiles*, London 1980
Gray, R. and Clarke, D., *A Catalogue of the Lancastrian Pottery at Manchester City Art Galleries*, exhibition catalogue, Manchester, 1982
W. Burton wrote several books and articles, of which a selection is given here: Burton, W., *A History and Description of English Porcelain*, London 1902; *A History and Description of English Earthenware and Stoneware, to the beginning of the nineteenth century*, London 1904; *Porcelain, Its nature, art and manufacture*, London 1906; *A general history of porcelain*, London 1921; 'The Palette of the Potter', *JSA* 44, February 1896, 319-34; 'Recent Advances in Pottery Decoration', *JSA* 49, February 1901, 213-21; 'Crystalline Glazes', *JSA* 52, May 1904, 595-603; 'Lustre Pottery', *JSA* 55, April 1907, 756-70.

30 Lion　　　　[PLATE 26; COLOUR PLATE VI]

Earthenware, press-moulded, white body, covered with green 'sunstone' glaze containing gold flecks. There are two firing holes at the top and between the feet.

MARKS None.

Made in 1899-1900 at Pilkington's Tile & Pottery Company Ltd, Clifton Junction, near Manchester (renamed Pilkington's Royal Lancastrian Pottery and Tiles in 1913), as an enlarged version of the cast-iron lions designed by Alfred Stevens for the British Museum (see Cat. 276-7).

H 60.8cm　1903,4-10,1　Given by William Burton, manager of Pilkington's from 1891 to 1915

William Burton was a chemist at Wedgwood from 1887 before being invited to manage the newly formed Pilkington Tile & Pottery Company in 1891. In 1895 he was joined by his brother Joseph (1868-1934), who was responsible for many of the glaze experiments, including 'sunstone' (see Lomax, 59-60, 152; Cross, 25-6).

Abraham Lomax, chemist at the factory from 1896 to 1911, records that a pair of lions with sunstone glaze were shown at the Paris Exhibition of 1900 and at an exhibition of Lancastrian pottery in London at the Graves Gallery in June 1904 (Lomax 1957, 24, 29). For the 1904 exhibition, Lomax quotes a press report describing 'the sunstone glaze with deep glint of innumerable crystals. What these can do in the way of actual application may be seen by the great lions cast from an original mould by Alfred Stevens, and now upstanding with a fine dignity and new but exquisite colour'. Lomax gives no reference for the Paris Exhibition of 1900 and the lions are not recorded in the official catalogue, but Pilkington's themselves produced a small illustrated catalogue of their exhibits (see Gray 1981, 175 and note 6). A copy of this catalogue is to be found in the Victoria and Albert Museum Library; it is undated and is titled simply 'Pilkington's Tile & Pottery Company Ltd' with no reference to the exhibition. However, on p. 8 is a map of the Paris exhibition buildings indicating the location of Pilkington's stand on the Esplanade des Invalides, together with the exhibits relating to the furniture and decoration of houses and public buildings. The catalogue comprises seventy-three items, all tiles, but at the very end, on p. 28, are three unnumbered items. The first is: 'item 00. LIONS. The lions, made in buff faience and glazed in "sunstone" glazes, are enlarged copies of the well-known lions designed by the late Alfred Stevens, which formerly decorated the railing round the British Museum.' (The other unnumbered items were two tile pavements designed by Lewis F. Day and samples of coloured glazes.) In his article on 'Modern Pottery at the Paris Exhibition' L. F. Day gave special praise to '...the sunstone glazes which the English firm of Pilkington's use in many of their tiles, and in the enlarged version of Alfred Stevens's lion mounting guard upon the little English stand: they are triumphs of technique, and sparkle like veritable aventurine' (*Art Journal Special Number. The Paris Exhibition, 1900-1901*, 98). A pair of similar green 'sunstone' lions is owned by Manchester City Art Gallery, though the green is a darker shade (see Manchester 1982, cat. no. 1). The lions are all made from the same coarse white clay body, described as 'faience', as that used by Pilkington's for tiles; it was developed into Pilkington's 'Parian faience' for architectural work (Gray 1981, 175).

It is likely that the Pilkington lions were manufactured with the aid of one of the bronze casts of the Stevens lions made by Messrs Brucciani & Co. after 1896, from which an enlarged mould could have been produced (see Stevens, cat. 276-7). Significantly, Lewis F. Day, who was hired by Pilkington's as designer and consultant in 1899, owned one of the bronze casts, which he had purchased at the sale of the contents of Stevens's studio, held after the sculptor's death on 19 July 1877 (see lot 122, 'A bronze casting of lion executed for the rails of the British Museum. Lewis F. Day. £4 5s.', quoted in Towndrow 1939, 270). Day was an admirer of Stevens and in his role as consultant to Pilkington's may have suggested the production of the lions to William Burton.

Burton, with his interest in ceramic history and technology, had close contacts with the British Museum, especially with Sir Charles Hercules Read, Keeper of the then Department of British and Medieval Antiquities from 1896 to 1921. Prior to the gift of the lion, Burton had presented to the Museum in March 1902 a series of small tiles with trial glazes (possibly from the 'arrangements of coloured glazes' shown at the Paris Exhibition). And in 1910 Burton gave Read a handsome covered jar in Pilkington's lustreware, decorated with heraldic lions by Gordon Forsyth and inscribed 'W. Burton 1910' 'C.H. Read' (Cross 1980, pl.XXXI; sold Christie's, London, 19 July 1989, lot 230; a similar, though less elaborate jar, given to the Victoria and Albert Museum by Forsyth's daughter in 1974, c.39 and a.1974, was originally intended for Read but never presented because the glaze had not succeeded).

In describing the panel of tiles in green sunstone glazes shown at the Paris Exhibition of 1900, Burton wrote: 'These glazes, which have been perfected on earthenware by our Mr Joseph Burton, contain clouds of golden crystals in the glaze, thus resembling the mineral known as Sunstone. We are now able to produce this new effect in a variety of colours.' Burton does not record when sunstone was first produced, but Lewis F. Day, writing on Lancastrian pottery in 1904, stated that Pilkington's used sunstone on tiles long before the 1900 exhibition (*Art Journal*, 1904, 201-4) and indeed tile panels with sunstone glazes were exhibited by Pilkington's at the Arts & Crafts Exhibition Society in 1896 (*Catalogue of the Fifth Exhibition*, 1896, 118-19, no. 478 b, c, g, i). The mineral sunstone, or aventurine feldspar, contains minute red, orange or green crystals. Pilkington's sunstone was produced in green (made by adding copper chromate to a rich lead glaze) and also in brown and yellow. In his 1901 paper to the Society of Arts, Burton explained that crystalline glazes resulted from the 'supersaturation of a glaze with mineral compounds at a high temperature, and the subsequent separation of these in crystalline form on cooling'; he contrasted 'sunstone', in which the crystals were 'diffused throughout the mass of the glaze in golden clouds' with the glazes produced in Denmark, France and Germany, in which the crystals appeared in patches on the surface of the glaze (Burton 1901, 217). For an example of French starry crystalline glaze, see Sèvres, Cat. 269. In his later paper of 1904 (p. 599), Burton noted that on high-fired wares, the 'sunstone' glazes developed a steely-blue colour, and that the glazes were similar to the aventurine or tiger-eye glazes produced at the Rookwood Pottery in America (see Cat. 260).

Castle Hedingham Pottery 1837-1905

Bradley, R.J. 'The Story of Castle Hedingham pottery', *Connoisseur*, Part 1, February 1968, 77-83; Part 2, March 1968, 152-7; Part 3, April 1968, 210-16

The Castle Hedingham Pottery was founded in 1837 by Edward Bingham senior; ornamental wares, in the form of red terracotta baskets, were first produced in 1853 by his son, Edward (b.1829, date of death unknown). The peak production of glazed wares ran from the mid 1870s to the end of the 1880s. The Pottery is noted for its pastiches of archaeological and historical models, ranging from Greek vases to wall-reliefs after Da Vinci, as well as the popular loving-cups and tygs to commemorate births and weddings. With their simple methods of manufacture, the copies were not intended to deceive and usually bore one of the Pottery's marks. At the Hertford Fine Arts Exhibition of 1880 the Pottery's exhibits were purchased by the School of Fine Art at South Kensington, while Lord Braybrooke commissioned a special drinking cup for Audley End (Bradley 1, fig. 10). From 1899 the pottery was run by the founder's grandson, Edward W. Bingham (b.1862), under whom it was renamed the Essex Art Pottery, with new marks, from 1901 to 1905.

31 Tyg [PLATE 4]

Earthenware, glazed brown, with four double handles and applied moulded relief ornaments in the form of fleur-de-lys, rosettes, etc., and the date '1612' also in applied relief. All applied details glazed white. Firing crack to rim.

MARKS None.

Designed by Edward Bingham senior and made at the Castle Hedingham Pottery c.1875-1901.

H 9.3cm   1926,2-20,1   Given by Mrs L. A. Akers

Bradley, 3, 210, gives a list of numbered wares produced at the Pottery and suggests that it began to number wares from the later 1880s when they became more commercial. Thus unnumbered wares are probably among the earlier products. Nos 3 and 34 are both listed as 'Four-handled tyg dated 1612'.

32 Jug [PLATE 4]

Earthenware, glazed matt brown with rough, lumpy finish, with an inscription in applied slip glazed blue 'CONSIDER WELL YE END OF ALL THAT U INTEND'. A further band of relief ornament in blue around the rim and on the front. The handle decorated with an applied lizard, glazed blue.

MARKS On the base, applied castle-keep relief mark incorporating a scroll with 'E. Bingham' below.

Designed and made by Edward Bingham senior at the Castle Hedingham Pottery c.1865-99.

H 16.1cm   1930,10-22,1   Given by T.G. Arnold

According to Bradley, 2, 156, this is the earliest of the keep marks used by Bingham senior and is not usually found on the better-quality wares of the late 1870s and 1880s.

33 Mug [PLATE 4]

Earthenware, glazed blue outside and buff inside, with applied moulded relief decoration in the form of Hedingham Castle among trees, glazed buff and green, with 'Hedingham' applied in relief to the left and 'castle' to the right.

MARKS The base incised 'E W Bingham England'.

Designed by Edward or Edward W. Bingham and made by E.W. Bingham at the Castle Hedingham Pottery c.1880-1901.

H 10.2 cm   OA (Old Acquisition) 10710

E. W. Bingham began to assist his father in 1874 at the age of twelve; he was certainly signing his works by 1880. In Bradley's list of numbered wares, this is no. 201 'Tapered mug with Hedingham Castle design on front' (1968, 211). This mid-blue became known as the pottery's finest colour.

Chashnik, Ilya Grigorevich 1902-29

Ilja Tschashnik, exhibition catalogue, Kunstmuseum, Düsseldorf, 1978

34 Plate   [PLATE 142]

Hard-paste porcelain, glazed white and painted in overglaze colours of black and matt grey. A rectangle of matt grey is placed off-centre and surrounded by lines and blocks of grey and black on a white ground; the rim entirely black. The plate slightly warped in the firing.

MARKS Printed underglaze dark green mark of the Imperial Porcelain Factory with the cypher of Nicholas II and the date '1906'; hammer, sickle and cogwheel mark of the State Porcelain Factory with the date '1923' painted in overglaze blue; the word 'SUPREMATISM' in Cyrillic capitals and the Suprematist logo of a square within a square painted in black; 'after the design of Il. Chashnik' in Cyrillic script (the word for 'design' is abbreviated), and the numbers '447/983' also painted in black.

Decorated in 1923 at the State Porcelain Factory, Petrograd, on a pre-revolutionary blank.

D 23.7 cm   1988,6-9,2

Chashnik was a pupil of Malevich at the Vitebsk Practical Art Institute from 1920 to 1922, when he followed Malevich and his fellow-student, Suetin, to Petrograd. He worked with Suetin (see Cat. 278-80) at the State Porcelain Factory from 1923 to 1924; he then assisted Malevich in his work on architectural models at the State Institute of Artistic Culture (Inkhuk).

Chashnik's output was sadly cut short by his early death at the age of twenty-seven. The revolutionary use of a colour range limited to black, grey and white is characteristic of Chashnik's Suprematist designs for porcelain; see Oxford and London 1984, 17, no. 24, for a dinner service of 1923 in the Museum of the Lomonossov Porcelain Factory, Leningrad; Lobanov–Rostovsky 1990, nos 150-51, in the same collection. The design on the British Museum plate, with its solid black rim, disguises the traditional shape on which it is painted; Suprematist designs are not always so well suited to the shapes that they decorate.

For a group of Chashnik's designs for the decoration of plates, together with porcelain plates painted with his designs, see Düsseldorf 1978, nos 32-47, pp. 16-17 and pp. 63-7 (the designs from a private collection, Düsseldorf, formerly Chashnik estate). See also Andreeva 1975, pls 225-9; Franzke 1977, figs 2 and 6; Franzke 1982, figs 8-9 and pl. II.

Chekhonin, Sergei Vasilievich 1878-1936

Efros, A. and Punin, N., *S. Chekhonin*, Moscow n.d. (1924)
Chekhonin's designs for porcelain are also discussed in contemporary Russian publications on porcelain: Gollerbach 1922 (also published in French); Gollerbach and Farmakovski 1924 (with French summary); Lukomski 1924; Lunacharsky et al. 1927. For more recent Russian literature, see Moscow 1962; Nikiforova 1973; Lansere 1974; Andreeva 1975; Baranova 1983.

For other recent literature, see Lianda 1980; Oxford and London 1984; Venice 1988; Lobanov-Rostovsky 1990 (with further bibliography).

See also Recent Acquisitions, Cat. 340-41.

35 Plate   [PLATE 139]

Hard-paste porcelain, painted in overglaze colours. In the centre, a hammer and sickle with the word 'KOMMUNA' on a background of multicoloured sun-rays, bordered with oak leaves in green and gold. Round the rim, a large, five-pointed red star with the slogan in black Cyrillic letters on a cream ground 'There will be no end to the rule of the workers and the peasants'.

MARKS Painted dark green oval obliterating the underglaze printed mark of the Imperial Porcelain Factory; hammer, sickle and cogwheel mark of the State Porcelain Factory with the date '1920' painted in overglaze blue.

The decoration designed and painted in 1920, after Chekhonin's design, at the State Porcelain Factory, Petrograd, on an undecorated plate made before the Revolution.

D 24.1 cm   1981,12-8,1

When Chekhonin joined the State Porcelain Factory in 1918 he was an established graphic artist; previously his varied career had included book illustration, typographic design, designs for architectural ceramics and directing a school for enamel work. The Imperial Porcelain Factory was renamed the State Porcelain Factory in 1917 and Chekhonin was its artistic director from 1918 to 1923 and again from 1925 to 1927. In addition to his own considerable output of new designs, he was responsible for retraining the factory's painters and for recruiting other outstanding artists to make new designs.

The post-1917 ceramic production was used as a propaganda tool to disseminate the slogans and symbols of the new republic. Chekhonin's design for this plate, signed and dated 1920, is illustrated in Efros and Punin, 105. Characteristically, it combines pre-revolutionary decorative elements, such as the gilded oak-leaf border, with a dynamic Futurist-style motif in the centre; the effect is striking, but the stylised letters of 'KOMMUNA' (commune) are almost lost against the vivid background.

In general, artists' designs were copied by the factory painters, using the stocks of undecorated blanks held in reserve at the Imperial Porcelain Factory. From 1918 to 1921-2, the Imperial factory mark, incorporating the Imperial monogram, was obliterated; Gollerbach, writing in 1922 (p. 22), stated that this practice was begun in 1918, when the Soviet government was established in Moscow and the factory received an order to cover the tsarist mark, but that it was now no longer done.

A number of other examples of plates with this design are known, e.g. Lobanov-Rostovsky 1990, no. 14, and others sold in recent London auctions.

Christiansen, Hans 1866-1945

M. Zimmermann-Degen, *Hans Christiansen, Leben und Werk eines Jugendstilkünstlers*, Königstein/Taunus 1981

36 Wine glass   [PLATE 95]

Clear glass with optic mould-blown bowl and tall stem expanding towards the centre.

MARKS None.

Designed in 1900-1 for the exhibition held at the Darmstadt artists' colony in 1901 and made by the Theresienthaler Krystallglasfabrik, Theresienthal, Zwiesel, Bavaria.

H 25.2 cm   1987,10-8,1   Given by Victor Arwas

Christiansen trained as a painter and graphic artist in Hamburg and then at the Kunstgewerbeschule in Munich. He studied in Europe and America before spending the years 1899-1902 at the Darmstadt artists' colony.

This large white-wine glass and its accompanying six-piece service were widely illustrated in contemporary publications: Darmstadt 1901, 59; *DK & D* IX, November 1901, 62, 69; Koch 1902, 254, 258, 261 (where the glasses are shown on the table and sideboard in the dining-room of Christiansen's house). For examples in the Hessisches Landesmuseum, Darmstadt, see Heller 1982, no. 40 (two large wine glasses) and 41 (the six-piece service, with Christiansen family provenance). See also Darmstadt 1976, Bd 4, 48, no. 104; Zimmermann-Degen, 329, pl. 209; Ulmer 1990, no. 75. According to Koch 1902, the glasses were retailed through Louis Noack, Darmstadt.

The Theresienthal glassworks, founded in 1836, were run from 1861 by three generations of the family of Michael von Poschinger (1834-1908). In 1897 Michael von Poschinger handed the works to his son Benedikt (1864-1915). From 1915 the firm was run by Benedikt's sons Hans (1892-1951) and Egon (1894-1977). The works were taken over by Hutschenreuther AG, Selb, in 1982 (see Hilschenz 1973 and Seyfert 1988). A slightly different account is given by Killinger (1986, 55), according to whom Michael von Poschinger's son Egon (not Benedikt) left the factory to his two sons in 1922.

This service was produced at least until 1907, when it appears in a Theresienthal catalogue of that year, with two other services, acknowledged as the design of Prof. Christiansen. The catalogue illustrates a stoppered decanter and four different glasses for each service (information kindly supplied by W. Vollmer, Theresienthal Krystallglas- und Porzellanmanufaktur, as it is called today).

37 Five pieces of cutlery   [PLATE 89]

Silver, cast, comprising a meat knife, meat fork and spoon, the knife with steel blade and hollow-cast handle, and a fish fork and tea spoon. All decorated with linear ornament representing a stylised peacock feather on the handles.

MARKS Each piece stamped with the German silver standard mark 800 with crescent and crown, together with maker's mark, an eagle, for the firm of P. Bruckmann & Söhne, Heilbronn. The knife blade stamped 'ROSTFREI SOLINGEN', the table spoon stamped with the Munich retailer's mark, 'M. T. WETZLAR'.

Designed *c.*1901 and made by P. Bruckmann & Söhne, Heilbronn, Württemberg.

37a Knife: L 24.4 cm   1982,5-10,1
37b Fork: L 21.2 cm   1982,5-10,2
37c Spoon: L 21.9 cm   1982,5-10,3
37d Fish fork: L 17.3 cm   1982,5-10,4
37e Tea spoon: L 14.6 cm   1982,5-10,5

This service is a variant of the design made for the Darmstadt Exhibition of 1901, which had pistol-shaped handles; see *DK & D*, 1901-2, 62, 82, where the cutlery is shown on the dining table in Christiansen's house. It is described as by L.

Viëtor, Darmstadt (a retailer and silversmith). Both variants, with straight or curved handles, were included in *P. Bruckmann & Söhne: Preis-Liste über Silberne-Bestecke*, September 1911, 14, no. 3001 1/2 (quoted in Solingen 1979, no. 29).

For further examples, see Heller 1982, no. 37 (meat cutlery with straight handles, Hessisches Landesmuseum, Darmstadt); Spielmann 1979, no. 248 a-f (meat and fish cutlery with straight handles, one knife with curved handle, Museum für Kunst und Gewerbe, Hamburg); Flensburg 1972, pl. 8b (Flensburg Museum, quoted by Heller and Spielmann); Brussels 1977, no. 198 (a pair of salad servers in a private collection); Ulmer 1990, cat. no. 77 (Museum der Künstlerkolonie, Darmstadt).

38 Plate   [PLATE 83]

Hard-paste porcelain, decorated with a border of stylised roses, the monogram 'HC' beneath one of the roses and a double gold line round the rim, all stencilled in gold.

MARKS Printed on the base in green 'Krautheim, SELB, BAVARIA' with crown above, 'Louis Noack' printed in red.

Designed *c.*1903 and decorated by Krautheim & Adelberg, Selb, Bavaria on blanks made by L. Hutschenreuther, Selb. Retailed by Louis Noack, Darmstadt.

D 25.2 cm   1981,6-10,1

According to Zimmermann-Degen, 269-70, no. K45, the rose motif was designed by Christiansen for a drinking-glass service and was adapted to decorate existing porcelain shapes which were not of Christiansen's design. The dinner service was decorated on blanks made by L. Hutschenreuther: for examples bearing the Hutschenreuther factory mark, see Brussels 1977, no. 339; Darmstadt 1976, Bd 4, no. 103, and Ulmer 1990, cat. no. 65. The Darmstadt retailer Louis Noack may have been involved in the commissioning of this service, obtaining cheap blanks from Hutschenreuther.

There was a matching coffee service also decorated by Krautheim & Adelberg but using blanks made by Porzellanfabrik F. Thomas, Marktredwitz, Oberpfalz, Bavaria. For a sweet dish bearing the Thomas factory mark, see Heller 1982, no. 52. This sweet dish was bequeathed to the Hessisches Landesmuseum, Darmstadt, by Frau Adams-Christiansen, together with other pieces from the service bearing the Krautheim & Adelberg mark only. The Porzellanfabrik F. Thomas was founded in 1903. The service is therefore dated *c.*1903, although Christiansen had used similar rose motifs in his designs for the interior furnishings of his house at the time of the Darmstadt Exhibition of 1901. The rose decoration for the porcelain service was also executed in blue-grey (see Zimmermann-Degen, who acknowledges Herr Georg Krautheim, son of the manufacturer, for information about the porcelain service).

For Hutschenreuther, see Hohenberg 1989.

Christy, John Fell   active *c.*1840-50

For a brief account of Christy's activities in the 1840s, see Wakefield 1982, 64 and 68, and Morris 1978, 52, 54 and 56.

39 Tazza   [PLATE 8]

Opaque white glass, painted inside the bowl with a bust of a man with balding head and beard, wearing a red robe lined in white. The border pattern is executed mainly in gilding with some red. The exterior with gilded rims on bowl and foot.

MARKS Painted on the base in red 'Christy, Stangate, London'.

Made c.1845-50 by John Fell Christy, Stangate Glass Works, Lambeth, London.

H 11.1 cm, D of bowl 21.3 cm   1880,5-13,3   Presented by A.W. Franks

Very little is known about the glassworks of J.F. Christy at Lambeth. Surviving examples attributable to his firm all date from the late 1840s, when he was producing painted opaline glass in the manner of Richardson's of Stourbridge, who were the leading producers of painted glass at this time. Like Richardson's, he produced ornamental wares inspired by Greek vases and by contemporary French opaline glass. For a vase of dark blue, nearly black, glass, painted in pinkish enamel to imitate Greek pottery, see Morris 1978, pl. 31. For a white opaline vase painted and gilded with a pair of lovers in eighteenth-century costume, see Wakefield 1982, pl. 60 (both vases in the Victoria and Albert Museum). Christy also executed some of the designs by the artist Richard Redgrave for Felix Summerly's Art Manufactures, an enterprise founded by Henry Cole in 1847. Cole himself designed under the pseudonym of Felix Summerly as well as commissioning artists such as Redgrave, whose 'Well Spring' water jug, carafe or vase enamelled with water plants was made by Christy; the design was registered on 3 June 1847 (Morris 1978, pl. 35). A matching 'Water Lily' goblet made by Christy was registered on 25 October of the same year.

Clichy, Cristalleries de   1837-85

There is no detailed discussion of the Clichy factory. Information in this entry has been compiled from Sauzay 1868, Barrelet 1953 and Bloch-Dermant 1983.

40 Tazza   [PLATE 7]

Free-blown clear glass, the bowl, stem and foot wheel-engraved with foliate scrolls and tendrils. The matt areas of the engraving are interspersed with polished dots.

MARKS None.

Designed and made in 1862 for the International Exhibition in London by the Cristalleries de Clichy, Clichy-la-Garenne, near Paris.

H 16.1 cm, D of bowl 18.1 cm   Slade Collection 829   Bequeathed in 1868 by Felix Slade FSA

The Cristalleries de Clichy, founded initially by Rouyer & Maës in 1837 at Billancourt (Pont de Sèvres), moved to Clichy in 1839. Under the direction of Louis Clémandot and Joseph Maës, the firm exhibited in London in 1851 and 1862 (*Art Journal Illustrated Catalogue*, 1862, 213) and in Paris in 1867 (*Art Journal Illustrated Catalogue*, 1867, 301). In 1885 the firm was absorbed by the former glass factory at Sèvres as the Cristallerie de Sèvres et Clichy.

The catalogue of the Slade Collection of glass, published in 1871 (Nesbitt 1871, no. 829, quoted in London 1968, no. 250), notes that this tazza 'was selected as one of the best examples of engraving on glass in the [1862] Exhibition, and this must be the excuse for introducing so modern a specimen into this catalogue'. It is included in the full-page illustration of Clichy glass (Fig. 6) in the *Art Journal Illustrated Catalogue*, 1862, 213.

This tazza combines foliate ornament derived from German engraved glass of the eighteenth century with a Venetian-style shape, widely popular in nineteenth-century historicist glass. Further engraved glass by the Cristalleries de Clichy is illustrated in Sauzay 1868, 168, who praised the graceful interlaced foliate motifs of Clichy glass, compared with the overelaborate subjects of contemporary Bohemian engraved glass.

The Commondale Brick, Pipe and Pottery Company Ltd   1880-82

Little has been published on the Commondale Pottery; information in this entry has been taken from J. LeVine, *Teesside Pottery*, Teesside Museums and Art Galleries, 1974 and J. & J. Cockerill, 'The Commondale Works and Commondale Pottery', Bulletin of the Cleveland and Teesside Local History Society, no. 59, Autumn 1990.

41-2 Two stoppered bottles or 'water-coolers'   [PLATE 42]

Red terracotta, turned.
41 With matching saucer. The bottle ornamented with a rouletted relief band edged with white beading on neck and body, painted with dark red outlines on stopper and neck; saucer with similar relief band.
42 Plain, with slightly raised band at top and bottom and at the base of the neck. The stopper is repaired.

MARKS 41 the bottle unmarked, the saucer impressed 'CROSSLEY COMMONDALE'. 42 impressed 'COMMONDALE POTTERY' in a circular stamp.

Made at the Commondale Brick, Pipe and Pottery Company Ltd, near Guisborough, North Yorkshire, between 1880 and 1882.

41 H 27 cm (with stopper), D of saucer 16 cm   1907,11-7,1
42 H 21.3 cm (with stopper), 19 cm (without stopper)   1907,11-7,2
Given by Arthur Hurst (1858-1940), from 1917 honorary curator of ceramics of the Yorkshire Philosophical Society, to whom he bequeathed part of his collection of Yorkshire pottery and silver.

The short-lived Commondale Pottery was set up by John Crossley, a retailer of building products from Stockton-on-Tees, on the site of a former brickworks which Crossley had acquired in 1872. The manufacture of art and domestic pottery was begun in April 1880, as an addition to the manufacture of bricks, tiles and pipes. The Commondale Pottery produced a wide range of domestic wares in both red and buff terracotta, some with elaborate painted and glazed decoration. A similar enterprise on the site of a former brickworks, the Linthorpe Art Pottery, had begun in 1879 in nearby Middlesbrough (see Cat. 96-103).

The *Pottery Gazette* for 2 May 1881 reported that John Crossley had sold the works to a new company, which remained in production at least until April 1882, when Crossley's son Alfred, who managed the pottery, left for America. The company appears to have ceased production at some point after this date, and, despite a brief revival in the spring of 1883, production had discontinued by 1884. The Commondale Brick & Pipe Works traded again from the late 1880s or early 1890s until 1947. J. and J. Cockerill have suggested that the 'Commondale Pottery' mark, without Crossley's name, may have been used after Crossley sold the works in 1881. (I am much indebted to J. and J. Cockerill and to Peter Hall of the Yorkshire Museum for their assistance.) Similar bottles and stands were advertised as 'water-coolers' in *The Silber and Fleming Glass and China Book* (n.d., c.1890), Wordsworth Editions 1992, 50.

Similar unglazed terracotta wares were produced at the same period from local clays in South Devon, at the Watcombe Pottery and the Torquay Terracotta Company.

Copeland, W.T. & Sons Ltd founded 1847

There is no monograph on W.T. Copeland & Sons. For the history of the factory and its production, see Jewitt 1883, 381-93; Shin 1971; Atterbury, P. ed. 1989.

43-8 Six Assyrian-style figures [PLATES 12-14]

Parian porcelain. 43-5 Three standing figures on plinths, impressed on the front of the plinths: 'SENNACHERIB B.C.721.'; 'SARDANAPALUS 662 BC'; 'THE QUEEN.OF SARDANAPALUS.650 B.C.'. 46-7 Two book-ends in the form of a winged human-headed bull and a winged human-headed lion. 48 Vase in the form of the head of a human-headed bull, impressed on the front of the plinth 'NIMROD'.

MARKS Sennacherib: impressed on the sides and back of the plinth 'COPELAND COPYRIGHT RESERVED'; oval blue printed mark inside the plinth 'ALFRED JARVIS WILLES ROAD LONDON NW'; Sardanapalus: impressed marks as above, with the addition of 'BY.A. HAYS' on the back of the plinth; Queen of Sardanapalus: impressed marks as on Sardanapalus with 'N93' for November 1893; blue printed mark as on Sennacherib; Winged bull and lion: 'COPYRIGHT RESERVED COPELAND' and 'M82' for March 1882; Nimrod vase: impressed on the base 'COPELAND' and 'J82' for January 1882.

Modelled by Aaron Hays, issued by Alfred Jarvis and made by W.T. Copeland & Sons, Spode Works, Stoke-on-Trent, between 1868 and 1893: the book-ends and the Nimrod vase dated 1882, the Queen of Sardanapalus dated 1893.

43 Sennacherib H 33.8cm   1985,3-8,2
44 Sardanapalus H 30.5cm   1985,3-8,3
45 Queen of Sardanapalus H 29.5cm   1989,5-8,1
46 Winged lion H 23.4cm   1987,1-9,2
47 Winged bull H 22.5cm   1987,1-9,1
48 Nimrod vase H 16.7cm   1986,3-3,1

The Assyrian sculptures discovered by Henry Layard at Nimrud between 1845 and 1851 and subsequently by his successors at Nineveh created a sensation when they were put on display at the British Museum during the late 1840s and 1850s. When the Crystal Palace was moved from Hyde Park to Sydenham in south London, casts of the Nimrud reliefs and the colossal winged bulls and lions were installed in a 'Nineveh Court', so called after Layard's *Monuments of Nineveh*, vol. 1, published in 1849. Layard initially thought he had discovered Nineveh, and so although this volume describes Nimrud, Nineveh was the name that caught the public imagination.

Hays and Jarvis both worked at the British Museum as attendants, Hays from 1845 to 1876 and Jarvis from 1869 to 1900. Little else is known about them, though when Jarvis retired at sixty his pension was reduced for 'grave misconduct', but the nature of his misdemeanour is not recorded. Hays appears to have been an amateur sculptor; as part of his application for employment in 1845 he submitted a number of sketches, mainly of sculpture, and a letter of recommendation from Richard Westmacott, who had recently designed the pedimental sculpture for the façade of the Museum. Hays exhibited the three standing figures of Sennacherib, Sardanapalus and his queen at the International Exhibition in London of 1871; the statuettes, dated 1868 in the exhibition catalogue, cost £1 10s. each (*Official Catalogue, Fine Arts Depart-*

ment, Sculpture, nos 2564-6). Initially the series comprised these three figures only; the Nimrod vase and the winged gateway figures, together with a lion weight and a relief plaque of Ashurbanipal and his queen in a garden scene, were added later.

For a figure of Sennacherib marked 'A Hays Pub. March 1868. Regd. Feb 25th 868' see Atterbury ed. 1989, 174, pl. 568). A notice in *The Athenaeum*, 6 July 1878, 17, describes the same three figures as 'a trio of statuettes in porcelain representing Sardanapalus and his queen, and the great King Sennacherib. The Statues . . . will be issued to a limited number of subscribers by Mr. Jarvis, of 43, Willes Road, N.W., who has obtained from Mr. Hays the right of reproducing them.' It does not mention any additions, but according to press opinions quoted in a publicity leaflet issued by Jarvis in 1893, the Nimrod head and the small lion weight (Atterbury, ed. 1989, 174, pl. 569) were in production by 1878. The winged bull and lion book-ends were certainly in production by 1882, the date of the British Museum examples. A pair of similar figures owned by Bolton Art Gallery is also dated 1882, and the figures are mentioned in a press notice of 1883 quoted in the publicity leaflet printed by Jarvis when the series was re-issued in 1893. By this time it had acquired the eighth and last piece: a relief plaque of a garden scene in the palace of Ashurbanipal. According to Atterbury ed., 137 and 175, pl. 570, the relief plaque was modelled by the sculptor and water-colour painter Owen Hale, and was first issued in 1886, ten years after Hays had left the British Museum. The Bolton Art Gallery holds an example dated May 1886 with a design registration number for that year. The prices listed in 1893 are the same as they were in 1868. The statuettes were still selling at £1 10s. each; the winged bull and lion sold for £2 2s. and Nimrod's head for 10s. The complete series of eight works cost £11.

In his leaflet Jarvis claimed the patronage of 'Her Majesty the Queen; H.I.H. The Grand Duke Constantine of Russia; Science and Art Museum, Dublin; Chadwick Museum, Bolton; Sheffield Museum; Astor Library, New York; Smithsonian Institution, U.S.A.; and various other public institutions'. These patrons had presumably subscribed to the whole series; a complete set is held by the Bolton Art Gallery.

Following the reissue in 1893, an exhibition of the series was held at the Royal Institution; the *Magazine of Art* (November 1895-October 1896, 5104) published an article on 'Assyrian art three thousand years ago' which was illustrated entirely with the Copeland reproductions, described as 'desirable ornaments for the drawing-room and boudoir' and 'especially welcome . . . to those who are unable to study the famous originals'. Layard had died in 1894 and so the exhibition may have been held in his honour.

Jarvis titled his leaflet 'Nineveh Reproductions from the Assyrian Sculptures'. Hays's figures are in fact taken from the sculptures of Nimrud, Khorsabad and Nineveh. The statuette of Sennacherib is based on the king as he appears seated in one of the sculptures of the siege of Lachish from Sennacherib's palace at Nineveh; the king is shown inspecting the booty (Reade 1983, fig. 73, Department of Western Asiatic Antiquities 124911). He holds his bow in his right hand and wears a full-length robe with elaborate border pattern, copied accurately by Hays. His head has been mutilated in antiquity and so Hays has substituted the tiara worn by Ashurbanipal in the lion-hunt reliefs from Ashurbanipal's palace at Nineveh (Reade 1983, fig. 82).

Hays has confused the dates of Sennacherib's reign (705-681 BC) with those of Sargon II (721-705 BC). Sardanapalus (Ashurbanipal) is taken from another lion-hunt relief showing him killing a wounded lion with his sword (Reade 1983, fig. 87; WAA 124875). The king's robe is short at the front and long at the back and there are many details that Hays has copied accurately, but the posture is thoroughly Victorian, despite Jarvis's claim that the statuettes were 'faithful reproductions, modified . . . only so far as was unavoidably necessary in the transfer from the relief to the round'. The Queen of Sardanapalus is based on the seated figure of the Queen of Assyria as she appears with Ashurbanipal in the garden scene that inspired the plaque of 1886 (Reade 1983, figs 102-3; WAA 124920). She is drinking from a bowl held in her right hand. The chronology of Assyrian kings was roughly right by the mid-1870s; the date '662 BC' for Sardanapalus (ruled 668-627 BC) and '650 BC' for his queen are reasonable guesses.

The book-ends are based on the colossal guardian figures from Nimrud and Khorsabad. The winged lion is taken from the figure flanking the doorway in the throne-room of Ashurnasirpal II in the North-West palace at Nimrud (WAA 118873), while the winged bull is taken from one of the gateway figures in the palace of Sargon at Khorsabad (Reade 1983, fig. 2, WAA 118808). In common with the originals Hays's animals have five legs, so that they appear correct whether viewed from the front or the side, but unlike the originals Hays's figures are double-sided. The Nimrod vase is based on the head of a bull from the palace of Esarhaddon at Nimrud (Barnett and Faulkner 1962, pl. CXIII; WAA 118893).

Parian porcelain, a type of white or tinted porcelain resembling marble, was first produced at the Copeland factory in 1844. Other factories followed this lead, but it is not known why Jarvis chose Copeland for the production of his Assyrian series, nor is it clear how he was able to finance the production of the figures by Copeland and to obtain such a prestigious list of subscribers.

For jewellery inspired by the Assyrian sculptures, see Rudoe 1989; the British Museum also holds Layard's silver-gilt Freedom casket, based on the Nimrud sculptures (Cat. 127). For information used in this entry I am grateful to Julian Reade of the Department of Western Antiquities, Christopher Date of the British Museum Archives, Brian Hughes of Bolton Art Gallery and Robert Copeland of Spode.

Copenhagen, Royal Porcelain Factory

founded 1774

Hayden, A., *Royal Copenhagen Porcelain*, London 1911
Grandjean, B., *Kongelig Dansk Porcelain 1775-1884*, Copenhagen 1962
Winstone, H.V.F., *Royal Copenhagen*, London 1984

49 Cup and saucer [PLATE 122]

Hard-paste porcelain, moulded, each piece painted in overglaze colours with three flower sprays in red, purple, pink and blue, with gilded rims, the handle partly gilt.

MARKS On the cup, underglaze blue mark of the Royal Copenhagen factory and the factory numbers '482/8500' and '50X' painted in overglaze green. On the saucer, as above, plus printed underglaze green factory mark in use after 1922: 'ROYAL COPENHAGEN DENMARK' with a crown in the centre, impressed number '8500V'.

Made by the Royal Copenhagen Porcelain Factory, Denmark, after 1922.

H of cup 5.9 cm, D of saucer 14.6 cm   1989,11-5,1-1a   Given by Lady Eva Wilson

This is based on traditional nineteenth-century shapes and patterns that remained popular into the twentieth century; see, for example, a page of patterns for similar faceted wares with floral decoration of the 1840s and a sugar-bowl of 1844 (Grandjean 1962, pls 183 and 190). The cup and saucer was formerly part of a service owned by the donor's great-aunt, who died in the mid 1930s.

For a Royal Copenhagen Porcelain Art Nouveau waist-clasp in the Hull Grundy Gift, designed by Christian Thomsen with silver mounts dated 1902, see C. Gere in Gere et al. 1984, no. 1115.

Copier, Andries Dirk 1901-91

Leerdam Unica: 50 jaar modern Nederlands Glas, exhibition catalogue, Kunstmuseum Düsseldorf and Museum Boymans–van Beuningen, Rotterdam 1977 (contains article by Copier 'Gedachten van een glasontwerper')
Haarman-Engelberts, C., 'Leerdam glas naar ontwerp van Copier', *Antiek* 15, Jaargang no. 5, December 1980, 278-86
Ghent 1986. Galerij Novecento, *Andries Dirk Copier. Leerdams Glas 1923-1971. Unica Serica Gebruiksglas*, ed. M. Heiremans
Liefkes, R., 1986/7. 'Master of Pure Form', *Dutch Heights*, Winter, I, 38-41
Liefkes, R., *Copier, glasontwerper/glaskunstenaar*, Amsterdam 1989 (with parallel English text)

50 Three glasses [PLATE 120]

Wine glass, champagne glass and tumbler, clear glass, free-blown bowls and stems, the feet moulded.

MARKS Each glass acid-etched on the base with Copier/Leerdam serial glass signet, a 'c' within an 'L', in use from 1924 to c.1945.

Designed in 1923-4 as part of the 'Romanda' table-glass service and made by the NV Glasfabriek Leerdam, Holland, between 1924 and c.1945.

Wine glass: H 18.6 cm   1988,7-7,1
Champagne glass: H 13.8 cm   1988,7-7,2
Tumbler: H 10.6 cm   1988,7-7,3

Copier joined the etching department at Leerdam in 1914 at the age of thirteen. He later trained as a typographer in Utrecht from 1918 to 1919 and then at the Art Academy in Rotterdam under the graphic designer J. Jongert until 1924. His studies were largely financed by the Leerdam factory, under the enlightened directorship of P.M. Cochius (1874-1938), who had become general director in 1912. Cochius, a theosophist, Catholic priest and freeman, was determined to promote contact between artists and industry, following the example of the Deutsche Werkbund, founded in 1907. He was instrumental in setting up a similar association in Holland which eventually came into being in 1924 as the Nederlandsche Bond voor Kunst in Industrie (Netherlands Association for Art in Industry). Foreign competition in utilitarian glassware, combined with his own concerns with series production for the general public, led Cochius to invite a number of outside artists to design for the company, beginning with the architect K.P.C. de Bazel in 1915.

Other artists commissioned by Cochius include the decorative artist C. de Lorm (see Cat. 77) from 1917, the ceramist Chris Lanooy (1881-1948) from 1919, the architect H.P. Berlage (1886-1934) from 1923 and Chris Lebeau (see Cat. 141) from 1924.

From 1921 Copier was asked to supervise the production of de Bazel's glassware and in 1922 he began to design publicity material for the new range of artist-designed glassware; he turned to the design of glass in 1922–3, but continued to design advertisements, as well as exhibition installations and showroom interiors. He thus became the company's first permanently employed designer for all aspects of the firm's output. In this, Cochius was inspired by the model of AEG in Germany, where Peter Behrens had been architect and designer since 1907. Copier became Leerdam's artistic director in 1927 and remained with the company until 1971.

The tall, elegant 'Romanda' glasses, with their baluster stems and flared rims, are reminiscent of traditional Venetian forms, but because of their shape the glasses were difficult to blow, which made their production expensive. Nevertheless 'Romanda' was very successful and was widely exported during the 1930s; it was sold at Altmans in New York as 'modern Dutch glass' (see *Arts & Decoration* 40, March 1934, 60). For a sketch for the wine-glass from the 'Romanda' service, remade by Copier in 1969 and owned by the Gemeente Museum, The Hague, see Haarman-Engelberts 1980-1, 282. For the complete service, see van der Kley-Blekxtoon 1984, 77.

At the same time as designing tableware, Copier also created the 'Leerdam-Unica' range of individually made pieces, some of which were produced as 'Serica' pieces, i.e. in a limited edition. The tableware or serial glass always bore the designer's monogram and was designed for production in large numbers, yet it remained expensive to produce. In the 1930s economic difficulties led to the manufacture of a cheaper range, sold without the designer's signature under the name 'Sonoor'. Made of semi-crystal, the models were often very close to the artist-designed pieces, but were generally simplified.

For a general account of Leerdam glass at this period, see van Gent 1937; Amsterdam 1985. For full discussion of Copier's work, see Liefkes 1989. Glasses from the 'Romanda' service are to be found in a number of museums in Holland, and in the Kunstmuseum, Düsseldorf (Leipzig 1989, no. 410).

51 Two glasses [PLATE 119]

Wine glass and champagne glass, amethyst-coloured glass, free-blown bowls, the stems and feet moulded and then cut to produce ten facets.

MARKS Each glass acid-etched on the base with Copier/Leerdam serial glass signet in use from 1924 to *c*.1945.

Designed in 1926-7 as part of the 'Peer' (pear) service and made by the NV Glasfabriek Leerdam, Holland, between 1927 and *c*.1945.

Wine glass: H 15.6 cm 1988,7-8,1
Champagne glass: H 15.8 cm 1988,7-8,2

The 'Peer' service is regarded as Copier's most successful introduction of cut-glass decoration in combination with geometric porportions and natural forms. Copier's construction drawings (in the Gemeente Museum, The Hague) show how the bowl is based on an inverted pear shape, while the circumference of a pear and the ten-faceted foot of the glass fit into a pentagon (see Haarman-Engelberts 1980, 282). For the complete service, see

van der Kley-Blekxtoon 1984, 81. In common with many of Copier's designs the 'Peer' service was widely exhibited abroad; for example, at the Leipzig Fair of 1927 (see Leipzig 1928, pl. 68).

52 Whisky decanter and stopper [PLATE 120]

Mould-blown green glass, the neck and stopper cut, each with eight facets.

MARKS Acid-etched on the base with the Copier/Leerdam serial glass signet in use from 1924 to *c*.1945.

Designed in 1927 and made by the NV Glasfabriek Leerdam, Holland, between 1927 and *c*.1945.

H 26.3 cm (with stopper)   H 21.2 cm (without stopper)
H of stopper 8.3 cm   1988,7-6,1

This decanter was designed with matching glasses and punch-bowl; see van der Kley-Blekxtoon 1984, 84.

53 Wine glass [PLATE 119]

Clear glass, free-blown.

MARKS Acid-etched on the base with the Copier/Leerdam serial glass signet in use from 1924 to *c*.1945 and the signet of the Vereniging van Nederlandse Wijnhandelaren (Dutch Association of Wine Merchants), the letters 'VNLW' between a cross.

Designed in 1930 as part of the 'Gilde' service, so called because it was created in cooperation with the wine-merchants' guild. Made by the NV Glasfabriek Leerdam, Holland, between 1930 and 1945.

H 15.3 cm   1988,7-9,1

The 'Gilde' glass service is Copier's most successful design for mass-production and is still in production, though since 1958 it has been machine-made. It is characteristic of his 1930s designs, many of which were influenced by the De Stijl movement and the new functional style in architecture. This led Copier to use simple geometric shapes based, in this case, on the golden mean, which determines the proportion of the bowl's height to that of the stem.

For Copier's sketch for the 'Gilde' service, remade in 1969, see Haarman-Engelberts 1980, 286. The sketch (in the Gemeente Museum, The Hague) shows that the profiles of the glasses are based on segments of concentric circles. They were initially manufactured in three sizes, small and large wine glasses and a port glass. Later other pieces were added: see van der Kley-Blekxtoon 1984, 93.

54 Vase [PLATE 120]

Free-blown glass, pale amber cased with several thick layers of colourless glass so that the walls increase in thickness round the rim.

MARKS Acid-etched on the base with the Copier/Leerdam serial glass signet in use from 1924 to *c*.1945.

Designed *c*.1936 and made by the NV Glasfabriek Leerdam, Holland, between *c*.1936 and *c*.1945.

H 21.6 cm, D of rim 17.1 cm   1980,7-3,1

This vase is characteristic of Copier's preoccupation during the second half of the 1930s with the optical effects of a thick wall of glass; the expanding thickness of the wall produces variations between the inner and the outer contour so that the inner form is optically distorted by the thick glass. A similar vase is illustrated in an article on 'The New Glass Ware' published in *The*

Studio 113, April 1937, 207. For two similar vases dated *c.*1935, see Ghent 1986, pls 42-3.

Crane, Walter 1845-1915

'The Work of Walter Crane', *Art Journal Easter Annual*, 1898
Spencer, I., *Walter Crane*, London 1975
Walter Crane 1845-1915 Artist, Designer and Socialist, exhibition catalogue, Whitworth Art Gallery, Manchester, 1989
Crane's own publications on art include the following: *The claims of decorative art*, London 1892; *The Bases of Design*, London 1898; *Line and form*, London 1900; *Moot points. Friendly disputes on art and industry between Walter Crane and Lewis F. Day*, London 1903; *An artist's reminiscences*, London 1907.

55 Vase [PLATE 24]

Earthenware, hand-thrown, bulging body painted with mermaids and foliate ornament in deep red lustre on a cream-coloured ground.

MARKS Painted on the body near the base with the artist's device, a crane and a 'w' within a 'c'.

Designed in 1889 and made by Maw & Company, Benthal Works, Broseley, Shropshire.

H 22.4 cm, D 22.7 cm   1983,10-11,1

Crane's first ceramic designs were made for Wedgwood creamware between 1867 and 1871. He then designed tiles for Maw & Company, together with his friend, Lewis F. Day, from the mid 1870s. Maw & Co. was one of the first firms to produce lustrewares under industrial conditions; they exhibited lustre pottery by Lewis F. Day at the first exhibition of the Arts & Crafts Exhibition Society at the New Gallery, Regent Street, London, (Arts & Crafts Exhibition Society, *Catalogue of the First Exhibition*, 1888, 161, no. 382). Two years later they exhibited a 'case containing vases in lustre ware', designed by Walter Crane and executed by 'Childe, Jones, Rutter and Brown' (Arts & Crafts Exhibition Society, *Catalogue of the Third Exhibition*, 1890, 210, no. 416). These were almost certainly the series of seven pots illustrated in the *Art Journal Easter Annual*, 1898, 31 (the same illustration is reproduced in Coysh 1976, pl. 51). The Art Journal special number is accompanied by Crane's own account, in which he records that he gave sectional drawings to the thrower and then painted the design on a biscuit pot as a model. This was afterwards copied on duplicate vases in ruby lustre (presumably by the four factory artists listed in the Arts & Crafts Exhibition Society catalogue). Crane discusses the Maw pots immediately after his description of a series of tiles designed for the Paris Exhibition of 1889 and also made by Maw & Company, suggesting that the pots may have been designed in that year. They all have bulging forms with decoration in red lustre and cream.

The series continued in production for some years. In 1902 Crane organised the Arts & Crafts Exhibition Society's display at the Turin Exhibition of that year and he included the Maw pots although they were no longer new work (*DK & D* XI, 1902-3, 235). The 'swan' vase is the best known of the series and examples are to be found in the Victoria and Albert Museum (illustrated in Spencer, 112) and in the Fitzwilliam Museum, Cambridge (formerly Handley-Read collection; see London 1972, G25). The V & A also holds an example of the 'mermaid'

vase (Circ. 312.1953, given by Maw & Co.; see London 1952, M53); the lustre is a bright orange-red and the vase is painted on the base with the factory name and date '1901'. The orange lustre was probably not intentional, but the lustre tones vary considerably between different pieces; the deep ruby lustre of the British Museum vase has not fired successfully: there are murky patches and pitted surface areas.

56 Vase [PLATE 25; COLOUR PLATE IV]

Earthenware, painted in gold lustre on a scarlet red ground with the daughters of Hesperus guarding the golden apples: three dancing maidens in classical dress hold hands before the apple trees, protected by a serpent. Between each maiden is a lily branch. The red glaze covers the base, which is painted with the monograms of designer and painter in gold lustre. The glaze is perfectly fired.

MARKS Impressed on the base with the Pilkington factory mark and year-letters for 1906, together with the painted monogram of the designer, Walter Crane, with the Latin 'DES' below, and the painted monogram of the painter, Richard Joyce, with 'PINX' below.

The decoration designed by Walter Crane and painted by Richard Joyce (1873-1931) in 1906 at Pilkington's Tile & Pottery Company, Clifton Junction, Manchester, on a shape probably designed by Lewis F. Day.

H 33.9 cm   1989,11-3,1

Pilkington's manager, William Burton (see Cat. 30), was primarily a glaze chemist; he therefore hired three of the most distinguished designers of the period; Lewis F. Day, Walter Crane and C.F.A. Voysey. Day acted as artistic consultant as well as designer; his contract stated that he was to design pottery solely for Pilkington's, who would guarantee to find him consulting work for a retainer of £100 per annum (Manchester 1982, no. 1). Day made a number of tile designs for the company and contemporary accounts record that he was also responsible for many of the pottery shapes (*Pottery Gazette*, April 1906, 441).

Crane's designs for Pilkington's were made at the end of his career, first in 1900, when he designed a series of tiles and then between 1904 and 1906, when he made a few designs for pottery. Examples are recorded of eleven of Crane's designs; a photographic record book in the Pilkington factory archive illustrates the same designs, suggesting that this was the limit of Crane's involvement. Few examples of each design appear to have been executed and so surviving pieces are rare, by comparison with designs of the factory artists, Gordon Forsyth, Richard Joyce or W.S. Mycock. Crane's designs were executed by Joyce, Mycock and Charles Cundall.

The daughters of Hesperus vase appears in the photographic record book as 'shape LL 6171, Ht.13¼ins'. However, it is clear from the photograph that the figures were executed in a dark lustre on a pale ground (the photograph is illustrated in Gray 1981, pl. 101c); the red ground in the British Museum vase is unusual. The only other recorded example of this design has the figures in relief, with dull, murky glazes (Cross 1980, pl. IV, where it is dated *c.*1919). The report of the Arts & Crafts Exhibition Society's exhibition at the Grafton Galleries in 1906 in the *Pottery Gazette* (April 1906, 441) gave a detailed description of the Lancastrian lustrewares, including 'a pair of fine vases with figures executed in slip under the glaze, designed by Walter Crane and executed under the direction of William Burton'. No other Crane designs in relief are recorded and so it is likely that the description refers to vases of this design. Another contemporary account described 'a few large pots' decorated after designs by Walter Crane as 'not amongst the least successful' (*Journal of the Society of Arts* 55, 5 July 1907, 849) Curiously, the Arts & Crafts Exhibition Society's 1906 catalogue does not mention any designs by Crane.

Crane's designs for Pilkington's tend to reproduce his own highly individual style of some twenty years earlier. One of the vases that he designed for Maw & Co. has a similar frieze of female figures (Manchester 1989, Cat. K8v). Richard Gray has noted the similarity of the daughters of Hesperus to Crane's cotton print 'the British Empire', with its frieze of dancing figures linking hands, in classical drapery; the print was produced by Edmund Potter & Company of Manchester in 1887 (Gray 1981, pl. 101a). Both designs are derived from Roman reliefs of dancing maidens placed as if dancing in a circle, with alternating back and front views, clinging 'wet' drapery and fluttering folds (see, for example, the 'Borghese dancers', P. Bober & R. Rubinstein, *Renaissance artists and antique sculpture*, Oxford 1986, pl. 59A). The classical figure theme in Pilkington's lustre is further discussed in Gray 1981.

Crane's designs were all executed in Pilkington's new 'Lancastrian Lustre'. Burton began experimenting with lustre effects in 1903, but did not perfect the technique until 1906, the daughters of Hesperus vase being among the earliest successful pieces. The processes used at Pilkington's were fully described by William Burton in his paper on lustre pottery given to the Society of Arts in 1907 (*JSA* 1907, 764-6): sulphides, oxides or carbonates of silver or copper (for red lustres) were mixed with china clay or red-brick clay and painted over the previously fired glaze using an ordinary potter's medium. The piece was then re-fired in a muffle kiln fed by reducing gases at the right temperature and intensity. Curiously, Burton does not mention the use of gold for lustre. He concluded his paper by saying that 'every piece of lustre we produce is unique . . . in cases where we have been fortunate enough to obtain designs from distinguished decorative artists like Mr Walter Crane no two pieces are reproduced the same way'.

Crane's designs are listed below, in order of shape number where this is known, with recorded examples; the factory names are given in inverted commas; 'LL' refers to Lancastrian Lustre. For items in the Manchester City Art Galleries that were included in the exhibition of Lancastrian pottery held in 1982, the exhibition catalogue reference is given.

1. **'George and Dragon'** Photo album, shape LL 6167.
   Whitworth Art Gallery: Cross, pl. X, dated 1910.
2. **'Sea Maiden'** Photo album, shape LL 6169.
   a Manchester 1982, no. 72, dated 1912.
   b Manchester City Art Gallery 1983.210, dated 1921.
   c Portsmouth City Museum: London 1972, G38 (ex Handley-Read Collection).
   d-f Cross, pl. V, dated 1907 and 1906.
3. **'Bon Accorde'** (sic) Photo album, shape LL 6170.
   Manchester 1982, no. 110, dated 1907.
4. **'The daughters of Hesperus'** Photo album, shape LL 6171.
   a British Museum: Manchester 1989, no. K13, dated 1906.
   b Cross, pl. IV, figures in relief, c.1919.
5. **'Lion Bowl'** Photo album, shape LL 6172.
   a Manchester 1982, no. 186, dated 1911.
   b Cross, pl. III. A number of other versions are known, e.g. Godden 1961b.

6. **'Moon Flask'** Photo album, shape LL 6173.
   Female figure of Enterprise on one side, Manchester city arms on the other.
   a Cross, pl. 59, dated 1907.
   b Manchester City Art Gallery 1982.128, dated 1932.
7. **'Figures Ogee'** Photo album, shape LL 6174.
   Cross, pl. II, dated 1910.
8. **'Figures Striped'** Photo album, shape LL 6175.
   a Manchester 1982, no. 118, dated 1910.
   b Cross, pl. II, dated 1910.
9. **'Dog Pot'** Photo album, shape LL 6176.
   The design to which this name refers is uncertain, but it is thought to be the design illustrated in Cross, pl. 57.
10. **'Night and Morning'** Cross, pl. VII, dated 1906.
11. **'Peacock'** Victoria and Albert Museum, 1438-1920: Cross, pl. VIII, dated 1912.
12. **'Moon flask with Pegasus'** Known from Crane's watercolour design only, Cross, pl. 58.

Deck, Joseph-Théodore 1823-91

There is no monograph on Deck. For his own writing, see T. Deck, *La Faïence*, Paris 1887. Other contemporary accounts include two articles by E. Gerspach in *La Revue des Arts Décoratifs* III, 1883, 289-98 and XI, 1891, 353-8. For full bibliography, see Cologne 1974.

57 Dish   [PLATE 22]

Earthenware, painted in enamel colours of blue, deep turquoise, pale turquoise, green and red over white slip containing tin oxide and covered with a transparent lead glaze. Inside the dish is a floral pattern and on the outside, a band of leaves and flowers with stylised foliate ornament round the foot. The pattern is enamelled in low relief.

MARKS Impressed beneath rim of foot 'TH DECK' (the 'TH' conjoined).

Designed and made in the factory of Théodore Deck, Paris between 1861 and c.1878.

L 54.8cm, W 38.7cm, H 12.5cm 1986,10-19,1 Bequeathed by Freda Swain FRCM.

Théodore Deck, a native of Alsace, trained as a chemist and sculptor, working initially in pottery-stove factories in Strasbourg, Vienna and Berlin before setting up his own atelier in Paris in 1856. His early products included Renaissance-style historicist wares. A number of artists designed for him, though most of the Isnik-style pieces such as this dish were his own compositions.

According to Burty (1869, 116) Deck was introduced to Islamic styles and techniques by Adalbert de Beaumont, whose *Recueil de dessins pour l'art et l'industrie* of 1859, based on his travels in the Middle East, was one of the earliest sourcebooks for Islamic decoration. It later reached a much wider audience when it was reissued between 1871 and 1883 as a series of volumes of chromolithographs entitled *Encyclopédie des Arts Décoratifs de l'Orient*. Gerspach (1883, 292) records that Deck learnt his so-called 'Persian' process from a damaged Persian tile that he owned; the process consisted of covering the earthenware body with a white slip made with tin oxide which was fired and then painted with enamel colours beneath a clear glaze.

For Deck's own description of his methods and his glaze compositions, see Deck 1887, 245-58.

Deck's Isnik-style wares, with their celebrated turquoise blue, were first shown at the *Exposition des arts industriels* in Paris in 1861 (Deck 1887, 245-6) and then at the London International Exhibition of 1862 (Waring 1862, III, pl. 297). They continued to be admired at international exhibitions in Paris in 1867, London in 1871 (*Art Journal Illustrated Catalogue*, 59) and Vienna in 1873. The decoration was based on Turkish pottery of the sixteenth century, now known as Isnik pottery, Isnik being the chief pottery-producing city in Turkey. The Musée de Cluny acquired a group of Isnik vessels from Rhodes in the early 1860s; as a result Deck's wares were often known at the time as 'Rhodes' pottery.

Burty acknowledged that Deck had succeeded better than any other furnace in reproducing Isnik colours, but noted that 'even his red has not all the desirable brilliancy', while his 'blue-green, composed of oxide of copper, cannot resist great heat, and is very unstable' (Burty 116). Similar low-relief enamelling was practised by Deck's rival and Beaumont's collaborator, Eugène Victor Collinot: as described by Burty, the pattern was drawn on the body with an oxide 'which had the property of remaining fixed where it was laid as well as that of rejecting the proximity of those colouring enamels intended to form the tone of which the ...pattern...was composed. In the baking, the enamel, always distanced by this line, which remains as thin as a thread, swells up into a sort of little eminence, like the earth piled up on each side of a newly-made ditch' (Burty, 117). The relief caught the light and so the decoration was shown off to best advantage. When Collinot called his enamelling '*cloisonné*', despite its flat outlines, Deck accused him of inaccuracy and of using unauthentic designs (Victoria and Albert Museum 1987, 127).

Deck's patterns rarely imitate the asymmetry of their Isnik models, being usually centred and symmetrical. For comparable Isnik-style pieces by Deck, see Mundt 1973, no. 61 (acquired by the Kunstgewerbemuseum, Berlin from the 1867 Paris Exhibition); Munich 1972, nos 86-90 and no. 92, a plate acquired by the Victoria and Albert Museum in 1878 with floral motif similar to this dish; Philadelphia 1978, no. IV-14; Mundt 1981, fig. 180.

From the late 1870s Deck worked in other styles, especially Far Eastern, and ended his career as Director at Sèvres from 1888 until his death in 1891.

De Feure, Georges 1868-1943

There is no monograph on de Feure. His designs for the applied arts are widely illustrated in contemporary journals and his work for Bing's Maison de l'Art Nouveau is fully discussed in Weisberg 1986. For biographical details, see Houston 1976. See also G. Weisberg, 'Georges van Sluijters called "De Feure": an identity unmasked', *Gazette des Beaux-Arts*, 84, 1974, 231-2; I. Millman, 'Georges De Feure, The Forgotten Dutch master of Symbolism and Art Nouveau', *Arts Magazine* (Europe), September/October 1983, vol. 6, no. 1, 41-7; I. Millman, 'Georges de Feure, A Turn-of-the-Century Universal Artist', *Apollo*, November 1988, 314-19; G. Weisberg, 'Siegfried Bing and Industry, The Hidden Side of L'Art Nouveau', *Apollo*, November 1988, 326-9.

58 Vase [PLATE 76]

Hard-paste porcelain, cast in two parts, with moulded low-relief decoration painted in underglaze high-temperature colours. At the base, two peonies, with sweeping stems rising to a broad band of decoration on the upper part with two flying swans in white low relief outlined in grey, against a background of deep blue above and pale green below, with two peonies in two shades of pale green and deep blue, all on a grey background. The petals of the flowers are emphasised with a low-relief white outline. Firing faults have produced occasional smoky patches on the grey ground and the vase is slightly warped.

MARKS Printed in green on the base with the monogram of G. De Feure, the monogram 'ANB' for L'Art Nouveau Bing, both in a rectangle, and 'LEUCONOË', with incised factory number '528'.

Designed in 1901-2 for Siegfried Bing's gallery, the Maison de L'Art Nouveau at 22 rue de Provence, Paris and made by the firm of Gérard, Dufraissex & Abbot, Limoges, France, before 1903.

H 30.9 cm, max. W 14.8 cm   1980,7-11,1

The Dutch artist Georges de Feure (born Georges Joseph van Sluijters) went in 1890 to Paris, where he studied under Jules Chéret. He came to Bing's attention through his poster designs and his illustrations for Parisian periodicals; he specialised in images of seductive *femmes fatales*. He first exhibited furniture and ceramics at the Salon de la Société Nationale des Beaux-Arts in 1894. As both painter and decorative arts designer he was ideally suited to work in Bing's atelier, producing interior furnishings and fittings for Bing's gallery. By 1899 de Feure was working principally for Bing (Weisberg 1986, 151). De Feure was responsible for two rooms of the Pavillon Bing at the 1900 Paris Exhibition and in 1903 Bing mounted a de Feure exhibition. De Feure designed for all branches of the decorative arts, founding his own independent Atelier de Feure with the architect T. Cossmann. He later designed for the theatre and taught at the École Nationale des Beaux-Arts.

A vase of this design was shown at the Société des Beaux-Arts Salon of 1902; see *Art et Décoration* 28, July 1902, 26. De Feure's '*porcelaines grand feu*' were here praised for their pure white glaze and restrained decoration in low relief: '*il bossèle rarement les objets qu'il décore d'un relief ornemental, et s'il le fait, c'est très légèrement qu'il variera ses surfaces*'. See also *DK & D* XII, 1903, 316. For a similar vase with the same marks in the Metropolitan Museum, New York (inv. no. 26.228.9), see Weisberg 1986, 204, pl. 199 and Houston 1976, no. 279; the colours on this vase include pink as well as blue and green. According to Weisberg (1986, 189) this vase was one of Bing's best-selling items. At the Salon of 1901, where de Feure's porcelains by Gérard, Dufraissex & Abbot were first exhibited, their rich colours were noted as exceptional for '*grand feu*' colours (*L'Art Décoratif* III, June 1901, 116-24). *The Studio* (23, 1901, 68-9) also noted the '*grand feu*' colours, though it mistook the moulded relief for 'coloured pâte appliquée'; it described the manufacturers, Gérard, Dufraissex & Cie, as one of the best firms in Limoges.

From the early 1890s the firm of Gérard, Dufraissex & Cie (known as Gérard, Dufraissex & Abbot from 1900) was noted for its high-fire colours: for a detailed account of the porcelains shown at the Chicago Exhibition of 1893, see *La Revue des Arts Décoratifs* 13, 1893, 387-94. Before opening the Maison de l'Art Nouveau, Bing had acquired considerable experience in the French ceramic industry. His family firm, Gebrüder Bing, in Hamburg, imported French porcelain and glass. From 1863 to

1881 Bing (born 1838) was associated with the Paris firm of Leuillier, making popular rococo-style porcelains. From the mid 1870s he began to collect Japanese art and it is possible that the contact with Gérard, Dufraissex & Abbot came about through Bing's fellow collector Charles Haviland, director of the Limoges firm of that name. Gérard, Dufraissex & Abbot was approached by Bing initially in 1899 (d'Albis and Romanet, 148) to execute pieces from drawings submitted by de Feure and Edouard Colonna, with Bing retaining the right of rejection and oversight; the first porcelains were ready in early 1901 (Weisberg 1986, 188).

The collaboration between Bing and Gérard, Dufraissex & Abbot was cut short in 1903 by the ill health of Bing, who died in 1905. The company continued to make de Feure's designs, but later versions bear the firm's mark, 'GDA France'. Among the group of de Feure porcelains given to the Musée National de la Céramique, Limoges, in 1911 by E. Gérard are examples with various combinations of marks which differ from the monograms found on this vase: the factory mark in conjunction with 'Art Nouveau Paris', or either mark on its own (information kindly supplied by Chantal Meslin-Perrier). Possibly Bing purchased some for L'Art Nouveau, while others were sold by the factory. D'Albis and Romanet state that later productions, i.e. after 1903, bear GDA's mark. For further discussion of Bing's relationship with GDA and other industrial firms, see Weisberg 1988. The significance of 'LEUCONOË' is not known: Weisberg initially described it as probably a trade mark (Weisberg 1978), but he later suggested that it may have something to do with Bing's association with Leuillier (Weisberg 1986, 278, note 19), though this is not explained.

For further discussion, see A. Dawson, *French Porcelain. A Catalogue of the British Museum Collection*, London 1994, cat. 238.

D'Humy, P. R. de F. (Vasa Murrhina Glass Company) 1878-83

There is almost no literature on this short-lived venture; brief contemporary accounts may be found in the *Art Journal*, 1879, 253; the *Pottery Gazette*, 1 April 1880, 208. See also Revi 1967, 215-17.

59-76 Group of glass vessels and wasters

[PLATES 55-6; COLOUR PLATE III]

Blown glass, with gold or platinum embedded inside the glass or encrusted on the surface, comprising twenty-five items in all.

MARKS Each item bears the manufacturer's original paper label with description, dated '1 [or 2] April 1878'.

Presented by Paul Raoul de Facheux D'Humy on 3 April 1878. In the British Museum's acquisition register D'Humy is described as 'Managing Director, Aurora Glass Company Limited, 21 Litchfield Street, Soho, London WC'.

In the list that follows, the manufacturer's descriptions are given in quotes; these are taken from the paper labels on the base of most pieces. After each description is D'Humy's name and address as above, followed by 'Inventor' (see Cat. 68, plate 56). D'Humy also supplied an accompanying list that repeats these descriptions.

Vessels with embedded decoration

59 'Antique Water Bottle Craquelé Unique', clear glass cased with blue; gold foil sandwiched between the two layers; the gold has separated in patches. H 24.1 cm   1878,4-13,1

60 'Antique vase with Stripes the Gold fused and incrusted inside and outside the glass', blue glass, blown into a mould lined with gold rods cased in clear glass; the blue has filled the spaces between the rods, leaving fused gold and crystal as a stripe on the surface. H 20.9 cm   1878,4-13,2

61 'Antique Vase Craquelé Blown at the Furnace', clear glass; during blowing pale blue powder has been picked up on the marver and then gold foil applied, which has cracked as the glass was worked; bubbles have also entered at this stage. The arrangement of the patches so that the gold is always outlined in blue is remarkable. H 21.4 cm   1878,4-13,5

62 'Blue Bottle Antique with Stripes Blown in the mould with Gold Rods & covered with Crystal & Blue afterwards', a variation of 60: the gold rods are here covered with clear glass and sandwiched between two layers of blue. H 14.9 cm   1878,4-13,3

63 'Antique blue bottle incrusted with platinum & again coated with crystal.' H 13 cm   1878,4-13,6

64 'Crystal plate with Gold fused and embedded in the glass', gold foil sandwiched between two heavy layers of clear glass. D 19.6 cm   1878,4-13,8

65 'Plate, with Gold inside of Glass, coated with glass, coated with Platinum, and coated again with glass.' Here, gold and platinum are embedded between separate layers of blue glass, comprising five layers in all, but nevertheless astonishingly thin. D 12.1 cm   1878,4-13,19

66 'Liqueur Glass Gold Stripes inside glass Blown at the Furnace', clear glass applied with stripes of blue and gold and then cased in clear glass. H 5.4 cm   1878,4-13,16

Vessels with encrusted decoration

67 'Green Bottle Antique Blown with Blowpipe with Platinum on surface.' This bottle is extremely thin-walled. H 16.4 cm   1878,4-13,4

68 'Plate Unique in the World, the Gold inside the plate, the most inexplicable work extant', pink glass, very thin, with gold on the upper surface. D 16.6 cm   1878,4-13,7

69 'Antique Vase coated with Gold while the glass in fusion, Blown at the furnace', clear glass, the gold evenly coated, the base star-cut. H 14.1 cm   1878,4-13,9

70 'Champagne Cup with gold encrusted on the surface of the glass, Blown at the Furnace', the gold even but not so dense as 68, the foot also coated, the stem left in clear glass. H 10.8 cm   1878,4-13,10

71 'Wine Glass Platinum with Gold & Crystal foot; ruby rim round foot', the bowl in blue glass thickly encrusted with platinum applied in strips on the surface, the foot in clear glass with ruby rim and encrusted with gold on the surface. The ribbed stem in clear glass has three ruby rings, the central ring applied with opaque turquoise blue dots. The stem restored. H 13.4 cm   1878,4-13,11

72 'Wine Glass Finished Ruby, Patchy and Sandy Blue foot', ruby bowl, blue glass foot with applied turquoise rim and patchy gold on the surface, the stem in clear glass with two ruby rings and a central deep blue ring applied with opaque turquoise dots. H 13.4 cm   1878,4-13,12

73 'Champagne Glass Gold incrusted blown at the Furnace.' Here the gold is evenly crackled all over the surface. The stem is clear with turquoise blue knop and deep blue foot encrusted with gold. H 19.5 cm   1878,4-13,14

74 'Crystal Scent Bottle incrusted with platinum', with ruby rim and knop to stopper, the platinum applied in strips. H 14.7 cm   1878,4-13,15

75 Cage vase, 'Scent Bottle Blown in wire work', deep blue glass blown into woven copper wire with basketwork rims. H 13.5 cm   1878,4-13,13

76 Fragments (not illustrated)
a two sections of letter weight with gold embedded between blue and clear glass layers. Max W 5.4 and 4.1 cm   1878,4-13,18
b a solid clear-glass cylinder described as 'First attempt of Incrustation of Gold Dust into the Glass while in fusion.' L 12 cm   1878,4-13,17
c a piece of the end of the blowing iron, pink glass coated with gold. L 4 cm   1878,4-13,22
d-h five waste pieces cut from a vase during the process of manufacture, illustrating the techniques described above.
d pink with patchy gold on one surface. L 10.1 cm   1878,4-13,20
e blue thickly coated with gold on one side. L 9.6 cm   1878,4-13,21
f blue coated with platinum on one surface. L 21.7 cm   1878,4-13,23

g blue with patchy gold on one surface. L 8.5cm   1878,4-13,24
h pink glass cased with clear glass and coated with gold on one surface. L 9cm   1878,4-13,25

The first record of D'Humy in England occurs on 31 October 1876, when he took out patent number 4217 for ornamenting glass with gold leaf or other metal. But he was not necessarily living in London before 1878, when he presented his glass to the British Museum from Litchfield Street; he took out a second patent in the same year, but is not listed in the London Post Office Directories until 1881, when he appears not as 'Aurora Glass Company' as in the British Museum records, but as 'Vasa Murrhina Glass Company'. The Directories give the Litchfield Street address as well as a gallery at 294 Regent Street and, significantly, a manufactory in York Place, York Road, Battersea. By 1882 D'Humy had opened another office at 5 and 6 Great Winchester Street, EC, but by 1883 only the address of the manufactory is given, suggesting that the Regent Street Gallery had closed, and by 1884 D'Humy is no longer listed at all. He took out one further patent in 1888 (Patent Abridgements, Glass, 31 March, no. 4878), for ornamenting lamp globes with wire-threaded beads.

In relation to developments in England it is interesting to note that Powell & Sons, Whitefriars Glass Works, were experimenting at precisely this time with similar methods of decoration. In his 'Notes of a Flint-Glass Works Manager' (*Journal of the Society of Glass Technology*, 1916, 241), H. J. Powell records decorating glass by 'marvering on gold or platinum leaf' between 1877 and 1879. A much later development was that of Northwood's 'Silveria' glass produced by Stevens & Williams in Stourbridge at the turn of the century. This involved sandwiching silver foil between two layers of clear or coloured glass; the primary bulb was blown almost to full size before the foil was picked up from the marver, and it was then coated by dipping it into a pot of molten glass (Revi 1967, 215).

The process patented by D'Humy differed in that the primary bulb was not blown to full size before picking up the foil from the marver; consequently, when the bulb was expanded to full size the foil tore apart, giving a patchy effect. This explains why the encrustation is denser on the smaller pieces, which required less blowing. According to D'Humy's 1876 patent (Patent Abridgements, Glass, 31 October, no. 4217), a glass cylinder was covered with gold leaf and heated until the gold and glass had united. The coated cylinder was then passed into a larger but closely fitting glass cylinder left open at one end. The two cylinders were then united by heat and elongated to part the metal into strips, after which the glass was blown to the required shape. Revi (1967, 215-17) records a later patent of 13 February 1878, which varies slightly: 'a bulb covered with sheet or powdered metal is blown inside another bulb and has in turn a third bulb blown inside it. The whole is then fused together and finished as usual. Metal leaf may be attached to the inner or outer surfaces of articles by simply heating, or by means of enamel.' (Patent Abridgements, Glass, 13 February 1878, no. 600). Many modifications and special devices are mentioned, including the forming of patterns by splitting metal surfaces by enlarging the article (see items **59** and **61**), and the blowing of glass into a wire network (item **75**). (The patent references were kindly supplied by Charles Hajdamach.)

A similar process of applying a layer of gold between two layers of glass was patented in England on 29 November 1878 by Messrs Monot, Père & Fils, & Stumpf, of Paris: a mixture of copper and gold was sandwiched between the glass to produce an effect known as 'Chiné'; this technique was shown at the Paris Exhibition of 1878 (Revi 1967, 217; see also *Gazette des Beaux-Arts* 18, 1878, 2e période, 198, of Monot & Stumpf: '*Leurs chinés or craquelé sont une création, une de ces inventions tant à la mode qui déguisent absolument la matière employée*'). A notice in the *Furniture Gazette* for 3 January 1880, announcing 'A Novelty in Decorative Glass' and describing D'Humy's invention, refers to examples of the technique at the Paris Exhibition of 1878 and states that it was now manufactured in England by the Aurora Glass Company. This suggests that D'Humy's process was developed in France, and the *Art Journal* account notes that he engaged glass blowers from the Continent, but further research is required to ascertain D'Humy's origins and early career.

From 1879 D'Humy was promoting his glass as 'reproductions of the Murrhine vases of the ancients' (*Art Journal*, 1879, 253). D'Humy is here alluding to the 'vasa murrhina' mentioned by many ancient authors. According to Pliny 'myrrhina' were hardstone vessels made of carved fluorspar, introduced by Pompey in 62-61 BC and highly prized for their glistening veins of purple and white (*Natural History*, XXXVII, VII-VIII, 18-22). However, Pliny also refers to the manufacture of glass to imitate murrhine vessels (*Natural History*, XXXVI, LXVII, 198). Pliny's imitation murrhine was no doubt one of the several types of Roman millefiori or mosaic glass of the first century BC to the first century AD formed of bands of different colours (see Corning 1987, no. 16). However, D'Humy's encrusted glass is closer in technique to a different type of banded glass, known as gold-band or gold-sandwich glass (Corning 1987, nos 17-18). In these examples dark blue, green, yellow-brown and white bands alternate with clear glass bands encasing gold foil. Examples of both types of Roman glass are to be found in the Slade Collection, bequeathed to the British Museum in 1868. D'Humy would certainly have known the Slade pieces, the best of which were illustrated in colour lithographs in Nesbitt's catalogue of 1871. Colour plate 3 illustrates a remarkably fine alabastron with bands of emerald green and dark blue containing a central white thread, separated by a band of powdered gold within clear glass (Nesbitt, no. 75), while colour plate 2 shows an ampulla or perfume bottle of similar colours with bands of gold foil embedded in clear glass (Nesbitt, no. 76).

Pliny's murrhine vessels were not identified securely as fluorspar until the middle of the present century (see Harden and Loewenthal 1949 and Bromhead 1952). In the late nineteenth century the word 'murrhine' was used indiscriminately to denote all mosaic and millefiori coloured glass made in imitation of semi-precious stones, whether or not it contained gold inclusions. It is still so used today (e.g. Vicenza 1982, 64). Roman mosaic and millefiori glassware was copied by Salviati of Venice, who showed 'murrhine' glass vessels at the Paris Exhibition of 1878. Thus when D'Humy changed the name of his company to the Vasa Murrhina Company, he may have done so in direct rivalry to Salviati, whose retail outlet in London had moved by 1882 from St James's to 311A Regent Street, a few doors from D'Humy's gallery at number 294. The possibility that D'Humy employed Italian glass blowers must also be considered; the small liqueur cup with gold stripes is very close to contemporary Venetian models.

The cagework bottle was also inspired by Roman models; it is a combination of two different types, one of which has a direct prototype in the Slade Collection which D'Humy could well have known. It is a cobalt-blue beaker blown into a silver cage, though the cage is formed of sheet silver which has been pierced, rather than of woven wire (London 1968, no. 74; Corning 1987, no. 78). The second Roman type is a common mould-blown vase of the third or fourth century AD, where the lower body is covered with a honeycomb pattern of raised bosses resembling a bunch of grapes (e.g. Klein and Lloyd eds 1984, 37).

In the *Art Journal* account the Regent Street gallery was praised for its display of 'these beautiful objects, principally of an artistic character'. The *Pottery Gazette* was more cautious in its acclaim, criticising the lack of attention to form, which was 'the more to be regretted seeing that the invention itself is one that deserves all the care that can be bestowed upon it'. The wirework vessels were considered so simple and graceless that 'we were sorry to find M. D'Humy taking special pride in them, and voting their production something beyond the ken of ordinary mortals ...they reminded us of nothing more aesthetic than the wire-cased bottles in which seltzer and other mineral waters are sold' (1 April 1880, 208, reference supplied by Charles Hajdamach). As a trade journal the *Pottery Gazette* was also concerned about the high prices; a comparatively small goblet cost thirty shillings. They predicted that it was too expensive to be commercially successful, a prediction confirmed by D'Humy's disappearance soon after from the London trade directory.

Nevertheless, pieces appear to have been highly regarded at the time. An encrusted gold goblet identical in technique and effect to the tall champagne glass has recently been acquired by Broadfield House Glass Museum, Kingswinford. It is so close that its attribution to D'Humy is without doubt. The bowl only is of glass and is mounted in a silver-gilt stem and foot, bearing the maker's mark of Thomas Johnson (see Cat. 82) and the London date-letter for 1879 (I am grateful to John Smith, who first drew this goblet to my attention; he and Charles Hajdamach have made helpful comments on the techniques of manufacture).

De Lorm, Cornelis 1875-1942

Cornelis de Lorm – ontwerper 1875-1942, exhibition catalogue, J. R. de Lorm, Drents Museum, Assen and Nederlands Postmuseum, The Hague, 1987

77 Wine glass [PLATE 119]

Clear glass, free-blown, with raised foot.

MARKS Acid-etched on the base with de Lorm's serial glass signet comprising the designer's monogram in combination with 'LG' for Leerdam Glas.

Designed between 1920 and 1923 as part of a service known as 'Normaal I' and made by the NV Glasfabriek, Leerdam, Holland.
H 14.1 cm, D of bowl 6.8 cm   1988,7-10,1

When de Lorm began to work for Leerdam in 1917 he was well known as a graphic artist, especially for his work on the post office building in The Hague. Before this he had worked for the interior design gallery het Binnenhuis in Amsterdam in the early 1900s and in 1917 had opened his own modern design shop, De Zonnebloem, in The Hague, where he sold ceramics and glass

by himself and others until 1928. As president of the association Kunst Aan Allen founded in 1907 (see Assen and The Hague 1987, 25-8) and a member of the Bond voor Kunst in Industrie, de Lorm shared the preoccupations of Leerdam's director, P. M. Cochius, with series production. Nevertheless, in common with much of the new glassware commissioned by Cochius, de Lorm's glass was largely handmade.

De Lorm began designing 'Normaal I' in 1920; it was put into production in 1923, and followed by 'Normaal II', a taller and thinner version, in 1926. The 'Normaal' service was his most successful design for Leerdam. It was designed in association with the Nederlandse Wijnkopersbond (Dutch Guild of Wine Merchants – see also Cat. 53) who pronounced the bulb-shaped bowl ideal for the retention of the bouquet and the everted rim easy to drink from (van den Kley-Blekxtoon, 52). The name 'Normaal' derives from the desire 'to achieve the norm, obtained through harmony of function and material' (quoted in Assen and The Hague 1987, 91). The raised feet set this service apart from conventional factory-made glasses with flat feet, as did the continuous line between bowl and stem. In fact the bowls and stems are made separately, joined together and stretched on the rod to give a unified effect. It was this new method of production, developed under de Bazel, that made the 'Normaal' shape possible. De Lorm was the first Leerdam designer to use coloured and lustred glass, but the 'Normaal' service was always in clear glass, except for the white wine glass, which was made in *annagroen* (bright yellow-green), with the occasional use of lustre. The service was produced into the 1930s.

For further examples of de Lorm's designs for Leerdam, see van der Kley-Blekxtoon 1984 and Assen and The Hague 1987. For the role of Cochius, see Cat. 50.

De Morgan, William Frend 1839-1917

Morris, May, 'William De Morgan, Recollections', *Burlington Magazine*, August and September 1917, 77-89 and 91-7

Sterling, A.W.N., *William De Morgan and his wife*, 1922

Gaunt, W. and Clayton-Stamm, M.D.E., *William De Morgan*, London 1971

Pinkham, R., *Catalogue of Pottery by William De Morgan*, Victoria and Albert Museum, London 1973

Catleugh, J., *William De Morgan Tiles*, London 1983

Greenwood, M., *The Designs of William De Morgan*, Ilminster 1989 (catalogue of De Morgan's pottery designs in the Victoria and Albert Museum)

See also De Morgan's own article 'Lustre ware', *Journal of the Society of Arts* 40, 1892, 756-67.

78 Dish [PLATES 23-4; COLOUR PLATE V]

Tin-glazed earthenware, painted in red copper lustre over a white slip with two running deer facing to the left among orange trees. Two tones of red lustre are used: the deer in deep red, the trees in a brighter pinkish-red; the deer have pale pink highlights and the oranges are yellow. The reverse is painted with a border of leaves and a central circle surrounded by rays.

MARKS Impressed on the reverse with the number '24'.

Decorated in 1880 at the Orange House Pottery, 36 Cheyne Row, Chelsea, London, on a Staffordshire blank.

D 36 cm, H 5.2 cm   1928,7-25,1   Bequeathed by De Morgan's associate, the architect Halsey Ralph Ricardo (1854-1928)

De Morgan started his career as a painter and then a stained-glass artist, before turning to ceramics in 1869. The Orange House Pottery was in production from 1873 to 1882, when De Morgan moved to Merton Abbey, Surrey, close to the Morris & Company works. From 1888 to 1898 De Morgan worked in partnership with Halsey Ricardo at the Sands End Pottery in Fulham. For Ricardo's designs for De Morgan (mainly tiles and tile panels), see Greenwood 1989, 18-19. De Morgan made pottery at Sands End until 1907, becoming a successful novelist for the remaining years of his life. His partners from 1898, Charles and Fred Passenger and Frank Iles, continued to work at Sands End until 1911.

The British Museum acquisition register records that this dish was made at the Orange House Pottery in 1880; this information was presumably supplied by Ricardo himself, with the bequest. Ricardo's will (kindly checked by Christopher Date) lists the dish but gives no details of when or where the dish was made. However, animal subjects painted in ruby lustre on a white slip are characteristic of De Morgan's Chelsea period.

De Morgan's water-colour design for a closely similar subject (Fig. 8) is included among the 1248 sheets of original drawings bequeathed by his widow in 1917 to the Victoria and Albert Museum (Greenwood 1989, pl. 37, Department of Prints & Drawings, E.1218-1917, D 14 ins). The design is executed in reverse, with the deer running to the right. This is consistent with the method of transfer of designs to the ceramic body: the outline of the design was pricked through from the reverse (see Greenwood, 15-16). Comparison of the design and the plate shows that the deer are identical, but the background differs in that the trees are differently disposed; those on the plate are painted in more detail with individual leaves and bear oranges, which do not appear in the design. From the reverse of the drawing the pin-pricks are clear: the outlines of the deer are densely pricked, suggesting that the design was used more than once, while the outline of the trees is very lightly pricked. A dish that corresponds exactly with the design is to be found in the De Morgan Foundation, Cardiff. It bears the painted marks 'W.D.M. FULHAM' and the decorator's initials 'C.P.' for Charles Passenger (Greenwood 1989, pl. 38, illustrated back to front, with the deer running to the right). Greenwood states erroneously that this dish is impressed 'WEDGWOOD' on the base; it has no factory mark). The V & A designs also include a number of sketches for decoration, as distinct from designs for specific items; among these is a page of running deer (Greenwood 1989, 92, E.1397-1917, illustrated by May Morris in 1917, pl. 1).

The blanks for these large 14-inch dishes, known as rice dishes, were supplied by other firms; some were supplied by Wedgwood, but most of the blanks were from the firm of Davis of Hanley, Staffordshire.

For De Morgan's own account of his development of lustre glazes, see JSA 40, 1892, 762ff. (reprinted in Gaunt and Clayton-Stamm 1971, 156-65). His experiments with lustres were inspired by the iridescence of silver in the paint used on stained glass and he gives detailed recipes for his processes: 'The best of the first lustres I made on Staffordshire ware were on ironstone or granite. The body was repellent in colour, but the glaze particularly good. Latterly, we have used the common opaque white made with tin . . . The pigment consists simply of white clay, mixed with copper scale or oxide of silver, in proportions varying to the strength of colour we desire to get. It is painted on the already fused glaze with water. . . .' After firing, the clay of the pigment lay on the surface where it had been painted, but it was not fused to the glaze and had to be rubbed off. The metallic part of the pigment which had separated from the clay during firing was then revealed as a metallic film deposited in the surface of the glaze. De Morgan's lustre technique is further discussed, with reference to tiles, by A. Caiger-Smith in Catleugh 1983, 152-6, while the method of transferring the designs to the body is discussed in Greenwood 1989, 15-16.

Among other contemporary revivalists of lustreware, De Morgan admired especially the French artist potter Clément Massier and the Cantagalli factory in Florence, where, for health reasons, De Morgan spent many winters during the 1890s. His interest in the Italian lustre revival led to his use of red lustre, as found in Renaissance maiolica from Gubbio and Deruta, but the subject here is inspired rather by Hispano-Moresque pottery. For discussion of oriental influences on De Morgan, see Pinkham in Munich 1972, 69-70.

79 Vase [PLATE 24]

Tin-glazed earthenware, of double-gourd shape, painted in two tones of red copper lustre on an opaque white tin glaze with three grotesque birds on a ground strewn with tufts of grass and flowers. At the top, a band of stylised ornament. The birds and flowers are in deep red on a pink ground, with details left in white.

MARKS Painted in blue on the base 'W.DE.M.&.CO. J.J.'.

Decorated c. 1890 by Joe Juster at the Sands End Pottery, Townmead Road, Fulham, London.

H 31 cm, D 18 cm   1983,10-9,1

For comparable gourd vases with decoration of birds among grasses, dated to c. 1890, see Greenwood 1989, pls 166 and 168. For De Morgan's designs for gourd vases of this shape but with different decoration, see Greenwood 1989, 76 and 230, pl. 205. For contemporary illustrations of vases of similar gourd shape, the shape inspired by Chinese models, see The Studio 18, 1900, 279. See also Sterling 1922, 96. The De Morgan designs in the Victoria and Albert Museum include several sketches for fanciful birds, but none corresponds with the bird on this vase.

Joe Juster joined De Morgan during the latter part of the Chelsea period (1872-82) and came to be regarded among the most skilful of De Morgan's painters (Gaunt and Clayton-Stamm 1971, 21).

This vase illustrates De Morgan's use of different tones of lustre, obtained by varying the concentrations of silver and copper in the clay medium used for the pigment (see Cat. 78).

Writing shortly before he gave up decorating pottery, De Morgan listed the type of work done at Sands End in order of importance: painted panels, patterned tiles, plain coloured tiles and 'Miscellaneous decorated pots – good for wedding presents and the like, but of no use except to put flowers in when they do not run – as indeed now and then they do not. It is very possible that a little further evolution of this work might have really satisfactory results. As it is, it pays as well as anything we do' (quoted by May Morris 1917, 78).

Doat, Taxile-Maximilien 1851-1939

There is no monograph on Doat, but Doat himself wrote widely on his high-fire ceramics, see: Doat, T., *Grand feu ceramics: A Practical Treatise on the Making of Fine Porcelain and Grès*, Syracuse, New York 1905 (translated by Samuel E. Robineau). Also published as a series of fourteen articles in *Keramic Studio*, edited by the ceramist Adelaide Alsop Robineau, between July 1903 and September 1904, and in *Art et Décoration* xx, 1906, 87-104 and 153-63, and xxi, 1907, 69-80. For more recent bibliography, see Cologne 1974.

80 Vase [PLATE 77]

Hard-paste porcelain (*pâte nouvelle*), cast. Four circular medallions in *pâte-sur-pâte* depicting Notre-Dame, the Hôtel de Ville, the Louvre and the Arc de Triomphe hang from a garland of flowers round the neck. The garlands comprise naturalistically depicted flowers such as fuchsias, roses, daisies and poppies. Each medallion is enclosed in a cartouche containing a ship, the emblem of Paris, and surmounted by a gateway. Between each cartouche are pale green laurel-leaf garlands incorporating the dates of major events in the history of Paris: '56 avant JC', '1358', '1789', '1870-71'. Round the rim is a band of dolphins with the city's motto 'PARIS FLUCTUAT NEC MERGITUR' (Paris floats and does not sink). The decoration is all executed in low-relief *pâte-sur-pâte*: the medallions, floral garlands, dates and motto are in dark green outlined in white, the laurel-leaf garlands are in a lighter green and the background decoration in very low-relief pale green on a celadon ground. The interior is white. The foot is made separately and attached to the body with a metal fitting; there is slight restoration to the foot.

MARKS The date '1895' and 'T.DOAT' (the T and D ligatured) incorporated into the design beneath the date 1870-71. '96' in an oval printed in black on the base and '97' in an oval printed in green inside the neck. A series of partly legible numbers, letters and symbols are impressed inside the foot rim: '4 93 9 PN' (?).

Made at the Sèvres factory, Paris, between 1895 and 12 June 1897, when the vase was fired. The shape – *vase d'Entrecolles* – designed by an unknown modeller in 1875, the decoration executed by Doat and his assistant Lucas, the designer of the decoration unknown.

H 90.3 cm   1901,4-25,1   Presented by the French Government through the Ministre de l'Instruction Publique

Doat worked at Sèvres (see Cat. 269) as a sculptor, modeller and decorator from 1887 to 1909, when he left for the United States and established the University City Pottery at St Louis, Missouri. He returned to France in 1915. Doat specialised in the *pâte-sur-pâte* technique of building up a raised surface by successive applications of liquid slip using a brush. For full details of Doat's methods and recipes for porcelain bodies and pastes, see Dawson 1986.

This vase, known at the factory as the *vase de Paris*, was presented to the British Museum in March 1901 by the French Government in return for thirty thousand pamphlets on the French Revolution which had been given to the Bibliothèque Nationale and the Municipal Library of Paris. This huge vase was so expensive that it did not sell and was selected as a presentation piece in 1899. It was stipulated that it was to be shown at the Paris Exhibition of 1900, but it has not been possible to confirm that this was so, though *pâte-sur-pâte* wares by Doat were certainly included (see *Art Journal Special Number. The Paris Exhibition* 1900, 97-102, an article by L.F. Day on 'Modern Pottery at the Paris Exhibition'). The shape takes its name from the Jesuit, Père d'Entrecolles, whose celebrated letters of 1712 and 1722 described the manufacture of Chinese porcelain. *Pâte nouvelle* was a new porcelain body introduced in 1884 to take a wider range of colours.

For further detailed discussion, see Tait 1985, Dawson 1986 and A. Dawson, *French Porcelain. A Catalogue of the British Museum Collection*, London 1994, cat. 191, where full references are cited from the Sèvres factory archive for the costings and hours worked.

Dominick & Haff 1872-1928

There is no monograph on this firm. For the history of the company, see Rainwater 1975 and New York 1986, 421.

81 Silver jug [PLATES 49-50]

The body hand-raised with repoussé decoration of naturalistic plants, the handle cast and chased with relief ornament of overlapping flowers and scrolls, the ends of the handle in the form of baroque cartouches. The plant ornament on the body is different on each side of the jug and is executed in very high relief: some of the leaves curl back on themselves. The fine hammering of the background is executed with graduated tools, so that the punch marks expand towards the centre and decrease at the base and at the neck, which is left plain.

MARKS Stamped on the base with the firm's trade mark, a circle flanked by the silver standard '925' in a rectangle and the date, in this case '1883', in a lozenge (Rainwater 1975, 43). The letters 'D & H' which normally accompany this mark are very worn. Also stamped with the name of the retailer 'SHREVE, CRUMP & LOW'.

Designed and made by the firm of Dominick & Haff, manufacturing silversmiths, Newark and New York, in 1883. Sold through the Shreve, Crump & Low Company, Boston, Massachusetts.

H 22.6 cm   1989,5-12,1

The firm of Dominick & Haff was founded as William Gale & Son in 1821, becoming Gale & North in 1860 and then Gale, North & Dominick in 1868, when Henry Blanchard Dominick (1847-1928) entered the business. When Leroy B. Haff became a partner in 1870, after working for three years in the retail department, the firm changed its name to Gale, Dominick & Haff. It is first listed as Dominick & Haff in 1872. From 1875 to 1893 the firm had premises in Bond Street, New York, moving to 860 Broadway until 1904. In about 1880 the firm reportedly acquired the silverware tools and patterns of Adams & Shaw, who had been absorbed by Tiffany & Co. In 1928, the year of H.B. Dominick's death, Dominick & Haff was itself absorbed by Reed & Barton of Taunton, Massachusetts.

Beyond these purely historical details little is known about the firm and its designers. This jug skilfully juxtaposes two different plant motifs. The hammered ground, characteristic of American Japanesque silver of the 1880s, and the decorative motifs, inspired ultimately by Far Eastern ornament, are here developed in a highly original way, combined with high-relief repoussé work of very fine quality.

Comparable pieces of repoussé naturalistic silver were produced in the 1880s by larger firms, such as Tiffany & Co. and the Whiting Manufacturing Company, North Attleborough, Massachusetts and New York (see, for example, New York 1986, 254, fig. 8.2, though the decoration here is much denser). A square-shaped coffee service by Dominick & Haff in the Japanese taste, retailed by Bailey, Banks & Biddle of Philadelphia, has similar heavy baroque cartouche terminals to the handles (New York 1986, 271, fig. 8.10).

For further discussion of American silver of the Aesthetic Movement, see New York 1986.

The Shreve, Crump & Low Company sold fine-quality silverwares and, according to Rainwater (1975), some of the designs they sold were created specially for them.

Dresser, Christopher 1834-1904

A selection of Dresser's own writings and literature of general relevance to the objects catalogued here is given below. Bibliography specific to metalwork, pottery and glass is given in the relevant sections.

Writings by Dresser: *Unity in Variety*, London 1859; *The Art of Decorative Design*, London 1862; *The Development of Ornamental Art in the International Exhibition*, London 1862; *Principles of Decorative Design*, London 1873 (previously published as a series of essays in *The Technical Educator*, 1870-72); *Studies in Design*, 1874-6; *Japan, its architecture, art and art manufactures*, London 1882; *Modern Ornamentation*, London 1886; *The Chromolithograph*, 1867-9; *Furniture Gazette*, 1880-81.

General literature:

The Studio, Vol. xv, November 1899, 104-14, 'The Work of Christopher Dresser'

Pevsner, N., 'Minor Masters of the xixth Century: Christopher Dresser, Industrial Designer', *Architectural Review*, 1937, 183-6

Dennis, R. and Jesse, J., *Christopher Dresser 1834-1904*, exhibition catalogue, London, Fine Art Society, 1972

Collins, M., *Christopher Dresser 1834-1904*, exhibition catalogue, London, Camden Arts Centre and Middlesbrough, Dorman Museum, 1979

Joppien, R., *Christopher Dresser, ein Viktorianische Designer*, exhibition catalogue, Cologne, Kunstgewerbemuseum, 1981

Halén, W., *Christopher Dresser*, Oxford 1990

Metalwork

Bury, S., 'The Silver Designs of Dr Christopher Dresser', *Apollo*, 1962, 766-70; Bury 1971, 54-7; Birmingham 1973, section E; Crisp Jones ed., 1981, 167-8; Tilbrook, A., 'Christopher Dresser; Designs for Elkington & Co.', *Journal of the Decorative Arts Society* no. 9, 1985, 23-8

Following his visit to Japan in 1877 Dresser supplied designs to a number of metalwork firms. Many of his metalwork designs are essays in the development of bold, geometric shapes inspired by Far Eastern models, such as the spun-brass candlestick (Cat. 94) or the rectangular teapot (Cat. 90), but adhering to the doctrine of fitness for purpose outlined in his *Principles of Decorative Design*. The strikingly original shapes of many of his vessels relate directly to his theory of 'the law governing the application of handles and spouts to vessels': the handle and spout should form a right-angle through the centre of gravity, so that the weight of the vessel is well balanced during pouring (*Principles* 139-42). Examples of this principle may be seen in Cat. 85, 90-91. Dresser's electroplated nickel-silver metalwork also illustrates his concern to design for industrial processes: the body and feet of the rectangular teapot (Cat. 90) are cut from one sheet of metal; in other cases, standardised elements are used for handles, spouts and Dresser's characteristic claw-feet. The electroplate wares generally have minimal decoration and ebonised wood or ivory handles, often in the form of a cylindrical or square-section bar, derived from Japanese bamboo handles.

Dresser supplied designs for electroplated wares to Hukin & Heath of Birmingham and London, and James Dixon & Sons of Sheffield, while Elkington & Co. of Birmingham made both silver and electroplated wares to Dresser's designs. The copper and brass wares were made by Benham & Froud of London or Perry & Co. of Wolverhampton.

The firm of Hukin & Heath (1855-1953) was established by Jonathan Wilson Hukin and John Thomas Heath as manufacturing silversmiths and electroplaters. They entered silver marks in London in 1879, by which time they had established showrooms at 19 Charterhouse Street, Holborn (Culme 1987, I, 243). The firm's collaboration with Dresser was noted by the *Art Journal*, 1879, 222: the showrooms were described as 'redolent of art', while the art works were produced without increasing the cost, exhibiting 'grace combined with the useful, simplicity and purity of form with readiness of application to the purposes to which they are to be applied'. Hukin & Heath also apparently made reproductions of Persian and Japanese models 'by the electric process' (i.e. electrotyped): 'such specimens, being selected by Dr Dresser, are of course always beautiful examples of art'. Hukin & Heath's trade mark comprised the initials 'H & H' with an eagle; they registered designs by Dresser from 1878 until at least 1881 and the models were produced into the early 1900s. The firm's design books were destroyed before it closed down in 1953. Hukin & Heath also had silver wares executed to Dresser designs which were hallmarked in London (Birmingham 1973, nos E3-10).

The firm of James Dixon & Sons of Sheffield was founded c.1806, initially working in Britannia metal only and later in silver and electroplate as well. London showrooms were opened in 1873 at 37 Ludgate Hill. The firm was still trading in 1987 (for a full account, see Culme 1987, I, 121-3. The trade mark of James Dixon & Sons comprised the initials 'J.D. & S' with a bugle; they appear to have registered designs by Dresser from 1880 and these were produced at least until 1885, when a trade catalogue containing many of Dresser's models was issued. This catalogue was included in the 1979 London exhibition on Dresser (Collins 1979, no. 55, with ill.). For a second page from the catalogue, see Joppien 1981, 34. A costing book of Dixon & Sons, dating from 1879, and containing photographs of electroplated wares designed by Dresser, was included in the 1972 London exhibition on Dresser (Dennis and Jesse 1972, back cover). The costing book indicated that not all of Dresser's designs were put into production (Bury 1962). However, the present location of both these documents is unknown.

Further designs by Dresser for Dixon & Sons may be seen in pages from Dresser's design and account book, dated 1881 (Pevsner, 1937, pl. 7 and Joppien, 1981, 22-3, also now unlocated).

Many of Dresser's silver and electroplate designs were registered for protection by the firms who purchased them; the pieces therefore bear diamond-shaped design registration marks incorporating the date on which the design was registered, together with the parcel number which identified the manufacturer or registration agent (the Registers of Ornamental Designs may be consulted at the Public Record Office at Kew). Most examples with such marks also bear the facsimile signature of Christopher Dresser, probably at his insistence.

The metalwork is grouped as follows: silver, Cat. 82-3; electroplate by Hukin & Heath, Cat. 84-9; electroplate by James Dixon & Sons, Cat. 90-93; copper and brass, Cat. 94-5.

82 Ashtray   [PLATE 38]

Silver, hand-raised, in the form of a spread-eagled male figure, the head made in two parts soldered together. There are traces of repair to the join between the head and the tray. Foot ring on the underside.

MARKS Stamped on the base with London hallmarks for 1881 and maker's mark 'TJ'.

L 17 cm, W 11 cm   1983,10-10,1

Designed c.1879-80 and made by the firm of Thomas Johnson, London in 1881.

For a vessel of the same shape executed in earthenware by Linthorpe Pottery and for discussion of the source for this shape, see Cat. 96. No other silver version has yet been recorded.

The firm of Thomas Johnson, smallworkers, is recorded c.1850-98. This mark was entered in November 1881, when the firm was at 32 John Street, Bedford Row, trading under the style of Johnson, Sons & Edmunds. They made a wide range of silver small work and supplied several retailers including Thornhill of New Bond Street (see Culme 1987, I, 260-61 and II, 291-2).

83 Teaset   [PLATE 30]

Silver, comprising teapot, sugar basin and milk jug, the body of each vessel based on spherical or hemispherical drum shapes. All pieces with bands of three engraved lines echoing the shape and further engraved decoration round the body and handles, the teapot lid and the spout of the jug engraved with a sun-ray motif. The teapot handle has ivory insulators. The interiors are gilded.

MARKS Each piece stamped on the base 'ELKINGTON & CO', with Birmingham hallmarks and date-letter for 1885, sponsor's mark 'FE' for Frederick Elkington, the model number '16678', and the design registration number '22865' for 1885.

Designed before 1885 and made for Elkington & Co. Ltd, Birmingham in 1885.

83a Teapot: H 16.2 cm   1980,11-12,1
83b Sugar bowl: H 7 cm   1980,11-12,2
83c Milk jug: H 6.6 cm   1980,11-12,3

This is one of several Dresser designs for silver and electroplated wares put into production by Elkington in 1885. Volume 2 of the Elkington design books (now in the Victoria and Albert Museum Archive of Art & Design) contains some twenty-four drawings for teasets, sugar bowls, claret jugs, kettles, cruets, baskets, a tureen and a tankard, all annotated 'Dresser' and with dates ranging from 1881 to 1893, though the majority are dated 1885 (Tilbrook 1985, pls 4-11). Each drawing has the model number in the top left corner and a five-figure design registration number in the top right corner. For the design for this teaset, see Tilbrook pl. 5a, dated 15 March 1885.

In addition the Elkington Pattern Book vol. 2, one of three such books preserved in the Birmingham Public Library, contains a reduced-scale pencil drawing for these three pieces as model no. 16678, but, like the drawing in the design books, it bears only the triple-line engraved decoration and not the other details (Fig. 10; Birmingham Public Library, Archive Department, ref. ZZ323 (660631), p. 329). Comparison of the design with the teaset shows that Dresser's characteristically elongated feet have been cut down in the execution. Since the Elkington records do not give any names, attributions to Dresser are only possible from the annotated design books.

For examples of other Dresser designs in silver and electroplate for Elkington, see Birmingham 1973, section E, nos E11-14, Col-

lins 1979, nos 56-60 and 62-5, and Halén 1990, pls 165-9. According to Halén, 145-6 and pl. 165, Dresser was associated with Elkington's from the late 1860s, but few pieces dating from this time are recorded.

84 Kettle   [PLATE 29]

Electroplate, with angular spout supported on one of the four hook-shaped feet, the bar handle of ebonised wood supported on two vertical uprights above the body. The lid is hinged at right angles to the spout and has a wooden knop. An applied band with raised bosses encircles the horizontal arm of the spout. On one side of the body is an engraved owner's monogram.

MARKS Stamped on the base 'DESIGNED BY DR C DRESSER', Hukin & Heath trade mark ('H & H' with eagle) and design registration mark for 6 May 1878 (parcel 6).

Designed in 1878 and made by Hukin & Heath, Birmingham and London, between 1878 and c.1900.

H 22.9 cm (including handle), W 20.8 cm   1980,5-18,1

In the book of sketches and design studies by Dresser in the Ipswich Museum is a sketch for a similar kettle with angular spout and hook feet, one of which supports the spout. The sketch shows a side handle and a more domed lid, but has the same band of beading, applied at the join of the spout and the body (Fig. 11). The sketchbook was purchased by Captain C.A. Orchard at a sale of architectural drawings at Christie's in about 1925-6 and presented to the Ipswich Museum in 1972.

For a version of this design with side instead of top handle and matching cream jug and sugar bowl, see Dennis and Jesse 1972, no. 128. See also Joppien 1981, no. 3 (the British Museum kettle).

The bar handles are a favourite motif of Dresser's: he included illustrations of Japanese metalwork with bar-handles in the *Furniture Gazette* XIV, 1880.

85 Kettle with stand and burner   [PLATE 33]

Electroplate, the cone-shaped kettle with ebonised wood handle with angled ends, and push-on lid. The stand has three legs holding a triangular plate for the burner, which has an ebonised wood handle.

MARKS The base of the kettle stamped 'DESIGNED BY DR CHRISTOPHER DRESSER', with the Hukin & Heath trade mark ('H & H' with eagle). The pot, stand and burner each bear the stamped design registration mark for 6 May 1878, flanked by the date '1878'.

Designed in 1878 and made by Hukin & Heath, Birmingham and London, between 1878 and c.1900.

Total H 17.2 cm. Pot: H 11.6 cm, W 20.4 cm. Stand: H 5.9 cm, W 15.4 cm   1980,11-11,1

86 Cruet set   [PLATE 35]

Electroplate, with three glass cruets set into a triangular base with cut corners, two legs at each corner, the handle with hemispherical knop. The plating is worn where the stand has been repaired in the centre.

MARKS Stamped on the base 'DESIGNED BY DR C. DRESSER', the Hukin & Heath trade mark ('H & H' with eagle), the number '1939' and design registration mark for 9 October 1878 (parcel 11).

Designed in 1878 and made by Hukin & Heath, Birmingham and London, between 1878 and c.1900.

H 13.4 cm, W 11.4 cm   1982,12-4,1

For variants of this design, see Joppien 1981, no. 2, enlarged to hold six glass cruets, and no. 27, of similar size but in silver, with silver-mounted salt and pepper pots, and a fourth hole containing a small bottle.

87 Cruet set [PLATE 35]

Electroplate, with six egg-cup-shaped containers and a D-shaped handle. The frame contains three glass cruet bottles with stoppers, a salt or pepper shaker and mustard pot. One container is empty.

MARKS Stamped on the base 'DESIGNED BY DR CHRISTOPHER DRESSER', the Hukin & Heath trade mark ('H & H' with eagle), the number '1996', and on the side of one of the containers the design registration mark for 8 October 1878 (parcel 11).

Designed in 1878 and made by Hukin & Heath, Birmingham and London, between 1878 and c.1900.

H 18.5 cm, W 16 cm   1980,2-2,1

This model was illustrated by Pevsner in his 1937 article on Dresser (pl. 4). For a variant of this design with four instead of six containers, see Dennis and Jesse 1972, no. 121.

88 Tureen and cover with ladle [PLATE 33]

Electroplate, the spun body on three cast feet with matching ivory bar-handles to bowl and cover; the ladle with stem angled above the bowl and terminating in an ivory handle.

MARKS Stamped on the base of the tureen 'DESIGNED BY DR. C. DRESSER', Hukin & Heath trade mark ('H & H' with eagle), and the number '2123'. The ladle stamped with design registration mark for 28 July 1880 (parcel 8).

Designed in 1880 and made by Hukin & Heath, Birmingham and London, between 1880 and c.1900.

88a Tureen: H 20 cm (with cover), W 31.1 cm (with handles), D of cover 23.5 cm
88b Ladle: L 35 cm, D of bowl 8.3 cm   1982,11-2,1

Several versions of this design are known, in varying sizes, with handles in ivory or ebonised wood. This version is unusual in having three identical bar-handles instead of the more customary knop-shaped handle to the cover. For examples with knop-shaped handle to the cover, see Dennis and Jesse 1972, nos 116-18; London 1972, D.161-2 (in the Victoria and Albert Museum, formerly Handley-Read collection); Collins 1979, no. 19; Joppien 1981, nos 13-14.

The design for this tureen and ladle, registered by Hukin & Heath on 28 July 1880, is recorded as no. 352892 in the Registers of Ornamental Designs held by the Public Record Office (Vol. No. BT 43/47).

89 Letter rack [PLATE 31]

Electroplate, with movable struts on a curved base resting on bun feet. Slots in the base allow the struts to slide into a more upright position.

MARKS Stamped on the base with the Hukin & Heath trade mark ('H & H' with eagle), the number, '2555' and design registration mark for 9 May 1881 (parcel 5).

Designed in 1881 and made by Hukin & Heath, Birmingham and London, between 1881 and c.1900.

H 12.3 cm, W 10.4 cm   1980,10-14,1

There were a number of variations on this design: the version with fixed supports was model no. 2556 (Dennis & Jesse 1972, no. 125; Collins 1979, no. 44, both described as toast racks); examples were also made with an open base, model no. 2655 (Collins 1979, no. 45). A further variant served as combined book-end and letter rack, comprising half the model with closed-in base for solidity, the lowest rack set horizontally, with a bend to hold pens (Collins 1979, no. 43). It should be noted that none of these examples bears Dresser's facsimile signature.

90 Teapot [PLATE 34]

Electroplate, of rectangular form, the hinged lid with square knop, ebonised wood bar-handle of square section with angular top support. The sides and feet are cut from one sheet of metal.

MARKS Stamped on the base with facsimile signature 'Chr Dresser', Dixon and Sons' trademark and 'EP, NC 0193, 4'.

Designed c.1878-9 and made by James Dixon and Sons, Sheffield, between c.1879 and 1885 or later.

H 18.5 cm, W 23.3 cm   1981,10-5,1

A photograph of this model, lacking the knop to the lid, was included in Dixon & Sons' costing book of 1879 (Dennis & Jesse 1972, back cover). A sketch for a teapot of similar form appears in Dresser's design and account book of 1881, though the spout is angled instead of straight (Pevsner 1937, fig. 7, and Joppien 1981, 22). This teapot appears to be the only recorded example of this model, which is inspired by Chinese eighteenth-century metal teapots of similar shape.

91 Teapot [PLATE 32]

Electroplate, an inverted cone shape on three legs with angled handle and spout, hinged lid with cone-shaped knop.

MARKS Stamped on the base with facsimile signature 'Chr Dresser', Dixon and Sons' trade mark ('DIXON' with bugle instead of 'J.D. & S' with bugle as on Cat. 90, 91 and 93), and the number '2278'.

Designed in 1880 and made by James Dixon & Sons, Sheffield, c.1880-85 or later.

H 10 cm, W 18 cm   1982,1-8,4

The complete 'afternoon tea set' with milk jug and sugar bowl was advertised in J. Dixon & Sons' 1885 catalogue at 58s. for the pot, 40s. each for the jug and bowl. For an example of the milk jug, see Collins 1979, no. 52. For a silver version, see Dennis and Jesse 1972, no. 137.

92 Sugar basin [PLATE 32]

Electroplate, of hemispherical shape, supported on four legs, the interior gilded.

MARKS Stamped on the base with facsimile signature 'Chr Dresser', Dixon and Sons' trade mark ('DIXON' with bugle instead of 'J.D. & S' with bugle as on Cat. 90, 91 and 93), and the number '2278'.

Made by James Dixon & Sons, Sheffield, c.1885 or later.

H 9.9 cm, D 11.2 cm   1980,2-5,1

Illustrated in J. Dixon & Sons' trade catalogue of 1885 (Collins 1979, no. 55); the sugar bowl cost 35s., the full set with tea pot and creamer cost £6 7s. A design for a closely similar set with three legs is included in the Elkington & Co. Pattern Book, vol. 2, pattern 16611 (Collins 1979, no. 67). For a variant in electroplate with lids to the jug and bowl, see Dennis & Jesse 1972, no. 148.

93 Toast rack [PLATE 31]

Electroplate, in the form of a double row of hexagons set on an openwork rectangular frame, the triangular handle rising from the centre to form a lozenge above the hexagons.

MARKS Stamped on the base with facsimile signature 'Chr Dresser', Dixon and Sons' trade mark, 'EP', and the number '68'.

Made by James Dixon & Sons, Sheffield, c.1885 or later.

H 13.4 cm, L 16.2 cm, W 12.3 cm   1980,5-3,1

This is one of Dresser's most original designs. It was illustrated in J. Dixon & Sons' trade catalogue of 1885, price 29s. (Joppien 1981, 34). It was also produced in silver.

94 Candlestick [PLATE 36]

Spun brass, painted crimson-red, formed of a hemispherical base with a smaller, shallower drip tray, joined by a cylinder, with polished brass mount supporting a curved wooden bar-handle.

MARKS Stamped on the brass handle-mount 'DR DRESSER'S DESIGN' with design registration mark for 30 October 1883 (parcel 13). Stamped on the base 'Perry, Son & Co' within a rope device.

Designed in 1883 and made by Richard Perry, Son & Company, Wolverhampton, after 1883.
H 14.7 cm, W 19.3 cm   1980,6-8,1

The red colour is here inspired by Japanese lacquered wood wares of the eighteenth century; the shape recalls lacquered drums used for the Noh theatre, while the bamboo handle, suggested by the knobbled brass mounts as well as the wooden bar, completes the Japanese effect, though the shape is pure Dresser.

These candlesticks seem to have been the only metalwork designed by Dresser to have been sold by Liberty's; examples are recorded marked 'Liberty & Co, London' (e.g. Phillips, Son & Neale sale catalogue, 18 June 1987, lot 143). They were advertised by Liberty's under the name of 'Kordofan' candlesticks in 'Liberty art colours', which included yellow, turquoise and deep green (London 1975, no. C25). They were also sold in plain polished brass (Morris 1989, 78). Kordofan is a province of Sudan; Liberty's trade name was doubtless intended to sound romantic and eastern.

Perry & Co. of Wolverhampton specialised in japanned and tinned iron wares; the firm had a retail outlet in London at 72 New Bond Street until 1890, when they moved to 17 Grafton Street. According to an undated catalogue of lighting appliances in the Victoria and Albert Museum Library, the business was sold to Burt's of Wardour Street in 1925.

95 Kettle [PLATE 36]

Spun copper with brass handle and three brass legs. Wooden knop slightly damaged.

MARKS None.

Made by Benham & Froud Ltd., London, c.1885.

H 21.5 cm   1980,6-13,1

Although unmarked, this example was almost certainly made by Benham & Froud, by comparison with identical examples bearing the firm's trade mark, the bell and cross of St Paul's Cathedral (e.g. Collins 1979, no. 69).

It is interesting to note that an alternative and more daring model, also made by Benham & Froud, was illustrated by Pevsner in his 1937 article on Dresser (p. 184), where it is dated c.1885 (see also Collins 1979, no. 68). The Pevsner model has no horizontal moulding breaking the line of the spherical body, the rim rises almost vertically above the inset lid, and, most significantly, the handle is in the form of a high, horizontal bar on vertical supports, one of which bends at the base to join the angled handle. These characteristic Dresser motifs give a much bolder and more geometric effect than the example catalogued here, with its horizontal moulding and traditional handle and spout. Possibly these were modifications made by the factory.

Benham & Froud are recorded from 1860 as copper and brass manufacturers at 40-42 Chandos Street, Charing Cross EC; they exhibited at the London Exhibition of 1862 (Culme 1987, I, 39). According to a catalogue of 1878 in the Victoria and Albert Museum Library, they specialised in 'art metal and wood work'. A later catalogue, issued after 1904, gives the firm's address as 'Chandos House', Store Street (off Tottenham Court Road) and Chandos Works, Chandos Road, Willesden Junction. By 1913 the firm had been succeeded by Herbert Benham & Co. of 4 Ramillies Place, Great Marlborough Street.

Linthorpe Art Pottery

Jewitt, L., *The Ceramic Art of Great Britain*, 2nd edn 1883 (reprinted Poole 1985, 308-9; Moreland, A., 'Linthorpe: A Forgotten English Pottery', *Connoisseur* XXXIX, June 1914, 85-8; *Pottery Gazette* XL, 1915, 849-53; Lee, R., 'A forgotten Yorkshire Pottery', *The Heaton Review* 7, 1934, 37ff.; Bracegirdle, C., 'Linthorpe: The Forgotten Pottery', *Country Life*, 29 April 1971, 1022-5; Le Vine, J.R.A., *Linthorpe Pottery, An Interim Report*, Teesside Museums and Art Galleries Service, 1970; See also Coysh 1976, 54-6 and Haslam 1975, 24-5 and 95-7 (reprint of 'Notes on Linthorpe Ware' from a trade brochure, c.1886); Hart, C., *Linthorpe Art Pottery*, Aisling Publications, 1988.

The Linthorpe Pottery at Middlesbrough, then in Yorkshire, was set up by Dresser in association with the businessman John Harrison, in 1879. According to an anonymous article in the *Pottery Gazette* XL, 1915, Harrison met Dresser as a result of reports in the local press of Dresser's lectures on art at Whitby and Darlington. Harrison owned the land, noted for its red brick-clay and it was intended that the pottery would produce original art wares and at the same time alleviate local unemployment by employing up to a hundred staff. But several workers were brought in from outside Middlesbrough, including skilled staff from the potteries in Staffordshire and fourteen artists from Kensington. On Dresser's recommendation, Henry Tooth, an artist who had worked as a boy in the local brickworks, returned to Middlesbrough from the Isle of Wight, where Dresser had met him, and was appointed pottery manager despite his lack of experience in pottery making. Dresser served as Art Director for three years until 1882, when Tooth left to establish the Bretby Art Pottery in 1883 at Woodville, Derbyshire, with William Ault. The latter set up his own Ault Pottery at Swadlincote, Derbyshire in 1887, in competition with Linthorpe. Linthorpe closed in 1889 following Harrison's death in May of that year; the moulds were publicly auctioned and many of them were acquired by Ault, who continued to produce Dresser designs at least until Dresser's death in 1904.

Linthorpe pots designed by Dresser usually bear the following impressed marks: Dresser's facsimile signature (which varies in size and detail); the factory name 'LINTHORPE'; model number and 'HT' conjoined for Henry Tooth. Thus it can be seen that Dresser's designs were executed for the most part before 1882, when Tooth left Linthorpe. The two pieces catalogued below that do not bear the initials 'HT' (Cat. 96, 98) have therefore been dated to 1879-89. According to Jewitt, Dresser's name was impressed only for the first three or four years of production.

Advertisements for Linthorpe Pottery appeared regularly in the *Furniture Gazette* while it was under the editorship of Dresser from 1880 to 1881. At that time the pottery was available through Dresser & Holme, a wholesale warehouse for imported oriental goods in Farringdon Road, run by Dresser from 1879 to 1882 in partnership with Charles Holme, a Bradford businessman who later founded *The Studio*. From the middle of 1880 Linthorpe Pottery was also sold through the Art Furnishers Alliance at 157 New Bond Street, set up to supply artistic household furnishings with the backing of G.H. Chubb of the firm of safe manufacturers; John Harrison was one of the directors. The author of the *Studio* article on Dresser of 1899 remembered the avant-garde displays and the 'attendants robed in many aesthetic costumes of the period, in demure art colours'. By contrast, the writer who announced the opening of the Alliance in the trade journal of the pottery industry, the *Pottery Gazette*, complained of 'yet another company under the above designation . . . we know not whether to laugh or be indignant over this new venture'. The Alliance was liquidated in 1883. Linthorpe pottery was also exhibited at the Society of Arts Exhibition of Modern English Pottery in 1882 (*JSA* 30, 769-71, 908-12, 917-22; Bracegirdle 1025).

Jewitt, writing in 1883, noted that Linthorpe had cast off 'the rigid severity of angular outlines on the one hand and grotesque combinations and distortions on the other . . . the peculiar ware for which it first gained so enviable a notoriety'. Yet he reserved praise for the never-ending variety and effect of the 'Linthorpe glaze'. The glazes range from olive, red, yellow and brown in varying shades, smooth or mottled and streaked, often with accidental patterns. The two different body fabrics, the local red clay and a white clay that was brought into the pottery, were skilfully used to achieve different effects with the different glazes. Many of the pots were cast in moulds and then incised or pierced decoration (Cat. 99, 102) was executed in the leather-hard stage. The Linthorpe factory collection in the Dorman Museum, Middlesbrough includes a number of undecorated blanks (in both red clay and white clay, Collins 1979, nos 160-72) as well as plaster moulds. Dresser's designs tend to have relatively low model numbers; there are few higher than 870 (recorded numbers go up to about 2500).

Dresser's work for Linthorpe divides itself into two groups: first, the extraordinary shapes derived from Far Eastern, Islamic, Peruvian or Fijian prototypes, sometimes contemporary, as in the case of the Fiji ritual dish (Cat. 96), or ancient, as in the case of the Pre-Colombian Peruvian bridge-spouted vessel (Cat. 97); secondly, the stylised animal and plant motifs developed from Dresser's botanical studies (Cat. 102-3).

96 Ashtray   [PLATE 38]

Earthenware, red body, in the form of a spread-eagled male figure, the head unglazed, the body covered with a streaked yellow, green and rust glaze.

MARKS Impressed on the base with facsimile signature 'Chr Dresser', 'LINTHORPE' and model number '293'.

Designed in 1879-80 and made by the Linthorpe Art Pottery, Middlesbrough, between 1879 and 1889.

L 18 cm. Franks Collection, OA (Old Acquisition) 10711. The object bears a Franks Collection number 'AF' ligatured and '91', but this can not be identified with the corresponding number in the Franks Bequest of 1897, or with the ancillary Franks Collection lists.

This unusual shape is included among the advertisements for Linthorpe Pottery in the *Furniture Gazette*, 22 May, 1880. It is based on a type of shallow, saucer-like dish made in Fiji as a priest's ritual drinking vessel and carved in wood in the form of human or animal images. Such dishes are known as *yaqona* dishes, *yaqona* being the narcotic drink used in the ritual; for an example in the form of a human image in the Fiji Museum, see F. Clunie, *Yalo i Viti. Shades of Viti: A Fiji Museum Catalogue*, Suva 1986, no. 130. Dresser is likely to have been familiar with the *yaqona* dish in the form of a male figure acquired by the British Museum in 1842 (Department of Ethnography, 1842. 12-10.127). He may also have known the illustration of a group of *yaqona* dishes, including a male figure dish, in T. Williams's *Fiji and the Fijians*, published in 1858 (p. 60). This illustration (Fig. 12) is of particular interest because some of the forms of the other dishes in the group reappear in modified form in other shapes designed by Dresser for Linthorpe Pottery. Both the 1858 dish and the British Museum dish are more elongated than Dresser's version. A dish of broader form exists in the Oldman Collection in Auckland, New Zealand, but its history does not go back to the 1880s (*Journal of the Polynesian Society* 52, 1943, supplement to the March issue entitled 'The Oldman Collection of Polynesian Artefacts'. I am grateful to Dorota Starzecka and Dr Steven Hooper for references to the Fijian models). The head, however, bears no relation to the heads of the Fijian dishes; the idea of a clay head is derived from ancient South American art, but the features of Dresser's head are more oriental. A similar head occurs in one of Dresser's most eccentric designs of Japanese inspiration for Linthorpe: a bottle-vase in which the head emerges from the neck of the vase and two hands extrude at the shoulders (see London 1990, no. 63); a vase of this design is held by the Dorman Museum, Middlesbrough.

Unlike some of the Linthorpe models, which survive in large numbers, few examples of this pottery ashtray are recorded. Two further examples are among the Linthorpe factory collection in the Dorman Museum, Middlesbrough; they are both in white clay with unglazed heads, the body glazed green or brown. A further pottery example with purple glass eyes and an amber-coloured glaze has recently been recorded (Phillips, London, 16 October 1990, lot 382), but it bears the mark of the Burmantofts Pottery at Leeds, not the Linthorpe mark. Like Linthorpe, Burmantofts was also a brickworks using local clays, before the introduction of art pottery in about 1880; they may have acquired the Linthorpe mould after 1889, when Linthorpe closed and the moulds were auctioned.

The shape was almost certainly designed originally for execution in pottery, but for a rare silver version, see Cat. 82.

97 Vessel   [PLATE 37]

Earthenware, red body, of sea-urchin shape with vertical lines of raised bosses and a bridge handle joining double spouts, the whole covered with mottled green and brown glaze.

MARKS Impressed on the base with facsimile signature 'Chr Dresser', 'LINTHORPE', the monogram 'HT' for Henry Tooth and model number '312'.

Designed in 1879-80 and made by Linthorpe Art Pottery, Middlesbrough, between 1879 and 1882.

H 17 cm, D 15.1 cm   1980,3-6,1

A vase of this design was advertised in the *Furniture Gazette*, 12 June 1880 (Collins 1979, 14). The shape is inspired by Pre-Columbian Peruvian vessels. Dresser designed several 'Pre-

Columbian' shapes for Linthorpe Pottery including another bridge-spouted vessel with a human face (Collins 1979, no. 158).

98 Vase [PLATE 37]

Earthenware, red body, of flattened spherical shape with two handles. On each side an incised circular band with raised bosses, containing a raised spiral motif. The body in mottled green and the spiral motif in brown glaze, with blue splashes.

MARKS Impressed on the base with facsimile signature 'Chr Dresser', the other marks hidden beneath thick glaze.

Designed c.1879-80 and made by Linthorpe Art Pottery, Middlesbrough, between 1879 and 1889.

H 20.1 cm   1980,10-12,1

For other vases of the same shape, all impressed with Linthorpe model number 337, see Dennis and Jesse 1972, nos 44-47; this group included two alternative relief motifs and a jug with a lip spout replacing one handle. A related vase shape with two small handles at the neck was advertised in the *Furniture Gazette*, 29 May 1880; known examples of this shape bear the model number 336.

99 Vessel [PLATE 37]

Earthenware, red body, of camel-back form, the handle evolving out of the neck and spout. Streaked green and rust glaze over incised geometric decoration in the form of a star motif on the hump and a band of rosettes round the body with a larger rosette at the front.

MARKS Impressed on base with facsimile signature 'Chr Dresser', 'LINTHORPE' and the monogram 'HT'; the model number '347' is incised instead of impressed.

Designed c.1879-80 and made by Linthorpe Art Pottery, Middlesbrough, between 1879 and 1882.

H 18.4 cm, W 16.3 cm   1980,10-13,1

For the same model with different glazes, see Dennis and Jesse 1972, no. 52; Collins 1979, no. 145 (in the Dorman Museum, Middlesbrough) and Joppien 1981, no. 58. This model is one of a small group of models with incised rather than stamped numbers; the reason for this is not known. The Dorman Museum also owns an unmarked version of this model of slightly larger size, in which the incised decoration lacks definition, suggesting that it is an after-cast from an original Linthorpe piece.

100 Vase [PLATE 37]

Earthenware, red body, of dimpled double-gourd shape, with streaked yellow brown glaze on upper part, merging to bottle green and turquoise below; applied gilded decoration of cloud motifs.

MARKS Impressed on the base with the facsimile signature 'Chr Dresser', the monogram 'HT' and model number '838' (or '833'). The factory name is not visible beneath the thick glaze. The number '30611' is painted with gold over the glaze, on top of the Dresser signature.

Designed c.1880-81 and made by Linthorpe Art Pottery, Middlesbrough, between 1879 and 1882.

H 20.1 cm   1980,5-4,1

For a similar double-gourd vase with model number 327, see Dennis and Jesse 1972, no. 38. See also a gourd vase in the Dorman Museum with the model number 140 (Collins 1979, no. 128). The gilded decoration on the British Museum vase is unusual and it is likely that it was added by the factory.

Two designs for gourd vases are included in Dresser's design and account book among a group of sketches headed 'Aug. 29th 1881. Sent to J. Harrison Esq. 41 Designs for Linthorpe' (Joppien 1981, 23).

101 Coffee-pot, cup and saucer [PLATE 39]

Earthenware, white body, with angular handles, the pot with vertical spout joined to body at the neck. Covered with yellow-ochre glaze over a design of blossom branches painted in underglaze black. The interior of pot and cup glazed turquoise.

MARKS All pieces impressed on the base with facsimile signature 'Chr Dresser', 'LINTHORPE', the monogram 'HT', the model number '664' on the coffee pot and '639' on the cups and saucers.

Designed c.1879-80 and made by Linthorpe Art Pottery, Middlesbrough, between 1879 and 1882.

101a Coffee pot: H 26.4 cm, D 15.4 cm   1980,5-6,1
101b Cup: H 6.5 cm. Saucer: D 12 cm   1980,5-5,1 and 2

This service occurs in plain glazes without the blossom pattern (Collins 1979, no. 177); there was also an alternative model for the coffee-pot, model no. 646 (Dennis and Jesse 1972, no. 68), a larger size cylindrical cup, model no. 640 (Dennis and Jesse, no. 68) shallow cups of rounded shape, model no. 641 (Dennis and Jesse, no. 69), a sugar basin, model no. 637 (Dennis and Jesse 1972, no. 66, and a creamer, model no. 636.

102 Plate [PLATE 40; COLOUR PLATE VI]

Earthenware, white body, with olive-green glaze. In the centre, a pierced roundel with a stylized moth among flowers and leaves, surrounded by a further band of pierced floral ornament, the pierced areas in mauve, orange and white.

MARKS Impressed on the base and the inside rim of foot with the facsimile signature 'Chr Dresser', 'LINTHORPE' and, inside rim of foot, the monogram 'HT'. There is no model number.

Designed c.1867-80 and made by Linthorpe Art Pottery, Middlesbrough, between 1879 and 1882.

D 41 cm, H 7 cm   1980,11-10,1

The design for this plate was originally supplied to Minton, but apparently not executed; the water-colour design, signed by Dresser and entitled 'Summer', survives in the Minton factory archive (Collins 1979, no. 116). A large number of designs for both shape and decoration were supplied to Minton by Dresser and his studio; recorded Minton pieces decorated with Dresser designs bear Minton date cyphers for the period c.1867-80 (Collins 1979, nos 103-5).

A plate of this design was advertised in the *Furniture Gazette*, 1 May 1880. This example appears to be the only recorded version of this elaborate and successful design; the coloured glazes have not run, and the pierced work is exceptional.

103 Plate [PLATE 39]

Earthenware, white body, olive-green glaze with a band of relief floral ornament in deep yellow and turquoise blue.

MARKS Impressed on the base with facsimile signature 'Chr Dresser', 'LINTHORPE', the monogram 'HT' and model number '299'.

Designed c.1879-80 and made by Linthorpe Art Pottery, Middlesbrough, between 1879 and 1882.

D 30.6 cm   1980,6-6,1

For a plate of the same design with flowers in brown, yellow and red, see Dennis and Jesse 1972, no. 30.

Old Hall Earthenware Company

104 Soup bowl and dinner plate   [PLATE 40]

Earthenware, of square shape with broad flat rims and angled corners. The bowl (104a) has a depression on one side continuing into the foot. The plate (104b) has two circular depressions at each corner of the flat rim. Both plates decorated with a transfer-printed floral motif in yellow, rust and buff with black outlines.

MARKS Transfer-printed facsimile signature 'Chr Dresser', pattern name 'SHANGHAI' and a partially legible design registration number for 1884.

The design registered in 1884 and made by Old Hall Earthenware Company Ltd, Old Hall Pottery, Hanley, Staffordshire, between 1884 and 1902.

w 22.8 cm (both)   1982, 1-8,5 and 6

The Old Hall Earthenware Company, formerly Charles Meigh & Son, was founded in 1861; it was known as the Old Hall Porcelain Works Ltd from 1886 and remained in production until 1902. This bowl and plate are from a dinner service with three different patterns designed by Dresser and registered by the Company in 1884. The patterns were called 'Persian', 'Shanghai' and 'Hampden'. For an illustration of all three, see Halén 1990, pl. 107. For examples of 'Shanghai' pattern with clearly legible design registration number 8723 for 1884, see London, Fischer Fine Art, 1986, no. 106; for an example of a 'Persian' pattern plate with registration number 4136 for 1884, see Collins 1979, no. 201. A number of other Old Hall patterns have been attributed to Dresser, but these three patterns appear to be the only ones that occur in conjunction with Dresser's facsimile signature.

The article on Dresser in The Studio of 1899 describes one of these dinner services, 'whereby the simple addition of hollows in the rim of the plate, such as a potter might make with his thumb, receptacles were provided for salt, mustard and the like condiments' (vol. 15, 112).

The pattern name 'Shanghai' is misleading, for the pattern, with its scrolling fleshy leaves, a characteristic Dresser motif, is rather a combination of Persian and medieval sources, as illustrated by Owen Jones in The Grammar of Ornament, pls XLVI, LXIX and LXXI. The 'Shanghai' pattern was also executed in an alternative colour scheme of greens, blues and khaki (information kindly supplied by David Coachworth).

'Clutha' Glass

Useful contemporary sources include The Studio 15, 1899, 104–14 and Liberty & Co.'s Yule-Tide Gifts catalogues for the 1890s (held by Westminster Library Archive Department). For more recent bibliography, see Fleming, A., Scottish and Jacobite Glass, Glasgow 1938; Revi, A.C., Nineteenth Century Glass, New York 1967, 205-6; Blench, B., 'The Elusive James Couper Snr', Scottish Pottery Society Historical Review 8, 1984, 20-27; Blench, B., 'Christopher Dresser and his Glass Designs', Annales du 9e Congrès de l'Association Internationale pour l'Histoire du Verre, Nancy 22-8 May 1983, Liège 1985; Morris 1989, 70-71.

The production of Dresser's designs for the Glasgow glass manufacturers James Couper & Sons seems to date from the late 1880s to the early 1900s and so is considerably later than the pottery. The glassware was sold under the trade name of 'Clutha', an old word for the River Clyde, which runs through Glasgow. The glass, like its name, was consciously archaic in its use of bubbled and streaked glass, in shades of green, brown, amber and pink, with striations in white, red, blue and aventurine. For the method used, see Revi, 205.

It has been suggested that 'Clutha' glass was in production by about 1883 (Halén 1990, 192), but the first secure evidence appears in 1888, when Couper & Sons registered the trade mark 'CLUTHA' in Roman capitals, recorded in the Trade Marks Journal, and indeed in the same year Couper's complained that their 'Clutha' glass was being imitated by the Stourbridge firm of Thomas Webb (Morris 1978, 184). However, the 'CLUTHA' trade mark appears on few pieces. Much more common is the circular acid-etched trade mark 'CLUTHA' in mock-Celtic script with the words 'DESIGNED BY C.D. REGISTERED' enclosing the Liberty & Co. lotus-flower trade mark, suggesting that much of the production was sold by Liberty & Co. 'Clutha' glass was advertised throughout the 1890s in Liberty's Yule-Tide Gifts catalogues as 'Decorative, Quaint, Original and Artistic', but, in accordance with Liberty's policy of not acknowledging the designers of the goods they sold, Dresser's name is never mentioned. The circular trade mark is thus exceptional: the assumption is that Dresser himself insisted that his initials should be incorporated, just as his facsimile signature had appeared on the metalwork and pottery.

Couper & Sons exhibited their new glassware at the Arts & Crafts Exhibition Society in London in 1890; the catalogue entry describes them as 'specimens of Clutha glass, designed by Christopher Dresser' (Arts & Crafts Exhibition Society, Catalogue of the Third Exhibition, 1890, 184, no. 271; further entries list specimens of Clutha glass exhibited by Couper & Sons, but no designer is given; see nos 306, 320, 326). Couper's introduction to the Arts & Crafts Exhibition Society may have come through the Glasgow architect George Walton, who was exhibiting with the Society at this time and who also designed glass for Couper (the Walton glass was sold at Liberty's from 1896; see Morris 1989, 71).

The shapes of 'Clutha' glass relate closely in their reliance on ancient and Near Eastern forms to the Linthorpe Pottery shapes; some of the designs registered by Couper & Sons were identical to shapes produced ten years earlier in pottery at Linthorpe (for example, Patent Office Design Registration numbers 121729-31, entered on 22 June 1893; reference kindly supplied by Brian Blench).

Couper & Sons, established in 1850-51, were manufacturers of utilitarian wares such as globes for gas and electric lighting and for Napier's Patent coffee-machine, lenses for harbour and ship lights, and a range of coloured glass for leaded glass work called 'St Mungo' glass. This may have led them to experiment with table wares using similar glass mixtures. Examples of St Mungo ornamental glass in green with bubbles and swirls of red, brown and blue, are held by Glasgow City Museum and Art Gallery. Couper & Sons ceased to blow glass in 1911.

105 Vase   [PLATE 41]

Free-blown green bubbled glass with red streaks, a conical base with tall stem and flared wavy rim.

MARKS Acid-etched on base with circular trade mark incorporating the Liberty & Co. lotus-flower and the words 'CLUTHA DESIGNED BY C.D. REGISTERED'. This is in a smaller format than the mark on the jug (Cat. 107); the words and flower are matt. There is also a very faint etched mark in the form of a trefoil surrounded by the words 'CLUTHA REG^D TRADE MARK'.

Designed c.1880-90 and made by James Couper & Sons, Glasgow, between the late 1880s and 1911.

H 42.2 cm, D of base 11.5 cm   1980,5-17,1

A similar vase, in which the foot has a slightly different profile, is illustrated in the *Art Journal*, 1892, 376, in an article by Aymer Vallance on 'The Furnishings and Decoration of the House': '"Clutha" glass, so named from the river Clyde, is conspicuous for its beauty and quaintness of form, as well as for its richness and variety of colouring. It has, moreover, the little specks and bubbles which . . . help to emphasise the shape of glass vessels' (p. 377).

A vase of this shape also appears in Liberty's *Yule-Tide Gifts* catalogue for 1895-6; it was offered in two sizes: 10-in (25 cm) at 5s. 6d. or 16-in (40 cm) at 7s. 6d. For a similar vase with the alternative acid-etched mark 'CLUTHA', with 'JC & S' and 'Registered', see Joppien 1981, no. 61. See also Dennis and Jesse 1972, no. 110.

106 Vase   [PLATE 41]

Free-blown pale green bubbled glass with red streaks, bulbous base with tall stem.

MARKS Acid-etched on base with circular trade mark incorporating the Liberty & Co. lotus-flower and the words 'CLUTHA DESIGNED BY C.D. REGISTERED'. This is arranged in a large circular format as on the jug (Cat. 107) but in reverse, i.e. the background is matt. There is also a faint etched trefoil mark with the words 'CLUTHA REG^D TRADE MARK', as on Cat. 105.

Designed c.1880-90 and made by James Couper & Sons, Glasgow, between the late 1880s and 1911.

H 40.9 cm, D of base 13.4 cm   1980,6-7,1

107 Jug   [PLATE 42]

Free-blown green bubbled glass.

MARKS Acid-etched on base with circular trade mark incorporating the Liberty & Co. lotus-flower and the words 'CLUTHA DESIGNED BY C.D. REGISTERED'. The words and flower are matt (for variants, see Cat. 105-6).

Designed c.1880-90 and made by James Couper & Sons, Glasgow, between the late 1880s and 1911.

H 17.3 cm   1980,2-4,1

Dufrène, Maurice 1876-1955

There is no monograph on Dufrène. The most useful accounts of his designs for the applied arts are to be found in contemporary articles, for example 'Maurice Dufrène décorateur', *Art et Décoration*, 1906, 73-84; 'Maurice Dufrène', *Art et Décoration*, May 1921, 129-42 (written by himself). A volume of his designs for jewellery in the Art Nouveau style is held in the British Museum's Department of Medieval and Later Antiquities (*Les Bijoux par Maurice Dufrène*, Librairie des Arts Décoratifs, n.d.).

108 Milk jug and sugar bowl   [PLATE 76]

Hard-paste porcelain, cast in two-piece moulds and painted in overglaze red and olive green with sinuous plant forms on a white ground. The handles are moulded in one piece with the body, continuing the line of both rim and base. The curvilinear decoration emphasises the form by running in a continuous loop along the rim and from body to handle. The lid to the sugar bowl is also moulded in one piece, the decoration running round the rim and over the top of the handle. The green is paler than other surviving examples from this service and is probably overfired.

MARKS Printed on the base in black 'LA MAISON MODERNE 82 R. des Petits Champs' with the monogram 'LMM'.

Designed c.1902-3 for La Maison Moderne, Paris and made probably in Limoges, manufacturer unknown, before 1903, when La Maison Moderne closed down.

108a Milk jug: H 9.1 cm, max. W 11.5 cm   1982, 12-3,5a
108b Sugar bowl: H 12.4 cm, max. W 17.7 cm   1982,12-3,5b

Dufrène studied at the École des Arts Décoratifs and was a founder member of the Société des Artistes-Décorateurs in 1901. From 1912 to 1923 he taught at the École Boulle and in 1921 founded his own shop in Paris, La Maîtrise. In 1900, while he was still at the École des Arts Décoratifs, Dufrène was engaged as chief designer for La Maison Moderne (*DK & D* XII, 1903, 551), the gallery of modern design established in Paris in 1898 by the writer and art critic Julius Meier-Graefe as a rival to Siegfried Bing's Maison de l'Art Nouveau.

This service was executed with an alternative decoration of stylised roses; see *Der Moderne Stil* 5, 1903, pl. 80; *DK & D* VI, 1903, 557; *A & D* XIX, 1906, 77 (ill.) and 82 (text); *The Studio Yearbook* 1908, F31. Another variant, of similar shape but with relief decoration is known from contemporary illustration only: see *A & D* XII, 1902, 24; *Der Moderne Stil* 5, 1903, pl. 10; *DK & D* VI, 1903, 556. The service as catalogued here, with sinuous plant decoration, does not appear in any of these contemporary sources, but it is assumed that this decoration was designed at about the same time as the roses pattern, illustrated in 1903.

For other examples of pieces from this service with the sinuous plant decoration, see Bröhan II/2, 1977, nos 435-6 and Heller 1982, no. 84. See also Mosel 1971, no. 91, a complete teaset, the milk jug signed on the shoulder in grey 'M.DUFRENE', but with no other marks; Düsseldorf 1974, no. 62: parts of this service are stamped on the base in green 'Le Parthénon, Paris' as well as 'La Maison Moderne'; Wichmann 1988, 50, including a coffee-pot with the artist's signature and a saucer stamped 'Le Parthénon Paris'. 'Le Parthénon' may be another retailer's mark, but if so, it is curious that it should appear with 'La Maison Moderne' unless it was applied later. None of these examples bears a manufacturer's mark, but it is likely that the Maison Moderne porcelain, like that sold at La Maison de l'Art Nouveau, was made in Limoges and supplied without manufacturer's marks at the request of Meier-Graefe (see de Feure, Cat. 58).

Eisenlöffel, Jan W. 1876-1957

There is no monograph on Eisenlöffel. For biographical details and Eisenlöffel's association with the Amstelhoek factory, see Leeuwarden 1986. There are also a number of contemporary sources, e.g. van de Velde, H., 'Einige Künstler Holland's und die Austellung Hugo Koch's in Düsseldorf', *Innen-Dekoration*, August 1902, 201-6; Vogelsang, W., 'Für den Weltmarkt: Metallarbeiten von Jan Eisenlöffel', *Die Kunst* 8, 1902-3, 383-9; Walenkamp, H., 'Het Metalwerk van Jan Eisenlöffel', *Onze Kunst* 1903, 10-21; Warlich, H., 'Jan Eisenlöffel', *Kunst und Handwerk*, 1909-10, 239-50.

109 Kettle and stand with spirit lamp [PLATE 78]

Brass, with engraved linear ornament, a wooden knop to the lid, the handle bound with wicker. The handle is attached to the body with rivets which form part of the decoration. Rivets are also used decoratively in the construction of the stand. The burner lacks the wick-adjusting knob.

MARKS Stamped on the kettle and on one of the legs of the stand with a circular signet enclosing the monogram 'JE' and the name 'JAN EISENLOEFFEL'.

Designed for the Turin Exhibition of 1902 and made in Eisenlöffel's workshop at Overveen, near Haarlem, Holland, between 1903 and 1908.

Total H 34.7cm, H of kettle 21.3cm (with handle raised), w of kettle 33.4cm, H of stand 13.4cm, w of stand 20.6cm   1987,1-10,1

After studying at the Rijksnormaalschool from 1892 to 1896 Eisenlöffel joined the silversmiths Hoeker & Son, Amsterdam, designing mainly works in revivalist styles. Following eight months in St Petersburg, where he learnt enamelling and niello techniques, Eisenlöffel developed his own style. In 1900 he became artistic director of the newly installed metal workshop at the Amstelhoek factory, working in his new style for the first time. The Amstelhoek factory was founded in 1897 by W.C. Hoeker (of Hoeker & Son), initially as a ceramic factory, the metalwork and furniture departments being later additions. Hoeker wished to produce modern designs in non-precious metals such as copper and brass; the production of silver at Amstelhoek was always associated with his family's firm. The factory name was derived from the telegraphic address: Amsterdam-Hoeker.

In September 1900, on the initiative of the architect H.P. Berlage and the designer Jacob P. van den Bosch, a new design gallery, het Binnenhuis, opened in Amsterdam as a retail outlet for the applied arts, with Eisenlöffel among the collaborators. Eisenlöffel's metalwork enjoyed wide distribution through Amstelhoek displays at het Binnenhuis, but in January 1902, he left Amstelhoek and het Binnenhuis to run his own workshop, designing copper and brass objects for machine production. In 1903 he founded a rival interior design firm, De Woning, together with W. Penaat, who had directed the furniture department at Amstelhoek.

This kettle is illustrated in *Die Kunst* 8, 1902-3, 49 as part of the report on the Dutch section at the Turin Exhibition (identical article printed in *Dekorative Kunst* VI, November 1902). It is shown on an iron floor-stand while a variant with more rounded outline and higher handle is shown on a similar table-stand to that which occurs with this example. See also *Onze Kunst*, 1903, 75 and 83, where the rounded version appears in Jong Holland's Huis, a small design shop in Breda.

During 1903 Eisenlöffel began to use the large circular signet which appears on the kettle stand. The monogram in the centre of this signet was registered as a silver mark in January 1903 (Leeuwarden 1986, 90). Thus the kettle is likely to have been made between early 1903 and January 1908, when Eisenlöffel left for Munich, where he worked for the Vereinigte Werkstätten. After his return from Munich at the end of 1908 he worked to commission in Laren but continued to produce his earlier designs at De Woning's request (see *Onze Kunst*, 1912, 94, an interior executed by De Woning). However, these productions usually bear the number 8 or no mark at all (information supplied by J.D. v. Dam).

Eisenlöffel's metalwork was first shown in Germany at the Kunstausstellung in Dresden in 1901 and then in Düsseldorf in 1902. Henry van de Velde praised Eisenlöffel's purity of line and form, writing 'At present, I know of no metalworker in the world, who has achieved such perfection of creativity' (van de Velde 1902). For an illustration of this kettle and stand as part of an exhibition of the Deutsche Werkstätten in Munich, see *DK & D* XVII, 1908, 251. The Deutsche Werkstätten comprised the Münchener Werkstätten für Wohnungs-Einrichtung, founded in 1902, and the Dresdener Werkstätten für Handwerkskunst founded at Hellerau, near Dresden, in 1898. The two workshops merged in 1907 and so Eisenlöffel's designs were also sold in Dresden; for this kettle, see *DK & D* XXII, 1908, 210. See also *Deutsche Werkstätten für Handwerkskunst Dresden und München, Preisbuch 1909*, 26 and 29. The various workshops for applied art in Germany are fully discussed in Heskett 1986.

Further examples of this kettle are to be found in the Stedelijk Museum, Amsterdam and the Amsterdams Historisch Museum, where it is described as a chocolate kettle. Eisenlöffel's metalwork is represented elsewhere in Europe, in the Kunstgewerbe-museum, Zurich, which acquired three brass kettles with burners directly from De Woning in 1905 and 1906 (see Gysling-Billeter 1975, nos 43-5), and in the Hessisches Landes-museum, Darmstadt (Heller 1982, no. 93, a silver teaset). For other examples of metalwork by Eisenlöffel, see Leeuwarden 1986; Leidelmeijer and van der Cingel 70-74. The latter also discusses het Binnenhuis and De Woning (pp. 64-6).

The influence of W.A.S. Benson (see Cat. 19-23) on Eisenlöffel has often been stated. The copper and brass designs of both workshops rely on simple forms with minimal decoration and on the repetition of favourite motifs or elements, but Eisenlöffel's angular shapes are in general more uncompromisingly severe than Benson's. That Eisenlöffel's work was thought similar to Benson's at the time can be shown by a curious suite of events following the exhibition of Dutch decorative arts in Copenhagen in 1904. Eisenlöffel sent some twenty pieces of metalwork, accompanied by his own thumbnail sketches showing which items were to be displayed together (the sketches include this kettle). The exhibition was held in the Kunstindustrimuseum in Copenhagen, then under the direction of Pietro Krohn, and the museum acquired some seven pieces by Eisenlöffel. But in 1908, under Krohn's successor, all but one of those pieces were sold at an auction in the museum itself, miscatalogued as the work of Benson, London (Burgers 1972, 14-15, pl. 9).

Follot, Paul 1877-1941

Riotor, L., *Paul Follot*, Paris 1925

Salmon, A., 'Un Artisan Français', *Art Vivant* 17, 1 September 1925, 19-25

Rutherford, J., 'Paul Follot', *Connoisseur*, June 1980, 86-91

Batkin, M., 'Wedgwood Ware designed by Paul Follot', *Journal of the Decorative Arts Society* 7, 1983, 26-33

110 Jardinière [PLATE 112]

Earthenware (creamware), with clear lead glaze over white slip and ornamented in high relief with apples and leaves.

MARKS Impressed 'WEDGWOOD', printed in black 'WEDGWOOD ETRURIA ENGLAND 1921'.

Designed in 1912-13 as part of the 'Pomona' range and made at the Wedgwood factory, Etruria, Staffordshire in 1921, the modelling executed by Bert Bentley.

H 21.7 cm, D 31.5 cm   1984,1-6,1

Follot studied under Eugène Grasset in the late 1890s, producing designs for jewellery, metalwork and fabrics for La Maison Moderne. He was a founder member of the Société des Artistes Décorateurs in 1904 and worked for all branches of the decorative arts.

In 1901 Wedgwood had opened a shop in Paris and established an agency with Georges Rouard, a leading French retailer. Under the control of John Goodwin, who was appointed art director to Wedgwood in 1904 and who understood the needs of foreign markets, Rouard commissioned Follot to design for Wedgwood; a two-year contract was signed in 1912. Work was interrupted by the outbreak of war in 1914 and not resumed until 1919; the 'Pomona' range finally went into production in 1921. Goodwin concentrated on the production of commercial wares, leaving the production of art wares to Alfred and Louise Powell (see Cat. 233).

The high-relief modelling, a feature of Follot's carved and gilt furniture, was difficult to manufacture in pottery. Bert Bentley (active 1891-1936) recorded in his price book in 1921 the amount of time spent in decorating a set of Pomona pieces: the jardinière took 12 hours, while the large lidded bowl (Batkin 1982, pl. 9) took 24 hours. 'Pomona' wares were also made in basalt, but few in either basalt or creamware seem to have been produced, presumably because of the time involved. The factory records are fully discussed in Dawson 1984, 145-6. For further Follot designs for the 'Pomona' range and for other patterns designed by Follot for Wedgwood, see Batkin 1982 and 1983; *Pottery Gazette*, February 1922; *Art et Décoration*, June 1921, 161-4. Wedgwood's 'Pomona' wares were exhibited at the Paris Exhibition of 1925.

Follot adopted the name 'Pomona', the Roman goddess of fruit and fruit trees, for his Atelier Pomone design studio attached to the Paris department store, Le Bon Marché, which he directed from 1923. He continued to work in a decorative style, remaining resolutely opposed to modernism.

Fox, Charles Thomas & George 1841-1921

For the most recent history of the firm, see Culme 1987; see also E.J.G. Smith, 'The Fox family – Victorian silversmiths', I and II, *Antique Dealer and Collectors' Guide*, August and September 1974; sale catalogue, Phillips, Son & Neale, London, 23 September 1988.

111 Caster   [PLATE 46]

Silver, the body cast, with applied dragon coiled round the neck. The top hand-pierced. The surface, excluding the dragon, has an overall matt texture.

MARKS Stamped on the neck with London hallmarks and date-letter for 1860-61, and the maker's mark 'GF' in a pierced quatrefoil. The base is also stamped with the maker's mark and the London lion and Queen's head.

Made by the firm of C.T. & G. Fox, manufacturing silversmiths, 13 Queen Street, Soho, London in 1861.

H 8.8 cm   1980,11-7,1   Given by Professor and Mrs John Hull Grundy

The firm of C.T. & G. Fox was established probably in 1801 as Turner & Fox; it was run by Charles Thomas Fox (c.1801-72) and George Fox (c.1816-1910) from 1841. C.T. Fox retired at the end of December 1860, leaving George Fox as sole partner. The latter entered the mark that appears on this caster on 11 March 1861 (Culme 1987, 11, 111). The caster bears the date-letter for 1860, i.e. in use from 30 May 1860 to 29 May 1861 (given that the new date-letter has been struck at the end of May since 1660) and so this caster must have been hallmarked between March and May 1861.

C.T. & G. Fox are known for their 'novelty' silverwares, often copying historical models. This caster is directly inspired by Far Eastern models, either Chinese porcelain vases of the eighteenth century or their Japanese copies in bronze or silver of the nineteenth century. Japanese art objects were first shown in England in quantity at the 1862 International Exhibition in London and the Japanese taste in decorative arts did not become widely fashionable until the later 1860s. It thus seems more likely that the inspiration here comes from Chinese porcelain, which was known and collected before this date. However, the matt surface texture suggests a knowledge of Japanese metalwork and so this may be a very early instance of the Japanese taste in English silver.

Friedländer, Marguerite Wildenhain
1896-1985

There is no monograph on Friedländer. For biographical details see Cologne 1978; Stahlke, W., 'Marguerite Wildenhain – Franz Rudolf Wildenhain: Die Holländische Zeit 1933-1947', *Keramos* 93/81, 103-6; Schneider, K., 'Keramik der Kunstgewerbeschule Burg-Giebichenstein 1925-1933, Arbeiten von Marguerite Friedländer, Franz Rudolf Wildenhain und Gerhard Marcks', *Keramos* 118/87, 13-64. See also Nauhaus 1981, Grzesiak 1987 and Berlin 1989.

112 Tableware   [PLATE 133]

Hard-paste porcelain, comprising two candlesticks, a coffee cup and saucer, a teacup and saucer, a plate, cream jug, sugar basin and cover, and an eggcup and saucer. All in white with border decoration of painted matt gold bands.

MARKS On base of each piece: the underglaze blue sceptre and printed red Imperial orb with 'KPM', factory mark of the Staatliche Porzellanmanufaktur Berlin; the printed black mark of the Kunstgewerbeschule Halle at Burg Giebichenstein (not on candlesticks, plate or eggcup); the decoration number '84/116' and painter's marks painted in black; impressed lower-case Greek year-letters on most pieces for 1934-8 (see details below and Köllmann & Jarchow 1987).

The shape designed by Friedländer in 1929 as part of the service known as 'Hallesche Form', with decoration 'Goldringe' designed by Trude Petri in 1931. The shape first produced by the Staatliche Porzellanmanufaktur, Berlin in 1930; these pieces made between 1934 and 1938.

112a Candlesticks: H 6.5 cm, D of base 8 cm, date-letter *nu* for 1938   1980,10-17,1
112b Coffee cup: H 5 cm, saucer D 13 cm, date-letter *mu* for 1937   1980,10-17,2
112c Teacup: H 5 cm, no date-letter; saucer D 15.5 cm, date-letter *iota* for 1934   1980,10-17,3
112d Plate: D 19 cm, date-letter *kappa* for 1935   1980, 10-17,4
112e Cream jug: H 7.5 cm, no date-letter   1980,10-17,5

112f Sugar basin H 10cm, no date-letter 1980,10-17,6
112g Eggcup: H 5.2cm, no date-letter; saucer D 9.4cm, date-letter *kappa* for 1935 1980,10-17,7

In 1929 Günther von Pechmann became the new director of the Staatliche Porzellanmanufaktur (SPM). Pechmann, a committed member of the Deutsche Werkbund, had previously directed the Neue Sammlung in Munich, founded in 1925, and had already exhibited works from Halle there. In November 1929 he set up an association between the Porzellanmanufaktur in Berlin and the Kunstgewerbeschule Halle at Burg Giebichenstein, where an experimental porcelain kiln had been installed earlier that year. The prototypes were designed at Halle and then modified until they had passed mass-production tests carried out in Berlin, where they were then industrially manufactured. The whole process could take up to two years. The Berlin factory paid for all costs in Halle and brought Friedländer to Berlin to study production techniques for porcelain.

It is thus all the more remarkable that the coffee and chocolate service known as 'Hallesche Form' was first advertised by the SPM as early as February 1930 (*Die Form*, 5 Jahrgang, Heft 3, February 1930, 103; *Keramische Rundschau*, Jahrgang 38, no. 8, 1930, p. ix). The design for the tea service followed in June-July 1930 (Schneider 1987, pl. 43, 38). When it was first offered in plain white it created a sensation (Hirzel 1953, 51), but soon various decorative patterns appeared; these consisted of simple coloured rims so that the form was not obscured. 'Goldringe' was introduced in 1931 and remained among the most popular patterns (for a complete service, see Berlin 1989, cat. no. 199). From 1932 the service was also produced in celadon green. Köllmann & Jarchow 1987, pl. 500 illustrates a later painted decoration of doves. For further discussion and full contemporary literature, see Passarge 1937, 78; Bröhan III, 1985, 42; Schneider 1987 and Berlin 1989, 154-70. Like Petri's 'Urbino' service (see Cat. 231), 'Hallesche Form' sought to apply the simple unornamented forms of industrial porcelain to tableware.

After training at the Bauhaus under Gerhard Marcks and then in the Pottery Workshop at Dornburg from 1919 to 1925, Friedländer directed the pottery workshop at Burg Giebichenstein, Halle, together with Marcks until 1933, when she emigrated to Holland and set up a workshop with her husband, Franz Wildenhain, at Putten. In 1940 they moved to California. 'Hallesche Form' was illustrated in *The Studio Yearbook* for 1933, 137, as designed by Friedländer with decoration by Petri; when it appeared in a later issue (1939, 126) it is described as by the 'Werkstätten der Stadt Halle'. Friedländer's name had been suppressed in Germany, but ironically the opposite page shows ceramics from the Wildenhain Workshop at Putten.

Geddes, Norman Bel 1893-1958

There is no monograph on Bel Geddes. For biographical details, see Bush 1975 and Meikle 1979. For Geddes's own writing, see *Horizons*, Boston 1932; *Miracle in the Evening*, New York 1960 (unfinished autobiography to 1925).

113 Cocktail shaker [PLATE 125]

Chromium-plated stainless steel, stamped with vertical ridges. Inside, a removal liner.

MARKS Stamped on the base 'REVERE ROME NY'.

Designed in Bel Geddes's studio in 1934 and made by Revere Copper & Brass Company, Rome, New York.

H 33.3cm 1988,1-8,1

Geddes worked as an advertising artist, stage designer and window designer before setting up his own industrial design firm in 1927. By the early 1930s he had developed streamlined designs for trains, cars, aeroplanes and a wide range of industrial products, including a few small-scale household items such as cocktail shakers and soda siphons.

An advertisement for three new cocktail shakers made by the Revere Company published in *Arts & Decoration* 43, March 1935, 45, includes this shaker at a cost of $4 and provides evidence that the shaker was in production by early 1935. It was made with matching chrome glasses and tray (see Brooklyn 1986, 329, pl. 8.84). See also Bush 1975, pl. 133.

The Norman Bel Geddes Collection at the University of Texas contains detailed archive material relating to Bel Geddes's giftware line for Revere. Firstly there are nine alternative designs for cocktail shakers represented in a total of twenty-one drawings, of which nos 102.1 and 102.3 bear a strong visual resemblance to the British Museum shaker. Both drawings are marked with origin dates and revision dates in 1934. All the drawings are signed and initialled by different employees in the Bel Geddes studio, many of whom are identified, but the initials 'C.B.' on the drawings relating to the shaker in question remain at present unidentified. Surviving patent information confirms that a number of items in the range went into production in 1935, while 1935 Revere catalogues feature several other items in the line, though not this shaker. (The above information is derived from the Bel Geddes job file ♯290, identified as Revere Copper and Brass, in the Norman Bel Geddes Collection, Theater Arts Library, Harry Ransom Humanities Research Center, The University of Texas at Austin, by permission of Edith Lutyens Bel Geddes, executrix. The information was supplied by Melissa Miller-Quinlan, who kindly checked the file on my behalf.)

It is interesting to note that a silver cocktail shaker of similar shape, with vertical fluted pattern, was designed by Kay Fisker for the firm of Michelsen in Copenhagen, at about the same time.

For another example of Geddes's streamlining on a small scale, see his 1933 medal for the twenty-fifth anniversary of General Motors (illustrated in Collins 1987, 74, fig. 77; Department of Coins and Medals 1934, 6-2,1).

Godwin, Edward William 1833-86

Harbron, D., *The Conscious Stone: the life of Edward William Godwin*, London 1949
Aslin, E., *E.W. Godwin Furniture and Interior Decoration*, London 1986

114 Ceremonial trowel [PLATE 3]

Silver gilt with ebony handle, the blade engraved with St Michael and the dragon within a mandorla, set within a triangle, the spandrels of which are decorated with conventionalised Gothic leaves. The handle mounts are pierced with quatrefoils and stylised leaf-forms; the shaft joining handle to blade is encrusted with rosettes and twisted wirework. The end of the handle is engraved with the monogram 'PP' within a shield, the reverse of the blade is engraved with a sexfoil containing the inscription in Black Letter script 'Presented to the worshipful Mayor of

Northampton, Pickering Phipps. Esq. by the Town Council, on the occasion of his laying the Foundation Stone of the New Town Hall. Oct.22.1861'.

MARKS Stamped on reverse of blade with Birmingham hallmarks and date-letter for 1861, the maker's mark rubbed and illegible.

Designed in 1861 and presented to Pickering Phipps, Mayor of Northampton, on 22 October 1861, by John Jeffery, Town Clerk, on the laying of the foundation stone of Northampton Town Hall. Made in Birmingham in 1861, maker unknown.

L 28.6cm   1980,2-3,1

Northampton Town Hall, built in the Gothic-revival style, was Godwin's first major commission; he won the competition for the design in April 1861 and the building was officially opened on 17 May 1864.

Pickering Phipps, JP (1827-90) was head of the brewing concern of Phipps & Co. and several times Mayor of Northampton and MP for Northampton. Following the completion of the town hall, Phipps engaged Godwin to design two houses (Harbron, 29).

Godwin's drawing for this trowel (Fig. 3) is preserved among his designs for Northampton Town Hall in the Victoria and Albert Museum (Department of Prints and Drawings, E.598-1963; gift of Edward Godwin, son of the artist). The pencil drawing, on the reverse of the plan for the tiled floor, is less elaborate than the trowel as executed, especially in the design of the handle. The decorative motifs used on the trowel appear also in the town hall: for example, the foliage in the spandrels of the blade echoes the foliate spandrels on the roof of the town hall, while the zigzag pattern with dots within the mandorla frame occurs on the building as a horizontal band of decoration. The sculptural decoration of the building includes figures of St Michael with St George.

The Northampton County Archives contain no further information about the commissioning and manufacture of the trowel and so it has not been possible to identify the Birmingham maker (the records were kindly checked by Rachel Watson, archivist).

Gorham Manufacturing Company

founded 1863

Carpenter, C.H. Jr., *Gorham Silver 1831-1981*, New York 1982

115 Coffee-pot

[PLATE 20; COLOUR PLATE II]

Copper, with hammered surface patinated in a rich wine-red colour. At the base of the neck is an applied die-rolled silver band with stylised sunflowers in relief; the band has been oxidised so that the lower areas of the relief are intentionally blackened. The rim of the pot and the lid are also mounted in silver, with silver hinge. The handle is fitted with ivory insulators attached with silver pins, the interior of the pot is tinned. The patinated red finish is in remarkably good condition.

MARKS Stamped on the base 'GORHAM CO' with the Gorham anchor symbol for Rhode Island, the Gorham date-letter 'o' for 1882 and the production code 'E 40'.

Made by the Gorham Manufacturing Company, Providence, Rhode Island, in 1882.

H32.5cm   1989,7-3,1

Founded in the early nineteenth century by Jabez Gorham (1792–1869), the firm became the Gorham Manufacturing Company in 1863. On Gorham's retirement in 1848 his son John (1820-98) took over the running of the firm and became

the driving force behind its development in the 1850s and 1860s, when he visited England, where he recruited craftsmen and began to assemble a reference library on historical and Far Eastern ornament. After John Gorham's bankruptcy in 1878 the firm was managed by William Crins, a Providence businessman, until 1894. Many of the company's designers, as well as its craftsmen, were English: George Wilkinson, the company's chief designer from 1860 to 1891, came from Birmingham in 1854; Thomas J. Pairpoint joined Gorham from the London firm of Lambert & Rawlings from 1868 to 1877, during which time he was responsible for Renaissance and classical-style designs; A.J. Barratt of Hunt & Roskell also joined Gorham in the late 1860s. However, it is rarely possible to attribute specific designs to any of these artists (New York, 1986, 433).

Gorham's copper line was introduced in 1881 and was produced for a few years only, until about 1885. Production was small owing to the amount of hand labour involved. The taste for coloured metals in the Japanese manner was developed to a far greater extent in America than in Europe, and became almost a hallmark of American metalwork of the Aesthetic Movement. The coloured metals were either inlaid and applied (see Tiffany & Co., Cat. 283) or patinated, as in this instance. The patinated wares, with their rich red tones, are probably inspired by Japanese lacquered wood rather than metalwares. The tall coffee-pot with its graceful spout was a favourite Gorham form, based on contemporary Turkish or Persian models. It was also made in plain copper, without the silver appliqués, and in solid silver. The *Jewelers' Circular and Horological Review* for January 1882 printed a lengthy description of the new copper wares, including 'a pot for black after-dinner coffee of silver in purest Persian shape' (quoted in Carpenter 1982, 113). The American metalwork shown at the Exposition des Beaux-Arts in Paris in 1884 included a teapot 'en cuivre auquel on donne par un oxyde une patine rouge vernie très étrange' (*La Revue des Arts Décoratifs* 4, 1884, 117). The makers are not specified, but it is likely that this refers to a Gorham piece.

According to Carpenter the processes used to obtain the coloured surfaces are not known, but there were a number of standard procedures, such as heating the copper to produce a thin film of red-to-brown copper oxide or cuprite (Cu_2O). The surface was then polished, and waxed or lacquered for protection. A similar process was described in a manual on the chemical colouring of metals published in England in 1925; the colour had the trade name 'Royal Copper'. After the heat treatment to produce the film of cuprite, the article was polished with soft felt and a paste of rouge powder and methylated spirits, to achieve an 'excellent enamel lustre surface' (Field & Bonney 1925, 150). With heat treatment alone it was difficult to obtain an even colour over the whole article. As an alternative a number of colouring solutions were used, in conjunction with heat treatment. Most of the standard recipes were for shades of brown; recipes for red copper include immersion in a hot solution of copper sulphate and sodium chloride (Field & Bonney, 149-50), or of ammonium sulphide (Herbert Maryon 1954, 261), or immersion in molten sodium nitrate for five minutes to ensure an even red oxide film (Fishlock 1962, 196). The colour tones could be varied by varying the length of time or temperature of the treatment.

Surface analysis by X-ray fluorescence of the British Museum coffee-pot (by Susan La Niece of the British Museum Research

Laboratory) has detected only copper with a trace of iron. However, the red patina is almost certainly cuprite, by analogy with that of the candlesticks (see Cat. 116), where it was possible to take a small sample. It is thus likely that the colour was achieved by heat treatment alone as described above, but no evidence for the patination process was found, on either the coffee-pot or the candlesticks.

A version of this coffee-pot with more elaborate appliqués is currently on loan to the Metropolitan Museum of Art, New York and corresponds more closely to the description in the *Jewelers' Circular*. For other patinated copper pieces by Gorham, see Carpenter 1982 and Christie's, New York, 19-20 January 1990, lots 58-9, a lamp and a tea-caddy. Similar patinated copper wares were also made by Tiffany & Co.: for a red-coloured chocolate pot with silver appliqués, see New York 1986, 267, fig. 8.13 and 264, fig. 8.14. For further discussion of American metalwork of the Aesthetic Movement, see New York 1986.

It is interesting to note that Japanese-style red-coloured wares in silver-gilt and red lacquer were made from c.1880 to 1917 by the Moscow firm of Ovchinnikov (see Solodkoff 1981, pl. 75; Sotheby's, New York, 15-17 November 1988, lot 38 and 15 December 1988, lot 347). See also Ovchinnikov, Cat. 230.

116 Pair of candlesticks [PLATE II]

Copper and bronze, with square bases, tapering square-section stems and removable drip trays resting on a rectangular block. The cast bronze stems are ornamented with relief decoration of palmettes and leaves. The bases, drip trays and blocks are in copper, stamped and hand-finished, and patinated in a rich deep reddish-brown colour, in good condition.

MARKS Stamped on the base 'GORHAM CO' with the Gorham anchor symbol, the date-letter 'o' for 1882 and the model number 'Y 9' (the prefix 'Y' was used for copper).

Made by the Gorham Manufacturing Company, Providence, Rhode Island, in 1882.

H 21.7cm, Base 11 × 11cm   1989,7-3,2 and 3

The harmonious combination of different elements is here skilfully achieved in the use of Japanese-style red patination for the plain areas, contrasting with the bronze of the neo-classical stems, which are based on eighteenth-century models.

Analysis by X-ray diffraction of a small sample from a scratched area on the base of 1989,7-3,3 (carried out by Susan La Niece of the British Museum Research Laboratory) has identified the patina as copper oxide or cuprite (Cu_2O). For discussion of the patination process, see Cat. 115.

Goupy, Marcel 1886-1980

There is no monograph on Goupy. For biographical details, see Arwas 1987, 154-7; Paris 1976; Schmitt 1989.

117 Plate [PLATE III]

Earthenware, with stencilled and hand-painted decoration of a vase of flowers in underglaze colours of blue, green and yellow, surrounded by blue and black stripes on a white ground.

MARKS Printed on the reverse in black 'WEDGWOOD ETRURIA MADE IN ENGLAND'; impressed 'WEDGWOOD' with date code '4XA' and 'M'; painted in black with the pattern number 'A64879' and a cross.

The decoration, known as 'Goupy' pattern, designed before 1915 in collaboration with John Goodwin, to the commission of Georges

Rouard. Made by Wedgwood, Etruria, Stoke-on-Trent in 1924, the shape known as 'Catherine table'.

D 25.3cm   1986,5-8,1

Goupy studied at the École Nationale des Arts Décoratifs in Paris. He collaborated with the Paris retailer Georges Rouard from 1909; on Rouard's death in 1929 Goupy became artistic director of the firm, and remained so until 1954, designing models and decoration for ceramics and glass, including matching sets of table glass and porcelain. For examples of Goupy's decorations for faience made in Belgium and porcelain made by Théodore Haviland in Limoges, see Paris 1966, 104-5. For examples of his decorated glass, see Arwas 1987.

Wedgwood established contact with Rouard following the opening of their Paris showroom in 1901. In 1904 John Goodwin was appointed art director at Wedgwood and worked closely with Rouard, who was instrumental in commissioning designs from French artists such as Paul Follot (see Cat. 110) and Marcel Goupy to be executed by Wedgwood.

Goupy's work for Wedgwood is further discussed in Batkin 1982, 120, pls 282-3. This pattern is first recorded in the Wedgwood Factory Estimates Book in December 1915; the entry indicates that a leadless glaze was used and that the decoration was stencilled and hand-painted. It also refers to the blue as 'matt', though on this plate it is not. Advertisements for 'Goupy' pattern occur from the 1920s (e.g. *Pottery Gazette and Glass Trade Review*, 23 June 1923, 72) and the appearance of the pattern in Wedgwood's publicity leaflets at this time suggests that it was not produced in quantity until the 1920s (references kindly supplied by Sharon Gater).

The Victoria and Albert Museum holds a meat plate and covered vegetable dish made in 1925, acquired via the British Institute of Industrial Art (c.478a, 479-1934).

Gray-Stan Glass 1926-36

There is no monograph on Gray-Stan glass. For a history of the studio, see: Revi, A.C., 'Gray-Stan', *The Spinning Wheel*, May 1963; Dodsworth, R., 'Gray-Stan (1926-1936)', *British glass between the wars*, exhibition catalogue, Broadfield House Glass Museum, Kingswinford, 1987, 15-17; Loveridge, B., 'Gray-Stan Glass', *The Antique Collector*, November 1989, 114-19.

For Elizabeth Graydon-Stannus's own writing, see Graydon-Stannus, E., *Old Irish Glass*, London 1920; 'Irish glass, old and new', *Journal of the Royal Society of Arts*, 1925, 292-305.

118 Vase [PLATE 116]

Flint glass, mould-blown (wrythen-moulded), pale cloudy green with vertical white opalescent stripes.

MARKS Engraved on the base 'Gray-Stan'.

Designed and made in the Gray-Stan studio, 69 and 71 High Street, Battersea, London between 1926 and 1936.

H 18.3cm   1988,4-3,1   Given by Paul Reeves

Mrs Graydon-Stannus (1873-1961) dealt in antique Irish glass from her own gallery in Earls Court Square before turning to the manufacture of reproduction Irish glass in 1922. Experiments in coloured art glass were made from 1925. The studio closed down in 1936.

The Gray-Stan studio specialised in complex colour effects. In her 1925 paper to the Royal Society of Arts Mrs Graydon-Stannus wrote that she was 'trying with some little success to shade colours, getting more of a pastel effect'. These effects were achieved by coating clear glass with coloured enamels. Gray-Stan's cloudy colours were a highly original, though not isolated, contribution, for cloudy colours were also produced at this time by J. Powell & Sons and by Monart in Perth. This piece, with its wrythen-moulding (achieved by blowing into a diamond rib-mould and twisting the glass in the mould) is typical of British decorative glass c.1930.

Gretsch, Hermann 1895-1950

There is no monograph on Gretsch, but Gretsch's own writings on his porcelain designs and other contemporary texts are reprinted in Bröhan III, 1985, e.g.:

Gretsch, H., 'Porzellan als Gebrauchsgegenstand', *Das Hausgerät* 36, 1936, 77ff. (Bröhan III, 3-4)

Gretsch, H., 'Grundsätze der Geschirrgestaltung', *Hausrat, der zu uns passt, Heft 1: Essgeräte*, Stuttgart 1940, 20ff. (Bröhan III, 5-8)

Hermann Gretsch (Werkstattbericht 10 des Kunstdienstes), Berlin 1941 (reprinted in Bröhan III, 16-17)

See also: *Arzberg 1382, a shape that made history*, exhibition catalogue, Arzberg 1981.

119 Coffee service [PLATE 134]

Hard-paste porcelain, comprising coffee-pot, milk jug, sugar basin and six plates, glazed white.

MARKS The base of each piece printed in green 'Porzellanfabrik Arzberg, Arzberg (Bayern)'; the jug with impressed model number '1382' and '81'.

Designed in 1931 as part of the table service 'Arzberg 1382' and made by Porzellanfabrik Arzberg, Bavaria.

119a Coffee-pot: H 18.7cm   1981,3-10,4
119b Milk jug: H 8.8cm   1981,3-10,5
119c Sugar basin: H 8cm   1981,3-10,6
119d-i Plates: D 18.4cm   1981,3-10,7-12

Gretsch trained as an architect before studying ceramics at the Kunstgewerbeschule in Stuttgart under Bernhard Pankok from 1922 to 1923. He completed a doctoral thesis on 'technical features of South German fayence manufacture' in 1928. In 1931 he became artistic adviser to Arzberg at the instigation of Fritz Kreikemeier, director of the factory, and Heinrich Schindhelm, representative of the Kahla Konzern, an association of five Bavarian porcelain factories.

'Arzberg 1382' was the first and most widely acclaimed of Gretsch's designs for Arzberg. An indication of its immediate and lasting success may be gained from the many references in contemporary publications from the 1930s onwards, too numerous to list here, but covering some three pages in the Bröhan catalogue (III, 1985, 9-11). 'Arzberg 1382' won a gold medal at the Milan Triennale of 1936 and an award at the Paris Exhibition of 1937. It was described in the 1950s as the 'first up-to-date porcelain service for daily use' (*Innenarchitektur* 11, 1954, 148-52) and is still in production today. For a study of 'Arzberg 1382' in the context of a desire for timeless forms in everyday wares, see Schmidt 1975, where attention is drawn to the repercussions of the exhibition 'Ewige Formen' (Timeless Forms)

installed by W. von Wersin in the Neue Sammlung, Munich, in 1930.

The shape was designed without decoration, but Gretsch stipulated that if decoration was to be applied it should suit the form. The examples in the Bröhan collection have red rims (pattern 4884). However, the factory did not heed Gretsch's wishes and later patterns included the '*hässliche Blumenmotive*' (the ugly flower patterns) that Gretsch rejected (Bröhan III, 2).

Grueby Pottery 1894-1911

There is no monograph on the Grueby Pottery. For a recent account of the Pottery, see Eidelberg, M., 'The Ceramic Arts of William H. Grueby', *The American Connoisseur* 184, September 1973, 47-54; Evans, 2nd edn 1987, 118-23. There are also a number of contemporary sources, e.g. *The House Beautiful* V, December 1898, 3-9; Saulnier, C., 'Les Poteries de la Cie Grueby (Boston)', *L'Art Décoratif*, III, August 1901, 203-8; *Brush and Pencil* IX, January 1902, 236-43.

120 Vase [PLATE 110]

Earthenware, yellow body, heavy hand-thrown form with applied leaves and matt deep green glaze. The veins of the leaves are modelled in high relief and the yellow body clay shows through at the edges, where the leaf curls over. The interior of the neck glazed matt green, the interior of the body glazed buff.

MARKS Impressed on the base with circular mark 'GRUEBY POTTERY BOSTON USA' surrounding a lotus flower and factory number '88'.

The form designed by George Prentise Kendrick c.1897-8 and made at the Grueby Pottery, Boston, after 1899, when the Grueby Pottery trade mark was registered.

H 30cm, D 21.2cm   1984,11-7,2

William Henry Grueby (1867-1925) trained at the Low Art Tile Works before setting up his own architectural faience company, which was incorporated as the Grueby Faience Company in 1897. From 1894 he had begun to develop his matt glazes, which he always called 'enamels' to distinguish them from the clear glazes popular at the time, but initially the matt glazes were applied to architectural decoration. The first display of Grueby art pottery was at the first exhibition of the Society of Arts & Crafts of Boston in 1897. Among the twelve pieces shown were four vases and lamps designed by George Prentise Kendrick (Evans 1987, 121).

Kendrick was a Boston craftsman who had previously worked in brass and silver; he designed the forms of Grueby art pottery from 1897 to 1901. The modelling and decoration were executed largely by young women graduates from local art schools (*Brush and Pencil* op. cit., 241). Designing always remained the responsibility of a single person, initially Kendrick and later others, which gave the pottery a uniform appearance; the decoration is distinguished by its vertical emphasis. The technique used was peculiar to the Grueby Pottery: the clay was rolled out, applied in thin strips and modelled to shape while the vessel was still damp; it was then biscuit-fired and glazed.

A closely similar vase, of the same form but with the addition of handles on the upper part, was illustrated in *The House Beautiful* V, December 1898, 5, suggesting that this model is likely to have been designed at about the same time. It may have been one of the four vases and lamps shown at the 1897 Boston exhibition. Both this and the handled model are known to have been used as both vases and lamps: for an illustration of the handled model with oil-lamp fitting and leaded-glass shade, see *Brush and Pencil* op. cit., 240. An example of the model without handles with its original bronze oil-lamp fitting and glass shade made by the Boston firm of Bigelow & Kennard was in the possession of Cathers & Dembrovsky Gallery, New York in 1988; in this case the base was pierced between the leaves. L.C. Tiffany & Co. also occasionally made shades for Grueby bases suitable for oil-lamps.

For an example of this vase in a bright yellow glaze, see New York 1987, pl. 110; for discussion of the variation in quality found in this particular model, see Rago 1987.

For the influence on Grueby of French potters such as Delaherche, see Eidelberg 1975, 49. Grueby's agent in Europe was Siegfried Bing, through whom the Victoria and Albert Museum and the Museum of Decorative Art in Copenhagen purchased examples around 1900.

Hart & Huyshe, the Guild of Handicraft

For the history of the Guild of Handicraft after Ashbee's departure, see McCarthy 1981 and Cheltenham 1988.

121 Bowl [PLATE 67]

Hammered brass, with repoussé acorn and oak-leaf decoration in the centre and a twisted wirework border.

MARKS Stamped on the reverse 'HART & HUYSHE CAMPDEN GLOS' in a rectangle.

Designed c.1920 and made in the workshop of George Hart and Reynell Huyshe, Chipping Campden, Gloucestershire, c.1918-27.

D 26.8cm, H 6cm   1980,5-7,1

After the liquidation of the Guild of Handicraft in 1908 (see Ashbee, Cat. 4) some of the Guildsmen stayed on at Chipping Campden. They formed themselves into a Trust, which lasted until 1919, but continued to practise their own trades. The metalworking shop has remained in uninterrupted existence to the present day, under the direction of various members of the Hart family, and is still located on the first floor of the Silk Mill, which housed the metal workshop when the Guild first came to Campden in 1902.

George Hart (1882-1973) and his brother Will, a woodcarver, were recruited to the Guild by Ashbee in their home town of Hitchin, where Ashbee had come to judge an Arts & Crafts competition. By 1914 George Hart had three assistants in the metalworking shop, but little was produced during the war. From the late 1920s Hart established himself primarily as a silversmith, specialising in presentation pieces and church silver, and supplying work to the Goldsmiths' and Silversmiths' Company in London and then Omar Ramsden (see Cat. 249-53). Some of his own pieces are illustrated in his book *Metalwork for Craftsmen* of 1932. The workshop was carried on by his two sons, George and Henry, and is now run by Henry's son David.

During the 1920s George Hart formed a partnership with his half-brother, Reynell Huyshe, whose father, Wentworth Huyshe, had married the Hart brothers' mother after their father's death in 1882. Wentworth Huyshe arrived in Campden in 1906; he worked intermittently as a heraldic draughtsman, but was not a fully-fledged member of the Guild (McCarthy

1981, 154-5). Reynell Huyshe probably joined the metal workshop before the outbreak of the First World War, but his main involvement was between 1918 and 1927 and the 'Hart & Huyshe' stamp was used during these years. George Hart spent much of this period farming and so this bowl is more likely to have been designed by Reynell Huyshe (information kindly supplied by Frank Johnson, The Guild of Handicraft Trust).

This bowl is inspired by late-medieval brass bowls known as Nuremberg alms dishes, though these were cast not hand-raised. It is likely that the Hart & Huyshe bowl is an earlier Guild model; there was a considerable vogue for medieval brass from Northern Europe in the 1880s (see *Art Journal*, 1887, 330-32) and 'Nuremberg dishes' were made at this time by other Arts & Crafts groups such as the Keswick School of Industrial Art (see Arts & Crafts Exhibition Society, *Catalogue of the Second Exhibition*, 1889, 159 no. 262).

Hentschel, Rudolf 1869-1951

There is no monograph on Rudolf Hentschel. For biographical details, see Jedding 1981 and Just 1983.

122 Dish [PLATE 83]

Hard-paste porcelain, painted with stylised wing motifs in underglaze colours of pale grey-green outlined in blue.

MARKS Meissen factory mark of crossed swords in underglaze blue on the base, with impressed shape number 'T 42 4 62' and underglaze blue '35'.

The shape, 'T glatt', designed jointly by Rudolf Hentschel and others at the Meissen factory in 1901, the decoration, 'Flügelmuster', designed by Rudolf Hentschel in 1901; made by the Porzellanmanufaktur Meissen, Dresden.

D 31.5cm, H 5.3cm   1981,7-15,1

Rudolf Hentschel was the son of the Meissen figure-painter Julius Hentschel; he trained at the Zeichenakademie of the Meissen porcelain factory, and studied at the Munich Academy and the Académie Julian in Paris before working for Meissen as painter and modeller from 1895 to 1933 (his brother, Konrad, worked for Meissen as a modeller from 1897 to his death in 1907).

The Meissen factory introduced a range of new patterns in the years around 1900; they then had to produce suitable new shapes. A competition was held among the factory workers for the 'Preparation of designs for handles and knops for tureens and lidded vessels', as it was felt that these were the elements in which changes in fashion were most visible. The first prize was awarded to Rudolf Hentschel and others went to the modellers Helmig, Lange and Stange and to the flower-painter Otto Voigt. This led to the joint development of a new service, 'T glatt', produced from 1901 for the next two decades. It was offered with several different decorations, the first of which was Hentschel's abstract linear design, anticipating van de Velde's dynamic 'Peitschenhieb' (see Cat. 294-5) by two years. For Hentschel's signed and dated water-colour drawing of 1901 for the 'Flügelmuster' and further discussion, see Just 1983, 127-9. 'Flügelmuster' was much admired in *L'Art Décoratif* (1904, 2e semestre, 144) for its flat plates with barely raised rims and for the placing of the three wing motifs to form a trefoil or clover leaf in the centre.

Illustrations of other pieces from this service can be found in the following publications: Düsseldorf 1974, no. 300 (a tureen and large plate in the Neue Sammlung, Munich; Bröhan II/2, 1977, no. 447 (this includes some twenty-seven pieces and gives references to contemporary literature from 1902); *Bulletin van het Rijksmuseum* 25, 1977, 1, 37, pls 18-20; Beaucamp-Markowsky 1980, no. 146 (with reference to a complete unpublished service in the Zwinger, Dresden); Jedding 1981, pl. 112; Wichmann 1985, 115.

In addition to the 'T glatt' service of 1901 two further services were commissioned by Meissen from outside artists: van de Velde (see Cat. 294-5) and Riemerschmid (see Cat. 256).

Hoffmann, Josef 1870-1956

Kleiner, L., *Josef Hoffmann*, Berlin 1927

Rochowanski, L. W., *Josef Hoffmann*, Vienna 1950

Neuwirth, W., *Josef Hoffmann, Bestecke für die Wiener Werkstätte*, Vienna 1982

Baroni, D. and D'Auria, A., *Josef Hoffmann und die Wiener Werkstätte*, Stuttgart 1984

Sekler, E. F., *Josef Hoffmann, The Architectural Work*, Princeton 1985

Noever, P. and Oberhuber, O., *Josef Hoffmann 1870-1956, Ornament zwischen Hoffnung und Verbrechen*, exhibition catalogue, Österreichisches Museum für angewandte Kunst, Vienna 1987.

123 Flower basket   [PLATE 106]

Silver, formed of sheet silver with stamped-out squares and square-shaped handle, a circular hole in the base. Containing the original clear-glass liner.

MARKS Stamped on the base: Hoffmann monogram; Wiener Werkstätte monogram and rose mark; 'WIENER WERKSTÄTTE'; monogram 'FK/KF' for the silversmith; Vienna Diana-head 900 silver standard mark in use 1872-1921.

Designed *c.*1905 for the Wiener Werkstätte, Vienna, executed between 1906 and 1921.

H 24 cm, W of base 4.2 cm   1981,6-5,1

Hoffmann trained under the architect Otto Wagner and worked alongside Olbrich in Wagner's studio. In 1899 he was appointed Professor at the Kunstgewerbeschule in Vienna, having joined the Vienna Secession in 1897. Both Mackintosh and Ashbee had a formative effect on Hoffmann, Mackintosh as the dominant artistic influence and Ashbee's Guild of Handicraft as a model on which to base a Viennese equivalent. But Hoffmann's Wiener Werkstätte, founded in 1903 with Koloman Moser, had, unlike Ashbee's Guild, strong financial backing, from the banker Fritz Wärndorfer. Hoffmann designed furniture, metalwork, glass and ceramics for the Wiener Werkstätte, but remained a designer only and did not execute his designs himself. For the Wiener Werkstätte, see Schweiger 1984 and Kallir 1986.

This flower basket was executed initially in painted metal (Noever and Oberhuber M9, 140) and from 1906 in silver (information kindly supplied by Elizabeth Schmuttermeier). The use of rectilinear square-pattern motifs or *Gitterwerk* (latticework) dominated the early metal designs of the Wiener Werkstätte and is closely associated with both Hoffmann (for whom it earned the nickname '*Quadratl*') and his collaborator, Moser. For related designs for flower stands, see Noever and Oberhuber Z152-5,

244, 249. The latticework was stamped outside the Wiener Werkstätte and used on a semi-manufactured basis, enabling the production of relatively inexpensive objects.

The maker's monogram 'FK/KF' is not identified and is referred to as the 'master FK' in current publications of the Österreichisches Museum für angewandte Kunst.

124 Four pieces of cutlery   [PLATE 105]

A silver snail pick, and three pieces in silvered alpacca: a crab fork with steel prongs, cheese knife with flat-ended blade and fruit knife, the handles slightly convex each side with rounded ends.

MARKS Snail pick: stamped on the handle with Wiener Werkstätte monogram and rose mark; Hoffmann monogram; monogram 'FK/KF' for the silversmith; Vienna Diana-head 900 silver standard mark in use from 1872 to 1921. Fruit knife: stamped on the blade with 'WW' monogram and rose mark; Hoffmann monogram; monogram 'FK/KF' for the silversmith. Crab fork: stamped on the handle with 'WW' monogram only. Cheese knife: stamped on the blade with 'WW' monogram only.

Designed as part of the 'Rundes Modell' service in 1906; the snail pick and fruit knife made in the Wiener Werkstätte, the crab fork and cheese knife made probably by Bachmann & Co., Vienna.

124a Snail pick: L 13.5 cm   1981,6-6,1
124b Crab fork: L 17.2 cm   1981,7-17,2
124c Cheese knife: L 16.7 cm   1981,6-6,2
124d Fruit knife: L 17.9 cm   1981,7-17,1

The designs for the 'Rundes Modell' are discussed and illustrated in Neuwirth 1982, 73-127. The service was shown in the exhibition 'Der gedeckte Tisch' held by the Wiener Werkstätte in autumn 1906 (*DK & D* XIX, 1906, 473 and Neuwirth 1982, pls 10-11. See also pls 99, 100, 103-4, 112 for the items catalogued here). Many of the shapes, including the snail pick and the cheese knife, were designed in 1904 for Hoffmann's earlier 'Flaches Modell', where the handles are flat and have straight, beaded ends (Noever & Oberhuber 1987, Z29).

X-ray fluorescence analysis of the three pieces with no silver standard mark has shown that both the cheese knife and the crab fork are plated with a thick layer of silver. The plating on the fruit knife is thinner and the base-metal core contains copper, nickel and zinc, which would be consistent with alpacca, an alloy of these three metals. Alpacca was commonly used as a silver substitute at this date.

According to Neuwirth (1982, 73) the silver pieces were made in the Wiener Werkstätte, but the silvered alpacca pieces were made for the Wiener Werkstätte by the firm of Bachmann & Co. If this is so, the appearance of the silversmith's mark on the silvered alpacca fruit knife is unusual. For a silvered alpacca 'Rundes Modell' service used in the Cabaret Fledermaus, see Vienna 1985, no. 13/2/41, 361-2. For further literature and examples, see Franzke 1987, no. 44.

The silversmith's monogram 'FK/KF' is not included in the *Lexikon der Wiener Gold- und Silberschmiede* (Neuwirth 1976-7), nor in the list of craftsmen's monograms in the Wiener Werkstätte '*Arbeitsprogram*' of 1905 (Neuwirth 1984, 23-4) and remains unidentified (see Cat. 123). For the registered trade marks of the Wiener Werkstätte, i.e. the rose mark and the 'WW' monogram (both registered in 1903), see Neuwirth 1985, where it is noted that a chronology for the unframed 'WW' monogram (as it appears on these examples) is being prepared for a planned second volume on the trade marks.

125 Coffee set [PLATE 104]

Electroplated nickel silver, comprising coffee-pot, milk jug and sugar basin, all of oval shape, the pot and jug with ebonised wood handles, the lids to pot and basin with beading at base of knop.

MARKS The coffee-pot and sugar basin stamped on base with the rose mark, 'WIENER/WERK/STÄTTE' block signet and Otto Prutscher monogram. On the base of the milk jug the rose mark, 'WIENER/WERK/STÄTTE' block signet and Hoffmann monogram. In addition, the coffee-pot is stamped with the letter 'A' and the sugar basin with the letter 'O'.

Designed c.1909-11 and made in the Wiener Werkstätte, Vienna, before 1919-20.

125a Coffee-pot: H 10.2 cm, L 19.8 cm (including handle), W 15.3 cm (including spout) 1982,1-7,1
125b Jug: H 4.5 cm, L 14.9 cm (including handle), W 7.4 cm (including spout) 1982,1-7,2
125c Basin: H 8 cm, L 8.5 cm, W 6.5 cm 1982,1-7,3

Hoffmann's original design drawings for this service survive in the Wiener Werkstätte archive in the Österreichisches Museum für angewandte Kunst, design numbers M.1881-89 (Fig. 28, OMAK inv. no. 12051/8, a page of designs including the coffee-pot, milk jug and sugar basin). The service was first executed in 1911 and produced until 1919-20 (information kindly supplied by Elizabeth Schmuttermeier).

For a related coffee-pot of c.1908, see Neuwirth 1984, no. 67, though this has a domed lid. A closer parallel is to be found in the tea service of 1910-11, which also has beaded knops, Neuwirth 1984, no. 80 and 1985, pl. 262, produced in brass and alpacca. Similar services are illustrated in *DK & D* 25, 1909-10, 368 and 33, 1913-14, 480. Hoffmann's use of plain surfaces decorated with beading dates from about 1909, when his style changed in favour of a return to the neo-classical forms of the early nineteenth century or Biedermeier period.

Both Hoffmann and Prutscher were designers only and did not execute the metalwork themselves. The appearance of Prutscher's monogram on the coffee-pot and sugar basin is misleading; the craftsman probably used the wrong designer stamp in error. (I am grateful to Elizabeth Schmuttermeier for this explanation.)

126 Vase [PLATE 128]

Blue glass, mould-blown, with fluting on bowl and foot.

MARKS None.

Designed c.1923 and made in Bohemia c.1923-28 for the Wiener Werkstätte.

H 23.2 cm, D of top 15.9 cm 1983,3-6,1

For an identical vase, see Neuwirth 1984, no. 154, in yellow-green glass, where it is stated that about four hundred examples were made. For a blue example, see *Die Wiener Werkstätte 1903-1928, Modernes Kunstgewerbe und Sein Weg*, published in Vienna in 1929 (unpaginated); see also Vienna 1985, no. 13/4/34. Many of Hoffmann's glass designs of this period were executed by the firm of Ludwig Moser & Söhne, Carlsbad, Czechoslovakia.

Hunt & Roskell 1843-97

There is no monograph on this firm. For the most recent account, see Culme 1987. See also Bury 1966, part 2, 157-8.

127 Casket [PLATES 15-16]

Silver-gilt, cast, with relief ornament based on the Assyrian sculptures from Nimrud. At each corner is a winged lion or bull, with relief scenes round the sides and on the lid. The body is heavily cast in one piece, the hinged lid is cast separately. Inside the lid is an inserted plaque engraved with the arms of Layard and of the City of London, and, below, the following inscription:

> At a Court of the COMMON COUNCIL holden in the GUILDHALL of the CITY OF LONDON on the Third day of MARCH, 1853. It was RESOLVED UNANIMOUSLY THAT THE FREEDOM OF THIS CITY, In a Box of the value of fifty guineas, be presented to AUSTEN HENRY LAYARD, Esqᵉ. D.C.L., M.P., as a testimonial of his persevering & zealous exertions in the discovery of the long lost Remains of Eastern Antiquity, & for securing them in so perfect a state as to demonstrate the ACCURACY OF SACRED HISTORY, & illustrate the early habits of the Human Race; and for his indefatigable labour and skill by which this Country has been enabled to place such valuable memorials of ancient grandeur amongst the collections of THE BRITISH MUSEUM.

At the top left is the name of the Lord Mayor, Challis, and at the lower right, the name of the Town Clerk, Merewether. The casket contains the Freedom Certificate (registration no. 1976,9-3,2).

MARKS Stamped on the lower edge of the right side, on the base and on the lid with the maker's mark of John S. Hunt of Hunt & Roskell with London hallmarks and date-letter for 1852-3. Engraved on the lower right edge of the front with the signature 'Alfred Brown. Sculpᵗ'.

Designed by the sculptor Alfred Brown (active c.1845-56) and made for the firm of Hunt & Roskell, London, in 1852-3.

L 15.7 cm, H 6.8 cm 1976,9-3,1 Bequeathed by A.H. Layard's great-granddaughter, Phyllis Layard

Hunt & Roskell, a firm of manufacturing and retail jewellers and silversmiths, was founded by Paul Storr in 1819, trading as Storr & Co. (1819-22), Storr & Mortimer (1822-38), Mortimer & Hunt (1838-43) and then Hunt & Roskell (1843-97). Hunt & Roskell had retail premises at 156 New Bond Street and a manufactory at 26 Harrison Street, near Clerkenwell. John Samuel Hunt, who had assisted Storr from the start, continued as a partner until his death in 1865, when he was succeeded by his son, John Hunt (d.1879). Robert Roskell, formerly a watchmaker and merchant of Liverpool, joined in 1844 and remained in the firm until his death in 1888. In 1889 the firm was taken over by J.W. Benson and continued in business as Hunt & Roskell Ltd until c.1965.

J.S. Hunt's first mark was entered in 1839 (Culme 1987, mark nos 8344-9) and was used concurrently with a joint mark for Mortimer & Hunt (Culme 1987, nos 8272-7). Mortimer retired in December 1843, and in January 1844 J.S. Hunt entered the mark that appears on this casket (Culme 1987, nos 8350-60) and which remained in use until his death; it was only in 1865 that his son entered a mark for J. Hunt & R. Roskell (Culme 1987, nos 8224-8). J. S. Hunt never served an apprenticeship as a silversmith; his mark was entered as a partner in the firm.

The firm was well known for its presentation plate in a wide variety of styles and was one of the first to exploit A.H. Layard's sensational discoveries: the Hunt & Roskell stand at the Great Exhibition of 1851 included 'Specimens of earrings, in emeralds, diamonds, carbuncles, &c. after the marbles from Nineveh' (*Official Catalogue*, Section III, Class 23, p. 688, jewellery). Assyrian-style jewellery in gold set with precious stones was also shown by Garrard & Co. (ibid, 689, no. 18), but no examples of jewellery or metalwork are known that can be securely associated with the 1851 exhibition. Most surviving pieces seem to have been made in the 1860s and 1870s (see Rudoe 1989 for detailed discussion of the taste for Assyrian-style jewellery). Thus this casket is one of the earliest surviving pieces of Assyrian-style metalwork.

Layard excavated in Assyria between 1845 and 1851. The colossal winged bulls and lions and the sculptured reliefs were shipped back to London and displayed in the British Museum from the late 1840s. Layard had discovered the palace of Ashurnasirpal II at Nimrud, but initially he thought he had found Nineveh and so his lavish two-volume publication of 1849 was called *Monuments of Nineveh*, although it is largely about Nimrud. This explains the reference to 'marbles from Nineveh' in Hunt & Roskell's description of the 1851 jewellery; Nineveh was actually discovered by Layard's successors during the 1850s.

The inscription inside the casket is a copy of the resolution of the Court of Common Council to award the Honorary Freedom of the City to Layard. As was customary with resolutions, the names of the Mayor and Town Clerk appear top left and lower right. Thomas Challis was Lord Mayor from 1852 to 1853, while Henry Alworth Merewether was Town Clerk from 1842 to 1859. Although the resolution was made on 3 March 1853, Layard did not attend the Guildhall to be admitted by the City Chamberlain until 9 February 1854. The Chamberlain's address and Layard's reply are published in *London's Roll of Fame....1757-1884* (London 1884, 31-2, 199-207). Honorary Freedom was reserved for distinguished recipients and the ceremony thus merited a report in the *Illustrated London News* (11 February 1854); the casket was illustrated with a drawing by Alfred Brown's brother, James. According to the report:

> the superintendance of the Box was delegated by the late Lord Mayor (Mr. Alderman Challis) to his deputy, Mr. Bennoch [Francis Bennoch, Deputy in 1853]; who, assisted by Mr. Scott, of the Chamberlain's Office [Benjamin Scott, principal clerk 1842-53], made certain suggestions, and confided the execution of the design and work to Mr. Alfred Brown, the sculptor ... the design is composed of copies from the Nimrud marbles ... to illustrate the manners and customs of the ancient Assyrians. At each angle of the Box is placed the human-headed Bull and Lion, so peculiar to Eastern Art. Between the angles are relievos of the Lion Hunt, as exhibiting their sport and pastimes; the Assyrian Horsemen chasing and overcoming the Arabs, as indicative of military prowess; the King in his chariot, led through the city with pomp and ceremony, showing something of municipal parade in those early times; and the winged deities, kneeling before the Sacred Roll, as descriptive of their religious faith and practice ... This is, we believe, the first practical use that has been made of the Layard sculptures in connection with art. ...

This last claim is slightly inaccurate in view of the Assyrian-style jewellery shown at the Great Exhibition. The lion hunt on the front of the casket is copied directly from Ashurnasirpal's palace at Nimrud of the ninth century BC (WAA 124579, illustrated in *Monuments of Nineveh*, I, pl. 31), as is the scene on the back, of two winged figures kneeling before the Sacred Tree (WAA 124580, *Monuments of Nineveh*, I, pl. 7A). The scene of Assyrian horsemen pursuing an Arab on a camel and the king in his chariot, on the sides of the casket, are both from the eighth-century BC palace of Tiglathpileser III (WAA 118878, *Monuments of Nineveh*, I, pl. 57, and 118908, not illustrated in *Monuments of Nineveh*). The lid is decorated with a winged warrior in a sun-disc, representing the highest Assyrian deity, Ashur, or the sun-God Shamash, copied from a relief in Ashurnasirpal's throne-room depicting the triumphal return of the king from battle (WAA 124551; *Monuments of Nineveh*, I, pl. 21). The mouldings along the edges of the casket were copied from the remains of tiles and bricks. The upper frieze was derived from painted ornaments with palmettes and lotus flowers (*Monuments of Nineveh*, I, pl. 86), while the lower frieze with winged horses and rosettes appears in the frontispiece to *Monuments* as one of the border motifs, together with the palmettes and lotus and the winged deity on the lid of the casket. The rectangular shape of the casket is undoubtedly inspired by Layard's reconstructions of Ashurnasirpal's palace in *Monuments* and is probably intended to suggest an Assyrian building with colossal figures flanking the entrance and relief sculptures decorating the walls. For further illustrations of the casket together with the Nimrud reliefs, see Rudoe 1987.

Little is known about the designer, Alfred Brown. According to Rupert Gunnis (n.d. 1964, 64), he won a Royal Academy Gold Medal in 1845, exhibited at the Academy from that year until 1855 and exhibited a statue of 'David before Saul' at the Great Exhibition of 1851. He is recorded as a designer of silver between 1851 and 1862. According to Bury 1966, 158, Hunt & Roskell financed Brown's training at the Royal Academy Schools. Brown was certainly working for Hunt & Roskell by the time of the 1851 exhibition, when Hunt & Roskell exhibited several of his works: four dessert stands with Indian figures (*Official Catalogue*, Section III, Class 23, p. 687, nos 14-17, modelled by Brown but designed by Frank Howard; *Art Journal Illustrated Catalogue* 57); a testimonial in the neo-classical style with the muses of drama and music, and a rococo-style candelabrum for the Marquess of Tweeddale (*Official Catalogue*, p. 687, nos 24 and 29; *Art Journal Illustrated Catalogue*, 1851, 57-8; Culme 1977, 119, and 1987, 246, note 34; sold Christie's, London, 22 May 1991, lot 6, from the collection of the late Hilmar Reksten). The essay on taste by R.N. Wornum printed at the back of the *Art Journal Illustrated Catalogue* refers to another centrepiece by Brown in the Renaissance style, criticised for its use of dead and burnished silver. Alfred Brown also designed and modelled a group of plate commissioned from Hunt & Roskell by the Goldsmiths' Company in 1853, as a result of a competition to 'test the state of art as applied to silver manufacture'. The group comprised a thirteen-light candelabrum representing the granting of the Charter to the Goldsmiths' Company by Edward III (Bury 1966, 158, fig. 16), two ten-light candelabra representing Michelangelo and Benvenuto Cellini, and two figure groups of Benevolence and Business Duties, all illustrated and described as the work of Brown in the *Illustrated London News*, 15 December 1855, 701 (reference kindly supplied by Lesley Leader; see also Carrington and Hughes 1926, 103-4 and 120-21). Thus in 1853 Brown was working for a major city livery company, so it is not surprising that he was approached for the design of the Layard casket. Further pieces by Brown designed and modelled for Hunt & Roskell include a silver centrepiece of 1856 for the Earl of Stamford (Gunnis, 64) and the Napier Testimonial shown at the 1862 International Exhibition in London (Culme 1977, 108).

Brown also worked for the firm of Watherston & Brogden, for whom he designed a large gold, jewelled and enamelled Renaissance-style vase (*Art Journal Illustrated Catalogue*, 1851, 251; Culme 1977, 212). Culme 1977 quotes a passage from M. Digby Wyatt (*Industrial Arts of the Nineteenth Century*, London 1853, pl. 66) stating that Watherston had assisted the young Brown and helped him secure his position at Hunt & Roskell, and that Brown had designed the vase in gratitude to Watherston.

For a series of Assyrian-style figures in Parian porcelain made by W.T. Copeland Ltd, see Cat. 43-8.

I am grateful to James Sewell, City Archivist, for information from the archives of the City of London.

P. Ipsens Enke, Kongelig Hof Terracotta-Fabrik founded 1843

Holst, B., *P. Ipsens Enke, En udstilling om en keramikfabrik*, Brønshøj 1984

128 Two containers [PLATES 9-10]

Low-fired earthenware, with classical-style ornament and scenes after Thorwaldsen, the ornament mostly reserved in the red unglazed body colour, the background painted black. Each container is constructed in three parts: a turned base with foot; a turned lid with central knop and vertical handles; beneath the lid a removable central tray with knop in the centre.

The bases are decorated with classical scenes flanked by palmettes, all reserved in the red body colour with outline details and background painted black. Cat. 128a depicts 'Briseis being taken from Achilles'; below, a band of Greek key pattern painted in black on the red body colour. Cat. 128b depicts 'Hector's farewell to Andromache', with the band of Greek key pattern reserved in the red body on a black ground.

The lids are decorated with the knop with a rosette pattern, the central tongues painted in deep red on the pale red body, the ground black, the handles with linear ornament reserved in the red body colour. The central trays are decorated on the exterior with a scrolling-leaf and flower pattern painted in black and white on the red body colour. The black ground shows horizontal brush lines, suggesting that it was applied while the pot was on the wheel, possibly over wax resist or a similar method to achieve the reserved areas.

MARKS The base of each impressed 'P Ipsen Kjobenhavn Eneret' with impressed model number '30' and a further number '433' painted in black. 'Eneret' (copyright) refers to the model. The inside of the lid of 128a is painted in black with 'Ds'.

Designed and made by P. Ipsens Enke, Kongelig Hof Terracotta-Fabrik, Norgesgade 33, Copenhagen, *c.*1874-1903.

H 24cm, D 17cm, H of base 12.7cm, H of central tray 4.1cm
128a 1986,3-2,1
128b 1986,3-2,2

The terracotta factory of P. Ipsens Enke (P. Ipsen's widow) became widely known for its Greek-style vases and other historicist ceramics exhibited throughout Europe during the 1870s. The *Art Journal Illustrated Catalogue of the Paris Exhibition of 1878*, 28, devoted a whole page to Ipsen's terracottas, which were to be seen at the factory's London agent, Messrs Arup Brothers of New Bond Street.

These containers appear in the factory's earliest recorded catalogue of 1875 (copy in Bornholms Museum, Rønne, Denmark); the shape only is illustrated, as model nos 30, 31, 47, 55, referring to the different sizes in which it was made

(according to the 1890 catalogue the heights were as follows: no. 31, 43cm; no. 47, 16cm; no. 55, 8cm). The shape is described as a 'Lepaste' (a term derived from the Greek word for limpet, no longer used in Greek vase studies) and was available in cream, red or black, with or without decoration. It also appears in the firm's catalogues of 1879 (copy in Royal Copenhagen Porcelain Factory library), 1890 and 1903 (copies in the Kunstindustrimuseum, Copenhagen). Both the 1879 and 1890 catalogues show model 30, with a light ground, decorated with 'nemesis on a chariot' after Thorwaldsen. Without decoration it cost 5 kroner (cream or red) or 7kr (black), with decoration 35kr (cream), 26kr (red) or 30kr (black). None of these catalogues (xeroxes kindly supplied by Gerd Bloxham, Kunstindustrimuseum, Copenhagen) discusses the intended use for these containers; it has been suggested that they were used for tobacco. The unglazed earthenware body is highly porous and so it is unlikely that they contained liquid. A container of identical shape is illustrated in the *Notice Historique et Descriptive sur les Galeries Royales d'Art Danois*, owned by A. Borgen & Company at 142 New Bond Street; this leaflet, published in 1874, lists tobacco jars among the articles available. For Borgen & Co., see J. Rudoe in Gere et al. 1984, no. 994.

Sometimes both shape and decoration were taken straight from an ancient vase; in other cases the shapes alone were derived from antiquity. The egg-shaped form of these containers is loosely based on the Greek hydria, but the lid is entirely nineteenth-century in conception: handles of similar form occur on the Greek hydria and crater but not placed vertically. The decoration is a mixture of classical and neo-classical elements. The technique imitates the Greek red-figure technique of the fifth-fourth centuries BC in which the figures are reserved in the colour of the red clay ground with painted linear detail, the background filled in with black. The central scenes, on the other hand, are copied directly from well-known marble reliefs by the Danish sculptor Bertel Thorwaldsen (1770-1844), housed in the Thorwaldsen Museum in Copenhagen since the nineteenth century: Briseis being taken from Achilles of 1803 (*Thorwaldsen's Museum Guide*, 1961, 43, no. 489; Hartmann 1979, pl. 85.2) and Hector's farewell to Andromache of 1837 (*Thorwaldsen's Museum Guide*, 1961, 44, no. 501A, ill.).

The subjects of Ipsen's vases were also copied after Flaxman and after the contemporary Danish artist and history painter Anker Lund, who began to make sketches for terracotta wares in 1871. For an elaborate volute crater in the Kunstindustrimuseet, Copenhagen, painted by T. Alvesen after Lund's designs *c.*1875, see Gelfer–Jørgensen 1982, 56. For further examples, see Hamburg 1977, no. 385, a hydria or water jug, *c.*1875 (not illustrated, but from the description this is likely to be after Thorwaldsen); Mundt 1981, pl. 24, two plates, *c.*1875. For further discussion of the Ipsen factory's production, see Gelfer-Jørgensen 1982 and Holst 1984.

Closely similar wares were produced by V. Wendrich of Copenhagen; see Hamburg 1977, no. 386, a hydria with the identical scene to that on one of the British Museum containers, 'Hector's farewell to Andromache' after Thorwaldsen. Little is known about Wendrich, but another major producer of Greek-style wares, usually imitating the black-figure technique, was the Terracottafabrik L. Hjorth at Rønne, Bornholm, Denmark, founded in 1859; see Hamburg 1977, no. 383; Gelfer-Jørgensen 1982, 57.

Jensen, Georg Arthur 1866-1935

See also **Nielsen**; **Rohde**

I.M. Olsen, *Sølvsmeden G J*, Copenhagen 1937
W. Schwartz, *G J*, Copenhagen 1958
Georg Jensen Silversmithy, exhibition catalogue, Renwick Gallery, Washington 1980
Møller, J.E.R., *Georg Jensen, The Danish Silversmith*, Copenhagen 1985

129 Brooch   [PLATE 102]

Silver, hand-raised, hollow-backed, with foliate and bud design, set with central amber stone, the pendant set with a further amber bead. Contained in the original leather case with paper label on top which reads 'Georg Jensen, Solvsmedie, Bredgade 36, Kjobenhavn'.

MARKS Stamped on reverse 'GEORG JENSEN COPENHAGEN 830s', the monogram 'GJ' (in use 1904-14), initials 'GI' and model number '80'.

Designed in 1910 and made in the workshops of Georg Jensen, Copenhagen, between 1910 and 1914.

L 11.4 cm, w 6.5 cm   1981,6-8,1

Jensen was apprenticed to a goldsmith in his teens; he later studied sculpture at the Kunstakademiet in Copenhagen. Unable to make a living as a sculptor, Jensen returned to silversmithing and worked for Mogens Ballin, whose fleshy and organic interpretation of Art Nouveau strongly influenced Jensen's own designs. Jensen's first workshop was set up in 1904. It is interesting to note that the first foreign exhibition of Jensen's work took place at the Karl Ernst Osthaus Museum in Hagen in 1905. Following the purchases of Osthaus and others in Germany, a Jensen shop was open in Berlin from 1909 to 1915.

This brooch can be dated by its model number from the company record books; a different series of numbers was allocated to each class of object, i.e. a different series for brooches, necklaces etc. It is made in the low silver standard current in Denmark at that time. Amber was traditionally used in Danish jewellery and it is characteristic of Jensen to achieve colour with few other materials, either amber or a semi-precious stone such as lapis. The jewellery was usually given an oxidised patina so that the surface appears matt grey.

An identical version of this design is in the Schmuckmuseum, Pforzheim (see Falk 1985, no. 136).

Karlsruhe, Majolika-Manufaktur

(founded 1901 as the Grossherzogliche Majolika-Manufaktur, renamed in 1927 the Staatliche Majolika-Manufaktur)
See also **König**; **Laeuger**; **Lindig**

N. Moufang, *Die Grossherzogliche Majolika-Manufaktur in Karlsruhe*, Heidelberg 1920
Karlsruher Majolika, exhibition catalogue, Badisches Landesmuseum, Karlsruhe, 1979

130 Bowl   [PLATE 130]

Red earthenware, turned, biscuit-fired and then gloss-fired over a layer of white slip. The cooling of the high-fired gloss glaze has produced a *craquelé* effect. The bowl has then been given a third firing in a smoky reduced atmosphere with silver lustre, which has caused stained yellow and silvery-brown patches. The base with transparent lead glaze.

MARKS The base incised with the number '1721'.

Made at the Majolika-Manufaktur Karlsruhe *c.*1930-33, the shape probably designed by Martha Katzer (1897-1947), the glaze developed by Gerda Conitz (b.1901).

D 18.2 cm   1984,2-7,3   Given in 1984 by Mr and Mrs John Gay, who received it as a gift from S. Stern, financial adviser to the factory from 1925 to 1933 (see also Cat. 135 and 139)

This is likely to be an experimental piece made around 1930 or shortly before. At this time the factory produced a range of vases and bowls of simple form with *craquelé* lustre glazes in several colours inspired by Persian or Far Eastern ceramics and known as 'Edelmajoliken' (*Badische Werkkunst* 1931), Sondernummer Heft 1, 17-18). The glazes were described as smoked (*geraucht*) because they were given a third firing in a reducing atmosphere after the biscuit and gloss firings. Further similar bowls, described as '*Craquelé-Schalen gelb und grau*' were illustrated in a catalogue issued by the Majolika-Manufaktur in October 1930 (a copy is held in the factory archive).

Conitz, who had trained at the Fachschule Bunzlau, was employed by the factory from 1928 to 1932 specially to develop new bodies and glazes. Katzer worked for the factory from *c.*1922 to the 1940s, designing several models for serial production, together with the '*Edelmajoliken*', which won a Grand Prix at the Paris Exhibition of 1937.

The examples in the possession of the factory are marked in a variety of ways: some have model numbers only, while others have the factory mark only (Karlsruhe 1979, nos 244-52). The colours include varying shades of yellow, white, grey, grey-blue, grey-black and grey-brown.

The shape and glaze of this bowl appear to derive from Japanese models of the seventeenth to nineteenth century.

I am grateful to Nigel Wood for his comments on the glazing techniques.

Kempen, J.M. van, en Zonen 1835-1919, from 1919 Van Kempen & Begeer

Menzen en Zilver, bijna twee eeuwen werken voor Van Kempen en Begeer, exhibition catalogue, Museum Boymans–van Beuningen, Rotterdam and De Zonnehof te Amersfoort, 1975-6
Industry & Design in the Netherlands 1850/1950, exhibition catalogue, Stedelijk Museum, Amsterdam 1985, chapter on Van Kempen & Begeer, 216-22

131 Spoon   [PLATE 79]

Silver, with four-leaf clover motif enamelled in light blue on the handle, the surface matt overall.

MARKS Stamped on the reverse of the bowl with the assay office mark for The Hague, the Dutch silver standard mark '934', date-letter for 1904 and rectangular maker's mark 'VK' beneath a crescent on its side flanked by two dots.

Designed by the design department of J.M. van Kempen & Sons under the direction of H.J. Valk and made in 1904 by the firm of J.M. van Kempen & Sons, Voorschoten, near The Hague, Holland.

L 18.2 cm   1988,1-12,1

The design department of the silver manufacturers Van Kempen & Sons comprised a team of draughtsmen, modellers and engravers; from 1886 to 1924 it was directed by H. J. Valk (1863-1940), but the names of individual designers were not revealed and so designs cannot be attributed to particular artists in the design team.

During the years around 1900 Van Kempen had produced silver in a curvilinear Art Nouveau style, but from about 1904 the firm turned to more geometric forms, often of surprising originality. For teaspoons and a sugar shovel of 1904 from the same service, see Rotterdam and Amersfoort 1975, no. A44; for a cake slice of 1905 also in matt silver but with the leaf motif enamelled in green, see Darmstadt 1962, no. 175 (Citroen Collection). These handmade pieces with high-quality enamelling did not sell in large numbers and were produced for a short time only; see Krekel-Aalberse 1989, 177-8

Keswick School of Industrial Arts 1884-1982

Little has been written on the Keswick School of Industrial Arts. For a brief account, see Anscombe and Gere 1978. See also *Canon Rawnsley, An Account of his Life*, by his second wife, Eleanor F. Rawnsley, Glasgow 1923, 65-8

132 Set of six spoons [PLATE 68]

Silver, hand-raised, the bowls with hammered surface, the stems of square-section with bud knops. Contained in the original case covered with mauve cloth and labelled inside the lid 'Keswick School of Industrial Arts'.

MARKS Each spoon stamped with Chester hallmarks and date-letter for 1917, with the maker's mark used by the School, the initials 'KSIA' in an oval.

Made at the Keswick School of Industrial Arts, Keswick, Cumberland, in 1917.

L of spoons 11.7cm. Case: 16.8 × 14.2cm 1980,11-13,1-6

The Keswick School of Industrial Arts was founded in 1884 by Canon Hardwicke Drummond Rawnsley (1851-1920) and his wife Edith (d.1916). Inspired by Ruskinian teaching, the school was intended to provide leisure-time occupation for local working men, with evening classes in metalwork and wood carving. According to Eleanor Rawnsley thirty people were employed after the first two years, and after four years sixty-seven people worked at the school. In 1894 the School's own building was erected, enabling the introduction of daytime classes.

The School participated in the exhibitions of the Arts & Crafts Exhibition Society from 1889; the catalogues frequently list the names of the metalworkers, while many designs of the 1890s were credited to Mrs Rawnsley. Later, designs are credited to Harold Stabler, who directed the School from 1898-1902, to Herbert Maryon, who taught at the School in the early 1900s, and to Robert Hilton, who taught there for seventeen years and was succeeded by G.A. Weekes. However, it has not been possible so far to associate these spoons with any of the above.

The shape of the spoons is derived from English fifteenth-century acorn-knop spoons, though late-medieval spoons have round-section or flattened stems.

Knox, Archibald 1864-1933

Tilbrook, A.J., *The Designs of Archibald Knox for Liberty & Co.*, London 1976
Levy, M., *Liberty Style*, London 1986

133 Spoon [PLATE 74]

Silver and enamel, cast, with relief interlace decoration and the inscription 'ANNO CORON: ER VII' on the bowl, the interlace enamelled in blue, green and purple. The flat, elliptical stem with hand-pierced interlace panel and pointed end.

MARKS Stamped on the reverse 'L & Co', 'CYMRIC', with Birmingham hallmarks and date-letter for 1901.

Designed by Knox, initially without the inscription and adapted for use as a souvenir of the Coronation of King Edward VII in 1902 by Liberty's. Made by W.H. Haseler, Birmingham, for Liberty & Co., London.

L 16.3cm 1980,5-13,1

After studying and teaching at the School of Art in Douglas, Isle of Man, Knox settled in London in 1897. It has been suggested (Tilbrook, 37) that he may have made contact with Liberty through the architect M.H. Baillie Scott, who was then practising in Douglas and had designed for the firm since 1893. Knox went back to the Isle of Man in 1900, supplying several designs to Liberty's from there, and returned to London in 1904. He continued to supply designs to Liberty while teaching as Head of Design at Kingston School of Art. It is unlikely that he supplied many designs after 1909, when Liberty designs were sold to the rival firm of Connell of Cheapside. In 1912 Knox resigned from Kingston, returning to teach in Douglas for the rest of his life.

Liberty's range of jewellery and silver sold under the trade name of 'Cymric' was launched in 1899. It was manufactured in association with W.H. Haseler of Birmingham, manufacturing jewellers and silversmiths; a subsidiary company known as Liberty & Co. (Cymric) Ltd was registered in May 1901, directed by William Hair Haseler and Frank Haseler, with J.H. Howe and John Llewellyn of Liberty's. This association ended in 1926 (see Culme 1987, I, 220-21). The Celtic-sounding trade names 'Cymric' and 'Tudric' (see Cat. 134) are thought to have been invented by Llewellyn (Levy, 92). For W.H. Haseler's role in the Liberty metalwork venture, see Bury 1977.

In March 1902 Liberty & Co. wrote to Knox, commissioning designs suitable for a Coronation year souvenir spoon:

'. . . We are also sending you a coronation spoon, being a copy of that used for the anointing of King Edward I and successive sovereigns of Great Britain.

We thought something of this kind might be made in the Cymric ware as a souvenir of the Coronation of Edward VII. The designs would have to be very clear so that it could be easily recognised by the ordinary individual as a commemerative [sic] spoon for the Coronation year.

We should require it in three sizes one as enclosed, one 6½ ins [16.5cm] long, one 8 ins. [20cm].

The form of the bowl we of course leave to you, but should like it practical and in the larger sizes applicable as a fruit or jam spoon.'
(Quoted from Tilbrook, 30).

It is not known what Knox produced in answer to this letter. Tilbrook (fig. 111) illustrates a plain version of this spoon without the inscription and without enamel, suggesting that Liberty's may have adapted an existing design.

Other examples of this design bear in addition the design registration number 391477 for 1902 (see London 1983, no. s42); the designs for the 'Cymric' range were not registered until that year, by which time their success was assured.

134 Tea and coffee set [PLATE 74]

Cast and hand-finished pewter, five pieces, comprising coffee-pot, teapot, milk jug, sugar bowl and tray, all with interlace ornament in relief of stylised honesty plants. The handles of both pots bound with wicker, the coffee-pot with wood thumb-rest to lid lever.

MARKS All pieces stamped on the base 'MADE IN ENGLAND'. In addition, the sugar bowl and tray stamped 'ENGLISH PEWTER'; the coffee pot stamped '2 TUDRIC PEWTER 0231 1 PINTS'; the teapot and milk jug stamped 'TUDRIC 0231 Rd 420290 H, the milk jug also stamped with the trademark 'SOLKETS' above crossed roses, used by W.H. Haseler (the trade mark was the firm's telegraphic address: a contraction of the words 'solitaires' and 'lockets', Haseler's original speciality; see Levy, 120-22).

Designed by Archibald Knox in 1903, the design registered in 1903. Made by W.H. Haseler, Birmingham, for Liberty & Co., between 1904 and 1926.

134a Coffee-pot: H 21.6cm 1980,5-11,1
134b Teapot: H 10cm 1980,5-11,2
134c Milk jug: H 7.1 cm 1980,5-11,3
134d Sugar bowl: H 6.5 cm 1980,5-11,4
134e Tray: 49 × 35.6cm 1980,5-11,5

Liberty's had been importing German pewter wares by the firms of J.P. Kayser & Sons of Krefeld, W. Scherf of Nuremberg and others since about 1896. The success of these wares encouraged Arthur Lasenby Liberty to work on the production of his own modern pewter range from the late 1890s (Tilbrook, 63-7). However, Max Haseler, son of W.H. Haseler, claimed that it was the Elizabethan pewter purchased by his father from the painter and antiquary Oliver Baker that inspired the launching in 1901 of the new range (Bury 1977, 18), sold under the trade name 'Tudric' (see Cat. 133).

Liberty, in his article on the revival of pewter for the *Journal of the Society of Arts* in 1904, illustrated this tray (p. 636), describing it as 'Tray with grip hands. Designed with hollow rim to give additional strength'. He illustrated several Knox designs in his article, along with contemporary German pewter, mostly Kayserzinn, but neither Knox's name, nor those of the German designers, are ever mentioned, in accordance with Liberty's policy of anonymity.

The teaset appears in Liberty catalogue no. 97, *Yule-Tide Gifts*, 1904, 37. For the complete service, with hot-water pot, see London 1975, C 176 A-F and Levy, 12.

That the 'Liberty style' enjoyed much success on the Continent is in large part due to Knox's bold interpretation of continental Art Nouveau combined with the use of Celtic ornament and interlace. Knox is exceptional among British designers in his absorption of continental Art Nouveau. For further discussion of Knox's designs for Liberty, see Morris 1989, chapter 4.

König, Ludwig 1891-1974

Karlsruher Majolika, exhibition catalogue, Badisches Landesmuseum, Karlsruhe 1979, 353 (biography), cat. no. 278-307

135 Frog [PLATE 130]

Red earthenware, cast, covered with dark grey-brown glaze, the base unglazed.

MARKS Impressed on the base with factory mark of the Majolika-Manufaktur, Karlsruhe, 'MM' beneath the arms of Baden, in use since 1908; 'LK' for Ludwig König with model number '1641', 'Made in Germany' and '10'.

Designed in 1922 and made by the Staatliche Majolika-Manufaktur, Karlsruhe, between 1922 and 1933.

H 9.8cm, L 16.8cm 1984,2-7,2 Given in 1984 by Mr and Mrs John Gay, who received it as a gift from Mr S. Stern, financial adviser to the Karlsruhe Majolika-Manufaktur from 1925 to 1933 (see also Cat. 130 and 139)

König was a pupil of Richard Riemerschmid in Cologne and a member of the Deutsche Werkbund. He worked as modeller for the Karlsruhe Majolika-Manufaktur from 1922 to 1929, designing both tableware and sculpture for serial production. König's compact, stylised forms were designed to be suitable for mass-production methods and were widely praised at the time (*Die Form*, 1927, 382 and 1929, 610-11). However, König later became disillusioned and in 1929 left the factory to concentrate on teaching, first in Karlsruhe and later in Cologne and Bunzlau.

For König's own writing on the modelling of ceramics for mass-production and the collaboration of artists with industry, see *Die Schaulade* 2, 1926, 156-66 (reprinted in Bröhan III, 1985, 288-9) and *Die Form* 5, 1930, 211-12.

For a contemporary illustration of the frog, described as a paperweight, see Pelka 1924, 165. For other examples of König's animal models, see Karlsruhe 1979, nos 292-4, 300-301, 304-5; Bröhan III, 1985, nos 280-81. The factory archive collection does not include an example of this frog. One other example in private ownership is recorded (Karlsruhe 1979, 402).

For the Majolika-Manufaktur, see also **Karlsruhe, Laeuger, Lindig.**

Köpping, Karl 1848-1914

There is no monograph on Köpping. For biographical details, see Hilschenz 1973, Pazaurek and Spiegl 1983 and Arwas 1987.

136 Liqueur glass [PLATE 95; COLOUR PLATE VI]

Lamp-blown thin-walled dark green lustrous glass.

MARKS Acid-etched in lustre on the upper surface of the foot '*Köpping*'.

Designed c. 1898 and made by the Grossherzoglich sächsiche Fachschule und Lehrwerkstatt für Glasinstrumentenmacher in Ilmenau, Thuringia, Germany.

H 11.8cm, D of rim 6.5cm 1982,11-2,2

Köpping trained as a painter and printmaker, studying in Munich and Paris. From 1890 he taught etching at the Berlin Academy and from 1896 replaced Meier-Graefe on the editorial board of the luxury art magazine *Pan*, where his early designs for fragile ornamental glasses were illustrated, in his own original etching (*Pan* II, Heft 3, December 1896, 253); the etching was illustrated by G. E. Pazaurek as the frontispiece to his *Moderne Gläser*, n.d. (1901).

Initially Köpping's glasses were made by the freelance Thuringian glass-blower Friedrich Zitzmann (1840-1906), who had previously worked in Lauscha, Thuringia and in Murano and had exhibited at the Chicago Exhibition of 1893. In 1895 Zitzmann was in Berlin, giving demonstrations in the Kunstgewerbemuseum, and it is likely that the association with Köpping was made at this time (Schack v. Wittenau 1971, 40). But the association between Zitzmann and Köpping lasted only a few months, from the end of 1895 to the summer of 1896, when Zitzmann was found to have sold his own work under the name of Köpping. Pietro Krohn, Director of the Kunstindustrimuseet in Copenhagen, visited Köpping in Berlin to buy glasses for Copenhagen, mentioning that he had heard about the Köpping glasses recently purchased by the Oslo Museum from the Berlin retailers E. Kayser. But as Köpping glass had never been sold by Kayser, it became clear that the Oslo Museum had acquired Zitzmann's glasses, produced without Köpping's permission. From then on, Köpping's glasses were made with his signature, as on this example, at the Fachschule in Ilmenau, a school and teaching workshop for glass instrument-makers, founded in 1894 under the patronage of the Grand Duke of Saxony. The glasses acquired by Copenhagen in 1896 were among the first to be made at Ilmenau; for detailed discussion, with reference to letters from Köpping to Krohn, see Schou-Christensen 1969.

Köpping's first ornamental glassware ('Ziergläser'), with twisted stems and applied tendrils, was exhibited by Bing at the Maison de L'Art Nouveau and at the Salon of the Champ de Mars in Paris in 1896 (The Studio 8, June 1896, 25-6). Köpping's glass is here described as 'delightfully simple and light, and supremely artistic. How infinitely preferable this plainly treated, graceful material, which is really glass, to the over-elaborate metallic complications of Tiffany'. See also Revue des Arts Décoratifs, June 1896, 186; Magazine of Art, May-October 1897, 27-9; Kunstgewerbeblatt 1897, 162-4 (with reference to the production of the glasses by the Fachschule in Ilmenau); DK & D III, October 1898-March 1899, 130); L'Art Décoratif, August 1899, 211; Bascou et al. 1988, 150 (acquired from Bing in 1896 by the Musée du Luxembourg, now in the Musée d'Orsay); two further examples with applied leaves and tendrils are in the Grassimuseum, Leipzig (Grassimuseum 1980, 21-2).

For Köpping's more utilitarian glasses ('Gebrauchsgläser') similar to the British Museum example, see L'Art Décoratif, December 1898, 133 and Revue des Arts Décoratifs, October 1899, 323, text 330, where even the simple glasses are dismissed as trifles. Pazaurek noted in 1901 that Köpping's glasses were made of such poor quality glass that decomposition was already producing cracks. In this respect the 'Gebrauchsgläser' have lasted better than the 'Ziergläser' (Pazaurek 1901, 1-3). A glass of the same design as that catalogued here was purchased from Bing's shop in about 1900 by the Nordenfjeldske Kunstindustrimuseum, Trondheim, Norway (Weisberg 1986, 71, pl. 70). Similar glasses were also shown at the Turin Exhibition of 1902 (Pica 1902-3, 316) and at the Dresden Exhibition of 1904 (DK & D, 14, 1904, 551). The Kunstindustrimuseet, Copenhagen, in addition to their 1896 group, acquired in 1899 a group of glasses with simple profiles and no applied decoration, from the Keller & Reiner gallery in Berlin (Schou-Christensen, 1969, 182). For further glasses of this type, in the Kunstmuseum, Düsseldorf, see Leipzig 1989, no. 338a and b, 339 and 340.

Examples of Zitzmann's glasses dating from before and after his association with Köpping are to be found in the Gewerbemuseum, Nuremberg (now part of the Germanisches Nationalmuseum). They belong to two separate groups, both purchased by the museum directly from Zitzmann. The first group, acquired in 1889 while Zitzmann was in Lauscha, comprises elaborate pastel-coloured glasses in the Venetian style with animal stems and handles; the second was bought in 1903 when Zitzmann was in Wiesbaden, and consists of simple forms in lustrous colours. Some of these have applied tendrils in the manner of Köpping's early glasses (see Bornfleth 1985, fig. 99), but in general the shapes are heavy and ungainly compared with Köp-

ping's balanced forms and the glass is opaque rather than transparent. (I am indebted to Elizabeth Bornfleth for information about the Gewerbemuseum glasses.) For a signed Zitzmann glass in the manner of Köpping, the signature in lustre on the foot, see Hilschenz 1973, no. 62.

For discussion of signed imitations of Köpping's ornamental glasses made in the 1970s by Karlheinz Feldbusch, Bremen, as well as unsigned copies see Leipzig 1989, no. F.13 A, B.

It should be noted that fragile glasses with spiralling stems were being produced in Murano in 1895 or soon after (Venice 1982, pl. 234); simple undecorated forms of this type were a radical departure from traditional Venetian products of the nineteenth century and may represent the influence of trends elsewhere in Europe.

Krause, Charlotte active c.1912

137 Jug [PLATE 100]

Stoneware, grey body with light brown 'Kölnisch braun' glaze; round the neck, a band of moulded relief ornament in the form of stylised vine leaves and bunches of grapes. Fitted with pewter lid and thumb-piece.

MARKS Impressed on the base 'R.MERKELBACH GRENZHAUSEN', with model number '2315', the letter 's' and 'KRAUSE'.

Designed by Charlotte Krause c.1912-15 and made by the firm of R. Merkelbach, Höhr-Grenzhausen, Rhineland.

H 26.4cm 1989,5-11,1 Given by Judy Rudoe

Very little is known about Charlotte Krause; she worked in Dresden-Hellerau, where she directed her own workshop, specialising in the decoration of porcelain, and in the design of jewellery and textiles. Between about 1912 and 1915 she made several designs for stoneware, characterised by densely arranged jewel-like foliate ornament. Her work has been compared to that of Munich decorative artists such as Adelbert Niemeyer, but there is no evidence that she studied in Munich (Kunsthandwerk Aktuell no. 2, March 1986, 14).

A jug of this design is illustrated in Die Kunst XXXII, 1915, 55, alongside designs by Niemeyer and by Wynand (see Cat. 330-32) for the Steinzeugwerke Höhr-Grenzhausen. Her contribution seems to have been on a fairly small scale compared with that of Wynand; in the Merkelbach price list of 1912 she is credited with eleven designs. Some of these were illustrated in the Jahrbuch of the Deutscher Werkbund, 1912, 62. For recently published stonewares designed by Krause, see Cologne 1978, nos 448-9 and 452, of which no. 449 bears the mark of the Dürerbund Werkbund Genossenschaft (see Cat. 332); Bonn 1987, nos 116, 154-8.

Laeuger, Max 1864-1952

Kessler-Slotta, E., Max Laeuger 1864-1952, Saarbrücken 1985

138 Tile [PLATE 87]

Earthenware, red body, decorated in underglaze slip beneath a transparent lead glaze with a Japanese ginkgo leaf in black relief on a yellow ground.

MARKS Impressed on the base with the factory mark of the Tonwerke Kandern 'Prof. Laeuger'sche Kunsttöpferei', in use 1895-1913, incorporating the letters 'MLK' (Max Laeuger Kandern) and the arms

of Baden; the model number '79' 'MUSTER GESETZL. GESCHÜTZT' and the incised letter 'K'.
Designed by Max Laeuger c.1900 and made at the Tonwerke Kandern, south of Freiburg in the Black Forest, Germany.

H 20.4cm   1989,1-5,1

Laeuger trained as a painter and was a self-taught ceramic artist. He directed the art pottery division of the Tonwerke Kandern from 1895 to 1913, specialising in the traditional Black Forest technique of underglaze slip decoration, but creating strikingly original designs incorporating Persian and Far Eastern motifs.

For a catalogue of Laeuger's designs for tiles with references to surviving examples, see Kessler-Slotta, 289-98, where one other example of this pattern is recorded in a private collection. Laeuger's tiles were designed mainly as fireplace surrounds and decorative wall panels. This example is unusual in that it shows no sign of having been mounted. For contemporary illustrations of similar tiles by Laeuger, see *Kunstgewerbeblatt*, 1901, 230 and Bormann 1902, 68-72, where they are described as among the best in Germany.

139 Vase   [PLATE 130]

Earthenware, red body, turned, leaf sprays painted in deep blue and black over a pinkish-grey slip, covered with clear matt alkali glaze. The interior with a transparent lead glaze which spills over the rim on to the upper body.

MARKS Brush-painted in black on the base 'M.L. 1924'.

Designed and made by Max Laeuger in 1924, in his own workshop in Karlsruhe.

H 6.5cm   1984,2-7,1   Given in 1984 by Mr and Mrs John Gay, who received it as a gift from S. Stern, financial adviser to the Karlsruhe Majolika-Manufaktur from 1925 to 1933 (see also Cat. 130 and 135)

In 1916 Laeuger took over as his own workshop the former premises of the Karlsruhe Majolika-Manufaktur in the Hoffstrasse. From 1921 to 1929 he collaborated with the Majolika-Manufaktur, supplying models for serial production as well as one-off studio pots.

Laeuger's association with the Majolika-Manufaktur took the form of three different types of production: commercial articles (*Handelswaren*) with relief slip decoration, series numbers 1800-1932 and 2000-2024; small vessels with underglaze painting and alkali glaze known as '*Edelmajoliken*', series numbers 3000-3048, and '*Originale*' or one-off pieces which were also sold and distributed through the factory. The '*Edelmajoliken*' were all painted by Laeuger himself in his Hoffstrasse workshop and thus can also be described as originals although they are not unique.

The commercial articles bear the impressed factory mark and impressed serial number, while the '*Edelmajoliken*' bear a brush-painted signature 'ML' and a painted serial number on the base. The '*Originale*' also bear the brush-painted initials 'ML' and often a brush-painted date as well, but no serial number. The factory's own archive collection contains numerous examples of these small vases with foliate decoration, many of which bear a brush-painted signature 'ML' in various forms or the impressed signature 'PROF. LAEUGER; none, however, is dated and they all bear a painted serial number. Thus this vase can with certainty be described as a one-off piece made in Laeuger's workshop. For three '*Originale*' with black brush-painted initials and dates, see Karlsruhe 1979, nos 337, 338 and 340, dated 1916-20.

Laeuger had made vases of similar shape and decoration

before 1913 at the Tonwerke Kandern; closely related vases with the Kandern mark are to be found in the archive collection of the Majolika-Manufaktur. For similar matt-glaze vases shown at the Kunsthalle, Mannheim, in 1931, see *Die Form*, 1931, 293-5. See also Hartlaub 1931, 74-5; Karlsruhe 1979, nos 334-5, made by the Majolika-Manufaktur, and Kessler-Slotta, no. 227, with matt glaze. These small pots are inspired by Japanese porcelain tea-caddies, though the decoration on this vase is more Chinese in style.

For the Karlsruhe Majolika-Manufaktur, see also **König** and **Lindig**.

Lalique, René 1860-1945

The following publications deal with Lalique's designs for glasswares, which became his main interest from about 1906. The British Museum acquired six pieces of jewellery designed by Lalique as part of the Hull Grundy Gift in 1978. These are described and illustrated in Gere et al., *The Art of the Jeweller; a Catalogue of the Hull Grundy Gift to the British Museum*, 2 vols 1984, nos 370, 371, 373, 1094, 1095, and 1177, the latter in moulded glass.

McClinton, K. Morrison, *Lalique Glass for Collectors*, 1975
Marcilhac, F., *R. Lalique, catalogue raisonné de l'oeuvre de verre*, Paris 1989
See also Arwas 1987; Bloch-Dermant 1983.

See also Recent Acquisitions, Cat. 344.

140 Inkwell   [PLATE 117]

Press-moulded glass, 'Quatre Sirènes', domed circular form with central depression forming the inkwell, depicting four mermaids in opalescent glass against a clear-glass ground. Separate lid.

MARKS The signature 'LALIQUE' moulded into the design and 'R Lalique, France, Nº 434' acid-etched on the side.

Designed in 1920 for Lalique's own firm in Paris and made before 1937, when this model was removed from the firm's catalogues.

D 16.2cm, H 5cm   1980,10-15,1

This is one of a group of inkwells of this form created in 1920, model number 1386 (body) and 1386 *bis* (lid); it was produced into the 1930s, but was not reintroduced after the Second World War; see Marcilhac 1989, no. 434.

Lebeau, Joris Johannes Christiaan 1878-1945

Chris Lebeau – ontwerper 1878-1945, exhibition catalogue, M. de Bois, Drents Museum, Assen and Frans Halsmuseum, Haarlem, 1987

141 Vase   [COLOUR PLATE XIV]

Mould-blown bowl of trumpet-shaped yellow-green glass, the rim ground and polished, set in a deep purple pressed-glass base of stepped form, echoing the outline of the bowl.

MARKS Acid-etched on the base of both pieces with the Lebeau/Leerdam serial glass signet comprising the designer's monogram.

Designed in 1924-5 and made by the NV Glasfabriek Leerdam, Holland, between 1925 and 1930.

Total H 27.5cm. Bowl: H 21.6cm, D 20.9cm. Base: H 7.5cm, D 14.9cm   1988,7-11,1

Chris Lebeau studied at the Amsterdamse Kunst Nijverheid

Teekenschool 'Quellinus' (the 'Quellinus' school of applied arts) from 1892 to 1895 and then at the Rijksschool voor Kunstnijverheid from 1895 to 1899. From 1898 to 1899 he also studied at the Vâhana-School, where he developed a geometric approach to design. By the early 1900s he was a reputed graphic and textile designer. He was largely responsible for the popularity of batik textiles in the Netherlands, setting up his own batik atelier in Haarlem in 1902 and selling the textiles through het Binnenhuis. He later taught in Antwerp and Haarlem.

He had made designs for glass as early as 1900 but they were never realised; at the request of Philips electric-light factory in 1922, he made sketches for items to be made from waste glass, but the collaboration came to nothing. Lebeau first met Leerdam's director, P.M. Cochius, at the funeral of the architect K.P.C. de Bazel, the first outside artist to design for Leerdam. For the role of Cochius in commissioning outside artists to design for Leerdam, see Cat. 50. Lebeau's first series for Leerdam was designed in 1924, put into production in 1925 and shown at the Paris Exhibition of that year, where the Musée des Arts Décoratifs acquired a large trumpet-shaped vase with separate base, also in green and purple (the vase is unpublished, but for an illustration of the same model, see van der Kley-Blekxtoon 1984, 68, pl.73, centre vase in group). Lebeau's vases continued to be shown at exhibitions in Holland and abroad, for example in New York, at the International Exhibition of Contemporary Glass and Rugs, held by the American Federation of Arts in 1929-30.

Lebeau found Leerdam's existing vase shapes too uniform; he therefore designed unusual shapes for specific flowers and plants, as well as double-sided vases that were usable either way up. His bizarre shapes were not always well received at the time: Karel Wasch in his book *Glas en Kristal* (1927) compared them to laboratory glass. Yet they were highly original and quite unlike anything else produced at the time in Holland, or indeed elsewhere. Those that were put into production are illustrated in the Leerdam trade catalogue of 1927 (see van der Kley-Blekxtoon 1984, pls 73-9, reproductions of the 1927 illustrations, and pl. 80). The vases were no longer produced after 1930.

The Leerdam colour range at the time included the popular bright yellow-green known as 'annagroen', bright orange-red, purple, amber and blue. The mould-blown bowls were made in pear-wood moulds, the pressed bases in iron moulds. A number of Lebeau's original water-colour sketches survive (see de Bois 1987, 171-7), including designs for items that were never produced. The pieces were executed from working drawings made by the factory's design department. For further discussions of manufacturing techniques see de Bois, 174-5. Unlike Copier, de Lorm and the other designers, Lebeau's tableware designs were limited to a single water glass and water carafe, finger bowl and fruit bowl; being teetotal, he designed no wine glasses.

Following conflict with Copier and Cochius, Lebeau left Leerdam in 1926 for the factory of Ludwig Moser in Winterberg, Bohemia, where he concentrated on the production of one-off pieces, often in *craquelé* glass in the manner of Copier's 'Unica' vases. But after 1929 Moser was no longer able to sell expensive, unique pieces; the factory could not persuade Lebeau to design for serial production and so the association came to an end (de Bois, 185). For the rest of his career Lebeau returned to painting and drawing. His anti-Nazi activities during the German occupation of Holland led to his arrest in 1943 and he died in Dachau in 1945.

Lessore, Thérèse 1884-1944

Very little has been written on Lessore. The most useful recent account of her career is the essay by Charlotte Haenlein in *The Sickert Women and the Sickert Girls*, exhibition catalogue, London, Parkin Gallery, 1974.

142-3 Two plates [PLATE III]

Earthenware (creamware), painted in silver lustre.
142 with a scene of two mothers and their babies on a park bench;
143 with people in the balcony of a theatre. The latter had been broken before its acquisition by the Museum and has been repaired by the Department of Conservation.

MARKS On each plate, impressed mark 'WEDGWOOD and the artist's monogram 'TL' painted in silver lustre.

Designed and painted by the artist on a Wedgwood creamware blank at the studio of Alfred and Louise Powell in Bloomsbury, London, between about 1920 and 1924.

142 D 23cm 1989,5-10,1
143 D 23.4cm 1989,5-9,1 Given by Richard Dennis

Thérèse Lessore was the daughter of the painter and etcher Jules Lessore. Her grandfather Émile Lessore (1805-76) was a French artist who had trained at Sèvres before working at Mintons and then at Wedgwood. Thérèse Lessore studied at the Slade School of Art from 1904 to 1909 and her work subsequently appeared in avant-garde group exhibitions, through which she was drawn into the circle of Walter Richard Sickert (1860-1942). In the early 1920s she lived at 20 Fitzroy Street; Sickert's studio was at no. 15. In 1926 she became his third wife. During the 1920s both she and Sickert decorated Wedgwood blanks at the Bloomsbury studio of Alfred Powell (see Cat. 233) and his wife Louise, Thérèse Lessore's sister. Lessore's work was strongly influenced by Sickert in its sketchy, impressionistic manner. These two plates illustrate well her affinity for the theatre and her fascination with passing moments in everyday life.

For an account of the work done by Lessore and Sickert in the Powells' studio and illustrations of the full range of painted plates and tableware, see Batkin 1982, 145, pls 361-6 and col. pl. XI.

A group of etchings and one drawing by Lessore are held in the Department of Prints and Drawings.

Lindig, Otto 1895-1966

There is no monograph on Lindig. For biographical details, see Janda, 1959; Kulz. W., 'Otto Lindig', *Keramos*, Heft 69, 1975, 65-74; Bernstiel, L., 'Otto Lindig', *Sigill* VI, i, Hamburg 1977; Berlin 1989.

144 Teapot [PLATE 132]

Earthenware, cast, red body with pale pink tin glaze all over including base.

MARKS Impressed in relief on the base with the factory mark of the Majolika-Manufaktur, Karlsruhe and the model number '4010/B'.

Designed in the late 1920s at the Dornburg Pottery Workshop, Weimar. This example made by the Majolika-Manufaktur, Karlsruhe between 1929 and 1962.

H 16cm to top of handle; 14.3cm to top of lid.
D. 17.4cm 1982,12-3,2

Lindig trained initially at the Weimar Kunstgewerbeschule under Henry van de Velde (see Cat. 290-95) and took a diploma in sculpture at the Weimar Academy before joining the Bauhaus as a sculptor in 1919. He moved to the Pottery Workshop at Dornburg, near Weimar, in 1920, becoming technical and then business director in 1924. In 1925 the Bauhaus moved from Weimar to Dessau, but the Pottery Workshop remained at Dornburg as part of the new Staatliche Bauhochschule in Weimar. Lindig stayed on as teacher and director of the Pottery Workshop until the closure of the Bauhochschule by the Nazis in 1930. In October 1930 he took over the Dornburg teaching workshop on his own account. Sometime before this date workshop photographs were taken depicting a tea service with two teapot models, one identical with this example, the other larger with top-set raffia handle (the original Dornburg workshop photograph from Lindig's catalogue is reproduced in Kulz 1975, 70). In 1931 Lindig issued a small catalogue which showed a variant of the teapot as produced at Karlsruhe (the catalogue is reproduced in Berlin 1989, pls 26-39).

The serial production by the Majolika-Manufaktur of Lindig's Dornburg service was initiated in 1929 as a result of the Bauhaus exhibition 'Die Gebrauchswohnung' held in the Dammerstock in Karlsruhe in 1928. The then director of the factory, Müller von Baczko, was so struck by this exhibition that he went to Dornburg to select models for production by the Karlsruhe Majolika-Manufaktur (Karlsruhe 1979, 67, citing a report of October 1928 in the factory archive). An account published in *Die Schaulade* for 1931 (Heft 10, June, 491-4) states that Lindig's designs were put into production at Karlsruhe because the Dornburg workshop could not meet the demands for regular supplies in large quantities, suggesting that the initiative may also have come partly from Lindig himself. For a complete list of models from Lindig's workshop which were produced at Karlsruhe, see Berlin 1989, 207. Some of these models were conceived as early as 1923 (see Cat. 145), but others, such as this teapot, are later works. In general, the shapes were modified slightly for casting in a thick-walled body, as distinct from the thin stoneware bodies of the Dornburg wares.

An early version of this teapot appears in a Karlsruhe manufactory *Werbeprospekt* of 1929 (Karlsruhe 1979, 68). For the version with top-set raffia handle, see *Badische Werkkunst* 2, Sondernummer Heft 1 (1931), 20; for the same model, but with metal handle, see *Die Schaulade*, 1931, 491. For the complete tea service executed by the Majolika-Manufaktur, see *Die Schaulade*, 1932, Heft 16, December, 687. See also Karlsruhe 1979, 431, cat. no. 358g, where it is stated that Lindig's models were produced until 1962 and that during the 1930s the service was made in a red high-fired body with a cream-coloured grey-white glaze, varying from grey to pink depending on the thickness of the glaze and the amount that the red body shows through it. Porous bodies with glazes of other colours or transparent glazes suggest a later date. The mottled pink-white glaze was coloured with zinc oxide and is still known at the factory as the 'Bauhaus' glaze. This teapot was also produced in a smaller size, model no. 3778, height 13.5 cm. The significance of the letter 'B' after the model number is not known. For further examples, see Bröhan III, 1985, no. 382, and Berlin 1989, no. 312.

From 1947 to 1960, Lindig taught at the Landeskunstschule in Hamburg, with Gerhard Marcks. His assistant there was Lieb-friede Bernstiel, who continued to make earlier designs from Lindig's own plaster moulds (the moulds are illustrated in her article on Lindig in *Sigill* VI, 1977). The original moulds were left in Dornburg, but Lindig remade them in Hamburg.

145 Cup, saucer and plate [PLATE 132]

Earthenware, cast and turned, red body, covered overall with *craquelé* tin glaze, the plate in pale pink, the cup and saucer in a deeper pink. Small chip to rim of cup.

MARKS The base of plate and saucer impressed with the factory mark of the Majolika-Manufaktur, Karlsruhe. The base of the cup impressed with model no. '4006'.

Designed jointly by Lindig and Theodor Bogler in 1923 at the Bauhaus Pottery Workshop, Dornburg; made by the Majolika-Manufaktur, Karlsruhe between 1929 and 1962.

145a Cup: H 4.2 cm (to rim), D 10.9 cm 1987,10-11,1
145b Saucer: D 16.9 cm 1987,10-11,1a
145c Plate: D 19.7 cm 1987,10-11,2

For the history of the Dornburg Workshop and the production of Lindig's designs at Karlsruhe, see Cat. 144. There are two variants of the cup: one with flared lip (as in this example), the other with more vertical profile. The design has traditionally been attributed to Lindig alone, but more recent sources (Berlin 1989, no. 314) credit it jointly to Lindig and Bogler, comparing the Karlsruhe production with an earlier model of 1923 which was designed at the Bauhaus by Bogler and executed by Lindig (Berlin 1989, no. 27, vertical profile; no. 28 flared profile).

For a similar place setting with the flared cup, see Bröhan III, 1985, no. 379, with the monogram 'OL' impressed on the base and made presumably at the Dornburg Pottery Workshop. For an example of the more vertical profile in Düsseldorf with the Bauhaus Pottery Workshop mark and therefore dating from before 1925, see Cologne 1978, no. 366. Both variants were made at Karlsruhe; see Bröhan III, 1985, no. 382 (vertical profile), and Karlsruhe 1979, no. 358e (flared profile). The plate is model no. 4009.

Lötz Witwe, Johann, Glasfabrik 1836-1940, attributed

H. Ricke, T. Vlček, A. Adlerová, E. Ploil (eds), *Lötz, Böhmisches Glas 1880-1940*, 2 vols, Munich 1989.

146 Sweet dish and cover [PLATE 106]

Mould-blown, white glass cased with clear glass, vertical blue lines over lid and bowl, with blue knop and blue ball-feet. The blue lines applied by placing the glass in a mould lined with blue canes.

MARKS None.

Made *c*.1914-20, possibly by the firm of Johann Lötz Witwe, Klostermühle bei Unterreichenstein, Böhmerwald, now in Czechoslovakia.

H 11.8 cm, D 12.4 cm 1982,2-4,1

Following the success of the vases with striped decoration made by Lötz to the designs of Powolny for the Werkbund exhibition in Cologne in 1914, the Lötz factory produced a range of similar vases of their own design. These factory variants have often been published as Powolny designs (see, for example, Bröhan II/1, 1976, nos 220-26), but the recent comprehensive publication of Lötz (Ricke et al. eds 1989) distinguishes clearly the group of Powolny designs (Ricke et al. 1989, Band, i, pl. 42, p. 266, factory archive photograph and cat. nos 340-43) from the 'Hüttenvarianten' (Band, ii, pl. i, p. 578, factory archive photographs and Band i, cat. nos 349-51).

This covered dish features in neither group, but the shape and the ball-feet relate more directly to the factory variants and other Lötz products. Thus it is possible that this piece was made by a Lötz factory worker as his own work or by another factory imitating Lötz glass.

Charles Rennie Mackintosh 1868-1928

Mackintosh Memorial Exhibition Catalogue, Glasgow, McLellan Galleries, 1933

Pevsner, N., *Studies in Art, Architecture and Design II, Victorian and after*, London 1968 (chapter on Mackintosh originally published in Milan, 1950)

Howarth, T., *Charles Rennie Mackintosh and the Modern Movement*, London, 2nd edn 1977 (with full bibliography)

Andrew McLaren Young, *Charles Rennie Mackintosh, Centenary exhibition*, Edinburgh Festival, 1968.

Macleod, R., *Charles Rennie Mackintosh*, London 1968

Billcliffe, R., *C. R. Mackintosh, the complete furniture, furniture drawings and interior designs*, 3rd edn 1986

147 Pudding spoon, soup spoon and meat fork [PLATE 70]

Silver, hand-raised, the flat elongated handles with tear-shaped perforation. The spoon handles continue over the back of the bowls to form a rectangular motif with incised parallel lines. Similar incised lines decorate the back of the fork.

MARKS Each piece stamped on the reverse of the handle with Glasgow hallmarks and date-letter for 1902 and maker's mark 'DWH' for David Hislop.

Designed *c*.1901-2, as part of a set of twelve place settings, for Francis Newbery, Director of Glasgow School of Art 1885-1917. Made by David Hislop, silversmith, Glasgow, in 1902. The cutlery remained in the Newbery family until it passed to Mrs Isobel F. Traill, who sold it at Christie's & Edminston's, Glasgow, 6 December 1979, lot 91. Mrs Traill was the niece of Sir John Richmond, a governor of Glasgow School of Art during the time that Newbery was Director; she may have received the cutlery as a gift from Newbery himself, or, more likely, from his daughter, Mary Newbery Sturrock, with whom she was friendly.

147a Pudding spoon: L 23.2 cm 1980,1-4,1
147b Soup spoon: L 26.8 cm 1980,1-4,2
147c Meat fork: L 25.8 cm 1980,1-4,3

An undated drawing for this set in pencil and wash is in the University of Glasgow Mackintosh collection, Q(b)7 (Fig. 21). The drawing shows a large and small fork, soup spoon and pudding spoon and a ladle in both plan and elevation. The small fork and pudding spoon are perforated closer to the end of the handle than the large fork and soup spoon, and the bowls of the two spoons have slightly different profiles. The drawing lists eight pudding spoons, twelve small forks, twelve soup spoons, two large forks, one ladle and four dividers (serving spoons). It is signed and bears the address 120 Mains Street, Blythswood Square. Apparently no knives were designed for this set.

The set was commissioned by Francis and Jessie Newbery as a gift from Jessie's parents; each setting comprised a soup spoon, meat fork, pudding spoon and pudding fork. For further examples, see Pevsner 1968, 168, and Edinburgh 1968, no. 197 (then owned by Mrs Mary Newbery Sturrock); London, Fine Art

Society, 1989, no. 62; Christie's, London, 31 January 1990, lot 24. The Art Gallery and Museum in Glasgow has recently acquired four pieces formerly owned by Mary Newbery Sturrock: a large fork, small fork and spoon, similarly hallmarked 1902 (EI 1989 L a,c,d), together with a presumed trial spoon with unfinished hammered surface and no hallmarks (EI 1989 L b).

Little is known about David Hislop; he worked for the Glasgow firm of Edwards and is recorded in 1904-5 in the Glasgow Post Office directories and Assay Office as 'Watchmaker, jeweller and dealer in stones' of 3 Argyle Arcade, Argyle Street, Glasgow (information kindly supplied by Simon Cottle). See Cat. 148-9 for other work executed by him after Mackintosh designs.

148-9 Two candlesticks [PLATES 71-2]

Ebonised wood with hand-raised silver sconces. Four shafts rise from a low pyramidal base and are joined at the top by a silver ring on which the sconces rest. One candlestick has flat-section shafts that taper inwards and are inlaid with mother-of-pearl squares at the base, the other has shafts that rise vertically. The sconces are therefore of different sizes, the sconce for the tapering shafts having a smaller bowl and wider rim. The bowl of each sconce has a small hole at the base. The vertical shafts are flat in section at the base, set at right angles, as with the tapering shafts, but change to a round section as they rise.

MARKS The sconce for the vertical shafts stamped on upper side of rim with Glasgow hallmarks and date-letter for 1904-5 and maker's mark 'DWH' for David Hislop; the other bears the same marks on the underside of the rim.

The tapering candlestick designed in 1904 for Hill House, Helensburgh, owned by the publisher Walter Blackie; the vertical candlestick designed in the same year for Hous'hill, Nitshill, Glasgow, owned by Miss Catherine Cranston. A number of candlesticks of each design were made for their respective houses, but these two examples, one of each design, were made for Mackintosh himself. On Mackintosh's death in 1928 they passed to his wife; they were included in the Mackintosh Memorial Exhibition at the McLellan Galleries, Glasgow, in 1933, where they were purchased by Alexander Kennedy, in whose family they remained until 1981, when they were exhibited at the Fine Art Society, London (London 1981, no. 61). The silver sconces made by David Hislop, the wooden stands by Alex Martin, in 1904.

148 Tapering candlestick: H 31.1 cm, D of sconce 9.2 cm, D of ring that holds sconce 6.4 cm 1981,6-4,2
149 Vertical candlestick: H 31 cm, D of sconce 10.4 cm, D of ring 9 cm 1981,6-4,1. Base of both candlesticks 15.4 × 14.8 cm

Although not listed in the catalogue of the 1933 exhibition, the candlesticks are clearly visible in an archive photograph of the exhibition in the University of Glasgow Mackintosh Collection (illustrated in Billcliffe 1986, 203, no. 1909.E). Kennedy paid £3 3s. for the two candlesticks (information from the receipt book of William Meldrum, Meldrum Papers, Mitchell Library, Glasgow). W. Meldrum was secretary of the Memorial Exhibition. The candlesticks were lent by Kennedy to the Edinburgh exhibition of 1968 (no. 254); from Kennedy's grandson, they passed to the Fine Art Society (London 1981, no. 61). A second non-matching pair was included in the 1968 Mackintosh exhibition (no. 253), lent by Mrs Norman Walker, née Blackie, apparently by family descent, suggesting that W. Blackie owned candlesticks of each design. See also Billcliffe 1986, no. 1904.18.

Both candlestick designs appear in Mackintosh's sketches for Hill House and Hous'hill, each design shown in its respective house. The sketch for a writing cabinet for Walter Blackie (Fig. 22), dated 1904, with the address 140 Bath Street, Glasgow, shows a tapering candlestick on top of the cabinet, the doors of which were designed to be inlaid with squares of mother-of-pearl, as on the candlesticks (University of Glasgow Mackintosh Collection, ref. no. M(e)5; Billcliffe 1986, 156, no. D. 1904.16). All three items in this drawing – the chair, writing desk and candlesticks – were duplicated by Mackintosh for his own home.

Two candlesticks of the Hill House design are owned by the Art Gallery and Museum, Glasgow; both have been previously converted for use with electricity and have holes at the base of the sconces, as on the British Museum examples, and there are further holes in the bases for the wire to pass through. At some later date the wires were removed and the original spikes to hold the candles replaced in the sconces.

The sketch for the Blue Bedroom at Hous'hill (Fig. 23) shows two pairs of vertical candlesticks placed in the alcoves above the bedside cupboards and on the mantelpiece (University of Glasgow Mackintosh Collection, ref. no. M(f)8; Billcliffe 1986, 170, no. D.1904.65). For a contemporary photograph of the White Bedroom showing the candlestick used to contain flowers, see Billcliffe, 164, no. 1904.1, and 264, no. 1904.L for a photograph with the candlesticks *in situ* in Hous'hill, again in the White Bedroom; see also 268, no. 1904.94 where five surviving examples of this candlestick are recorded, in addition to this one. Two of these are currently on display at Hill House, now owned by the National Trust (although this is not the house for which they were designed). See also *The Studio Yearbook*, 1907, 60.

Further information is provided by the bill books of Honeyman & Keppie, the Glasgow firm of architects which Mackintosh entered in 1889 and in which he became a partner in 1901. In the case of Hous'hill, it is difficult to know what the various quotes for candlesticks and their silver cups refer to, owing to a second candlestick design that was used at Hous'hill which has one central strut (Billcliffe 1986, 173, no. 1904.83). Under the bills for John Cochrane (husband of Catherine Cranston) at Hous'hill, David Hislop is recorded as quoting £1 14s. for four cups at 8s. 6d. each and £2 10s. for four cups at 12s. 6d. each for the Blue Bedroom, on 21 July 1904. On the same day Alex Martin is listed as quoting for wooden candlesticks for the Blue Bedroom, but no prices are given. On 6 December 1904 Hislop was paid 17s. for two cups (i.e. 8s. 6d. each) and £1 17s. 6d. for three cups (i.e. 12s. 6d. each). On 17 December 1904 Martin was paid £1 17s. 6d. for three candlesticks at 12s. 6d. each and for two candlesticks he received a total of 11s. (i.e. 5s. 6d. each). The cheaper candlestick must be the single-strut version; thus it appears that four of this type were commissioned but two paid for. Of the four-strut version, three were paid for, though Hislop's quote suggests that four were commissioned (University of Glasgow Mackintosh Collection, photographs of Honeyman & Keppie bill books, pp. 62-3).

Under the bills for Blackie at Hill House, Alex Martin quoted £2 10s. 6d. for three candlesticks and David Hislop quoted £1 17s. 10d. for three silver cups for the same on 4 February 1905. Payment for the three cups was received on 29 March 1905 and for the three candlesticks on 27 April (bill books, p. 74). Alex Martin ran a wholesale cabinet-making and upholstery business in Glasgow from 1898 to about 1909. Mackintosh was a major client from 1903 to 1905 (Glasgow 1984, 39).

The Hous'hill candlestick cost £1 5s., the Hill House version cost £1 9s. 4d. So when Kennedy bought them in 1933 for £3 3s., he paid just under 9s. more than they had cost in 1904-5.

150 Four pieces of cutlery [PLATE 66]

Electroplated nickel silver, comprising a jam spoon, dessert spoon, teaspoon and fish knife, the jam spoon and teaspoon with trefoil ends, the dessert spoon and fish knife with trifid ends, the fish knife with a rat's tail on the reverse.

MARKS Each piece stamped on the reverse of handle 'MISS CRANSTON'S'.

Designed *c.* 1905 for the series of four tearooms in Glasgow opened by Catherine Cranston (1850-1934) between 1884 and 1904.

150a Jam spoon: L 15.3cm 1979,12-1,1
150b Dessert spoon: L 18.3cm 1980,3-4,1
150c Teaspoon: L 12.7cm 1980,3-4,2
150d Fish knife: L 20.8cm 1980,3-4,3

Mackintosh was commissioned to design furniture and fittings for Miss Cranston's tearooms between 1896 and 1917. The Ingram Street Tea Room opened in 1900 and the Willow Tea Room in Sauchiehall Street opened in 1904. He had previously redesigned furniture and fittings for the Argyle Street Tea Room in 1897, and contributed to the design of the Buchanan Street Tea Room, opened in the previous year. See Howarth 1977, chapter 6.

These four pieces are from two different sets, with either trefoil or trifid ends. Although there are a number of contemporary illustrations of the various tearooms, the cutlery is not shown in detail and it is difficult to tell whether a particular set was used in a particular tearoom, but it is more likely that they were interchangeable. The manufacturer remains uncertain; most surviving examples are unmarked, but some pieces bear the mark of E. Bingham & Company, Sheffield; for example, Christie's, London, 18 July 1990, lot 118: six knives with the name in full on the blade and six spoons with trefoil ends, stamped on the handles 'E.B.&Co.' with the letters 'EP' (electroplate) and 'B'. David Hislop's name is also to be found on some pieces, including a third set with lollipop-shaped ends, suggesting that he was involved in some way in the manufacture or retail of the cutlery (reference to pieces with Hislop's name supplied by Simon Cottle).

For further illustrations of the tearoom cutlery, see Pevsner 1950, 127; Howarth 1977, pl. 51; Hughes 1967, pl. 242.

151 Clock [PLATE 73; COLOUR PLATE XI]

The case of oak, with a veneer of black stencilled chequerboard decoration; the face made up of squares of mother-of-pearl with four squares of ivory at the corners. The numbers are of wood, inset into the mother-of-pearl and the hands are metal painted blue. The face has a brass surround and is protected by a hinged cover. Beneath the face is set an oblong mirror. At the back are two doors, to the clock above and the pendulum below. There are some splits to the case and shrinkage to the wood, so that the lower door at the back no longer fits flush.

The clock dial has two slots cut into it on each side, indicating that it was once held by a pair of horizontal bars.

MARKS The case is unmarked. The clock movement is stamped 'MADE IN FRANCE' with the unidentified initials 'GB & E'.

Designed in 1919 for the guest bedroom of W. J. Bassett-Lowke's house at 78 Derngate, Northampton and incorporating an earlier, late-nineteenth century French movement; passed from W. J. Bassett-Lowke to his niece, Mrs Janet Dicks, and remained in her possession until 1979.

H 37cm. Base 25.2 × 13.8 cm 1980,5-19,1

Mackintosh left Glasgow in 1914; his transformation of a nineteenth-century terraced house in Northampton in 1917 for the engineering-model manufacturer Wenman Joseph Bassett-Lowke, was his last major commission. Bassett-Lowke was well aware of recent developments on the Continent, but, surprisingly, had not heard of Mackintosh before 1914 when he was recommended to him. The guest bedroom at Derngate was designed in 1919; Bassett-Lowke described it as 'perhaps the most daring in the house' (quoted in Billcliffe 1986, 246), with its striking black-and-white striped wallpaper carried up on to the ceiling. There were matching curtains and bedspread, and the furniture was edged with blue and black chequerboard decoration.

This clock was the largest of the clocks designed by Mackintosh for Bassett-Lowke (designs for a number of others are in the University of Glasgow Mackintosh Collection). A number of photographs in the Mackintosh Collection show the clock *in situ*, on the fireplace (for example, Fig. 24, where the fireplace is reflected in the long mirror, ref. no. G(h)19); see also Howarth 1977, pl. 77; Pevsner 1950, 139, and 1968, pl. 52; Billcliffe 1986, 247, no. 1919.7. A direct view of the mantelpiece with the clock was included in an article on the Derngate house in *Ideal Home*, September 1920, 95-6; by this time Mackintosh was so out of fashion that the article does not mention his name.

Billcliffe and Vergo (1977, 744, pls 13-14) have noted the influence of Otto Prutscher on Mackinstosh's design for this clock, which owes much to a clock design by Prutscher illustrated in *The Studio Yearbook*, 1908, item A.27.

Bassett-Lowke's furniture at Derngate was made either in his own works, or by local or London cabinet-makers, or by internees at the Knockaloe prison camp on the Isle of Man, under the supervision of Otto Matt, a skilled German cabinet-maker. Examples of furniture made on the Isle of Man are held by the Manx Museum and by the Victoria and Albert Museum, while two other clocks made for Bassett-Lowke are described by Billcliffe as having cases made by German internees on the Isle of Man (nos 1917.1 and 4). Both these clocks use ebonised wood and inlaid ivory and Erinoid, whereas the British Museum clock in its materials relates more closely to large-scale furniture for Derngate. The movement is a common late-nineteenth century French type, reused presumably because it was cheap and easily available.

In 1924 Bassett-Lowke decided to build a new house on the outskirts of Northampton, but had lost touch with Mackintosh, who was living in France; he therefore chose an avant-garde German architect: 'I could not find any other architect with modern ideas in England, and when looking through a German publication called *Werkbund Jahrbuch* of 1913 I saw some work by Professor Dr Peter Behrens which I thought was very simple, straightforward and modern in its atmosphere. I obtained Dr Behrens' address from the German Consul and got in touch with him' (quoted in Campbell 1986, 3). For Bassett-Lowke and his patronage of both Mackintosh and Behrens, see Campbell 1986.

152 Candlestick [PLATE 71]

Plastic (Erinoid), with black base and green stem, the upper part with turned decoration.

MARKS None.

Designed *c.* 1917, manufacturer unknown. Acquired by William Meldrum at the Mackintosh Memorial Exhibition in Glasgow in 1933; passed to his son, James Meldrum, by whom it was lent to the 1968 exhibition (no. 280) and thence to the latter's widow, in whose possession it remained until 1983.

H 40.2 cm, D of base 15 cm   1983,11-6,1

According to Billcliffe (231, no. 1917.8) Mackintosh began to use plastic in about 1910-11 in Glasgow as an inlay for furniture. A letter from Bassett-Lowke to Mackintosh of 12 January 1917 provides evidence that they were corresponding about Erinoid at this time, and suggests not only that Bassett-Lowke encouraged Mackintosh to use it as an inlay, but also that he had access to supplies, presumably difficult to obtain during the war: 'I presume the material you mention is similar to Erinoid which is now made in England and which I can obtain in any colour, an unpolished supply of which I enclose. Have you ever thought of using this in the decoration of furniture instead of wood inlays, or enamel stencil? as it appears to me that there are immense possibilities in this way considering the ease with which the material can be worked and the various colours and forms which it can be obtained in' (University of Glasgow Mackintosh Collection, ref. no. E(a)5). On 14 January Bassett-Lowke wrote, 'I am enclosing you herewith booklets on Erinoid which will doubtless be of interest to you.' This candlestick is apparently unique in being made entirely of plastic and is perhaps a result of Mackintosh's experiments with Erinoid at this time. For Mackintosh's use of green and purple Erinoid in his clocks for Bassett-Lowke, see Billcliffe 229, no. 1917.1, and 230 no. 1917.4. See also Brandt 1985, no. 61, an example in the Virginia Museum of Fine Arts. Further designs for clocks (in the University of Glasgow Mackintosh Collection) specify Erinoid inlays in several other colours (Billcliffe 229, no. 1917.2 and 230, no. 1917.5 and 6).

Erinoid is the trade name of a company based in Stroud, Gloucestershire, that produced a type of plastic known as casein from *c.* 1913-14 onwards. Casein is made from skimmed milk modified by formaldehyde; the name 'Erinoid' was adopted because the milk came from Ireland (see Katz 1978, 20).

Magnussen, Walter Claus 1869-1946

There is no monograph on Magnussen. For biographical details, see Cologne 1978.

153 Plate [PLATE 84]

High-fired earthenware, moulded, with relief ornament in the form of three cartouches round the rim. Within the cartouche and along the edge is a curvilinear pattern in underglaze colours outlined in deep blue-green and filled in with blue dots.

MARKS Printed in underglaze blue with the factory mark of J. Uffrecht & Co., incorporating the designer's initials 'WM' and the pattern name 'Isar'.

Designed in 1901 and made by the Steingutfabrik J. Uffrecht & Co., Neuhaldensleben, near Magdeburg.

D 32.1 cm   1990,10-18,1   Given by Graham Dry and Beate Dry-v. Zezschwitz

Walter Magnussen was the principal designer for J. J. Scharvogel's Kunsttöpferei in Munich in the early 1900s. Scharvogel (1854-1938) established his art pottery in 1898, specialising in flambé stoneware. Following the Paris Exhibition of 1900, in which he participated, he invited a number of artists to design new forms, among them Theo Schmuz-Baudiss, Paul Haustein and the progressive Munich artist Walter Magnussen. The latter's designs for Scharvogel are characterised by their bold relief ornament in a curvilinear style owing much to van de Velde and glazed usually in a lustrous deep brown (for examples with Magnussen's monogram, see Scheffler 1966, no. 150-52; Heller 1982, nos 268 and 270-72). See also *Kunst und Handwerk*, 1900, 379.

Scharvogel left Munich in 1904 to direct the Grossherzogliche Keramische Manufaktur in Darmstadt. Magnussen moved to Bremen (possibly before 1904), where he worked as an artist potter on his own account and from about 1929 directed the Werkstatt für Gebrauchs- und Zierkeramik der Kunstgewerbeschule Bremen. According to Heller 1982, he also taught at some time in Hanover.

Between 1901 and 1904 Magnussen designed a range of dinner services and wash services for J. Uffrecht & Co. of Neuhaldensleben. The service to which this plate belongs is illustrated in *Sprechsaal* no. 8, 1902, 277, where it is described as a moderately priced luncheon service in the modern style, with special praise for the subtle use of blue dots as infill for the pattern, instead of a solid blue band. The curvilinear blue pattern in sunken cartouches is a direct translation of Magnussen's relief designs for Scharvogel; see, for example, a closely similar linear motif on a bowl in the Kunstgewerbemuseum, Berlin (Scheffler 1966, no. 152).

Few other pieces from this service are recorded. For two egg-cups also decorated with the 'Isar' pattern, see Galerie Ketterer, Munich, 136 Auktion, 12 May 1989, lot 348.

A service with plates of the same shape, but decorated with a different pattern, is illustrated in *Die Kunst* 10, 1904, 104 and 106, and in Hermann Wahrlich's *Wohnung und Hausrat*, Munich 1908, 90.

Marcks, Gerhard 1889-1974

Busch, G. and Rudloff, M., *Gerhard Marcks, Das Plastische Werk*, Berlin 1977
See also Bayer et al. 1975; Wingler 1969 and 1981.

See also Recent Acquisitions, Cat. 346-8.

154 Coffee percolator [PLATE 134]

Fireproof glass with rubber fitting to secure the funnel in position beneath the upper vessel; ebonised wood handle. The neck of the lower vessel is encircled by a metal band which slots into the split wood handle clamped by a metal ring. The sieve and funnel are also of glass.

MARKS Acid-etched on the filter 'Jenaer Glas Schott & Gen. Jena' in a circle with four corners and 'Sintrax $\frac{3}{4}$ ltr'; on the base of the pot 'Schott & Gen. Jenaer Glas. $\frac{3}{4}$ ltr'.

Designed between 1925 and 1930 at Burg Giebichenstein and put into production from 1930 to 1939 by Schott & Genossen, Jena, Thuringia, Germany. The straight handle with spring clip is a later modification.

H 27.4cm, H of lower vessel 10.7 cm   1981,12-3,1

Marcks trained as a sculptor in Berlin before joining the Bauhaus in 1919. He was artistic director of the Bauhaus Pottery Workshop from 1919 to 1925. From 1925 to 1933 he taught ceramics at the Kunstgewerbeschule, Burg Giebichenstein, near Halle, becoming director of the school in 1928. In 1933 he was dismissed and barred from activity until after the war.

This is one of the first coffee percolators in fireproof glass and was illustrated by Herbert Read in 1934 (*Art and Industry*, 34) as a good example of modern design for mass production. Fire-

proof glass was developed by Schott initially for laboratory ware and applied to domestic glassware after the First World War. Schott's first fireproof-glass coffee-machine of 1925 was thought to look too much like a scientific instrument and so Erich Schott approached Gerhard Marcks at Burg Giebichenstein to create a new form. For E. Schott's account of his collaboration with Marcks, see *Baukunst und Werkform* 8, August 1954 (reference kindly supplied by Anne Marie Ittstein, Schott Glaswerke). The use of a glass sieve and funnel ensures that the coffee makes contact with glass only, preserving its full aroma.

For the earliest illustrated version of Marcks' Kaffeemaschine Sintrax, see *Die Form*, August 1928, 242, where it is shown with its own stand and spirit lamp; the lower vessel is larger than this example and has a spout, while the knop is above the top of the lid instead of being sunken. The handle curves downwards. However, by 1930 Sintrax was being produced with a sunken knop, as illustrated in *Die Schaulade*, 6 Jahrgang, Heft 9, July 1930, 593. Marcks' Sintrax was also produced in a 1½-litre size; for an example in the Bauhaus-Archiv Museum, Berlin, see Wingler 1981, no. 235. Some recent publications credit the straight handle to Wagenfeld (Bonn 1988, 10), but no source is given and the Schott archives contain no record of Wagenfeld's involvement with Sintrax.

The Sintrax coffee-machine underwent later modifications: for Bruno Mauder's version of 1949, see Hirzel 1953, 30; *Deutsche Warenkunde*, Stuttgart 1955, Blatt 2, 2/6, and *Schott Information* 3/1984, *100 Years of Schott*, 51. The Mauder version has a sunken knop and the lid is inset rather than following the profile of the upper vessel; the lower vessel is a flattened sphere rather than a cone and the handle curves downwards. Production of the Sintrax coffee-machine was discontinued in the late 1960s (information supplied by A. M. Ittstein).

Margold, Emanuel Josef 1888-1962

There is no monograph on Margold. For biographical details, see Darmstadt 1976; Schweiger 1982.

155 Storage jar [PLATE 129]

Earthenware, glazed white with simple outline decoration in blue on lid and body, the word 'GERSTE' (barley) printed in blue on one side.

MARKS Printed on the base with triangular mark 'ENTWURF MARGOLD DARMSTADT' incorporating the designer's monogram; printed factory mark of Ludwig Wessel AG, Bonn and the number '04010'. Impressed 'EDITH' (presumably a pattern name).

Designed at the Darmstadt artists' colony, certainly after 1911 and probably after the First World War, and made by Ludwig Wessel AG, Bonn.

H 20.9cm, max. W 12.1 cm   1981,3-10,14

Margold was trained initially as a cabinet-maker before studying under Hoffmann in the Vienna Kunstgewerbeschule. In 1908-9 he was assistant to Hoffmann in the master-class for architecture and a member of the Wiener Werkstätte. In 1911 he was invited to join the Darmstadt artists' colony and moved to Berlin in 1929.

For the Porzellan- und Steingutfabrik Wessel, see Kommern 1980.

156 Biscuit tin [COLOUR PLATE VIII]

Base metal, printed with stylised floral design in black, white, pink, yellow and grey on gold, with hinged lid.

MARKS Stamped on the base in raised letters 'H. Bahlsens Keks-Fabrik Hannover Weltaustellungen St Louis 1904 Brussels 1910 Turin 1911 Gent 1913 Grosser Preis Konigl. Preis Staats Medaille'.

Designed in 1914-15 for the Keksfabrik Hermann Bahlsen, Hanover.

L 17.8 cm, W 8.4 cm, H 4.2 cm 1982,12-3,7

As early as the 1890s Bahlsen's biscuit factory had begun to employ a range of artists for the design of packaging and publicity material; this was exceptional as it preceded by several years the founding in 1907 of the Deutsche Werkbund, which encouraged such policies. By 1913 fifteen artists had supplied designs for the firm, among them Behrens, Carl Otto Czeschka, Julius Diez, the sculptors Ludwig Vierthaler and Georg Herting, and the Hanover architect K. Siebrecht, who designed Bahlsen's new factory buildings in 1911-13. E. J. Margold worked for Bahlsen from 1914 to 1916 or 1917.

Bahlsen's new designs for ornamental giftware packaging were shown at the exhibition held by the Deutsche Werkbund in Cologne in 1914. They included ceramic boxes by Vierthaler and Margold as well as biscuit tins by Heinrich Mittag and Aenne Koken. The Margold biscuit tins were not shown in the exhibition. For a group of four biscuit tins with designs closely similar to this one, see DK & D, 34, 1914, 316. This example was advertised in the Werkbund Jahrbuch of 1915. The archive of the Bahlsen Museum holds several designs by Margold and his wife Ella, many of them dated to the years 1914 and 1915, but the design for this particular biscuit tin is not among them. (I am grateful to Beate Grubert for checking the Bahlsen archive.)

For full discussion of Bahlsen's display at the 1914 Werkbund exhibition, see Joppien 1984. For an identical tin in the Badisches Landesmuseum, Karlsruhe, see Franzke 1987, no. 226. For further tins with similar designs in the possession of Bahlsen's Keksfabrik, see Darmstadt 1976, Bd 4, no. 396 and Hauschild 1987. For examples in the Museum der Künstlerkolonie, Darmstadt, see Ulmer 1990, nos 218-21. For a ceramic biscuit box executed by the Vereinigte Wiener und Gmundner Keramik und Tonwarenfabrik Schleiss, see Heller 1982, no. 275.

Marks, Gilbert Leigh 1861-1905

There is no monograph on Gilbert Marks. For biographical details, see Culme 1987, I, 312-13. Useful contemporary articles are to be found in Art Journal, 1895, 251-2; The Studio 5, 1895, 219-20; Magazine of Art, 1895, 397-9, November 1895-October 1896, 437-40 and May-October 1897, 158-60; 1898, 564-5; 1899, 377-80; The Artist, 1898, 133-8. See also Harlow, K., 'Gilbert Marks, Forgotten Silversmith', Antique Collector, July 1984, 42-7.

157 Plate [PLATE 67]

Silver, hand-raised with repoussé border of wild roses and leaves.

MARKS Engraved on the front 'Gilbert Marks 1902'; stamped on the front with London hallmarks and date-letter for 1902 and maker's mark 'GM'.

Designed and made by Gilbert Marks in 1902.

D 22.1 cm 1980,10-7,6 Given by Professor and Mrs John Hull Grundy

Marks was the grandson of a working goldsmith and the nephew of the artist Henry Stacey Marks. He trained as a silversmith on leaving school, but by 1888 he was working in the City as a wool-broker's manager and appears to have continued to work in silver as a part-time occupation until at least 1896, when the Art Journal referred to him as 'someting in the City', practising his metalwork in his leisure, with the help of two assistants. He was subsequently associated with the firm of Johnson, Walker & Tolhurst of 80 Aldersgate Street, at whose showrooms he held regular exhibitions from 1895 to 1901. He also had an exhibition at the Fine Art Society in 1899. He registered two marks at Goldsmiths' Hall in 1896; before this his work was struck with the mark of Johnson, Walker & Tolhurst, though it seems always to have been engraved with his signature and the date. The earliest recorded piece with his signature dates from 1895 and the latest from 1902. This plate is one of his last works.

The exhibitions at Johnson, Walker & Tolhurst were favourably reviewed and Marks was praised for his masterly chasing of naturalistic floral ornament and for his rhythmical placing of the design to suit the form of the object: 'A spray of blossom does not seem to have fallen from some plant and to have been turned to metal upon a plate that happened to lie beneath it, as is so distinctive of the naturalistic Japanese metal-work' (Magazine of Art, 1896, 440). The same critic noted that Marks's work was not 'subjected to the ordinary polishing processes', while others praised the 'dull yet exquisite grey of unpolished silver' (Art Journal, 1897, 252) and the 'natural dull white colour in which silver looks at its best' (The Studio 5, 1895, 220).

Marks worked entirely by hand, evolving a rich individual style, strongly influenced by Dutch repoussé work of the late seventeenth century. He is best known for his ornamental domestic wares, but he also received a number of official commissions from City companies and other bodies. For an account of his methods, based largely on his own words, see The Artist, 1898, 133-8: 'I do the designs myself and never produce a duplicate. No dies or machinery are used and so the artist's fancy is at work upon the subject in hand from the moment when the design is first conceived to the time when the last detail has been wrought in the metal.'

From around 1904, by which time Marks was seriously ill, works in a very similar style appear, signed by Latino Movio and hallmarked by Johnson, Walker & Tolhurst or Holland, Aldwinckle & Slater (manufacturers for the former). Movio may have been one of Marks's assistants, continuing to work in his manner for the same firm.

Martin Brothers 1873-1915

The British Museum collection of Martinware comprises forty-one pieces, acquired from two eminent collectors: the first group was bequeathed to the Museum in 1945 by Ernest Marsh, the second group was given by Professor and Mrs John Hull Grundy in 1978, with additions in 1979, 1980 and 1981.

For full biographical details and discussions of Martinware production, see: Haslam, M., The Martin Brothers, Potters, London 1978 (with further bibliography).

The bibliography that follows has thus been limited to publications of particular relevance to the British Museum collection.

Beard, C.R., Catalogue of the Collection of Martinware formed by Mr. Frederick John Nettlefold, London 1936

Marsh, E., 'The Martin Brothers', Apollo XL, 1944, 94-6 and 127-32 (illustrated mostly by items in Marsh's collection)

Ullmann, A. (Anne Hull Grundy), 'The Genius of the Martin Brothers Pottery', Art & Design 2, no. 3, January 1948, 74-8

Hull Grundy, A., 'Salt-glazed Stoneware: The Martin Brothers', The Antique Dealer & Collectors' Guide, March 1959, 25-7

Hull Grundy, A., 'Martinware', Far and Wide, Autumn 1960, 44-7 (published by Guest, Keen & Nettlefold)

Summerfield, A., 'Pottery by the Martin Brothers', Antique Collector, November 1987, 92-7 (bequest of Ernest Marsh to the South London Art Gallery)

Dawson, A., The Hull Grundy Gift of Martinware, British Museum Occasional Paper 10, 1980, 35-45

Ernest Marsh was the son of a wealthy Quaker; he was introduced to the Martin brothers in 1887 by his brother, the lawyer John Marsh, and bought pots directly from them until Edwin's death in 1915. Marsh regularly lent his pieces to exhibitions; for example, the 'Exhibition of Pottery produced in London between the years 1872 and 1922', held at the South London Art Gallery in 1922 and the 'Exhibition of Fulham Pottery and Prints' held at the Central Library, Fulham in 1929. As Executive Committee Member of the Contemporary Art Society, he established a fund for the purchase of modern pottery and crafts. He wrote his reminiscences of the Martin brothers in 1936; they remain unpublished (copy in Southall Library) but formed the basis of his Apollo articles of 1944. In addition to his bequest to the British Museum, he left pieces to other London institutions, notably Southall Library, the South London Art Gallery and the Kingston-upon-Thames Museum. The Victoria and Albert Museum holds pieces given by Marsh in memory of his brother in 1920, while a further part of his collection was sold at Sotheby's, on 29 October 1946, after his death.

Anne Hull Grundy's interest in Martinware dates from 1944, when, as she records in her own annotated copy of the catalogue of the Nettlefold collection, under pl. 36, a pair of beakers with birds and flowers: 'Beaker like this decorated fish given me by John for 18th Birthday 1944 and began the collection.' She acquired her copy of the Nettlefold catalogue in 1946 and other annotations reveal that she saw several items sold at auction in 1946-7 and purchased a number for herself (for example, the jellyfish vase, Cat. 191). F. J. Nettlefold (d.1949) inherited the nucleus of his collection from his father, Frederick Nettlefold, who had collected Martinware from the mid 1870s and gave the brothers much-needed financial assistance. The elder Nettlefold died in 1913; his son then made important acquisitions from two further Martinware collections sold in the early 1920s: F. Hutchinson (Sotheby's, 25 November 1921, see Cat. 191) and Francis Henry Crittall (Sotheby's, 20 January 1922). Anne Hull Grundy also acquired items from the Marsh sale of 1946. She wrote her first article on Martinware in 1948 and by the 1950s had built up a significant collection. In addition to her gifts to the British Museum, she also gave Martinware to other museums, notably to the Castle Museum, Norwich (including thirty pieces purchased from the brothers by John Hull Grundy when a young boy), and to Southall Library. Martinware from her collection may also be seen at Pitshanger Manor, where it

is on loan to the London Borough of Ealing from the Trustees of the Hull Grundy Estate.

The forty-one pieces range in date from 1879 (Cat. 172) to 1907 (Cat. 192); but as the Martin brothers worked in the same styles and techniques over a number of years, the collection is catalogued here in groups of related material, rather than in strict chronological order, and the illustrations correspond to these groups. The collection includes pieces of extreme rarity, such as the figure of Cerberus (Cat. 161), the Toby jug (Cat. 171), the three tiny figures Cat. 167-9), the large jellyfish vase (Cat. 191) and the blue and white unglazed vase (Cat. 184).

The four Martin brothers who ran the pottery were sons of a wholesale stationer's clerk. Robert Wallace (1843-1923), the head of the firm, studied at the Lambeth School of Art from 1860 and at the Royal Academy Schools from 1864. During this time he worked in the studio of the sculptor Alexander Munro and in 1865 won a prize for the design of a medal for the South London Working Classes Industrial Exhibition (an example struck in bronze by Joseph Moore was presented to the British Museum by Professor and Mrs Hull Grundy in 1978, registration number 1978,10-1,1059; for the design, see Haslam 1978, 21, figs 16-17). R.W. Martin set up the first pottery in Fulham and was responsible for the characteristic 'Wally'-birds, the face jugs and other sculptural items. Charles Douglas (1846-1910) was the business manager and directed the showroom at 16 Brownlow Street, Holborn, opened by 1879. Walter Fraser (1857-1912) looked after the technical side, and was responsible for the coloured glazes, as well as throwing and decorating pots, and Edwin Bruce (1860-1915) was a thrower and decorator. Both Walter and Edwin had worked for about a year at Doulton's Lambeth factory, producing decorated stoneware. Walter was initially taught to throw pots by the French artist potter J.C. Cazin, a refugee in England during the Franco-Prussian war of 1870-71, who taught at Lambeth School of Art and worked at Bailey's Fulham Pottery, where Martin Brothers pottery was fired until 1874. The brothers employed a number of assistants, boys and designers, including H.W. Fawcett (see Cat. 173 and 181) and Edward Willy, who made designs for the naturalistic flower patterns (see Haslam 1978, 106, figs 59-60 and 108, fig. 169).

Most of the pieces bear incised marks on the body or on the base; these give the brothers' name in various forms and the date and place of manufacture, 'London and Southall', referring to the showroom in Holborn and the pottery at Southall, Middlesex, established in 1877. The date is sometimes given in full but it is usually just the month and the year. Up to 1899 there were two firings per year, in February and October; after that only one firing took place. Early wares are marked 'R.W.Martin' only up to about 1882, when '& Bros' was added. The full range of marks used is illustrated in Haslam 1978, 164-8.

Large sculptural pieces (158-62)

158-9 Two grotesque birds [PLATE 52]

Salt-glazed stoneware, decorated with coloured slips under the glaze in greens, blues, pinks and browns. The bodies are turned on the wheel, the wings, feet and other details added. The detachable heads, made separately, also on the wheel, in the form of balls, which are then dented and given added details to form the features. Both heads have necks hidden inside the body. The bodies of both birds are much repaired. One is set on a wooden stand (159) and bears inside the neck an original paper label from the Martin brothers' shop which reads:

'R.W. Martin & Bro's., Art Potters, 16 Brownlow Street, High Holborn'; the other has holes in the base for attaching to a stand.

MARKS
158 On the body, at the feet, in an oval blue panel 'RW Martin sc. London.1882'. On the neck 'RW Martin.London & Southall. 3.11.1882', and on the base 'Martin & B^{ros} London & Southall 3.11.1882'. H 47.8cm 1945,2-4,4
159 On the body, on the shoulder, 'RW.Martin London 1882' and on the neck, 'RW.Martin.s^c Southall.& London.1.10.1882.'
H 53.5cm 1945,2-4,5 Marsh Bequest

According to the *Magazine of Art*, 1882, 445, these covered jars were used as tobacco jars, but the lids are not airtight. Several comparable examples are illustrated in Haslam 1978, but the largest of these is 14½in (36.8cm) high. Thus these two, at 18 and 19in (45.7 and 48.3cm), are exceptionally large.

160 Two roaring lions [PLATE 52]

Salt-glazed stoneware, matt brown bodies with greyish-buff manes and jaws, blue eyes, pink teeth and bluish-pink toenails, set on rectangular stoneware bases, glazed black. Details of the fur are incised on the body. The lions are not identical; the modelling of the mane differs and one has a ball beneath his right paw (**160b**). The ball is in mottled greenish-black colours and has a glossy glaze. This figure has a slight chip to the right ear.

MARKS On both, on the side of the base, 'Martin Bros. London & Southall 1893'.

160a H 36cm 1945,2-4,11
160b H 36cm 1945,2-4,12 Marsh Bequest

For a similar pair of lions dated 1887, see Haslam 1978, 101, fig. 148.

161 Jar and cover in the form of Cerberus [PLATE 52]

Salt-glazed stoneware, dark brown and black with white teeth and ears and patches of green and blue on the snakes entwined around the body. Details of the fur are incised. Mounted on a turned wooden stand. The three heads form the cover.

MARKS On the rim of the lid, 'R.W.Martin Bros London & Southall'.

H 26.3cm 1978,7-4,6 Hull Grundy Gift

For another Cerberus jar, see Haslam 1978, 101, fig. 147, dated 1887. This is apparently the only other recorded version of this model.

162 Square plaque, Edwin Martin decorating a vase [PLATE 51]

Terracotta, portrait relief of Edwin Martin incising flowers into the surface of a two-handled vase, against a stippled ground.

MARKS On the front, 'Sgrafitto [sic] RW Martin S^c Southall Pottery'.

H 32.4cm 1981,2-5,1 Hull Grundy Gift

According to Haslam this subject was first modelled by Robert Wallace Martin in 1885. For another version, dated 1890 and showing Edwin incising orchids with an actual flower in the background, suggesting that he was drawing from nature, see Haslam 1978, 81-2, fig. 101. Mrs Hull Grundy records that she owned this plaque in 1960 (Hull Grundy 1960, 46).

Sgraffito (Italian: scratched) is a term used to describe a method of decoration in which the vessel is covered with slip of a contrasting colour, then incised or scratched to reveal the body colour beneath. Cat. 184 is done in this way, but is exceptional among Martinware production in being true sgraffito; the incised decoration on most Martinware pottery is not done through a layer of slip.

Smaller sculptural pieces (163-71)

163 Spoon-warmer [PLATE 52]

Salt-glazed stoneware, in the form of two grotesque monsters, their mouths forming the two larger openings, modelled with eyes and noses in relief. The two smaller funnel-like openings form the ears to both monsters and the base is modelled with 'claws' to suggest feet. Painted in coloured slip beneath the glaze, deep brown with patches of turquoise blue at the sides, the interior, openings and claws buff, the eyes and noses blue. There is a loop handle at the top.

MARKS On the base, '1.12.80 RW Martin London & Southall'.

H 22cm 1945,2-4,2 Marsh Bequest

W. Cosmo Monkhouse, in the first public acknowledgement of the Martin Brothers' achievements, records that these vessels in the form of grotesque monsters were intended as spoon-warmers. He compared them to nonsense nursery rhymes in the manner of Lewis Carroll: 'We have a hundred young sculptors who will model you a Venus or an Adonis as soon as look at you; but who save Mr. Martin could give you a Boojum or a Snark in the round?' (*Magazine of Art*, 1882, 444-5). For a group of similar spoon-warmers, see Haslam 1978, 62, fig. IX.

164-5 Two grotesque birds [PLATE 52]

Salt-glazed stoneware, with detachable heads and mounted on wooden bases. Painted in coloured slips under the glaze, in blues, greens, greys, pinks and browns.

MARKS On both at the base of the body, 'Martin Bros London & Southall'.

164 On the rim of the lid, 'Martin Bro^s 8-1890 London & Southall'.
H 18cm 1978,7-4,18
165 Lid unmarked. H 17.5cm 1978,7-4,19 Hull Grundy Gift

For a group of comparable small birds all dating from the 1880s, see Haslam 1978, 65, fig. XI.

166 Figure, 'Thrower' [PLATE 52]

Salt-glazed stoneware, painted in blue, buff and pale green.

MARKS On the side of the base, '"Thrower" RW.Martin. S^c. Southall 1885'.

H 17cm 1978,7-4,4 Hull Grundy Gift

This is always said to be a portrait of Walter Martin and is one of a series of three, the other two being 'Bench Boy' and 'Wheel Boy'. The complete series is in the Victoria and Albert Museum, the 'thrower' dated December 1879 (see also Haslam 1978, 79, fig. 97). The three figures were also produced as a high-relief plaque, see Haslam, fig. 98 and the *Magazine of Art*, 1882, 443, where Monkhouse describes the plaque in detail: the wheel boy is turning the potter's wheel, while the bench boy is making the balls of clay ready for the thrower. In the figural version the bench boy is shown wedging the clay.

167-9 Three tiny figures [PLATE 52]

Salt-glazed stoneware, brown, a kneeling helmeted soldier tying up a bundle of rods and two figures of Hercules wearing a lion skin, one seated on a rock, his hands poised as if clasping a club, which is missing, the other kneeling and grasping an object in his left hand. The latter appears to have misfired; the rock is a dull murky green and very cracked.

MARKS
167 Soldier, 'RW Martin Bros 1904'. H 7.8cm 1978,7-4,16
168 Seated Hercules, '1904'. H 7.3cm 1978,7-4,15

169 Kneeling Hercules, 'Southall RW Martin & Bros 1904'. H 6.8cm 1978,7-4,17 Hull Grundy Gift

Other figures of a comparable tiny scale include imps playing musical instruments dated 1906-10 (Haslam 1978, 134-5, figs 208-9), figures from the *Pickwick Papers* dated 1906 (Haslam 1978, 136, figs. 212-13) and the chess set dated 1902 in the Victoria and Albert Museum (133, fig. xxv). Slightly larger figures of 4-5in (10.2-12.7cm) in height include a fireman (25, fig. 21) and a pair of figures in medieval costume dated 1910 (30, fig. 26). However, no other versions of the soldier or of the Hercules figures have as yet been recorded.

170 Face jug [PLATES 51-2]

Salt-glazed stoneware, creamy buff colour with blue eyes, modelled on each side with two different grotesque faces, the spout to one side.

MARKS '5-1902. RW Martin and Bros. London & Southall'.

H 21.6cm 1945,2-4,14 Marsh Bequest

This jug is illustrated in J.F. Blacker's *The ABC of English Salt-Glaze Stoneware from Dwight to Doulton*, London 1922, 130, as collection of E. Marsh, and was also illustrated by Marsh himself in his 1944 articles (1, 96). Marsh owned several more face jugs, many of which were included in the 1946 sale of his collection. For similar jugs, see Beard 1936, pl. 63; Haslam 1978, 94, figs 134-5 dated 1890 and 1899; 131, figs 200-201 and 146 dated 1899 and 1910; 146, fig. 229, dated 1897.

171 Toby jug [PLATE 52]

Salt-glazed stoneware, with coloured slips in green, pale blue and browns, beneath the glaze.

MARKS 'R.W.Martin & Bros. London & Southall. 17.9.1903.'

H 25.3cm 1978,7-4,20 Hull Grundy Gift

Aileen Dawson has noted that this jug may be one of the two Toby jugs exhibited at Fulham Public Library in 1929 (London 1929, 34, Case K. nos 12 and 18); the jugs belonged to Jonathan Hutchinson and Ernest Marsh. That owned by Hutchinson (no. 12) was described as 'a very good coloured and finished one'. The catalogue text, written by Marsh, states that Wallace made three Toby jugs. A third example, also dated 1903, was owned by Richard Dennis in 1979, but so far only one other example has been recorded, see Sotheby's, 26 March 1991, lot 29, dated '11-1903'. During the nineteenth century lead-glazed earthenware Toby jugs were made in large numbers in Stafford-shire, while stoneware examples were made in the Brampton and Chesterfield area in the mid nineteenth century. They were also made around 1870 at Bailey's Fulham Pottery, where R.W. Martin's early stonewares were fired (Dawson 1980, 36).

Incised decoration 1 (172-6)

This group comprises classical, Renaissance and Far Eastern styles, the decoration executed in blues and browns (Cat. 172 and 176) or in buff on a brown ground. The decoration is incised into the buff fabric, the outline coloured dark brown or black and the background filled in with brown. There are traces of colour suggested in thinly applied slips beneath the glaze.

172 Large vase [PLATE 53]

Salt-glazed stoneware, painted in brown, grey and blue, with two angular handles, decorated with a central band of incised nereids and tritons in the classical style, the outlines and background painted in blue. Above is a frieze of palmettes, painted blue, the background incised with a geometric pattern in grey. The dividing bands are in brown, the neck and foot blue, the handles grey and brown. The glaze has misfired on one side and round the foot, which has some firing cracks with infill and overpainting.

MARKS Round the rim of the foot, 'RW Martin – London & Southall 10.79'.

H 40cm 1978,7-4,1 Hull Grundy Gift

This is a good illustration of the Martin Brothers' early classical style with characteristic geometric borders and is an exceptionally large piece. Ernest Marsh much preferred their later styles, explaining these early Greek-style pieces as the result of 'an unfortunate visit by some of our Museum people to their Brownlow Street shop, who urged them to follow the Greek forms and traditions'.

173 Pair of vases [PLATE 53]

Salt-glazed stoneware, the incised decoration predominantly in buff on brown, with solid flat handles of the same shape as Cat. 172. On one side dancing maidens in the classical style, one bearing a garland of flowers, the other playing a triangle; on the other side a Renaissance-style design of foliate scrolls and grotesques. The decoration is painted with touches of coloured slips beneath the glaze: the floral garland in white and brown, the drapery in green. Both the figures and the foliate designs are contained within a cartouche, the background areas with incised foliate decoration in blue on a deep brown ground.

MARKS On both, '2.5.84 RW Martin Bros London & Southall'.

173a (figure with garland) H 24.2cm 1978,7-4,2
173b (figure with triangle) H 24.3cm 1978,7-4,3 Hull Grundy Gift

For a group of vases and jugs with similar Renaissance-style ornament dating from 1879 to 1906, see Haslam 1978, 58, fig. VII and 103, fig. 152, a vase of 1896. A number of Renaissance-style designs appear to have been sketched by the artist H.W. Fawcett, who had previously worked with William De Morgan and who stayed with the Martin Brothers from 1879 for a year or two at the most. For pages from the Fawcett sketch-book, see Haslam 1978, 67, figs 78 and 80. See also the *Magazine of Art*, 1882, 445-6.

174 Bulbous vase [PLATE 53]

Salt-glazed stoneware, incised decoration in buff on brown of foliate scrolls inhabited by animals: a frog, mouse, beetle and several lizards. The animals painted with green and white coloured slips beneath the glaze. The neck incised with parallel lines.

MARKS '9-1890 RW Martin & Bros. London & Southall'.

H 17cm 1945,2-4,9 Marsh Bequest

For a similar vase with frogs dated 1893 from the Nettlefold collection, see Beard 1936, pl. 41, formerly in the collection of F.H. Crittall.

175 Tall vase [PLATE 53]

Salt-glazed stoneware, buff and brown, incised with dragons and painted with pale green and white slips beneath the glaze.

MARKS '11-1896. Martin Bros London & Southall'.

H 35.5cm 1978,7-4,11 Hull Grundy Gift

The dragons are vigorously drawn. For comparable pieces with dragon decoration dating from 1893 to 1908, see Haslam 1978, 126, fig. XXIII. The Martin brothers owned a number of books of Japanese designs which they used as inspiration for their work. Similar dragon motifs were favoured by Mrs Nichols at the Rookwood Pottery (see Cat. 260). See also Cat. 183.

176 Vase [PLATE 53]

Salt-glazed stoneware, blue and grey, of slender shape, with decoration of chrysanthemums and a butterfly, incised and painted in blue, with additional greenish-brown slips beneath the glaze for the butterfly, the buds and the bands at top and bottom. The rim repaired.

MARKS '20 & 21.9.81 RW Martin London & Southall'.

H 24.1 cm   1945,2-4,3   Marsh Bequest

Incised decoration 2 (177-83)

This group comprises floral and Japanese-style decoration, mostly in dark colours on a buff or pale grey ground.

177 Pair of vases [PLATE 53]

Salt-glazed stoneware, baluster form, with incised decoration of passion flowers, painted in cream, pale green and greenish-blue slips thickly applied beneath the glaze on a buff ground. The pattern on each vase is not identical.

MARKS
177a '12.9.83. RW Martin & Bros. London & Southall'.
H 31.3 cm   1945,2-4,6
177b '10.9.83. RW Martin & Bros. London & Southall'.
H 31.2 cm   1945,2-4,18   Marsh Bequest

The decoration on these vases is close to designs by Edward Willy. Like the Wally-birds, the floral wares were in constant demand. For a vase with closely similar flowers, painted in blue, see Haslam 1978, 55, fig VI, dated 1889.

178 Jug [PLATE 53]

Salt-glazed stoneware, baluster form, with decoration of flowers and butterflies incised and painted in rust and browns on a buff ground. An incised geometric pattern round the rim. At the base of the handle, a foliate Renaissance-style motif.

MARKS '2.1886 RW Martin & Bros London & Southall'.

H 22.2 cm   1978,7-4,5   Hull Grundy Gift

The geometric band round the rim is characteristic of the floral wares of the 1880s; see, for example, Haslam 1978, 56, figs 62-3.

179 Vase [PLATE 53]

Salt-glazed stoneware, with incised decoration of irises, grasses and dragonflies. Painted with coloured slips beneath the glaze, the irises blue, the leaves and insects green, with touches of brown and pink. On the shoulders, a speckled brown area.

MARKS '6.1892 Martin Bros London & Southall'.

H 24.6 cm   1945,2-4,10   Marsh Bequest

The design on this vase is strikingly close to the decoration on the silver-gilt jug by the firm of Ovchinnikov in Moscow (Cat. 230), which itself is based on a Tiffany jug of the same design, suggesting that both are derived from a common source.

180 Jug [PLATE 53]

Salt-glazed stoneware, of square form, with decoration of herons amid bulrushes and grasses, with hovering dragonflies, incised and painted in shades of green and brown on a buff ground. The rim restored.

MARKS '10-1895 Martin Bros London & Southall'.

H 17.7 cm   1978,7-4,10   Hull Grundy Gift

181 Jardinière [PLATE 53]

Salt-glazed stoneware, light brown ground, incised with geese flying through bulrushes and grasses. The geese painted in deep brown, white and bluish-green slips.

MARKS '1.1900. Martin Bros London & Southall'.

H 21.7 cm   1945,2-4,13   Marsh Bequest

The design on this piece is very close to designs in the Fawcett sketchbook; see Haslam 1978, 69, fig. 81. A pair of closely similar bowls dated 1899 were owned by F.J. Nettlefold (Beard 1936, pls 59-60). Nettlefold acquired them from the sale of the collection of F. Hutchinson, Sotheby's, London 25 November 1921, lot 159. Mrs Hull Grundy's annotated copy of the Nettlefold catalogue records that she purchased them at the Nettlefold sale in 1946-7 for £30.

182 Jar and cover [PLATE 53]

Salt-glazed stoneware, with decoration of humming-birds and orchids incised and painted in yellows, greens and browns with touches of blue, white and pink, on a pale whitish-grey ground.

MARKS On the base and inside the lid, '10-1896 Martin Bros London & Southall'.

H 20.6 cm   1945,2-4,15   Marsh Bequest

This is a finely potted and decorated piece. It was illustrated by Ernest Marsh in his 1944 articles and described as a 'white covered vase thrown by Walter and decorated by Edwin' (Marsh 1944, II, 128). For jars of this shape with marine decoration, see Haslam 1978, 124-5, figs 192-3, both also of 1896.

183 Jug [PLATE 53]

Salt-glazed stoneware, incised with dragons outlined in deep brown on a buff ground with turquoise-green and white slips.

MARKS '11-1892 Martin Bros London & Southall'.

H 21.2 cm   1978,7-4,9   Hull Grundy Gift

See Cat. 175 for vase decorated with similar dragons in buff on a brown ground.

Unglazed incised ware

184 Vase [PLATE 54]

Stoneware, white body, covered with a deep blue slip and then deeply incised through the slip with decoration of orchids, grasses and humming birds. Further details then incised on the white areas. The inside of the neck blue.

MARKS '1-1898 Martin Brothers London & Southall'.

H 32.7 cm   1979,4-8,1   Hull Grundy Gift

This vase, with its true sgraffito decoration seems to be unparalleled in Martinware production. Its inspiration lies in Chinese reserve-decorated blue and white wares of the fifteenth century, though these do not have the incised detail.

Relief decoration: marine life, gourds and natural forms (185-95)

This group is mostly decorated in low relief built up with slips and then incised. Designs with fish and sea creatures predominate in the firm's work of the late 1890s and early 1900s. The two matt-finish high-relief pieces (Cat. 191-2) are unusual.

185 Ovoid jug   [PLATE 54; COLOUR PLATE VII]

Salt-glazed stoneware, with incised relief decoration of exotic fish and weeds in blues, greens and browns. On each of the flattened sides, an exotic fish, round the rest of the body a ray, eels, jellyfish and catfish. The relief built up with applied slips and then painted with coloured slips.

MARKS '10-1889. Martin Brothers. London & Southall'.

H 22.8cm   1978,7-4,7   Hull Grundy Gift

For a jug with comparable decoration, see Haslam 1978, 102, fig. 151.

186 Vase   [PLATE 54; COLOUR PLATE VII]

Salt-glazed stoneware, with square mouth and four vertical ribs pushed out from the inside; low-relief incised decoration of fish and jellyfish painted in pale green and greenish-blues on a greyish ground.

MARKS '12-1901. Martin Bros London & Southall'.

H 16.9cm   1978,7-4,13   Hull Grundy Gift

This is a transitional piece combining figurative ornament with a bulging ribbed form that was later developed into the bold, abstract, textured shapes illustrated by Cat. 194-5. A vase that appears to be closely similar to this one was owned by Ernest Marsh and illustrated in his 1944 articles (II, 127), described as a 'square vase in 4 panels: raised fish decoration greenish grey on a grey ground: mutton fat quality glaze'. The description of the glaze is precisely applicable to the British Museum vase. Marsh ascribed it to Edwin. In speaking of a 'mutton fat quality glaze' Marsh is referring to mutton fat jade, the most prized type of jade in China, imitated by Chinese potters with thick glazes.

187 Jug   [PLATE 54; COLOUR PLATE VII]

Salt-glazed stoneware, of ovoid form with slanting body, low relief and incised decoration of fish and water plants in turquoise-greens and browns on a buff ground.

MARKS 'Martin Bros London & Southall 2-1890'.

H 15.9cm   1978,7-4,8   Hull Grundy Gift

188 Small vase   [PLATE 54; COLOUR PLATE VII]

Stoneware, of amphora shape with two handles, low relief and incised decoration of crabs on each side in bluish-greens and brown, the background painted pale blue.

MARKS '2-1900. Martin Bros London'.

H 9.5cm   1978,7-4,12   Hull Grundy Gift

189 Small bowl   [PLATE 54; COLOUR PLATE VII]

Salt-glazed stoneware, with low-relief decoration of fish among water plants incised and painted in browns and greens on a patchy brown and buff ground.

MARKS '10-1890. Martin Bros. London & Southall'.

H 6.9cm   1945,2-4,8   Marsh Bequest

190 Hexagonal bowl   [PLATE 54; COLOUR PLATE VII]

Salt-glazed stoneware, with low-relief decoration of fish incised and painted in brown on a blue ground with horizontal incised lines to suggest the water, the rim painted brown. One of the panels has misfired.

MARKS '7-1903. Martin Bros. London & Southall'.

H 8.5cm   1945,2-4,16   Marsh Bequest

For vases with similarly painted fish on a ground with incised lines, see the *Art Journal*, 1905, 309.

191 Large bulbous vase   [PLATE 54; COLOUR PLATE VII]

Stoneware, with high-relief decoration of jellyfish applied in dark green, white and pink coloured slips and then covered with a pale greenish-white opaque glaze. The glaze is thicker on one side and has begun to melt but still retains a matt surface. On the other side it is very thin with a sandy surface. Beneath the glaze the pot has been brushed with a green oxide. The interior of the rim has a glossy honey-coloured glaze.

MARKS '8-1904. Martin Bros. London & Southall'.

H 29.8cm   1978,7-4,14   Hull Grundy Gift

This unusual vase, with its remarkably effective and subtle use of colour and relief, was purchased by Anne Hull Grundy from the Nettlefold sale in 1947; her copy of the Nettlefold catalogue (Beard 1936, 239, pl. 68) is annotated 'Given by me Anne Ullmann to my fiancé John Hull Grundy'. F. J. Nettlefold bought it for £14 at the sale of porcelain and pottery belonging to F. Hutchinson FRCS at Sotheby's, London, on 25 November 1921, lot 161; the sale catalogue described it as 'An important vase, globular without handles, with pattern of squids in slight relief in green on an unglazed ground, brown glazed rim, $11\frac{3}{4}$ in [29.8 cm], signed Martin Bros. 8-1904.' For a much smaller vase of similar bulbous shape dated 1894 with relief decoration, see Haslam 1978, 116, fig. 180.

192 Vase   [PLATE 54; COLOUR PLATE VII]

Stoneware, tapering shape with two loop handles, covered with a pink slip, the surface rough and bubbly, decorated with sea snails in high relief in greens and browns. The opening is glazed dark brown.

MARKS '6-1907. Martin Bros. London & Southall'.

H 21.9cm   1945,2-4,20   Marsh Bequest

193 Gourd vase   [PLATE 54; COLOUR PLATE VII]

Stoneware, ribbed, with incised decoration between the ribs, painted in patchy pale green over pinkish-brown.

MARKS '12-1903. Martin Bros London & Southall'.

H 18.1cm   1980,12-7,3   Hull Grundy Gift

For a similar vase, see *The Studio* 42, 1907-8, 114. See also Haslam 1978, 118, fig. XVIII.

194 Vase   [PLATE 54; COLOUR PLATE VII]

Stoneware, square mouth, with four bulging sides separated by four ribs. The surface of the lobes is incised all over to suggest the veins or markings of stone or bark. At each corner is an applied rib. Painted in coloured slips in green, cream and brown on a buff ground. The method of construction is obscured by the slips inside, but this is probably a slab pot, with holes cut in the sides into which the lobes have been inserted.

MARKS '1-1901. Martin Bros. London & Southall'.

H 11cm   1980,12-7,1   Hull Grundy Gift

This and Cat. 195 illustrate Edwin's introduction of abstract decoration and the creation of a boldly sculptural interpretation of Continental Art Nouveau forms and of the gourd-like vegetal forms favoured by the French art potters of the late nineteenth century. Forms based on vegetal shapes were apparently first produced by Edwin Martin in 1898 without knowledge of the French developments, to which he was introduced by the architect and future patron of the firm, Sydney Greenslade, whom he met in that year and who later made sketches of ribbed shapes for Edwin to execute (Haslam 1978, 121, fig. 190). Greenslade also took Edwin, Walter and Charles to the Paris Exhibition of 1900. In the words of The Studio's critic (42, 1907-8, 109), these wares relied on 'the manipulation of clays of varied texture and of coloured glazes'. For similar textured vases, see The Studio 42, 1907-8, 109, 111. Ernest Marsh noted that Edwin was 'expert in the inlaying of dots and honeycomb patternings, and was fond of . . . giving to the surface of some of his pieces a crackle-like finish of his own devising' (Marsh 1944, II, 129). Edwin's pots were collected by prominent members of the Arts & Crafts movement such as Edward Spencer and Nelson Dawson, but not by earlier collectors such as F. Nettlefold.

195 Vase   [PLATE 54; COLOUR PLATE VII]

Stoneware, of bulbous shape with five wing-like ribs, hollowed out to form openings at the top. In the centre of the top a rosette with central hole. The ribs painted deep greyish-black with a blue line down the outside, the body painted with blue spots circled in deep grey on a rust ground.

MARKS '12-1901. Martin Bro⁵ London & Southall'.

H 14.7 cm   1980,12-7,2   Hull Grundy Gift

Walter Martin experimented with metallic effects from the late 1890s. For a vase with similar spotted decoration on a deep-grey ground, see Haslam 1978, 118, fig. XVIII. It is possible that the reference to the successful production of 'a very fine dullish black, which has all the excellent qualities of the best Chinese prototypes' (The Studio 42, 1907-8, 111) is a description of the deep grey glaze on this vase. The collection of F. H. Crittall sold after his death included a 'vase, four-sided, with wide neck, 10 in [25 cm], glazed to represent black metal, dated 11-1905' (Sotheby's, London, 20 January 1922, lot 98).

Minton & Co.   founded 1793

See also **Pugin**

Jewitt, L., *The Ceramic Art Of Great Britain*, 2nd edn, London 1883, 393-414 (reprinted Poole 1985)
Aslin, E. & Atterbury, P., *Minton 1798-1910*, exhibition catalogue, Victoria and Albert Museum, London 1976 (with further bibliography)
Cecil, V., *Minton 'Majolica'*, exhibition catalogue, Jeremy Cooper Ltd, London 1982
Atterbury, P. and Batkin, M., *The Dictionary of Minton*, Woodbridge 1990

196 Garden seat   [PLATE 20]

Lead-glazed earthenware (majolica), cast and pierced with three 'windows' round the body and other smaller holes, with relief decoration in the 'Alhambra' style of interlaced strapwork, foliage and stylised flowers in bright colours, on a white ground. The strapwork in maroon and blue outlined in yellow, the foliage in shaded green, the flowers pink. One of the three feet is damaged.

MARKS Impressed on the base 'MINTON' only, mark in use c. 1862 to 1873, when the letter 's' was added to the end of the word (Godden 1964, no. 2706).

Designed before 1862, possibly by Christopher Dresser, and made by Minton & Co., Stoke-on-Trent, Staffordshire, before 1873.

H 45 cm, D of top 29.2 cm   1981,1-1,477   Woodward Bequest

The term 'majolica' was derived from the tin-glazed 'maiolica' made in Renaissance Italy, but was widely used to describe all brightly coloured earthenwares of the nineteenth century, often with elaborately modelled shapes that had nothing to do with the finely painted pictorial 'maiolica' of the sixteenth century. The only similarity was the use of a coating of opaque white glaze beneath the coloured glazes; in Renaissance Italy the white glaze was made with tin, whereas in the nineteenth century it was made with lead. Minton were the first firm to produce majolica glazes, developed by Léon Arnoux, Art Director from 1849 to 1892; the new wares were shown at the Great Exhibition of 1851 and were soon copied by other manufacturers, for example, Wedgwood (see Cat. 311).

This stool, although not stamped with a model number, can be identified as model no. 940 from an archive photograph owned by the factory (Minton Archives MSS 1618; reference kindly supplied by Joan Jones). This reference gives no date, but garden seat no. 940 was exhibited at the 1862 International Exhibition in London: there were two versions, with white ground or turquoise ground (*Catalogue of the Principle Works exhibited at the International Exhibition, by Minton & Co.*, Stoke-on-Trent, 1862, nos D84-5). Neither reference gives a designer, but Widar Halén has identified several designs by Christopher Dresser among the Minton exhibits at the 1862 exhibition (see Halén 1990, 119). Furthermore, the border pattern and interlace motifs on this seat are characteristic of Dresser's work of the 1860s (see Halén 1990, 120, pl. 123 for a page from Dresser's sketchbook, dated 1862 and showing borders for Minton & Co.). In his pamphlet on 'The Development of Ornamental Art in the International Exhibition of 1862' Dresser described the Minton stand, noting 'some fine vases and garden stools on the east side'. Thus it is possible that he is here admiring his own work. (I am grateful to Joan Jones for drawing my attention to Dresser's account.) For reference to a barrel-shaped oriental-style jardinière of 1878 with Dresser's facsimile signature below the rim, see Karmason and Stacke 1989, 56.

The Alhambra, the palace and fortress of the Moorish kings of Granada, Spain, was built during the thirteenth and fourteenth centuries. Its restoration, begun in 1828, excited great interest and inspired 'Alhambra' or Moorish-style decoration in the applied arts; the repertoire of motifs came initially from Owen Jones's *Plans, Elevations, Sections and Details of the Alhambra*, a lavishly illustrated volume published between 1836 and 1845. In 1854 Jones designed the 'Alhambra' court at the Crystal Palace in Sydenham, while his *Grammar of Ornament* of 1856 provided a pattern-book of historic and eastern ornament. In this seat the pierced 'windows', interlaced strapwork and foliate motifs are inspired by the architectural ornament of the Alhambra (see Jones, *Alhambra*, col. pl. XXXI and pl. 10), but the colours are typically Victorian.

For further Minton majolica in the 'Alhambra' style, see London 1976b, no. F.4; Jewitt, 1883, fig. 1130. The British Museum garden stool was still in production in the 1880s (see Atterbury and Batkin 1990, 330, for a page from the 1880s Majolica Catalogue). For a Minton majolica garden seat with Chinese-style decoration, see London 1972, no. C23 (now in the Cecil Higgins Art Gallery, Bedford). For Minton's Italian-style majolica, see Atterbury 1976.

197 Garden seat [PLATE 75]

Earthenware, cast, barrel-shaped with block-printed decoration: a central band of stylised yellow poppies with green leaves, on a patterned ground with floral motif in grey and white, bordered above and below with a row of raised bosses and a band of stylised wave scroll ornament in brown on a cream ground. The top with foliate ornament in brown on cream, with a pierced hole that serves as a handle in the centre.

MARKS Impressed on the base 'MINTONS ENGLAND' with date symbol for 1898: a swan enclosing the number '4', shape number '2638', the letter 'E' and '5'.

Made by Minton & Co., Stoke-on-Trent, Staffordshire, in 1898.

H 47.5 cm, D of top 31 cm   1981,1-1,476   Woodward Bequest

The barrel shape is derived from Chinese eighteenth-century blue and white porcelain garden seats, but the curvilinear decoration is more Japanese in inspiration and shows the influence of Continental Art Nouveau, which was never widely fashionable in England. Minton, however, had strong links with France through their French designers and painters, Léon Arnoux, Antonin Boullemier and M. L. E. Solon (see Cat. 273). Joan Jones has suggested that the decoration on this seat may have been designed by Léon Victor Solon (1872-1957, son of M. L. E. Solon), who specialised in slip-trailed Art Nouveau ornament and was joint designer of Minton's Secessionist ware.

Manchester City Art Gallery and Museum owns a jardinière with a similar, though not identical, pattern (1981.2) dated November 1907.

198 Tazza [PLATE 116]

Bone china, shallow bowl with two side handles on a stemmed foot. The interior with central roundel of a crowing cock at sunrise, the cock painted in bright matt colours of red, green, blue, magenta and yellow ochre, the flowers in red, orange, mauve and green on deep blue ground, all with gold outlining, the sun rays in yellow and pink. The rest glazed in mottled green shading to grey at the edge and lustred, with printed gold scroll-pattern border, the rim and handles also gilded. The exterior of the bowl glazed in a bright green shading to blue at the edge, the stem in mottled blue on a green ground, lustred, with gilded rims and scroll-pattern borders. Some restoration to foot and one of the handles.

MARKS The base with printed red standard Minton wreathed globe mark in use from c. 1912 (Godden 1964, no. 2716), with incised shape number '3682'.

Designed in 1925 and made by Minton & Co., Stoke-on-Trent, Staffordshire.

H 14.8 cm, max. W 28.8 cm   1981,1-1,478   Woodward Bequest

During the 1920s and 1930s Minton continued to produce richly decorated lustre wares of which this is a typical example. This tazza is described in the Minton Estimate Book for 21 October 1925 (Minton Archive MSS 1545) as 'Tazza, stippled ground, lustred and gold printed borders with Chanticleer centre' with decoration number OA 1508. This shape was also produced with 'Ship' or 'Babes in the Wood' centre (the above information kindly supplied by Joan Jones). For a bone china dish with the same central motif and mottled ground, see Atterbury and Batkin 1990, 122, where it is described as part of the 'Rotique' range.

Moore, Bernard 1850-1935

Dawson, A., *Bernard Moore, Master Potter 1850-1935*, London 1982 (including further bibliography and a list of Moore's own writings).

Bernard Moore, Master Potter 1850-1935, exhibition catalogue, Victoria and Albert Museum, London, compiled by A. Dawson and J. Opie. This exhibition included most of the pieces catalogued below as nos 12 (Cat. 200), 13 (Cat. 199), 14 (Cat. 201), 32 (Cat. 203), 33 (Cat. 202), 162 (Cat. 205) and 186 (Cat. 204).

The first six of the following pieces were given by the artist in July 1902. They were undoubtedly chosen to demonstrate Moore's mastery of complex glaze effects and are therefore catalogued together. They are all of high-fired earthenware (industrial earthenware).

After their father's death in 1867 Bernard Moore and his brother took over the running of the family china works at Longton, Staffordshire, which became known as Moore Brothers, manufacturing on a large scale a wide range of table and ornamental wares, often of Eastern inspiration. They exhibited successfully at Sydney in 1879, Melbourne in 1882 and at Chicago in 1893. Unfortunately little is known of Moore's career at the end of the nineteenth century and his reasons for closing the factory in 1905 and setting up a studio at Wolfe Street, Stoke-on-Trent, are unclear.

Moore had begun to experiment with coloured glazes in the 1890s, if not earlier, and Cat. 199-204, made at Longton before 1902, are the earliest securely datable examples of Moore's *rouge flambé* and other lustrous glazes. They are described in the British Museum's acquisitions register as 'the first results of attempts to produce Chinese flambé on porcelain'. If these are indeed his first results, they are highly accomplished pieces and may have been completed as early as 3 December 1901, as the Visitors' Book records that he visited the British Museum on that day. Further evidence to support this suggestion is that five of the pieces, the four vases and the bowl (Cat. 199-203), are illustrated in William Burton's *A History and Description of English Porcelain*, published in 1902 (pl. XXIV, opp. p. 186). Burton gave Moore due acknowledgement alongside French and German potters, ending his book with the following tribute: 'Mr. Bernard Moore of Longton has been equally successful, and, in addition to producing rich red and *sang-de-boeuf* glazes, has also produced novel and wonderful effects by the use of metals other than copper, treated in the same way. How rich and varied these effects can be is shown in the pieces illustrated.... The way in which the colour deepens and lightens over the piece, passing from the faintest grey to the richest brown or vivid ruby red, by imperceptible gradation, recalls the colouring of some piece of precious sardonyx or jasper, and is the final reward of days and nights of labour spent at the potter's kiln.' A vase with a fine red glaze, now in the Victoria and Albert Museum, was given by Moore to Burton, and is inscribed on its base: 'W.B. from B.M. Amicus

Amico' (see Munich 1972, no. 1448, V & A, Circ. 305-1953).

Rich, red glazes, produced by firing a copper glaze in a reducing atmosphere (i.e. without oxygen) were developed in China in the fourteenth century, the celebrated *flambé* or streaked glazes being especially popular in the eighteenth century (for an account of Chinese copper-red glazes, see Vainker 1991, ch. 7). Chinese red glazes began to be produced in Europe from the 1880s, both by artist potters and on a large scale by factories such as Sèvres and the Berlin porcelain factory. Collections and exhibitions of Chinese ceramics in England that Moore might have seen are fully discussed in Dawson 1982, 25-7.

Moore did not make his own pots in his Wolfe Street studio; many of the blanks which he glazed were from the Moore Brothers' range or made by other firms such as Minton, Wedgwood, and Copeland, sometimes to Moore's design and sometimes from current production. Thus pieces exist in different bodies: porcellanous stoneware, porcelain, bone china and earthenware. The early pieces, dating from before 1905, also presumably used blanks from Moore Brothers or elsewhere.

For the descriptions of the glazes, I am indebted to Nigel Wood.

199 Vase [PLATE 27; COLOUR PLATE V]

Wide base and straight neck: copper-red *flambé* glaze of varying shades of red with dark, grey-black patches. The interior glazed with the same colours.

MARKS Painted mark 'B.M.' on the base in blue, with remains of original Bernard Moore paper label.

H 26.6cm   1902,7-21,1   Given by the artist

The dark patches represent a concentration of copper in the glaze which has turned to copper oxide. The bright red patches were probably obtained with iron, while other variations in colour, for example the yellowish colour on the underside, suggest the application of other glazes to certain areas.

200 Vase [PLATE 27; COLOUR PLATE V]

Globular base and tapered neck: copper-red *flambé* glaze, crimson-red in tones varying from very bright to deep with black patches. A series of ducks is depicted round the body, silhouetted in a pale cream colour.

MARKS Remains of a Bernard Moore paper label on the base.

H 19.9cm   1902,7-21,2   Given by the artist

The method by which the decoration is achieved is uncertain; it is possible that the copper was painted on and then rubbed off and filled in, perhaps using the same glaze formula but without the copper. When fired, the two glazes melted smoothly, leaving the desired outline. Alternatively, another glaze may have been applied over the red, causing a bleaching effect.

201 Double-gourd vase [PLATE 27; COLOUR PLATE V]

Red *flambé* glaze with wave patterns in yellow varying to salmon pink or 'peach-blow' and deep bluish-purple patches.

MARKS Remains of a Bernard Moore label on the base.

H 19.9cm   1902,7-21,3   Given by the artist

The red glaze has been applied first with a yellow glaze on top; the brush strokes are clearly visible in the thinly applied areas. The variations in colour appear to be due to the thickness of the glaze and to the reduction visible on one side, so that the brightest yellow occurs where the glaze is thick and the 'peach-blow' and opal colours occur where the glaze is thinner and reduced; the red here is much deeper.

202 Bowl [PLATE 28]

Crinkled rim, pushed inwards to leave five peaks: deep red and grey patchy lustre glaze, heavily smoked. The interior also glazed.

MARKS Remains of a Bernard Moore label on the base.

H 5cm   1902,7-21,4   Given by the artist

The dark areas may have been produced by concentrations of lead in the smoke which has reduced down to the metal.

203 Ovoid vase [PLATE 28; COLOUR PLATE V]

Liverish-red and grey lustre glaze, reduced, the grey turning to pale yellow at the rim and on the base, where the glaze is thinner.

MARKS None.

H 12.7cm   1902,7-21,5   Given by the artist

204 Kylin, or seated figure of a Dog of Fo [PLATE 27; COLOUR PLATE V]

Right paw resting on a pierced ball, grey lustre glaze with patches of red on the lower parts.

MARKS Remains of a Bernard Moore label on the base.

H 7.7cm   1902,7-21,6   Given by the artist

The grey glaze (possibly rutile) has been applied first and appears to have been sprayed with red from underneath to produce red highlights on the under surfaces. The piece has then been smoked with lead to give a lustre effect, especially on the head.

The Dog of Fo or Kylin is closely related to late-nineteenth-century Japanese pieces made for the Western market and it may be that the models were imported from Japan and decorated by Moore. For a close Japanese parallel, see Dawson 1982, fig. 24. Moore made several versions of the Dog of Fo, but this is the earliest securely datable example.

205 Vase [PLATE 28; COLOUR PLATE V]

High-fired earthenware (industrial earthenware), *flambé*, decorated with a ship on a stormy sea with rolling waves. The ship and its oars are in red outlined in gold, the sea a deep turquoise blue and the spray highlighted with turquoise-blue enamel spots and gilding. The background is bright red with yellow patches applied over the red. The rim and foot are gilded and there are gilded circles over the red glaze inside and outside the rim. The interior is glazed white with splashes of red.

MARKS Printed black mark 'BERNARD MOORE' and printed stamp 'ENGLAND'.

Made in the studio of Bernard Moore in Wolfe Street, Stoke-on-Trent, Staffordshire, probably c. 1904-5.

H 19.7cm   1977,5-3,1   Given by Dr E. J. Dingwall

The red glaze covers the base, suggesting that it was applied first, with a resist for the boat. The deep blue glaze is a cobalt glaze, while the enamel spots are a mixture of cobalt and copper, and pure copper (turquoise). The use of enamels and gilding required several firings: first the glazes, at least two firings, then the enamels, then the gilding.

For a group of similar pieces with ships on stormy seas, see Dawson, col. pl. XII, and p. 24, where it is suggested that the ship motif was probably derived from the work of William De Morgan and was used by Moore from c. 1904-5 and later.

206 Bowl [PLATE 27; COLOUR PLATE V]

Porcelain, deep red *rouge flambé* copper glaze on interior and exterior, the base unglazed. At the rim, the glaze has pulled away, leaving a white edge.

MARKS Painted on the base in brown 'BM'.

Decorated in the studio of Bernard Moore in Stoke-on-Trent, Staffordshire, probably in the late 1920s or early 1930s.

H 4.1 cm   1990,1-9,1   Given by Geoffrey Hetherington, son of Arthur Lonsdale Hetherington, to whom it was given by the artist

This is a very fine piece; according to the donor it was regarded by Moore as a particularly successful imitation of Chinese *sang-de-boeuf*.

A. L. Hetherington (1881-1960) was a collector and scholar of Chinese ceramics and one of the founders of the Oriental Ceramic Society. His particular interest was in glazes and it is likely that Moore gave him the bowl when he was preparing his book on *Chinese Ceramic Glazes*, published in 1937. Hetherington probably met Moore through the Oriental Ceramic Society and had great admiration for him. He concluded his book on glazes with an account of a joint research project conducted by Moore and the scientist J. W. Mellor. Mellor writes: 'Mr Moore worked in his own way. I was very interested as a spectator. I was amazed at the unerring instinct displayed by my friend. Like a bloodhound on a fresh trail, he rapidly went ahead, and in my opinion he arrived at a successful solution of the problem in a very short time. . . . He was well on the way to the winning post before I was ready to start.' Hetherington's final comment places Moore in a league with Chinese potters. He argued that 'if a man versed in all the science of to-day could be coupled with a Chinese potter of a few centuries ago', it was probable that 'the man of science would add to his knowledge more than the Chinese potter would add to his understanding of the business'.

Hetherington's other publications include *The Art of the Chinese Potter*, 1923, which he wrote jointly with R. L. Hobson, then Keeper of the Department of Ceramics and Ethnography at the British Museum.

Moser, Koloman 1868-1918

Koloman Moser, exhibition catalogue, Hochschule für angewandte Kunst, Vienna 1979
Fenz, W., *Kolo Moser*, Salzburg and Vienna 1984
Baroni, D. and D'Aurio, A., *Koloman Moser*, New York 1986

207 Decanter, compote bowl and six glasses [PLATE 103]

Clear mould-blown glass with dimples. The glasses consist of a schnapps glass, a sherry glass, three sizes of wine glass and a champagne or sparkling wine glass. Slight chips to rims of bowl and champagne glass; both rims have been ground.

MARKS None.

Designed in 1899-1900 to the commission of E. Bakalowits & Söhne, glassware retailers, Vienna.

207a Decanter: H 21.2 cm   1982,10-6,1
207b Bowl: D 10.6 cm   1982,10-6,2
207c Schnapps glass: H 8.8 cm   1982,10-6,3
207d Sherry glass: H 10.6 cm   1982,10-6,4
207e-g Wine glasses: H 12.5, 13.5, 15.3 cm   1982,10-6,5-7
207h Champagne glass: H 11.2 cm   1982,10-6,8

After studying at the Kunstgewerbeschule in Vienna, Moser taught there, with Hoffmann, from 1899 until his death in 1918. He was a founder member of both the Vienna Secession in 1897 and the Wiener Werkstätte in 1903, and designed widely for the decorative arts.

This service won first prize for a '*Glasservice für einen einfachen Haushalt, 12 Personen*' (glass service for a simple household, 12 persons) at a competition for the design of applied arts held in Vienna, the prizes awarded out of state funds ('*Preisausschreibung für Entwürfe Kunstgewerbliche Objekte aus dem Hoftiteltaxfunde*'). The design is credited to Moser, and the service was submitted by Bakalowits (*Kunst & Kunsthandwerk*, 1900, 52 and 54). It was also exhibited at the fifth Secessionsaustellung in Vienna, 1899-1900, and at the Weinachtsaustellung of the K. K. Österreichisches Museum für Kunst und Industrie (later the Österreichisches Museum für angewandte Kunst) in 1900 (*Die Kunst* 2, 1899-1900, 238). It was sold at La Maison Moderne in Paris (*Art et Décoration* 10, 1901, 133) and shown at the Salon de la Libre Esthétique in Brussels (*L'Art Décoratif* 11, May 1901, 80ff.). See also Pazaurek n.d. (1901), 59, fig. 47.

In the autumn of 1906 the service was included in an exhibition held by the Wiener Werkstätte entitled 'Der gedeckte Tisch'; for a contemporary illustration showing the glasses, see *DK & D* XIX, 1906, 475. See also Pazaurek 1925, 24.

For similar services, see Rutherford & Beddoe, 1986, no. 3 (in the Art Gallery and Museum, Brighton) and Bascou et al. 1988, 175-6 (in the Musée D'Orsay, Paris, acquired from the Moser family, Vienna). This service was also produced without dimples and offered, in addition, water, lemonade and beer glasses, a jug and a fruit bowl. For a version of the service without dimples in the possession of E. Bakalowits & Söhne, Vienna, see Vienna 1985, no. 13/4/7. The service appears without dimples in the *Musterbuch E. Bakalowits*, held by the Österreichisches Museum für angewandt Kunst (see Neuwirth 1973, 413, where a page from the pattern-book showing this service is reproduced).

Glasses commissioned by Bakalowits were made by Bohemian firms such as Lötz Witwe or Meyr's Neffe, or by the Rheinische Glashütten, but the manufacturers of this service are not known.

Moser, Koloman (pupils of, at the Kunstgewerbeschule, Vienna)

208 Plate [PLATE 103]

Hard-paste porcelain, with stencilled blue border pattern of shield shapes on a white glazed ground. The plate is flat with no central depression and no rim. The edge has a slight upward curve.

MARKS Printed in overglaze black on the reverse 'Schule Prof. Kolo Moser' in a rectangle; impressed 'C3' above the number '69'.

Shape and decoration designed c.1901-2 by pupils of Koloman Moser at the Kunstgewerbeschule, Vienna and made by the firm of Josef Böck, Vienna.

D 24.4 cm   1981,12-5,1

From 1898 the firm of J. Böck collaborated closely with the Kunstgewerbeschule, Vienna, and in particular with Hoffmann, Moser and their pupils. Winter exhibitions of designs by the 'Schule Prof. Kolo Moser' were held in the Museum für angewandte Kunst in 1902-3 and 1903-4. The design for the decoration is included in the Böck archive now in the Museum für angewandte Kunst, Vienna. Several designs by the Schule Prof. Kolo Moser dating from 1898 to 1914 are reproduced in Neuwirth 1974b, but this particular design (Neuwirth 1974b, 437 and 442) is not signed or dated. For a contemporary illustration, see *The Studio Yearbook*, 1907, 222.

The shape of the plate, with total absence of a rim or central depression, is remarkable at this date and illustrates the tremendous risks taken by manufacturers such as Böck, who were prepared to make new moulds, an expensive process, to put avant-garde art-school work into production (see Sika, Cat. 270).

Müller, Albin 1871-1941

There is no monograph on Müller. For biographical details, see Darmstadt 1976. The most useful contemporary source is an article on Müller in *Die Kunst* XII, 1905, 316-27.

209 Pitcher with lid   [PLATE 92]

Pewter, cast, with pierced handle to lid, the body with relief ornament in two bands joined by a central rib.

MARKS Impressed in relief on the base with the monogram 'AM' in a square for Albin Müller and 'E. HUECK EDELZINN 1880' in a circle.

Designed in 1903-4 and made by Eduard Hueck Metallwarenfabrik, Lüdenscheid, Westphalia.

H 35.1 cm, D 22.5 cm (base)   1981,7-14,1

Müller taught at the Kunstgewerbeschule in Magdeburg from 1900 to 1906, and then at the Technische Hochschule in Darmstadt, where he was a member of the artists' colony from 1906 until its demise in 1918. He lived in Darmstadt until his death in 1941.

For a pitcher of this design exhibited by the Magdeburger Gruppe at the St Louis Exhibition of 1904, see *Die Kunst* 9, 1903-4, 311 and *DK & D* XIV, April-September 1904, 489. The Magdeburger Gruppe showed an entire suite of rooms at the St Louis Exhibition; Müller directed the execution and installation. Thus it is likely that the pitcher was designed specially for this display. Pitchers of this model are to be found in the Kestner Museum, Hanover (Mosel 1971, no. 35) and in the Museum der Künstlerkolonie, Darmstadt (Ulmer 1990, no. 253); see also Cologne 1976, no. 109.

210 Pitcher with lid   [PLATE 92]

Copper and brass, beaten copper body with cast brass handle and lid lever, the body of octagonal form with stylised leaf-and-bud motif from base to top and beak-shaped spout.

MARKS Stamped on the base with the monogram 'AM' in a square for Albin Müller and 'EDUARD HUECK 2028'.

Designed c.1904 and made by Eduard Hueck Metallwarenfabrik, Lüdenscheid, Westphalia.

H 30.2 cm   1982,12-3,6

For a contemporary illustration of this model, see *Innendekoration*, Jahrgang 15, 1904, 156 and 157. Another example is held by the Museum der Künstlerkolonie, Darmstadt (Ulmer 1990, no. 269).

211 Pair of candlesticks   [PLATE 93]

Cast brass with beaten-copper drip trays. Four rectangular uprights rise from the base in an indented curve. Between each upright at the base is set an oval cabochon of opaline glass.

MARKS None.

Designed c.1904-5 and made by the Württembergische Metallwarenfabrik, Geislingen, near Ulm.

H 26.4 cm, W 11.3 × 11.1 cm (base)   1980,1-3,1 and 2

A candlestick of this design is illustrated in an article on Müller in *Die Kunst* XII, 1905, 322. Similar candlesticks were shown in the Dresden Exhibition of 1906, in the *Herren-Arbeitszimmer* (man's study) designed by Müller in Magdeburg (*DK & D* XVIII, 1906, 633; *Offizieller Katalog der Dritten Deutschen Kunstgewerbe-Ausstellung*, Dresden 1906, Illustrierte Ausgabe, 35-6).

Further metalwork by Müller was exhibited in the architect's *Wohn-und Empfangszimmer* (living and reception room; *Offizieller Katalog*, 38-9), made by the firms of Hueck and Gerhardi of Lüdenscheid and by the WMF. Since the WMF did not always mark their products, it seems likely that they are the manufacturer of the candlesticks rather than the two Lüdenscheid firms, and indeed the candlesticks are to be found in WMF English export catalogues of 1906-c.1908: model no. 4352 E, described as 'copper, finished in Pompeiian green bronze colour'. Such an attribution would explain the illustration in *Die Kunst*, 1905, where the candlesticks are shown between two known WMF models. (Graham Dry first suggested that the candlesticks were made by the WMF and has kindly searched through all the surviving catalogues in the WMF factory archive in order to confirm the attribution. He has also noted that the candlesticks appear only in the factory's small selection of English catalogues and not in any of the German ones.)

For a similar candlestick in silvered brass with red glass stones, see Darmstadt 1976, no. 441.

212 Beer tankard   [PLATE 100]

Stoneware, buff body, salt-glazed, '*Kölnisch braun*' (Cologne brown) smooth glaze with a band of relief decoration incorporating four roundels with birds; pewter lid and thumb-piece.

MARKS Impressed on the base, 'R. MERKELBACH GRENZHAUSEN MADE IN GERMANY', with model number '2210 B'. This form of the Merkelbach mark was in use from c.1903-4 to 1916 (Dry-v. Zezschwitz 1981, 31).

Designed c.1910 and made by the firm of R. Merkelbach, Höhr-Grenzhausen, Rhineland.

H 13 cm, W 15.7 cm (with handle)   1980,12-10,1

A related model with decoration of stags instead of birds is illustrated in *Die Kunst* 22, 1910, 174 and *DK & D* XXVI, 1910, 258. The stag tankard was one of a series of tankards for which Müller won first prize in a competition held by the Kgl. Württembergische Landes-Gewerbemuseum, Stuttgart. The birds tankard is likely to belong to this series as both models bear a band of relief decoration interrupted by figurative panels. For illustrations of other beer tankards designed by Müller for Merkelbach, see Darmstadt 1976, no. 444; Bonn 1987.

213 Punch-bowl and cover   [PLATE 98]

Salt-glazed stoneware, grey body, with steeply domed lid, two handles and four scroll-shaped feet; relief decoration in cobalt blue in the form of a band round the rim of the bowl and down the centre of each side, with further decoration on the lid and a spiral pattern on the feet.

MARKS Impressed on the base with the factory mark of Simon Peter Gerz, a jug in a triangle, and the model number '1599 B'.

Designed *c.*1910 and made by the firm of S. P. Gerz, Höhr-Grenzhausen, Rhineland.

H 29.2 cm, W 27.3 cm (with handles)   1981,6-9,1

This punch-bowl is one of Müller's most architectural designs for a small-scale object and relates closely to his architectural and sculptural work for the Darmstadt artists' colony. Identical punch-bowls are held by the Kunstgewerbemuseum, Berlin (Scheffler 1966, no. 177; Darmstadt 1976, no. 443) and by the Museum der Künstlerkolonie, Darmstadt (Ulmer 1990, no. 238).

In 1911 the firms of S. P. Gerz, R. Hanke and W. Müller joined forces for retailing purposes with Merkelbach, which meant that Gerz and Hanke models appear in Merkelbach price lists with 'G' or 'H' in front of the model number. Thus this punch-bowl appears as model number G.1599 (R. Merkelbach Preiscourant, 1912, pl. 22). It was produced in three sizes: 7, 4 and 3 l, indicated by A, B and C respectively after the number. For contemporary illustrations of this model, see *Dekorative Kunst* 14, 1910-11, 180 (in an article by Gustav Pazaurek on 'Neues Steinzeug von Albin Müller') and *Kunstgewerbeblatt* 22, 1911, 7, where it is shown in a dining-room designed by Müller for an exhibition at the Keller & Reiner gallery, Berlin.

Müller designed at least two further punch-bowls: Rosskopf & Gerz advertised a similar punch-bowl with scroll feet in their trade catalogue of 1914, model no. 523, as a '*Weinbowle, hochmodern auf 4 Rollen*' (Dry-v. Zezschwitz 1982, pl. 13a); it was among the most expensive of the punch-bowl designs. Merkelbach also included a Müller punch-bowl in their price list of 1912, model no. 2220; it does not have the scroll feet and the decoration is different. An example has recently been acquired by the Hessisches Landesmuseum, Darmstadt (*Kunsthandwerk Aktuell*, Merkelbach-Goebel, March 1988, 16).

Müller-Munk, Peter 1907-67

There is no monograph on Müller-Munk. Useful contemporary sources include Müller-Munk's own article in *The Studio* 98, October 1929, 709-12 and a later article on his industrial design work in *Design* 47, May 1946, 8-9. For further bibliography, see Newhaven 1983, cat. no. 9.

214 Pitcher   [PLATE 124]

Chromium-plated brass, of tear-drop section, the body formed of a single sheet of metal bent to shape, with a tear-drop-shaped piece for the base, the join concealed beneath a strip which runs round the base, along the edge and round the rim. The handle is formed of a flat strip of metal expanding at the top to blend with the line of the rim.

MARKS Stamped on the base 'REVERE ROME NY'.

Designed in 1935 and made by the Revere Brass and Copper Company, Rome, New York.

H 30.5 cm, max. W 24 cm   1988,11-3,1

Peter Müller-Munk studied at the Kunstgewerbeschule in Berlin under the silversmith Waldemar Rämisch and emigrated to America in 1926. He designed briefly for Tiffany & Co. before setting up his own studio for handmade silver. In his article in *The Studio* 98, October 1929 (the same article appeared in the American magazine *Creative Art* 5, October 1929) Müller-Munk called for greater harmony of design and technique, criticising contemporary manufacturers in the silver and associated metal industries for striving to imitate handmade pieces with mass-production methods instead of adapting their merchandise to their machines; he despised the application of handmade ornament to a spun or stamped object and the 'artful practice' of cutting a hammered surface into the die. He claimed that the machine would not put the silversmith out of business: 'I still have the outmodish confidence that there will always remain a sufficient number of people who want the pleasure of owning a centre piece without being forced to share their joy of ownership with a few thousand other beings.' To illustrate his argument he included machine-made metalwork designed by Professor F. A. Breuhaus for WMF and his own handmade silver. He was soon to be proved wrong; the demand for silver was hit by the Depression and in the early 1930s he turned to industrial design. From 1935 to 1945 he taught at the Carnegie Institute of Technology, where he helped to organise the first college course in Industrial Design and Production Methods (*Design* 47, 9).

This pitcher was known as the 'Normandie' pitcher because its shape was blatantly derived from the smokestacks of the celebrated French ocean liner launched in 1935. The *Normandie* was a noted example of French modernist design and the image of the ship became familiar through Cassandre's popular poster. The 'Normandie' pitcher has been described as 'streamlining at its most elegant and practical, a perfect harmony of efficiency, material and the machine process' (Brooklyn 1986, 307); the spout pours perfectly. Another recent discussion notes the use of the tear-drop form with reference to Norman Bel Geddes's view that a drop of water was the perfect streamlined form. Streamlining thus suggests the flowing surface of water, thereby blurring the distinction between mechanistic and organic design – the pitcher could be grouped with either (New York, 1985, fig. 3.35, p. 120).

For examples of Müller-Munk's silver, see Newhaven 1983, cat. nos 9, 18, 68. Müller-Munk also participated in the Third International Exposition of Contemporary Industrial Art held at the Metropolitan Museum of Art, New York, in 1930-31, nos 396-7, with illustration. For an account of an exhibition of Müller-Munk's industrial design at the Philadelphia Art Alliance in 1946, see *Design* 47, May 1946, 8-9; the works exhibited ranged from electrical household goods and sewing machines to industrial canteens.

Murray, Keith Day Pierce 1892-1981

There is no recent monograph on Keith Murray, but useful sources are Batkin 1982 (Wedgwood ceramics) and D. Taylor in Kingswinford 1987 (glass). The most important contemporary articles, including Murray's own writing, are listed below.

Murray, K., 'The designer and his problem. 11. The design of table glass', *Design for Today* 1, June 1933, 53-6

Murray, K., 'Some views of a designer', *Journal of the Society of Glass Technology* 19, 1935 (reprinted in Dodsworth 1987)

Anderson, M. L., 'Industrial design in three materials', *Design for Today*, August 1935, 318-20

215 Vase   [PLATE 114]

Free-blown smoky green glass, with double ribbon round the lower part of the body, applied during the blowing so that the profile bulges slightly below the ribbon.

MARKS Acid-etched on the base with facsimile signature 'Keith Murray' and the Stevens & Williams trade mark, the letters 'sw' flanking a fleur-de-lys and 'BRIERLEY'.

Designed in 1933 and made by Stevens & Williams Ltd, Brierley Hill Glassworks, Stourbridge, Worcestershire.

H 26.2 cm   1980,3-3,1

An architect by training and New Zealander by birth, Murray turned to design in the early 1930s when architectural commissions were scarce. In his own account (*Design for Today*, June 1933) he acknowledges his debt to the Swedish, Viennese, Czech and Finnish glass that he saw at the Paris Exhibition of 1925, and records that he began making designs for glass 'some eighteen months ago', i.e. late 1931 or early 1932. He was introduced to Harry Trethowan (ceramic buyer for Heal & Son and a committed member of the Design & Industries Association) and to Marriot Powell (director of James Powell & Sons since the retirement of Harry Powell in 1919). Marriot Powell made some experimental pieces but found Murray's shapes unsuited to the Whitefriars manufacturing processes. Murray was eventually put in touch with Hubert Williams-Thomas, managing director of Stevens & Williams, who had already discussed the idea of a modern glass range with Gordon Russell and Ambrose Heal, both propagandists of industrial design. Williams-Thomas then put selected designs into production; these were first shown at a special display in Stevens & Williams's London showrooms in Holborn in September 1932 (*Pottery Gazette*, 1 September 1932, 1100-5).

For Murray, form in glass design was all important and decoration, if used at all, was to express the form of the object, not destroy it. The illustrations to his 1933 article include this vase in a group, described as: 'Flower vases in bottle green. These vases are made by hand without any mould. The rings in the centre specimen [Cat. 215] are put on at an intermediate stage of the making and rolled flat. The simple shapes are a natural expression of hand-made glass and they are comparatively cheap.'

Murray continued to design for Stevens & Williams until the outbreak of the Second World War, maintaining regular contact with the craftsmen and producing about one hundred and fifty new designs each year. Those that were made up for costings are recorded in the 'Keith Murray Works Description Book' held in the Royal Brierley Crystal Glass Museum (the firm became known as Royal Brierley Crystal in 1985); this vase appears as description no. 308a, with the date 1933.

Murray's glass was included in two large exhibitions of industrial art in London, 'British Industrial Art in Relation to the Home' at Dorland Hall in 1933 and 'British Art in Industry' at the Royal Academy in 1935, and in the Paris Exhibition of 1937.

For Stevens & Williams, see Williams-Thomas 1983.

216 Decanter   [PLATE 114]

Mould-blown clear glass, of conical form, with hand-cut stopper of hexagonal section.

MARKS Acid-etched on the base with facsimile signature 'Keith Murray' and the Stevens & Williams trade mark, the letters 'sw' flanking a fleur-de-lys and 'BRIERLEY'.

Designed in 1933 and made by Stevens & Williams Ltd, Brierley Hill Glassworks, Stourbridge, Worcestershire.

H 28.8 cm (with stopper), 24 cm (without stopper), H of stopper 7 cm
1980,6-12,1

Illustrated in Murray's 1933 article (*Design for Today*, June 1933, 56). The illustration is captioned 'sherry decanters and glasses in flint. Although these particular decanters were made by hand they were designed for blowing in moulds, and therefore for mass-production methods and prices. The stoppers are hand-made'. For another contemporary illustration, see *Pottery Gazette*, 1 July 1933, 847. This decanter appears as no. 318a in the Keith Murray Works Description Book, with the date 1933 (work numbers for this and Cat. 215 kindly supplied by S. Thompson of Royal Brierley Crystal). It was also made with applied black enamel lines.

217 Vase   [PLATE 114]

Mould-blown bubbled and cased green glass, the bubbles trapped during the making so that they increase in size towards the centre as the glass is elongated on the rod. The foot is applied separately.

MARKS Acid-etched on the base with facsimile signature 'Keith Murray' and the Stevens & Williams trade mark, the letters 'sw' flanking a fleur-de-lys and 'BRIERLEY'.

Designed in 1939 and made by Stevens & Williams Ltd, Brierley Hill Glassworks, Stourbridge, Worcestershire.

H 39 cm   1981,6-12,1

A vase of similar shape in 'river green' but without the bubbles was advertised by Heal's in 1934, described as 'fluent in form, decorated by one who knows how to begin and where to stop'. The plain version sold for 14s. 9d.; the cut and engraved pieces in the same advertisement ranged from 25s. to 52s 6d. (*Design for Today* II, July 1934, 275). According to factory records at Royal Brierley Crystal, this model, with bubbles, was produced from 1939.

218 Vase   [PLATE 113]

Earthenware, hand-thrown with lathe-cut decoration of horizontal ridges on the upper part, done before firing. Cream body with matt straw (yellow) glaze all over.

MARKS Printed on the base in black with facsimile signature 'Keith Murray', 'WEDGWOOD' and 'MADE IN ENGLAND'.

Designed in 1933 and made by Josiah Wedgwood & Sons Ltd, Burslem, Staffordshire, before 1940.

H 28.5 cm   1980,6-9,1

Murray was introduced to Felton Wreford, manager of Wedgwood's London showrooms, through his association with J. Powell & Sons (see Cat. 234-43). He began to design for Wedgwood on a regular basis from 1933, producing vases and tableware conceived on architectural lines and exploiting the new matt glazes being created at Wedgwood by Norman Wilson. These glazes were advertised by Wedgwood as 'Siennese glazes' (*Pottery Gazette*, 1 April 1933, 446) before their use on Keith Murray shapes advertised later in the year (for example, *Pottery Gazette*, 1 July 1933, 844 and 1 November 1933, 1310, with reference to the matt finish of the 'Siennese' glazes).

Many of Murray's designs were in production within a year of their design and were exhibited at John Lewis and Peter Jones (*Design for Today* I, 1933, 322). Murray's Wedgwood wares were shown at the exhibition 'British Industrial Art in Relation to the Home' at Dorland Hall, London in 1933, at the exhibition

'British Art in Industry' at the Royal Academy in 1935 and again that year at the Medici Galleries, Grafton Street, in an exhibition of Murray's glass, pottery and silver (see Anderson 1935, 320, for a vase of this shape; the silver was made by Mappin & Webb).

In the catalogue of the Royal Academy exhibition of 1935 (p. 13) this model appears as shape no. 3805, available in matt green, white, straw and grey, price 18s. 6d. Other glazes included blue, black basalt and brown basalt. Certain shapes and glazes remained in production into the 1950s, but the lathe-cut detail on the later pieces is not so sharp.

Most of the shapes were included in Wedgwood's *Catalogue of Glazes, Bodies and Shapes Current for 1940-50* (Batkin pls 513 and 517). It is interesting to note that by 1940 shape no. 3805 had been significantly modified. The line drawing in the 1935 Royal Academy catalogue shows it with straight sides and sharp, almost horizontal shoulders. In the 1940 Wedgwood shapes catalogue, it appears with slightly convex sides and more sloping shoulders, as in this example.

Murray was joint architect with C. S. White of the new Wedgwood factory opened at Barlaston in 1940; from this date the new location was incorporated into the factory mark.

219 Vase   [PLATE 113]

Earthenware, hand-thrown with lathe-cut decoration of sharply defined horizontal ridges, done before firing. Cream body with matt green glaze all over, the glaze wiped off so that the cream body shows through on the ridges.

MARKS Printed on the base in blue with facsimile signature 'Keith Murray', 'WEDGWOOD' and 'MADE IN ENGLAND'. Impressed potter's marks 'F' and 'H'.

Designed in 1933 and made by Josiah Wedgwood & Sons Ltd, Burslem, Staffordshire, before 1940.

H 16.5 cm, D 27.2 cm   1980,6-10,1

This model is illustrated in *The Studio* 106, September 1933, 186. It appears in the Royal Academy 1935 exhibition catalogue (p. 14) as shape no. 3820, available in matt green and white, price 19s. 6d. For further discussion see Cat. 218. See also Dawson 1984, 146-7 and col. pl. 16 for Cat. 218 and 219.

Nash, Arthur Douglas d.1940

There is no monograph on Nash. For a detailed biography, see Arwas, 1987.

220 Three glasses   [PLATE 126]

Two tumblers and a sherbet glass. Clear glass, free-blown bowls with moulded and cut square bases.

MARKS Acid-etched on the base 'Libbey' in a circle.

Designed in 1931-2 as part of the 'Knickerbocker' pattern and made by the Libbey Glass Manufacturing Company, Toledo, Ohio, between 1933 and 1942.

220a H 14.3 cm   1988,6-8,5
220b H 12.3 cm   1988,6-8,6
220c H 8.2 cm   1988,6-8,7

Arthur Douglas Nash was the son of Arthur J. Nash, an Englishman who worked in Stourbridge before emigrating in 1892 to the USA, where he ran L.C. Tiffany's glass studios until 1919.

From 1919 A.D. Nash ran the Tiffany Furnaces until their closure in 1928, when he formed his own firm, the A. Douglas Nash Corporation, but this too closed in 1931. He was then hired by Libbey to create a new line of luxury glassware. The series was formally introduced in 1933, with a catalogue and exhibition at the Waldorf Astoria Hotel in New York. Advertisements appear in *Arts and Decoration* 40, November and December 1933. The Libbey–Nash series comprised some eighty new patterns, but much of it proved too expensive; it was hit by the Depression and admitted a failure after two years. Nash left Libbey in 1935 and made no further designs for glass.

The complete 'Knickerbocker' service comprised a 12-oz tumbler, 10-oz tumbler, 6-oz sherbet, 4-oz cocktail and 1-oz cordial glass. It was a custom-built line – i.e. not regularly carried in stock – and so could be decorated at the factory with the purchaser's personal monogram, at an extra charge. The service was still in production in 1942, with the addition of a sugar bowl, cream pitcher and salt dips, not designed by Nash (Fauster 1979, 398, reprint of Libbey 1942 Modern American Glassware Catalogue). As the sales blurb rightly says, 'the heavy crystal block gives each item perfect balance and a delightful "feel"'.

Glasses with solid square bases were produced by other American firms in the early 1930s, notably the ranges designed by W.D. Teague for Steuben (Brooklyn 1986, 329, pl. 8.81) and by G. Sakier for Fostoria (see *The Studio Yearbook*, 1931, 149). Both these ranges were stemmed. The idea of placing the bowl directly on to the square base was already current in France, since the Paris Exhibition of 1925, when Baccarat exhibited a service with flared bowls on square bases designed by G. Chevalier. Later on, Jean Luce designed a straight-sided, square-based, clear-crystal service very similar to the Nash glasses. For illustrations of the Luce service, see *Mobilier et Décoration*, 1934, 179 and 196, and *Design for Today* III, June 1935, 212. For a square-based decanter and glasses designed by S. Gate for Orrefors, Sweden, see *Design for Today* II, 1934, 371.

Nichols, Maria Longworth 1849-1932

For bibliography, see **Rookwood Pottery**.

221 Vase   [PLATE 45]

Earthenware, moulded body biscuit-fired to a pale grey colour with applied decoration in high relief of a dragon encircling the vase, the front leg raised to form a handle at the neck. The dragon is painted in white and dark blue with black outlines. Further applied slip decoration in the form of cloud-like swirls decorates the rest of the body. The casting seam is clearly visible.

MARKS None.

Decorated by Maria Longworth Nichols, either in her studio at the commercial pottery of Frederick Dallas, Cincinnati, Ohio, between May 1879 and summer 1880, or at the Rookwood Pottery c.1880-81. According to Todd Volpe and Beth Cathers, the previous owners, this vase was formerly in the collection of Stanley Gano Burts, chief glaze chemist at Rookwood from 1892 to 1929.

H 26.2 cm, D 10.5 cm   1984,11-7,1

Mrs Nichols was the daughter of Joseph Longworth, a patron of the Cincinnati Art Museum. She married Colonel George Ward Nichols in 1867 and, with the aid of Longworth family money, became a significant figure in the American art pottery movement. She joined classes at the Cincinnati School of Design and began to decorate china in the mid 1870s along with several other Cincinnati women. From May 1879 she had studio space at the commercial pottery of Frederick Dallas, where she decorated commercially made blanks. Contemporary accounts refer to high-fired 'granite' ware (*Art Journal*, 1897), as well as 'Rockingham' clay, red clays of Ohio and other coloured clays (Perry, 1881, 837). Nichols established her own Rookwood Pottery in Cincinnati in the summer of 1880, taking with her the Dallas technicians, who used the same clays and the same moulds. This shape is included in the Rookwood Shape Book as shape no. 218, described as 'Vase. Old "Dallas" mold. Pressed. In June 1887 block altered and new mold made for casting' (Peck 1985, 57). The absence of the Rookwood shape number suggests a Dallas origin, and Dallas Pottery blanks of identical shape bearing the Dallas Pottery factory mark are known (information supplied by Beth Cathers in 1984). Rookwood marks were not standardised in the early years, making it more difficult to attribute the early pieces. The Cincinnati Art Museum owns unmarked pieces which are firmly documented as decorated by Nichols at Dallas (1952.406, a smear-glazed and gilded dragon vase) and at Rookwood (1881.25, a bowl with a blue-glazed dragon). This vase is therefore described as either Dallas or Rookwood.

Contemporary accounts describe the Dallas granite ware as 'a cheap white ware, hard as rock'. Mrs Nichols herself wrote 'I was constantly discouraged by the fact that the hard fire of the granite-ware kilns destroyed nearly every colour I used, except cobalt blue and black.' (*Art Journal*, 1897, 342). It is significant that these are the two main colours used on this vase, which is almost certainly an experimental piece as it has not been glazed. Among the 2,292 pieces of early Rookwood pottery formerly held by the Cincinnati Art Museum on behalf of the Pottery, was 'a large vase, gray clay – clear glaze outside, green glaze inside – modeled dragon with white and blue slip – spots of green glaze on outside – no mark' (Burt 1916, listed under 1880-81). The British Museum vase also uses modelled white and blue slip.

Three vases with closely similar decoration by Nichols of dragons and fish in high relief are known from an archive photograph in the Cincinnati Art Museum (illustrated in Trapp 1981, 57 and Barber 1909, 277). The photograph is dated May 1880 so the vases must have been decorated at the Dallas Pottery. The smaller vase in the centre of the photograph has a dragon coiled round the body with a front leg raised to form a handle at the neck. A very similar vase decorated by Nichols on a Dallas blank is in the Cooper-Hewitt Museum, New York (see Koehler 1987, no. 1, where it is dated 1879-80). A further unmarked Rookwood vase acquired by the Cincinnati Art Museum in 1881 (1881.43; see Boston 1987a, no. 6) is especially close in conception to the British Museum vase: the dragon is modelled in relief with black painted outlines and gloss glaze; it coils round the neck with a free-standing leg, while similar swirls of applied slip decorate the body (Fig. 13). For a related gloss-glazed dragon vase with free-standing leg, see New York 1987, no. 79.

During the early years of the Rookwood Pottery Nichols continued her repertoire of grotesque animals in the Japanese manner: 'the inevitable dragon coiled about the neck of the vase or at its base . . . monsters of the air and water . . . decorated in high relief, underglaze colour, incised design, and an overglaze enrichment of gold' (Perry 1881, quoted in Trapp 1981,

55). Mrs Nichols's interest in Japanese decorative motifs was first inspired by 'some little Japanese books of designs' given to her in 1875, while a large group of Japanese objects was shown for the first time in America at the Philadelphia Exhibition of 1876. Two exhibitions and sales of Japanese art were held in Cincinnati in 1878 and 1880, while Mrs Nichols herself owned a sizeable collection of Japanese bronzes, ceramics and textiles. Hokusai's *Manga* was certainly used as a sourcebook at Rookwood and the illustrations by Mrs Nichols to her husband's book of 1878 show that she was familiar with several others (Trapp 1973 and 1981). For a detailed account of the Japanese influence on American ceramics, see Syracuse 1989. This exhibition included Japanese nineteenth-century ceramics alongside the Rookwood pieces: of particular relevance to the British Museum vase are no. 60, with applied dragon, and no. 63, with applied lizard gripping the rim, given to the Cincinnati Art Museum by the Rookwood Pottery.

European ceramics shown at Philadelphia were also influential: both English and French models existed for vases with dragons in relief (for example by Théodore Deck, Minton & Co. and Royal Worcester), copied in some cases from Chinese rather than Japanese prototypes (S. Wichmann 1981, 336, 914-16). Indeed the Nichols vase itself bears comparison with contemporary nineteenth-century Chinese porcelain (see, for example, two vase from the Salting Bequest of 1910 to the V & A, c.986: with blue and white dragon in relief outlined in blue, or 993.1910: with glazed relief dragons on an unglazed ground).

I am grateful to Anita Ellis for details of items in the Cincinnati Museum of Art.

Nielsen, Harald 1892-1977

Harald Nielsen, exhibition catalogue, Georg Jensen Sølv, Copenhagen 1952
For further bibliography, see **Jensen**.

222 Four pieces of cutlery [PLATE 123]

Silver, pressed, a soup spoon, dessert spoon, knife and fork, with 'Pyramid' pattern handles, the knife with stainless-steel blade.

MARKS The fork stamped with the initials 'GI' in a circle (the mark used by the Jensen firm between ?1919 and 1933), London import marks and date-letter for 1930, '925.S' and importer's mark 'GS' for George Stockwell & Co. Ltd, 16-18 Finsbury Street EC and 8-10 Beak Street W, mark entered on 2 January 1925.

The spoons stamped with the initials 'GJ' in a square (the mark used by the Jensen firm between 1933 and 1944), London import marks and date-letter for 1934, 'STERLING DENMARK' and importer's mark 'G.J Ltd' in a cut-corner rectangle for Georg Jensen (Jensen's had a branch in London from 1921).

The knife with same marks as the spoons but with London date-letter for 1933, the blade marked 'JOHN WATT SHEFFIELD ENGLAND 1765'.

Designed in 1926 and made by the firm of Georg Jensen before 1930 (fork) or before 1933-4 (knife and spoons).

222a Soup spoon: L 15.6cm   1983,10-8,1
222b Dessert spoon: L 16.5cm   1983,10-8,2
222c Knife: L 20.4cm   1983,10-8,3
222d Fork: L 16.2cm   1983,10-8,4

Jensen's associates created under their own names and their initials usually appear on their designs; see Cat. 223. Harald

Nielsen, Georg Jensen's brother-in-law, was among a number of associates recruited from Jensen's own family. He worked with the firm from 1909 to 1969, initially as a chaser, taking over as artistic director on Jensen's death in 1935. He made a significant contribution to the Jensen style between the wars.

This cutlery pattern was the firm's first modernist design. It was illustrated in *Les Echos des Industries d'Art*, April 1929, 20, as an example of modern silver cutlery with broad, flat surfaces. It was also illustrated in *The Studio* 107, 1934, 325, as an example of 'a newer and simpler set of cutlery which is easy to clean' (see Cat. 223). For further pieces from the service, see Copenhagen 1952.

Most Jensen silver was imported into England by the London branch of the firm. However, George Stockwell & Co. Ltd were long-established importers and agents (see Culme 1987, 1, 434-5) and their mark frequently occurs on Jensen silver of the 1930s.

223 Jug
[PLATE 123]

Silver, hand-raised, the spout with undulating outline grows out of the body of the jug and the high handle, formed of a flat strip of silver, echoes the jug's rounded form.

MARKS Stamped on the base with the initials 'GJ' in a square (the mark used by the Jensen firm between 1933 and 1944), the designer's initials 'HN', model number '606A', '925.S' and 'DENMARK STERLING'.

Designed in 1930 and made in the Jensen workshops, Copenhagen, between 1933 and 1944.

H 15.5 cm, D 15.3 cm   1988,1-5,1

This jug was illustrated in *The Studio* 107, 1934, 323, as an example of 'simply designed silverware from the studio of Georg Jensen'. The article, entitled 'The Trend of Design in Silverware', praised a group of Nielsen designs (though not credited to him) for their reliance on 'balance and proportion and inherent beauty of material rather than perfunctory ornamentation'. See also Copenhagen 1952. The combination of organic and geometric elements is characteristic of Nielsen's attempt to streamline Jensen's naturalistic forms.

For further hollowware designs by Nielsen, see Hughes 1967, 14-17 and Møller 1985, 47.

Olbrich, Joseph Maria 1867-1908

Architektur von Olbrich, Berlin, published by Ernst Wasmuth, Berlin 1902-14 (reprinted 1988)

Joseph M. Olbrich 1867-1908, exhibition catalogue, Mathildenhöhe, Darmstadt 1983

Schreyl, K.H., *J.M. Olbrich. Die Zeichnungen in der Kunstbibliothek Berlin. Kritischer Katalog*, Berlin 1972

224 Fork
[PLATE 89]

Silvered metal, cast, with simple linear ornament in relief on the front of the handle; the reverse of the handle with engraved lines down the sides and motif of concentric ovals.

MARKS Stamped on the reverse with the monogram 'JO' in a square; 'CHRISTOFLE' in a rectangle (the Christofle factory mark for plated metal); the initials 'CC' flanking a pair of scales, with four stars above and two laurel branches below (the Christofle factory mark in use until the First World War).

Designed c.1900-01 and made by the firm of Christofle & Cie, Paris, for the firm's German subsidiary in Karlsruhe.

L 21.6 cm   1980,12-11,1   Given by John Jesse and Irina Laski

Olbrich trained as an architect in Vienna, working initially for Otto Wagner. He was a founder member of the Vienna Seccession in 1897, and in 1899 was called to the Darmstadt artists' colony, where he designed public buildings and artists' houses, as well as rooms for several international exhibitions.

This fork is part of a service designed for the 1901 exhibition of the Darmstadt artists' colony, where it was shown in Olbrich's own house (Darmstadt, 1901, 119). An undated drawing for the spoon from this service, with lotus-leaf-shaped bowl, is to be found in the Olbrich archive in the Kunstbibliothek, Berlin (Schreyl 1972, no. 11973). For the knives and forks from the service, see Heller 1982, nos 314-15.

Christofle had a marketing subsidiary in Karlsruhe from 1856, where patterns were distributed exclusively for the German market. Olbrich was commissioned by Christofle's agent in Nuremberg, George Leykauf, to design a new flatware pattern in the current German taste. Olbrich completed his design in 1900-01; Christofle modified some of the details and called it 'Modernes Besteck'. Contemporary praise for Olbrich's tasteful and practical design was widespread; see, for example, *Kunstgewerbeblatt* 1905, 15. According to a 1910 trade catalogue of Christofle, Karlsruhe, the service was model no. 5920a, and comprised a meat- and dessert-knife, fork and spoon, and a coffee-spoon. A letter in the Christofle archives, written by the director of the factory at St Denis in 1910, indicates that the firm had added several other items, including a range of spoons with lotus-leaf-shaped bowls, servers, ladles, etc. These were almost certainly the firm's designs, not Olbrich's.

The service remained in production until the First World War and was available only in Gemany and Austria (Christofle opened a retail outlet in Vienna in 1898). It does not appear in trade catalogues for the French market, being considered too modern at the time. In 1935, however, Christofle created a pattern called 'Louvre' inspired by Olbrich's design, of similar shape, but with simplified handles. (Much of the information in this entry was supplied by Christiane Jolly of the Musée Bouilhet-Christofle, Paris.)

225 Fish knife
[PLATE 89]

Silvered metal, cast, the blade pierced and engraved with three square motifs, the handle with relief linear ornament incorporating the monogram 'JO'. Further linear ornament on reverse of handle.

MARKS Stamped on the reverse with the factory mark of Clarfeld & Springmeyer (two figures holding an anchor, in a rectangle); the date '1904' in a rectangle and the number '60'.

Made by the firm of Clarfeld & Springmeyer, Neusilberwarenfabrik, Hemer, Westphalia, Germany, in 1904.

L 22.8 cm   1982,12-3,8

Clarfeld & Springmeyer were the second largest cutlery manufacturers in Germany before the First World War. The firm was founded in 1858 by the businessman Fritz Clarfeld and the engraver Heinrich Springmeyer. They made cutlery in nickel silver, alpacca and paktong, and, from the 1890s in silvered metal.

Often examples of cutlery from this Olbrich service are found that bear the marks of other firms, who acted as wholesalers and finishers only, but had their names stamped on goods by the factory. The half-finished wares were delivered to the wholesalers, who then had them silvered before retail. In this way the two main costs of the moulds and the silvering were shared between two different concerns (Sänger 1984, 200ff.). The fish knife and fork from the Darmstadt collection are also marked by Clarfeld & Springmeyer, but the servers bear the mark of C.B. Schroeder of Düsseldorf, founded in 1901 as electroplate manufacturers (Heller 1982, nos 310-11). The Hessisches Landesmuseum, Darmstadt, also holds examples of the meat cutlery from this service, with the mark of a third firm, Zoll & Co., of Pforzheim (Heller 1982, no. 326). A fourth mark of Ludwig Ziech & Co. of Hamburg is found on parts of the set in Karlsruhe (Franzke 1987 no. 46). See also Ulmer 1990, no. 306, for further examples in the Museum der Künstlerkolonie, Darmstadt, bearing the marks of Schroeder, Clarfeld & Springmeyer and Ziech.

The date '1904' stamped on the piece catalogued here suggests that it may have been made as part of the large group of Olbrich material which was shown in the exhibition at the Darmstadt artists' colony of that year or in the St Louis Exhibition, also held in 1904. A spoon from this service appears in an advertisement by Clarfeld & Springmeyer in the *Werkbund Jahrbuch* for 1912. The design date of this service is traditionally given as *c.*1900 in recent literature, but without reference to contemporary evidence.

226 Candlestick [PLATE 91]

Pewter, cast, with two branches issuing from a zoomorphic stem.

MARKS Impressed on the base 'EDELZINN E.HUECK', the model number '1819' in a circle and the monogram 'JO' in a square.

Designed *c.*1901-2 and made by Eduard Hueck Metallwarenfabrik, Lüdenscheid, Westphalia, Germany.

H 36.2cm, W of base 11.3cm, L of base 17.4cm   1980,5-16,1

The date of design of this candlestick is traditionally given as *c.*1901-2 (see Zons 1978, no. 268; *Architektur von Olbrich*, 1901-14, reprinted 1988, 30 and pl. 284, and recent publications listed below), but there does not appear to be a contemporary illustration of it before 1904. The candlestick was shown both at the St Louis Exhibition of 1904 (Nachtlicht 1904, pl. 43) and at the exhibition held at the Darmstadt artists' colony in the same year, where it was shown in the corner house of the 'Dreihäusergruppe' (Darmstadt 1904, 32; *Architektur von Olbrich*, 1901-14, reprinted 1988, pl. 71); it was also exhibited by the modern decorative arts gallery, K. Rittershaus, in Darmstadt. It was then included in an exhibition of pewter from the rival firms of Hueck and Gerhardi of Lüdenscheid organised by K.E. Osthaus in the Folkwang Museum, Hagen, in 1905 (Hagen 1984, 76); according to Funk-Jones (Hagen 1984, 78) there was no market for Hueck's artist-designed pewterware after about 1908.

Examples are to be found in several German museums, including the Hessisches Landesmuseum, Darmstadt (Heller 1982, no. 317), the Museum der Künsterkolonie, Darmstadt (Ulmer 1990, no. 313), Berlin (Scheffler 1966, no. 57), Kassel (Kassel 1968, no. 44), Hamburg, and Karlsruhe (Franzke 1987, no. 33, with further references). There are also examples in the Museum

of Modern Art, New York, and in the Virginia Museum, Richmond (Brandt 1985, 278).

227 Plate [PLATE 91]

Pewter, cast, of six-sided asymmetrical form with stylised plant ornament in relief on the border.

MARKS Impressed on the base 'EDELZINN E.HUECK'. the model number '1821' in a circle and the monogram 'JO' in a square.

Designed *c.*1903-4 and made by Eduard Hueck Metallwarenfabrik, Lüdenscheid, Westphalia.

W 26.4cm, H 25.8cm   1987,10-9,1

Plates of this design were shown at the St Louis Exhibition of 1904 (Nachtlicht 1904, pl. 42) and at the exhibition held at the Darmstadt artists' colony in the same year, where it was shown in the dining-room of the corner house of the 'Dreihäusergruppe' (see *Architektur von Olbrich*, 1901-14, reprinted 1988, 25 and pl. 71). The 'Dreihäusergruppe' was designed in 1903-4 as models for modern middle-class homes.

For other examples, see Darmstadt 1976, no. 516 (collection of Giorgio Silzer, Berlin), Darmstadt 1983, no. 412 (Frankfurt private collection) and Ulmer 1990, no. 314 (Museum der Künstlerkolonie, Darmstadt). These publications all date the design of this plate to *c.*1902, but as it does not appear to be documented before 1904, it is here dated to *c.*1903-4.

228 Clock [PLATE 90]

The case of blackened wood, inlaid with ivory, mother-of-pearl, abalone shell and aluminium, the hands of copper. The face is formed of a central octagonal panel with a painted veneer containing gold dust. It is surrounded by panels of stained yellow ivory and abalone shell outlined in aluminium. The numbers are incised into the ivory panels and filled in with a black compound, which has also been used to frame each ivory panel. A small piece of ivory is missing from the figure six. The two decorative motifs at the top are inlaid with abalone shell and mother-of-pearl framed in thin strips of ivory which also form the remaining linear and scroll inlays.

MARKS The clock movement bears the trade-mark 'AGU' for the Aktiengesellschaft für Uhrenfabrikation, Lenzkirch, in the Black Forest.

The case designed *c.*1902-3 and made by Robert Macco, Marqueterie und Kunstgewerbliche Anstalt, Heidelberg, with movement by AGU, Lenzkirch.

H 34.8cm, W of top 18.3cm   1980,3-5,1

A clock of this design is illustrated in *Velhagen & Klasing's Monatshefte* XVIII Jahrgang, Heft 1, September 1903, when it was displayed, along with other Olbrich clocks, at the Keller & Reiner art gallery in Berlin. Founded in 1899, the Keller & Reiner gallery was decorated by van de Velde and often acted as sole retailer for certain artists or firms. The 1903 article describes the clock as made by Macco; further support for this attribution is to be found in a closely related jewel box, of darkened maple, designed by Olbrich *c.*1901, which bears a label on the reverse signed 'Robert Macco, Kunstgew. Atelier, Hoflieferand, Heidelberg' (Darmstadt 1976, Bd 4, no. 478; Brussels 1977, no. 268A; Darmstadt 1983, no. 372). The inlaid details and the use of stained wood are closely comparable. This clock was included in the exhibition '*Ein Dokument Deutscher Kunst*', held in Darmstadt in 1976, no. 480. It appears to be the only known example of this model. For further clocks and jewel caskets designed by Olbrich with similar inlaid decoration, see *Architektur von Olbrich*, 1901-14, reprinted 1988, pls 263-4, 276.

Macco's marquetry workshop (founded in Paris in 1839) was at Bergheimerstrasse 49, Heidelberg. He won two gold medals at the Paris Exhibition of 1900 and executed most of the 'Intarsien' included in the Darmstadt exhibition of 1901 (Darmstadt 1901, 43 and 118). Macco advertised for 'Moderne Intarsien' in the catalogue of the 1904 exhibition at the Darmstadt artists' colony and he is again mentioned in the catalogue of the German section of the St Louis Exhibition of 1904 as an executor for Olbrich (no. 1456, p. 412 and no. 2457, p. 456).

AGU in Lenzkirch was founded in 1851 (see Abeler 1977); it had a reputation for good-quality movements, but went out of business in 1929 because its products were too expensive.

(Much of the information in this entry was kindly supplied by Graham Dry.)

229 Jug and wash basin [PLATE 90]

Earthenware, with transfer-printed decoration of a band of stylised flowers in blue and green.

MARKS On base of both pieces, printed factory mark 'Villeroy & Boch, Mettlach' with 'OLBRICH GLATT' both in overglaze green, the pattern number '1453' in black, and impressed mark 'FC 68' in a rectangle on the jug and 'HC 68' on the basin.

The shape designed in 1903 by J.M. Olbrich with decoration designed c.1910 possibly by Bruno Mauder. Made by Villeroy & Boch, Mettlach, Germany.

Jug: H 28.6cm. Basin: D 39.2cm, H 12.6cm   1981,3-9,1 (basin) and 2 (jug)

Olbrich's original drawing for this set in the Kunstbibliothek, Berlin (Fig. 25; Schreyl 1972, no. 12099), signed and dated 21 November 1903, differs in details such as the shape of the handle and the absence of a spout on the jug. The drawing shows a decoration of triangles, arranged in three stepped rows round the rim of both pieces. For contemporary illustrations of this pattern, see Architektur von Olbrich, 1901-14, reprinted 1988, pl. 198; The Studio Special Number; The Art Revival in Austria, 1906, pl. C54; DK & D XIX, 1906-7, 116, where the jug is illustrated on a washstand by Bruno Paul, as part of the display of the Vereinigte Werkstätten, Munich, at the Dresden exhibition. For examples, see Darmstadt 1983, no. 391 (private collection); Ulmer 1990, no. 299 (Museum der Künstlerkolonie, Darmstadt).

However, a number of other patterns are recorded on this shape and it is likely that they were designed as a group, probably by the same hand, after Olbrich's death. For examples, see Gysling-Billeter 1975, no. 534; Brussels 1977, no. 543; Christie's, London, 15 April 1987, lot 117, marked with pattern number 1454.

The attribution of this pattern to Mauder is based on closely similar designs included in Ornamente, a folio of designs published by Mauder in 1910 (Verlag Christian Stoll, Plauen; reference kindly supplied by Graham Dry). However, the pattern also bears comparison with a design for a frieze by Margold illustrated in The Studio 44, 1908-9, 235. It should further be noted that Albin Müller designed a pattern for this shape in a very different style (Ulmer 1990, no. 233). In the absence of further evidence, therefore, the attribution to Mauder must remain tentative. For Mauder, see Dry-v. Zezschwitz 1981; he was trained as a porcelain painter, becoming director of the Glasfachschule Zwiesel in 1910. He died in 1948.

Ovchinnikov, Pavel   workshop founded 1853, closed c.1917

There is no monograph on the firm of Ovchinnikov; for discussion of the firm's history and productions, see A. von Solodkoff, Russian Silver, Fribourg 1981.

230 Lidded jug [PLATE 48]

Silver, cast and partly gilded with surface punched to give a hammered effect. Applied and engraved decoration in the Japanese style. The body and handle applied with irises growing in a pond with carp and bamboo stick, two dragonflies above; the hinged lid with cast and applied lizard and fly; the handle, which is left smooth without hammered surface, has a cast and applied beetle. The handle, hinge and mouldings at top and shoulders of jug gilded, the applied work partly gilded. Engraved details to irises, dragonflies, carp and pond. The iris leaf that rises beneath the handle is broken and the top part is missing.

MARKS Stamped on the base with Moscow imperial eagle assay mark, silver standard mark '84' (equivalent to 875 silver), 'OVCHINNIKOV' in Cyrillic letters in a rectangular shield and the date '1882' beneath the letters 'AK' for the assay master.

Made in the workshop of Pavel Ovchinnikov, Moscow in 1882.

Total H 27.6cm, H without lid 23.2cm, D of base 13.5cm   1986,6-8,1

This jug is a close copy, in design though not in technique, of a jug by Tiffany & Co., without a lid, exhibited at the Paris Exhibition of 1878 (Bergerat 1878, 122). A version of the Tiffany pitcher is held by the Art Institute of Chicago (Antiques, October 1988, 830) and by the Musée d'Orsay, Paris. The latter example (Fig. 15) was exhibited together with this Ovchinnikov jug in the exhibition 'Le Japonisme' in Paris in 1988 (cat. nos 235 and 237), providing the opportunity for a detailed comparison. There are several differences in technique: the Tiffany jug is more sophisticated in its use of coloured metals for the appliqués, its fineness of detail and overall quality. Contrasts of colour in the Russian version are obtained by part-gilding only, and all the details are applied, so that the subtle distinction on the Tiffany jug between the tall iris leaves, which are applied, and the shorter clumps of reeds, which are engraved, is lost. The neck is left plain on the Tiffany version; it is also slightly shorter and the handle is angled upwards, creating a lighter effect than the heavy, rounded handle of the Ovchinnikov jug with its ungainly hinge and thumb-piece, recalling a Central European beer tankard.

Further differences of execution include the poor modelling of the fish on the Ovchinnikov version and the lack of ripples in the water around the fish and the reeds. The tallest iris leaf on the Tiffany jug is attached beneath the neck moulding, while the leaf underneath the handle (broken on the Ovchinnikov jug) continues up to the inside of the handle at the top, leaving a gap at the junction of the neck and body.

But it is the colours which give the Tiffany jug a much more Far Eastern feel. On the front (with handle to right), the dragonfly is in copper-coloured metal (probably red gold) with yellow-gold wings, the iris stems and details of the petals are also copper-coloured. On the reverse (handle to left) the bamboo stalk is a deep yellow-gold colour and the two fish have details in red or a copper-colour. The beetle on the handle is a deep coppery-brown.

However, the firm of Ovchinnikov also produced a range of Japanese-style wares with red patination imitating Japanese lacquer and with silver applied work; these items are very similar to those of Tiffany, Gorham (see Cat. 115-16) and other American firms and probably deliberately imitate them. For a silver-gilt and red lacquer teapot and sugar bowl with cast animals on the lids, see von Solodkoff 1981, pl. 75. A number of other examples have passed through the salerooms in recent years: for example, a silver-gilt and red lacquer tankard of 1882 with animals and flowers and a triangular tray with spider's web of 1884 (Sotheby's, Geneva, 15-17 November 1988 and Sotheby's, New York, 14 June 1989, lots 140-41); a small vase of 1882 with flowers, frogs and butterflies (Sotheby's, New York, 15 December 1988).

The Fabergé workshop also occasionally produced imitations of Japanese lacquer (Snowman 1979, 41) or cigarette cases and boxes with a hammered surface (Munich 1986, nos 147 and 151), but the Japanese taste was not widely popular in Russia as it was elsewhere in Europe.

For Tiffany metalwork, see Cat. 282-3.

Petri-Raben, Trude b. 1906

There is no monograph on Petri. For biographical details and Petri's work for the Staatliche Porzellanmanufaktur, see:

Jarchow, M., *Die Staatliche Porzellanmanufaktur Berlin (KPM) 1918-1938, Institution und Produktion*, PhD dissertation, Hamburg 1984

Köllmann, E. and Jarchow, M., *Berliner Porzellan 1763-1963*, Berlin 1987

Jarchow, M., *Berlin Porcelain in the 20th Century*, Berlin 1988.

231 Tea service   [PLATE 133]

Hard-paste porcelain, comprising teapot, sugar bowl and lid, milk jug, six cups and saucers and six plates, white with painted celadon-green knops and rims. The plates are almost flat with no central depression or border.

MARKS On base of each piece, the underglaze blue sceptre mark of the Staatliche Porzellanmanufaktur; the plates and saucers with impressed lower-case Greek year-letters λ for 1936 and μ for 1937 (Jarchow 1988, 314). The other pieces bear no date-letters.

The teapot designed in 1938 as part of the 'Urbino' tea service, the other pieces designed in 1931 as part of the 'Neu Berlin' tea service. Made by the Staatliche Porzellanmanufaktur, Berlin; the plates and saucers in 1936-7, the other items probably after 1938.

231a Teapot: H 15.7cm, D 14.3cm   1982,12-3,1a
231b Sugar bowl: H 9.8cm, D 8.8cm   1982,12-3,1b
231c Milk jug: H 8cm, D 8.3cm   1982,12-3,1c
231d-i Cups: H 4.2cm, saucers: D 15cm   1982,12-3,1d-i
231j-p Plates: D 19cm   1982,12-3,1j-p

Petri studied sculpture and painting at the Hochschule für Bildende Kunst in her native Hamburg. From 1927 to 1929 she attended the ceramic class of the Vereinigten Staatschulen in Berlin, before her appointment in 1929 as permanent designer to the Staatliche Porzellanmanufaktur, by the new director, G. von Pechmann. In 1953 she emigrated to America, but continued to design for the SPM on a freelance basis.

The tea service 'Neu Berlin' was designed in 1931 to complement Petri's 'Urbino' dinner service, also of 1931 (Köllmann & Jarchow 1987, pl. 344). The 'Neu Berlin' tea service appears in the factory workbooks from December 1931 (Jarchow 1988, 280); it was offered in white or celadon, or white with a celadon rim (as in these examples), or with a lily pattern designed by

Elsa Möckel. The use of white and celadon was inspired by Chinese porcelain, while the shape of the teapot was based on the traditional eighteenth-century shape which was still being produced by the factory as 'Alt Berlin' (for a plain white 'Alt Berlin' teaset of *c*.1850, see Jarchow 1984, pl. 8). The outline of the pot was virtually the same, but the handle and spout were streamlined by being stripped of rococo relief ornament (Jarchow 1984, 46-7; Köllmann & Jarchow, pl. 503). For an example of an eighteenth-century teapot of this form, see Köllman & Jarchow, pls 390-91.

The 'Neu Berlin' tea service was produced for only a few years and was replaced by the 'Urbino' tea service of 1938. The plates from the 'Neu Berlin' service were used for the 'Urbino' service, but the shape of the 'Urbino' teapot was modified; the 'Neu Berlin' teapot has slightly higher shoulders and straighter sides. After the war further modifications were made because the 'Urbino' moulds were destroyed; the service was reconstructed by Petri and a variety of patterns were used in the postwar years (e.g. Jarchow 1988, 56, 154).

The 'Urbino' dinner service was a huge success in the 1930s, winning the highest accolade of a Grand Prix at the Milan Triennale in 1936 and a gold medal at Paris in 1937. The dinner and tea services are still in production. The only other German 1930s service to have continued in production to the present day is Hermann Gretsch's 'Arzberg 1382' (see Cat. 119).

Poschinger'sche Krystallglasfabrik

For a detailed account of this factory, see Killinger 1986, 32-3; see also Arwas 1987, 51-2; Pazaurek and Spiegl 1983; Seyfert 1988.

232 Mug   [PLATE 128]

Glass, blown into an optic mould so that the upper part is faceted. Applied with green trails round the base and blue prunts round the centre.

MARKS None.

Designed and made *c*.1920-30 by the Poschinger'sche Krystallglasfabrik, Moosau bei Frauenau, Bayerischer Wald.

H 14.2cm   1980,5-12,1

This mug is closely similar to wares advertised by the Poschinger'sche Krystallglasfabrik, Frauenau (*Die Schaulade*, 1928, 228; reproduced in Killinger 1986, 39) which show comparable use of trails and prunts; known examples of the biscuit box illustrated in this advertisement use the same colours of blue and green as used on the mug (information supplied by Graham Dry). Stephan Freiherr von Poschinger, the current director of the firm, has confirmed that this mug was made in Frauenau and is still in production today. For a set of similar mugs with matching punch-bowl in which the blue prunts are applied on top of the green trails rather than above, see Galerie Wolfgang Ketterer, 153 Auktion, 10 November 1990, lot 193.

The Poschinger family has owned glassworks in Frauenau since 1605. The works have passed down through fourteen generations of the family until the present day. From the end of the nineteenth century the factory works have been situated at Moosau bei Frauenau. From 1901 to 1935 they were run by Eduard Benedikt von Poschinger, grandfather of the present director.

Glasses of similar design, with faceting and applied prunts, have recently been attributed to Koloman Moser; for example, a wine goblet with similar applied dots and faceted rim (New York 1978, 49) and a set of glasses with applied green prunts (Vienna 1985, no. 13/4/62). However, there seems to be no documentary evidence for such an attribution.

Powell, Alfred Hoare 1865-1960

233 Plaque [PLATE 67]

Earthenware, decorated with a view of Bisham Abbey among trees on the far side of a lake. The building is clearly reflected in the lake, with a daisy-strewn grassy bank in the foreground. The plaque is hand-painted in various shades of blue and green, with touches of red and yellow, the border with foliate pattern in blue and white. The foot rim is pierced with four suspension holes.

MARKS The reverse painted in blue 'BISHAM ABBEY' flanked by floral motifs, together with the monogram 'AP' incorporating a leaf motif for Alfred Powell and the number '3049'. Impressed marks 'WEDGWOOD MADE IN ENGLAND' and date code '4 CC' for 1926—i.e. fourth cycle of year-letters, potter's mark 'c' and letter 'c' for 1926; see Batkin 1982, 230).

Painted by Alfred H. Powell in his studio at 20 Red Lion Square, Bloomsbury, London, on a blank made in 1926 at the Wedgwood factory, Etruria, Staffordshire.

D 34.8 cm   1985,3-8,1

A. H. Powell trained as an architect at the Slade and worked with the architect J. D. Sedding from 1887 to 1892. He then practised as a freelance painter until 1901, when he joined the Cotswold Group, a craft revival movement established by Ernest Gimson and the Barnsley brothers. Both Gimson and Ernest Barnsley were also former pupils of Sedding. Powell's association with Wedgwood began in 1903, when he approached Wedgwood with his designs for ceramics. In 1907 he set up the Bloomsbury studio where he designed and decorated pottery for Wedgwood with his wife Louise (Ada Louise Lessore). The influence of the Powells reached a peak in the 1920s, when hand-painting for large-scale production was revived at Etruria itself, under the Powells' instruction, while other artists were encouraged to decorate pottery for Wedgwood in the Powells' London studio, notably W. R. Sickert and his wife Thérèse Lessore, Louise's sister (see Cat. 142-3; Batkin 1982, 139-45).

Bisham Abbey, near Marlow in Buckinghamshire, was the family home of the Powells and the plaque is likely to have been painted for a member of the family. This plaque is illustrated in Batkin 1982, pl. IV; no other examples with this scene have as yet come to light.

Powell, James & Sons, Whitefriars Glass Works, London 1834-1980

There is no monograph on James Powell & Sons. Some useful contemporary references for the period covered by the items catalogued here are therefore listed below.

Church, A. H., 'Powell's soda-lime glass', The Portfolio, 1890, 42-4

White, G., 'Domestic glass making in London', The Art Journal, 1896, 21-4

Sparrow, W. Shaw, The British Home of Today, 1904, pls G16-19 and Hints on House Furnishings, 1909, 247-61 (chapter on household glass illustrated by Powell glass)

'A two hundred and fiftieth anniversary: the Whitefriars glass-works', Apollo 12, 1930, 361-7

'Design in relation to the problem: hand-made glass – James Powell & Sons (Whitefriars) Ltd', Commercial Art & Industry, new series, 13, July-December 1932, 53-68

For Harry Powell's own writing, see The Principles of Glassmaking, London 1883; 'Table Glass' in Architectural Review 6, 1899, 51-5; 'Cut Glass' in Journal of the Society of Arts 54, 15 June 1906, 776-81; 'Glassmaking before and during the war', JRSA 67, 13 June 1919, 485-95; 'Some Incidental Notes of a Flint-glass Works Manager from 1875-1916' in Journal of the Society of Glass Technology 2, 1916, 241-6; 'The Development of Coloured Glass in England, JSGT 8, 1922, 249-55; Glassmaking in England, London 1923.

For more recent literature, see:

Angus-Butterworth, L. M., British Table and Ornamental Glass, London 1956 (chapter IX on Whitefriars)

Evans, W., 'Whitefriars glass in the 1920s and 30s', British Glass between the wars, exhibition catalogue, Broadfield House Glass Museum, Kingswinford, 1987, 17-20

There is also much relevant information in Morris 1978, Wakefield, 2nd edn 1982 and Manchester 1986.

See also Recent Acquisitions, Cat. 349.

The Whitefriars Glass Works were purchased by James Powell, a wine merchant, in 1834, as additional employment for his three sons, Arthur, Nathaniel and John Cotton. Nathaniel's son Harry (1853-1922), a man of extraordinary talent as designer, historian and scientist, entered the firm in 1873 and together with his cousin, James Crofts Powell (1847-1914), developed radically new forms, colours and decorative techniques, as well as creating special industrial glass for scientific uses.

When the factory closed in 1980 the surviving archive was presented to the Museum of London. Among an overwhelming array of design books, sourcebooks, notebooks, order books, photograph albums and trade catalogues, Wendy Evans of the Museum of London has located material relevant to the cataloguing of the following items and is here acknowledged for her invaluable help. The exhibition which she organised at the Museum of London during 1989 contained many items which will be referred to in the following entries. Powell & Sons' glass never bears a factory mark and rarely any other information.

Seven of the pieces catalogued here (Cat. 234-5, 237-41) were presented to the British Museum by Messrs Powell before the removal of the works to Harrow in 1923. The Museum's 'Book of Presents' has the following uninformative entry under 3 February 1923: 'Glass made at Whitefriars since 1870; seven specimens, three of them imitations of the antique. Given by Messrs Powell & Sons, Whitefriars Glass Works, 26 Tudor Street, Whitefriars, EC4'. A further clue as to how the glasses came to be acquired by the Museum is provided by a notice in the Daily Graphic of 17 January 1923 (reference supplied by Wendy Evans):

> Who would think that the guardians of our London Museums were so enterprising and up to date. Within a few hours of having seen in THE DAILY GRAPHIC, yesterday, the

photographs of the Whitefriars Glass Works, which will be demolished in a few days, an expert arrived at the works from the British Museum with a request that the proprietors would give the Museum some specimens of their glasswork, so that they could become a permanent exhibit in the museum's collection.

Not long afterwards, word came from the Victoria & Albert Museum that they, too, would like something to put on show.

The museum records do not reveal who made the choice at the Whitefriars factory, though it may have been William King, who was then in charge of ceramics and glass. It appears to be a somewhat random choice of pieces that happened to be in the factory; the three pieces copying eighteenth-century models (Cat. 239-41) had direct relevance to the Museum's collections, and the soda-lime vase (Cat. 237) was perhaps seen as an example of the revival of the use of soda glass, but the glasses designed by Webb (Cat. 234) and Jackson (Cat. 235) can have had little relevance, other than as typical examples of Whitefriars production, for the Museum was not at that time systematically collecting nineteenth and twentieth-century material. Since many Whitefriars models remained in production for decades, the items from this group have been catalogued in order of design date, but their date of manufacture could be at any time between the design date and the beginning of 1923.

234 Wine glass [PLATE 57]

Free-blown, with wavy profile, twisted quatrefoil stem and domed foot.

MARKS None.

Designed c.1860 by the architect Philip Webb (1831-1915) for Morris, Marshall, Faulkner & Co., and made by James Powell & Sons, Whitefriars Glass Works, London, before 1923.

H 9.9cm   1923,2-16,6   Given by Messrs Powell in February 1923

Webb was closely associated with William Morris from their first meeting in 1856; he designed the Red House for Morris at Bexley Heath in 1858 and in 1861 became a member of the newly founded Morris, Marshall, Faulkner & Co. Several of Webb's original designs for glass are preserved in the Victoria and Albert Museum, given by Miss Dorothy Walker. They consist of fourteen designs for simple, undecorated table glasses comprising a number of different ranges (E326-339), together with a single sheet of elaborate glasses with applied and enamelled decoration. This sheet is signed and dated 1860 and annotated 'Designs for Glass Vessels for W. Morris Esq.' (E340-1944). These elaborate glasses were intended for Morris's own use at the Red House. The simple glasses were sold by Morris, Marshall, Faulkner & Co. The glass catalogued here is a variant of E326 with modified profile; the drawing is annotated 'twist about a $\frac{1}{4}$ round' and measures 9.7cm (Fig. 17). The Powell & Sons archive in the Museum of London contains a factory working drawing for this glass on the same sheet as other glasses designed by T. G. Jackson (see Cat. 235 and Fig. 18). The quatrefoil-section quarter-twisted stem also occurs in the designs for William Morris.

Many of the simpler designs appear as thumbnail sketches in Webb's passbook for 1862-78, which also gives the prices paid to Webb for his designs: '20 designs for wine glasses at 5s. and ditto for tumblers . . . design for water cruet and tumbler, finger glass, liqueur glass, sugar basin £2 . . . jam dish & cover 10s.' (quoted in Morris 1978, 176; see also Morris 1989a). Barbara

Morris has also noted that during the 1860s glass made by Powell's to Webb's designs seems to have been sold exclusively by Morris & Co. (Morris 1978, 177) and it is clear from surviving Whitefriars trade catalogues for this period that Powell's normal range comprised the standard cut and engraved glass similar to that produced by other high-class glasshouses such as Apsley Pellatt. It was not until the 1870s that Powell's commissioned 'aesthetic' glass on their own account.

For further examples of glass designed by Webb for Morris & Co., and made by Powell's, see Morris 1978, pls 111-12 (in the Victoria and Albert Museum). Some of these were bequeathed to the V & A by May Morris in 1939 from Kelmscott Manor, but they do not figure among the Red House designs. Examples of Morris & Co. designs are also held by the Kunstgewerbemuseum, Zurich; see Gysling-Billeter 1975, no. 351. See also Powell 1923, 43, pl. 29A and B. The series remained in production for several decades. W. A. Thorpe, writing in 1935, regarded most of Webb's glasses as incompetent, especially for their 'meanness of stem'; he is here referring to the squat stuck shanks of many of them (Thorpe 1935, 243-4).

For further information about Philip Webb, see Lethaby 1932.

235 Liqueur glass, champagne glass and wine glass
[PLATE 58; COLOUR PLATE VI]

Free-blown, with wavy profiles and knopped stems. The liqueur glass in clear glass, the champagne glass in straw opal and the wine glass in green.

MARKS None.

Designed in 1870 by the architect Thomas Graham Jackson (1835-1924) and made by James Powell & Sons, Whitefriars Glass Works, London, probably all before 1923.

235a Liqueur glass: H 9.4cm   1923,2-16,7   Given by Messrs Powell in February 1923
235b Champagne glass: H 12.2cm   1988,6-7,1
235c Wine glass: H 14.8cm   1989,6-9,1

In his Recollections Jackson recalls that he first met James Crofts Powell in 1866, when he went to the Whitefriars Glass Works to order a window for Lyndon Church in Rutland, which he was then restoring (B. H. Jackson, ed., 1950, 118). His travels with J. C. Powell throughout Europe led him to turn his attention to stained glass and to design windows for Powell's. Of his table glass, he recalls, 'I used also at this time to design a good deal of table glass for the Powells. The agreement was that I was to have one piece of everything I designed, or the value of it. This paid me very well in the larger and more expensive articles, but not in the smaller. I remember, for instance, designing a wine-glass which caught the public taste, and at one time I used to see it everywhere when I dined out, together with the decanter and finger-glass that went with it, and I used to chaff Powell about the one wine-glass that formed my remuneration' (B. H. Jackson 1950, 116). Jackson later made a series of alterations to the Powell works at Whitefriars.

The original design, signed in monogram and dated 1870, for this service, comprising decanter, wine glass and champagne glass, is illustrated in Apollo 1930, 363, but no reference to its location was given and it is not in the Powell archive. The archive does, however, contain a design for a tazza and a footed jug with wavy outline similar to the decanter, similarly signed and dated 1870: H. J. Powell, however, dates the design of the table service to 1874 (Powell 1923, 132). The archive also contains a factory working drawing for six glasses (Fig. 18), including these three and the Webb glass (Cat. 234). There are also several undated archive photographs, in two photographic albums, c.1880-1900 (Ref. 80.547/3249, 3250), giving the model numbers of the champagne glass as 2002, selling at 24s. per dozen, the liqueur glass as 2007, selling at 14s. per dozen and the wine glass as 2101, selling at 21s. per dozen. The heights of the three glasses correspond exactly with the drawing, which includes two smaller-size wine glasses, one of which, shown on its side, combines a modified Webb bowl with a Jackson stem. The archive photographs show that there was also a small carafe with wavy outline and matching water glass (an example of the small carafe has recently been acquired, reg. no. 1991, 1-7, 1).

Jackson's designs for Powell & Sons are similar in their simple shapes and wavy outlines to those designed by Webb (see Cat. 234), but they were commissioned and sold by Powell's. W. A. Thorpe saw the Jackson glasses as a marked advance on the Webb designs in view of their tall stems flowing into the curves of the bowl (Thorpe 1935, 244). The range appears to have been most commonly executed in green. H. J. Powell, writing on table glass in 1899, recalls that the Jackson glasses were first made in 'a light dull green with a wealth of bubbles and irregularities. Owing to these so-called defects, the glass only appealed to a very select circle.' The colour was known as 'pale green' (Powell 1899, 51-5, illustrating the decanter, wine and champagne glass). In his 'Incidental Notes of a Flint-glass Works Manager' Powell records that straw opal was introduced in 1877-9 (Powell 1916). For a green decanter and stopper from the same service in the Victoria and Albert Museum, see Morris 1978, pl. 114. Further examples, a wine glass and finger-bowl, are held by Manchester City Polytechnic (Cooke 1986, 31). See also Gysling-Billeter 1975, 357, for three wine glasses in the Kunstgewerbemuseum, Zurich, acquired from Powell's in 1906.

Jackson's decanter and glasses were illustrated anonymously as examples of well-proportioned, reasonably priced table glass by Mrs Loftie in The Dining Room (1878, 96), part of the Macmillan 'Art at Home' series. The book was aimed at the middle-class artistic home and illustrated the Powell glass in outline (Morris 1978, 179). In common with the Webb series, the Jackson glasses were produced over several decades, but it is unlikely that they were still produced after the firm moved to Harrow in 1923; Harry Powell retired at the end of the First World War, and the firm was taken over by a cousin, Marriot Powell, under whom the production was radically changed.

236 Tazza [PLATE 59]

Free-blown glass, engraved and applied decoration. The bowl and foot in pale sea-green, the air-twist stem in a contrasting brighter green. The bowl engraved with four gannets flying above a web-like wave pattern in trailed deep-green glass. The engraving has been carried out on the underside of the glass before the application of the trailed pattern, which has then been acid-etched to produce a matt surface in selected areas. The wave pattern is also applied to the foot. The double-series air-twist stem comprises a multiple-ply spiral band outside a fine spiral gauze or multiple spiral.

MARKS None.

Designed by Harry J. Powell (1853-1922) before 1902 and made by James Powell & Sons, Whitefriars Glass Works, London.

H 21 cm 1988,4-2,1

An identical tazza is illustrated in The Studio, 1902, 256, in an article on the English section at the Turin Exhibition, described as 'tazza clouded with colours and engraved with sea-gulls. Designed by H. Powell . . .'

The Powell archive holds, among the drawings of this period, a sketch for this tazza by Harry Powell showing the waves on the bowl and annotated 'fine threading, green and white to look like waves', the stem annotated 'new air twist'. Next to it is a sketch for one of the flying birds labelled 'gannet' (Fig. 19, Harry Powell's source notebook, ref. 80.547/3251/1). The reverse of the sheet on which the tazza is drawn has designs for glasses annotated 'Glasgow 1901', suggesting that the tazza sketch was done about this time. In addition a photograph of the tazza is pasted into this book, with the caption 'Engraved sea-gulls, streaked bowl, air twist leg: sea-green'. It is difficult to tell from this description whether the tazza was ever executed with green and white threading as suggested in the sketch. No other examples of this tazza have so far been recorded, so this may be the one exhibited in Turin. In general Powell & Sons showed standard production pieces when they participated in exhibitions, both in England and abroad. They did on occasion make specially designed exhibition pieces, of which further versions were made if orders were received. At the most, two or three examples might have been made of such an elaborate piece.

The photograph in Harry Powell's notebook shows a clear glass body; thus The Studio's description 'clouded with colours' is probably inaccurate, especially as the photograph is the same as the illustration in The Studio. The photograph is further annotated 'book', indicating that it was used in Glassmaking in England, published in 1923 after Harry Powell's death; Powell illustrates the tazza as fig. 32 in his glossary of technical terms, with the caption 'air twist in leg, fine (modern)', characteristically omitting to acknowledge the tazza as his own design.

Harry Powell joined the firm in 1873 and from 1880 the firm's production came under his direct control. Although he devoted much of his energy to copying glass of earlier periods, he made several highly original designs c.1900 which were an important contribution to the Art Nouveau style. This tazza illustrates his preoccupation with Venetian and Venetian-style glass in the shape of the bowl and the tapering stem with its sharp merese at the top. The air-twist stems, derived from English eighteenth-century models, are especially characteristic of Harry Powell's designs of this period: the Powell archive includes a design for a goblet with similar air-twist stem dated 1899. A contemporary photograph shows a tazza with white enamel opaque-twist stem and shell-threaded foot and bowl. Shell-threaded decoration occurs in another design of 1899 for a tazza with plain tapering stem.

There are no other designs with comparable engraved decoration as early as 1902. The style of the engraving looks forward to Powell's engraved pieces of slightly later date such as the goblet with engraved fish (The Studio Yearbook, 1909, 114) or the blue glass bird and fish bowl of 1909 (shown in the exhibition of Whitefriars glass held at the Museum of London in 1989). Powell & Sons' chief engraver at this period was T. Hillebauer; little is known about him, but the fact that he is frequently acknowledged in contemporary literature (for example the catalogues of the Arts & Crafts Exhibition Society, 1896, 131, no. 553; 1903, 76-7, no. 179; 1906, 34, no. 87; The Studio 37, 1906, 223; and The Studio Yearbook, 1909, 114) suggests that he was highly regarded and may well have engraved this tazza. Alongside Hillebauer, Tommy Smith receives frequent mention as Whitefriars' master blower.

This tazza, with its innovative use of engraving and of threaded decoration, incorporating an apparently unique use of matt-etched areas, is among the most original examples of English glass of the period.

237 Vase [PLATE 60]

Free-blown soda-lime glass, turquoise-blue deepening in shade towards the base, with five dimpled sides and rigoree (applied band with milled edge) round the foot. The glass is extremely lightweight.

MARKS None.

Designed by Harry Powell before 1906 and made by James Powell & Sons, Whitefriars Glass Works, London, before 1923.

H 20.3 cm   1923,2-16,1   Given by Messrs Powell in February 1923

A design drawing for this vase appears in the firm's design book for 1903 and later: no. 1161, height 20.2 cm (ref. 80.547/ 3306). According to Wendy Evans the pattern number suggests a design date of c.1904-5. A vase of the same design is illustrated in The Studio Yearbook, 1906, 246, confirming this suggestion. No designer is given, but it is shown among documented Harry Powell designs and is characteristic of his work of the early 1900s. The tumbler shape is derived from Powell & Sons' copies of earlier models including Dutch seventeenth-century glasses (see Kingswinford 1987, no. 23) or the vase with applied tears copied from the Portinari altarpiece by Hugo van der Goes, for which Harry Powell's design dated 1901 survives in the Powell archive (shown in the 1989 exhibition). Harry's cousin, James Crofts Powell, was also much involved in what were known as 'glasses with histories', which he and Harry sketched during their visits to the Continent. In his article on Powell & Sons' new soda-lime glass (The Portfolio 1890), A. H. Church notes that J. C. Powell was responsible for selecting seventeenth-century models for reproduction in soda-lime glass and his article is illustrated with J. C. Powell's drawings.

Church gives an analysis of the composition of the firm's soda-lime glass, which he describes in delicate hues of honey-yellow, pale olive green and aquamarine blue. According to Harry Powell this blue was known as 'Alsatian'; it was achieved with iron, based on analysis of Roman glass, and was introduced in 1889 (Powell 1916, and 1923, 162). Powell's soda-lime glass was in production by 1888, when it was exhibited at the Arts & Crafts Exhibition Society (catalogue for 1888, 163, no. 386).

Harry Powell records that decanters and vases with dents in the body, to provide a secure grip, were produced by the firm from c.1880 (Powell 1923, 83). Forms with dented sides were still being made in the mid 1930s (see Dowling 1935, pl. XXII).

238 Wine glass [PLATE 60]

Free-blown clear glass, with tapered stem, ribbed foot and sharp merese between stem and bowl. The stem contains a double-series opaque twist: a four-ply white enamel band outside four spiral white enamel tapes.

MARKS None.

Designed by Harry Powell before 1896 and made by James Powell & Sons, Whitefriars Glass Works, London, before 1923.

H 14 cm   1923,2-16,4   Given by Messrs Powell in February 1923

A closely similar glass of the same shape with a double-series opaque-twist stem is illustrated in an article on Whitefriars glass by Gleeson White in the Art Journal, 1896, 24. For discussion of tapered air-twist stems, see Cat. 236. Mould-blown ribbed feet were also characteristic of Whitefriars glass of the late nineteenth and early twentieth century and are clearly visible in a number of contemporary illustrations.

239 Cider glass [PLATE 60]

Free-blown clear glass, thick stem with single-series air-twist, the bucket-shaped bowl wheel-engraved with a frieze of cider-apple branches, the engraving matt with a polished dot on each apple.

MARKS None.

Designed before 1905 and made by James Powell & Sons, Whitefriars Glass Works, London, before 1923.

H 16.3 cm   1923,2-16,3   Given by Messrs Powell in February 1923

An identical glass is illustrated in the Art Journal, 1905, 64, described as 'cider glass copied from a Gloucestershire original'. The mid-eighteenth-century original was at that time in the celebrated collection of eighteenth-century glass owned by A. Hartshorne, whose book Old English Glasses, published in 1897, illustrated this glass as pl. 51; he records that he obtained it in Hereford and describes it as having a 'brilliant air-twist stem, engraved in an admirable manner with an apple-branch border, which has been oil-gilded'. It has been published more recently by L. M. Bickerton (1986, pl. 414, height 6½ in (16.5 cm)). The Hartshorne collection is now at Worthing Museum, West Sussex.

The air-twist on the eighteenth-century original has a pair of corkscrews, while the Whitefriars copy has three corkscrews. Moreover, it does not reach along the entire stem, nor fill the stem across its width. Given that Powell's were able to produce air-twists of superb quality, it was probably a factory reject. But, as a copy of an eighteenth-century glass it was nevertheless considered a useful study piece for the British Museum.

240 Candlestick [PLATE 61]

Free-blown lead glass, the glass greyish and very heavy.

MARKS None.

Made by James Powell & Sons, Whitefriars Glass Works, London, before 1923.

H 29 cm   1923,2-16,2   Given by Messrs Powell in February 1923

The shape is close to that of English cut-glass candlesticks of c.1770 (see Powell 1923, 139, fig. 97; Thorpe 1929, pl. CXLIII); thus it is probably a blank for a copy of such a candlestick (I am grateful to John Smith for this suggestion). The Powell archive contains a number of designs for cut candlesticks of different sizes. A particularly close example of this shape and dimensions is no. 0 2923, height 28.8 cm, in the Special Designs Book of 1906-13, where the names of the clients are often recorded. The client for this candlestick was one Medhurst, and it sold for 50s. a pair; the design has later been annotated in 1926 with the price of £6 5s. a pair (Fig. 20). An example of a Powell & Sons cut-glass candlestick of this type is illustrated in the Architectural Review 62, July-December 1927, 90, in an article on modern table glass. The caption, 'Designer and craftsman: H. J. Powell', suggests that Harry Powell did the cutting himself. If so, then it must date earlier, before Powell's retirement.

The British Museum acquisitions register describes this piece as 'after an old model; the colour intentionally darkened'. The greyish colour, characteristic of eighteenth-century glass, is extremely deceptive and were it not for the provenance this candlestick could easily be mistaken for an eighteenth-century original.

241 Salt-cellar [PLATE 60]

Mould-blown and cut lead glass, with boat-shaped bowl and diamond-shaped foot, the bowl with wavy rim and four-petal motif, hexagonal faceted stem.

MARKS None.

Made by James Powell & Sons, Whitefriars Glass Works, London, before 1923.

H 8.8 cm, W 10.1 cm   1923,2-16,5   Given by Messrs Powell in February 1923

This is after a late-eighteenth century pattern of c.1790-1800, with characteristic boat-shaped cellar and lozenge-shaped foot (see Thorpe 1929, pl. CXLIV). However, it is more easily distinguishable as a copy than the candlestick; the foot would be thicker in an eighteenth-century example.

The design drawing for this salt-cellar is included in the 1906-13 Special Designs Book in the Powell archive, as shape no. 0 2876, height 9.1 cm, width 10.6 cm. The same pattern of cutting was used on several other items, including a salt-cellar with taller stem (0 2871-2) and a goblet (0 2455). In 1906 Harry Powell read a paper on the history of cut glass in England to the Society of Arts (JSA 54, 15 June 1906, 776-81). The lecture was given at the Whitefriars works, where several of the firm's 'copies of old specimens' were exhibited. It seems likely that many of the firm's copies of earlier cut glass date from this time. In 1906 a number of specimens of cut glass were exhibited by Powell & Sons at the Arts & Crafts Exhibition Society; the catalogue (no. 87) attributed the cutting to Longshaw.

242 Vase [PLATE 61]

Free-blown dark green glass, with pulled and blown claws, and applied threading at top and bottom, the lower threading applied before the claws were pulled. There is a rigoree round the neck and down the outside of each claw. The upper part broken and repaired.

MARKS None.

Made by James Powell & Sons, Whitefriars Glass Works, London, between 1883 and 1894.

H 27.1 cm   1894,5-20,2   Given by A. W. Franks

This is a copy of one of a group of celebrated glass claw-beakers from the Anglo-Saxon burial at Taplow, Berkshire, excavated in 1883 and acquired by the British Museum in that year. The Taplow excavations aroused enormous interest as the richest Anglo-Saxon burial then known, and contained no fewer than four claw-beakers, all of tall slender proportions, and among the most elegant examples of the type (see V. Evison, 'Anglo-Saxon glass claw-beakers', Archaeologia 107, 1982, 43-76). The prototype (Department of Medieval and Later Antiquities, 1883,12-14,13) was the only one of the group to be restored in 1883; the others were not restored until the 1970s.

The original is in a pale yellowish-green soda glass and is very thin-walled. The Whitefriars copy is much coarser and heavier. The dark-green colour is, according to Wendy Evans, typical of the 1890s. There are many other differences in both shape and technique: the copy is more bulgy and squat; the claws of the original are simply pulled from the body of the glass, whereas in the copy they are blown as well; the foot of the original is blown in one with the body and folded up, while the copy has a separate applied foot.

Sir A. W. Franks (1826-97) was Keeper of the Department of Antiquities and Ethnography from 1866 to 1896. Powell & Sons' interest in ancient glass is well documented: the firm made copies of a number of Roman and Anglo-Saxon glasses, including examples in the British Museum. Harry Powell's source notebook (ref. 80.547/3251/1) contains a page with five sketches of Roman and Anglo-Saxon glass (including a claw-beaker from Cambridgeshire) annotated 'BM. 20 1.94'. Franks presented the Taplow copy to the Museum in May 1894, and it is therefore very likely that the copy was made in the previous three months.

The Powell archive also contains a volume labelled 'Glasses with Histories', which includes a thumbnail sketch of a claw-beaker described as from Hythe, Kent, annotated with detailed measurements and the firm's pattern number 1377. The 1989 exhibition at the Museum of London showed the design drawing for this same beaker, dated 10 March 1909, and fully annotated with instructions to the glass-blower: 'Very light, between Alsatian and sea-green in colour, no rigoree used, very fine melted-in thread, lower thread coarser than upper thread, pipes solid at end, 4 upper, 4 lower pipes, upper pipe $1\frac{1}{2}$ in wide, lower pipe $1\frac{3}{4}$ in wide.' The drawing gives the total height as $6\frac{7}{8}$ in and the width of the top as $3\frac{1}{2}$ in. But no actual example based on this drawing has so far come to light, neither have any other copies of the Taplow beaker.

243 Vase [PLATE 116]

Mould-blown in an optic rib mould, with applied horizontal threads in deep green on a sea-green body.

MARKS None.

The shape originally designed c.1907 by Harry Powell; this is a modified version produced in the 1930s. Made by James Powell & Sons, Whitefriars Glassworks, Wealdstone, Harrow, Middlesex.

H 20.6 cm, D 16.4 cm   1988,1-14,1

The earlier version, shape no. 1257, is one of Harry Powell's 'Glass vases from Claypots', inspired by prehistoric earthenware pots of the 'beaker' culture, of which many examples are in the British Museum. The later version, shape no. 1258, appears in the firm's 1931 catalogue (archive, 225). Both shapes are illustrated in H. G. Dowling's A Survey of British Industrial Arts, 1935, pls XXI and XXII (the earlier version). A range of threaded vases including the later version of this shape is illustrated in a Whitefriars catalogue of 1938 in the Victoria and Albert Museum Library, pls 14-15. Shape 1258 was produced in two sizes, 8 in (20 cm) sold for 17s 0d. and 10 in (25 cm) for 25s. The colour variations advertised included dark blue or green threaded on sea-green (the traditional Whitefriars colour); amber threaded on gold amber; white on flint or clear glass; dark blue tinted on sea-green; ruby on flint. Examples are known to have been made with dark blue threading on pale blue (for a lamp base in these colours, see Kingswinford 1987, no. 264).

Although contemporary illustrations do not appear to be recorded before the 1930s, Powell & Sons were making threaded wares in the late 1920s. In 1929 the Manchester City Art Gallery acquired a bowl and bottle with widely spaced blue threads on green (1929.372 and 373). This fine threading should not be confused with the broader ribbon-threading which was introduced on a variety of shapes in the 1930s by Barnaby Powell.

Powolny, Michael 1871-1954

See also **Lötz**

A monograph on Powolny was published as this book was going to press and has therefore not been consulted: Frottier, E., *Michael Powolny-Keramik und Glas aus Wien 1900-1950*, Vienna 1990. See also Neuwirth 1974 and Rochowanski 1923.

244 Tumbler   [PLATE 106]

Machine-made glass, with engraved decoration of a putto carrying a pear branch, within a circle with a scalloped border which is repeated round the rim.

MARKS Acid-etched on the base with the Lobmeyr signet, two 'L's back to back for the two Lobmeyr brothers, intersected by a 'w' for Wien.

Designed c.1914 and made by the firm of J. & L. Lobmeyr, Vienna.

H 8.7cm, D of rim 8.2cm   1981,12-6,1

Powolny trained as a sculptor and ceramic artist at the Fachschule für Tonindustrie in Znaim, then at the Kunstgewerbeschule in Vienna, where he taught from 1909. He made several designs for engraved glass for Lobmeyr between about 1914 and 1925, including a series of similar tumblers. The starting point for these tumblers was a goblet designed in 1914 and ornamented with allegorical motifs, including the putto with pear branch (*DK & D* 34, 1914, 375; *Die Kunst* XXXII, 1914-15, 31; Eisler 1916, 161). The same motifs of putti were then used on the tumblers (*DK & D* 37, 1915-16, 100; *DK & D* 41, 1917-18, 105; Pazaurek 1925, 162-4, pls 174-5). For a goblet engraved with similar roundels shown at the Paris Exhibition of 1925, see Léon 1927, pl. LXXXVIII. Powolny's designs were apparently also used for jewellery; a rectangular amethyst glass brooch with the putto and pear-branch motif was sold at Christie's, Geneva, 10 May 1987, lot 211, described as moulded glass. For Lobmeyr, see Vienna 1973.

Prutscher, Otto 1880-1949

Eisler, M., *Otto Prutscher*, Leipzig and Vienna 1925

245 Wine glass   [PLATE 106; COLOUR PLATE VI]

Clear, mould-blown glass overcased in blue, the blue layer cut to form a pattern of squares on the stem and rim.

MARKS None.

Designed c.1907 and made probably by Meyr's Neffe K. K. priv. Kristallglasfabriken, Adolf, Adolfshütte Glassworks, near Winterberg, Böhmerwald, Czechoslovakia, for the retail glassware firm of Bakalowits & Söhne, Vienna.

H 21cm, D of base and rim 8.3cm   1982,5-12,3

Prutscher studied under Hoffmann at the Kunstgewerbeschule, Vienna, where he taught from 1909. He designed and executed metalwork for the Wiener Werkstätte (see Cat. 125), and

ceramics, furniture and glass for various firms (Neuwirth 1974a, 266), as well as several interior designs.

Neuwirth 1984, 200-3, states that the service to which this glass belongs was commissioned by Bakalowits & Söhne, Vienna, and executed probably by Meyr's Neffe. A glass of this design was illustrated in *DK & D* 20, 1907, 340 and was included in the Vienna Kunstschau of 1908 (see *DK* XVI, 1908, 542). This and other related designs were widely illustrated in succeeding years (*DK & D* 25, 1909-10, 376; *The Studio Yearbook*, 1912, 223).

This glass was made in several alternative colours: examples in dark red are owned by the Brighton Museum (Rutherford & Beddoe, no. 4) and the Bröhan collection (Bröhan II/1, 1976, no. 334); see also Christie's, London, 13 July 1988, lots 256-8, six glasses, cased in blue, red, purple, yellow, green and pink, and Neuwirth 1984, nos 182-6. Further variations included the addition of painted squares on the clear glass areas (e.g. Schmitt 1989, no. 132). However, Helmut Ricke (Leipzig 1989, no. 330) has noted that Meyr's Neffe produced their own modifications of the pattern, which they used on other shapes, so that not all glasses of this type can be attributed to Prutscher.

For the most recent and detailed account of Meyr's Neffe, see Schmitt 1989, 250-51.

Pugin, Augustus Welby Northmore 1812-52

Ferrey, B., *Recollections of Pugin*, first published London 1861, reprinted, with introduction and index by C. and J. Wainwright, London 1977
Trappes-Lomax, M., *Pugin, a medieval Victorian*, London 1932
Stanton, P., *Pugin*, London 1971
Victorian Church Art, exhibition catalogue, Victoria and Albert Museum, London 1971, section B: A. W. N. Pugin, 7-21

Pugin himself wrote widely on Gothic architecture and ornament. The following two publications are especially relevant for the items catalogued here: Pugin, A. W. N., *The Glossary of Ecclesiastical Ornament and Costume*, London 1844 and *Floriated Ornament: a series of thirty-nine designs*, London 1849.

246 Bread plate   [PLATE 2]

Buff earthenware, inlaid with blue and red-brown coloured clays. In the centre, a pattern of ears of wheat and foliate ornament; round the rim the inscription in black-letter script 'waste not want not'. The inscription and decoration is left in buff with the background inlaid in red-brown in the centre and blue for the border.

MARKS None.

Designed before 1849 and made by Minton & Co., Stoke-on-Trent.

D 32.5cm   1981,11-4,1

Pugin's Gothic-revival architecture was governed by the doctrine that Gothic architecture embodied the Catholic religion, to which he had converted in 1835. From the late 1830s he developed Gothic design in the applied arts, turning to Herbert Minton for the execution of his designs for 'encaustic' or inlaid tiles in the medieval manner for his Gothic-revival churches. By the early 1840s Minton had developed a modern method of imitating medieval tiles: the same inlay method was used for this bread plate, which is exceptional in being apparently Pugin's only other design for Minton to use this technique.

This plate is Minton shape number 430, described as 'Pugin's

Bread Tray – Encaustic' in one of the surviving shape record books in the Minton archive; the designs were entered in chronological order. It occurs in a variety of encaustic colours in different sizes and there is also a majolica version.

The bread plate was shown by Minton & Co. in the exhibition held in Birmingham in 1849 by the British Association for the Advancement of Science (*Catalogue of the articles in the Exhibition of Manufactures and Art*, Birmingham 1849, 22, no. 81: 'Pugin's Bread Tray, red, blue and buff'). An engraving of Pugin's design was illustrated in the *Journal of Design and Manufactures* III, 1850, 88, founded by Henry Cole as a vehicle for his ideas on design reform.

For an example formerly in the Handley-Read collection and now in the Fitzwilliam Museum, Cambridge, see London 1972, B39; For an example in the Victoria and Albert Museum (c.46.1972), see London 1976, D23 and Jervis 1983, pl. 65. For an example with impressed shape number 430, see London, Fine Art Society, 1981, no. 4.

247 Tazza [PLATE I]

Earthenware, on a low foot, decorated in transfer-printed cherry-red and green. Inside the bowl a central foliate roundel and border comprising a broad outer band with trefoils and an inner scroll. The outer motif is repeated on the foot, while the inner scroll is repeated on the outside edge of the bowl.

MARKS Impressed on the base with Minton year-cypher for 1856, together with the letters 'BB' for Best Body and 'NEW STONE'.

Designed c.1850-51 and put into production by Minton & Co., Stoke-on-Trent, Staffordshire, at the end of 1855. This example made in 1856, pattern number A2460.

D 30.5cm, H 6.9cm   1981,7-16,1

The Minton archive contains a group of water-colour designs by Pugin, many of which are signed, with the date 1850 or 1851. They bear the numbers S1-28, which are recorded as Pugin in the Art Catalogue of 1871 (Minton MSS 1234). Two of these designs, S13 and S15 (unsigned), illustrate motifs almost identical with those used for the central and border motifs on the tazza (Figs 1 and 2), illustrated in colour in Jones 1989, fig. 3. A third design, S9, signed and dated 1850, with foliate ornament and black-letter inscription 'ubi amor ibi fides', corresponds to a transfer-printed plate in the Victoria and Albert Museum (459-1852); see London 1976, D25.

The Minton Museum owns a plate with identical pattern to that used inside the tazza, but executed in three colours, turquoise blue, cherry red and buff. It bears the year-cypher for 1857 and the painted pattern number A2486. This pattern was executed in at least nine different colour combinations, all of which are recorded in the pattern-books in the Minton archive. The plate shape is described as 'table French', the pattern as 'Medieval' 'Printed by our New Press'. The nine variants listed below are dated between 27 November and 1 December 1855 and must therefore have been worked out by Minton's art department after Pugin's death in 1852, using his designs of 1850-51. Two-colour plates cost 4s. 6d., while three- or four-colour plates cost 5s. (presumably per dozen). The third or fourth colour was added to the bands and trefoils after the printing, hence the extra cost.

A2453	Turquoise angles and lines, cerise ground	(29 Nov 1855)
A2456	Turquoise angles and lines, cobalt ground	
A2460	Cerise and green	(27 Nov 1855)
A2464	Cobalt and cerise, buff bands	(1 Dec 1855)
A2465	Turquoise and cerise	(30 Nov 1855)
A2466	Turquoise and mazarine	(27 Nov 1855)
A2468	Cobalt and turquoise, coloured in buff	(29 Nov 1855)
A2485	Turquoise angles and lines, cerise ground, buff bands, green trefoils	
A2486	Cerise angles and lines, turquoise ground, buff bands	

These patterns were produced until at least 1868 as the numbers appear in the factory costing book at this date. The reference to 'New Press' indicates the use of the Collins and Reynolds process for printing on ceramics by lithography, patented in 1848 and subsequently acquired by Herbert Minton.

The Minton Museum collection also includes a plate and a lidded soup tureen with saucer, transfer-printed in blue and deep red with a different Pugin design and bearing the year-cypher for 1851, pattern number 8659 and pattern name 'Gothic' in underglaze blue. In these examples, the colours have flown. Two further examples of Pugin's Gothic-style transfer-printed designs for Minton are to be found in the V & A: an octofoil plate with vine leaves and grapes of c.1848 (c.33-1984) and a plate with the inscription 'souvenez vous de moi', dated 1851 (460-1852).

Puiforcat, Jean 1897-1945

Herbst, R., *Jean Puiforcat Orfèvre et Sculpteur*, Paris 1951
De Bonneville, F., *Jean Puiforcat*, Paris 1986 (with full bibliography including many contemporary articles)

248 Teaset [PLATE 118]

Silver and Brazilian rosewood, comprising teapot, milk jug, sugar bowl and biscuit jar with lid. The handles of both teapot and milk jug are formed of a thick block of wood with cylindrical grip. Both pieces are fitted inside with a sheet of silver across the front to prevent spillage, necessitated by the small spout. The sugar bowl and biscuit jar are set with rectangular panels of wood down the narrow sides and the lids of both jar and teapot have quadrant-shaped wood handles. All interiors are gilded except for the teapot.

MARKS All pieces stamped on the base 'JEAN E. PUIFORCAT PARIS' with lozenge-shaped maker's mark 'EP' flanking a pen-knife; French internal silver-standard mark erased and substituted with Minerva-head export mark (sugar bowl bears stamped signature only). Maker's mark and export mark also on inner rim of lids of teapot and biscuit jar. All pieces are stamped on upper edge with London Assay Office import mark, standard mark '925' and date-letter for 1964, together with sponsor's mark 'MB&S' for M. Beer & Son Ltd, London.

Designed in 1929 and made in the Puiforcat workshops, Paris. Given by Mr and Mrs John Cox in 1981. The donors acquired the set from George Attenborough & Sons, silver and jewellery merchants of Fleet Street, in 1966. According to information supplied by Attenborough's at that time, the set was originally purchased from them in 1930.

248a Teapot: H 13cm, L 22cm, W 10.5cm   1981,3-11,2
248b Milk jug: H 7.5cm, L 12.7cm, W 5.5cm   1981,3-11,3
248c Sugar bowl: H 7cm, L 12.3cm, W 7.7cm   1981,3-11,4
248d Biscuit jar: H 7cm (with handles, 9cm), L 12.4cm, W 7.4cm   1981,3-11,5

The son of a goldsmith, Puiforcat was self-taught as a designer, setting up his own workshop in 1922. He exhibited at the Paris Exhibition of 1925 and in 1928 joined the Union des Artistes Modernes, a breakaway modernist group favouring simplicity of design in reaction to the decorative style of the Société des Artistes Décorateurs. Puiforcat owned a celebrated collection of eighteenth-century silver and was also a distinguished athlete, being a tennis champion, a member of the French national Rugby football team and the Olympic ice-hockey team.

This teaset was designed for the 'Exposition de joaillerie et d'orfèvrerie du Musée Galliéra' in the summer of 1929 and is illustrated in *Art et Décoration* LVI, July-December 1929, 43 (as part of a review of the whole exhibition, pp. 33-50). The exhibition, organised by the Chambre Syndicale de la Bijouterie, Joaillerie et Orfèvrerie, was widely publicised in other journals, for example *Les Echos des Industries d'Art*, July 1929, 25-9, where Puiforcat was acclaimed as the innovator and guiding force behind modernist silver.

For further contemporary discussion of Puiforcat's silver, see Quenioux 1925 and Bouilhet 1941. This teaset was included in the Art Deco exhibition held in Minneapolis in 1971 (cat. no. 202). There are apparently no other published examples of this design.

Ramsden, Omar 1873-1939
Carr, Alwyn Charles Ellison 1872-1940

Omar Ramsden 1873-1939: centenary exhibition of silver, City
   Museum and Art Gallery, Birmingham, 1973
For Ramsden's own writing, see Ramsden, O., 'English silver and its future', *Journal of the Royal Society of Arts* 77, 1928, 51-71. See also Delieb, E., 'Omar Ramsden – me fecit', *Apollo* LXXV, 1961, 184-7. Ramsden & Carr's work was illustrated regularly in *The Studio*.

Omar Ramsden and Alwyn Carr met at the Sheffield School of Art, where Ramsden attended evening classes from 1890. They both won four-year scholarships at the School, Carr in 1893 and Ramsden a year later. Their partnership was formed by February 1898, when they registered a mark in London. They worked initially at the Stamford Bridge Studios in Chelsea, moving to the Albert Studios in Battersea in 1901, and then to St Dunstan's Studios, Fulham in 1905 (Birmingham 1973 above and Culme 1987). The partnership was dissolved in 1919, but Ramsden continued to run the workshop until his death in 1939. According to Birmingham 1973 above, Ramsden executed little silver himself; this was done by Carr and their assistants. The designing, up to 1919, seems to have been done mainly by Carr.

In addition to the silverwares discussed below, the British Museum also holds jewellery by Ramsden & Carr; see Gere et al., *The Art of the Jeweller, a Catalogue of the Hull Grundy Gift to the British Museum*, 1984, no. 1004 (a gold finger-ring made for the Bishop of Exeter in 1903), no. 1005 (a silver-gilt waist girdle made for Ramsden's wife in 1926) and no. 1010 (a set of six silver buttons in the form of Tudor roses), nos 1005 and 1010 made by Ramsden after the partnership had dissolved.

Ramsden & Carr 1898-1919

249 Menu holder [PLATE 69]

Silver, pierced and repoussé, in the form of a galleon.

MARKS Stamped on the feet 'RN & CR' together with London hallmarks and date-letter for 1908.

Made in the Ramsden & Carr workshop in 1908.

H 5.8 cm   1980,10-7,3   Given by Professor and Mrs John Hull Grundy

250 Bowl [PLATE 69]

Silver, hand-raised, with a band of repoussé ornament in the form of prunus blossom. The interior of the bowl is set with a circular plaque with translucent foiled green enamel applied with a silver flowering prunus branch and bordered with twisted wire.

MARKS The base of the bowl engraved 'OMAR RAMSDEN ET ALWYN CARR ME FECERUNT', and stamped with London hallmarks and date-letter for 1915 and makers' mark 'RN & CR'.

Made in the Ramsden & Carr workshop in 1915.

Max. D 12 cm, H 5.7 cm   1980,10-7,1   Given by Professor and Mrs John Hull Grundy

See Cat. 252 for a bowl of similar form with a different floral motif produced in Ramsden's workshops in 1934.

Ramsden, Omar 1919-1939

251 Desk ornament [PLATE 69]

Silver, cast, in the form of a nymph covered in clinging drapery, set on a weighted foot.

MARKS Stamped on the foot with the London hallmarks and date-letter for 1926 and maker's mark 'OR', registered in 1918.

Made in the workshop of Omar Ramsden in 1926.

H 13.3 cm   1980,10-7,4   Given by Professor and Mrs John Hull Grundy

252 Bowl [PLATE 69]

Silver, hand-raised, with a band of repoussé floral ornament. The interior of the bowl is set with a circular plaque enamelled in translucent blue and applied in silver with a spray of flowers and leaves, echoing those on the exterior.

MARKS The base of the bowl engraved 'OMAR RAMSDEN ME FECIT' and stamped with London hallmarks and date-letter for 1934 and maker's mark 'OR'.

Made in the workshop of Omar Ramsden in 1934.

Max. D 12 cm, H 5.8 cm   1980,10-7,2   Given by Professor and Mrs John Hull Grundy

253 Set of six dessert knives and forks [PLATE 115]

Silver, the knives with steel blades, the handles formed of two stamped halves, with engraved linear ornament.

MARKS Each piece stamped on the handle with London hallmarks and date-letter for 1935-6 and maker's mark 'OR'. The knife-blades stamped in black-letter script 'OMAR RAMSDEN Artist Goldsmith London, England'.

Made in the workshop of Omar Ramsden in 1935-6.

L of knife 17.7 cm, L of fork 14.9 cm   1980,10-16,1-12

This is an unusually modern design for the Ramsden workshops, which tended to produce works in traditional or revivalist styles. Ramsden scorned what he termed 'the intensely-regrettable cubism and other "isms" of our time' (Ramsden 1928, 56).

Reimann, Albert 1875-1976

Farbe und Form, Mitteilungen der Schule Reimann, 1-19, 1916-34
Farbe und Form, Sonderband; 25 Jahre Schule Reimann, Berlin
   1927
Reimann, A., *Die Reimann-Schule in Berlin*, Berlin 1966

Kunstschulreform in Deutschland 1900-1935, exhibition catalogue, Bauhaus-Archiv, Berlin 1977

254 Candlestick [PLATE 125]

Brass, the handle formed from the same sheet of brass as the base.

MARKS Stamped on the base with Sagittarius factory mark used by the Chase Brass & Copper Company and 'DESIGN BY REIMANN'.

Designed before 1931 and made by the Chase Brass & Copper Company, Waterbury, Connecticut.

H 15.3 cm, max. W 16.8 cm   1989,1-6,1

Albert Reimann was both sculptor and architect; he founded and directed a school of applied art in Berlin from 1902 to 1935. He then settled in London, where in 1937 his son opened a new Reimann School at 4-10 Regency Street, SW1, which survived until it was bombed in 1942.

Reimann visited New York in the late 1920s and early 1930s (information supplied in 1989 by his widow, the late Mrs E. Reimann). Metalwork from the Reimann Werkstätten in Berlin was included in the Third International Exhibition of Contemporary Industrial Art held by the American Federation of Arts at the Metropolitan Museum in New York and at museums in Boston, Chicago and Cleveland in 1930-31 (cat. nos 260-63). It may have been as a result of this exhibition that Reimann was commissioned by the Chase Company to design this candlestick. According to an article in *Creative Art* 9, 1931, 475-82, Reimann sent his designs from Germany; the candlestick is illustrated on p. 479. The article discusses the large-scale machine production of metal household goods to high aesthetic standards. Other items made by the Chase Brass & Copper Company are illustrated, but individual designers are not credited. Nor is Reimann credited with any of the items listed in the Chase Company's chrome-ware catalogue of 1936-7, which does not include the candlestick (Koch ed. 1978). Thus it is not possible to identify the full range of designs made by Reimann for Chase. However, one further item stamped with the Chase factory mark and 'Design by Reimann' is known to the present author: a four-branch cross-shaped candlestick executed in both brass and copper. (I am grateful to Ken Forster for drawing this to my attention.)

The British Museum's candlestick, with its use of thick-gauge brass, involved considerable hand-work. The stem probably used stamped parts, but the base and handle are almost certainly cut and worked by hand from the thick brass sheet. The scarcity of surviving examples of Chase metalwork designed by Reimann suggests that his designs may not have been ideally suited to mass-production techniques. Certainly examples of this candlestick are not common; for an identical pair of candlesticks in copper in the Metropolitan Museum of Art (inv. no. 1976.382.4), see Duncan 1987, 94.

Reimann's designs for Chase are exceptional in that he himself made few designs for objects; the metal workshop at the Reimann-Schule in Berlin was directed by Karl Heubler and contemporary illustrations are always captioned 'Schule Reimann, under the direction of Heubler'. The simple geometric forms of the candlestick may be compared with Reimann-Schule metalwork illustrated in *Farbe und Form* during the early 1930s. The Reimann-Schule was a private school, as distinct from the state-run Bauhaus, but like the Bauhaus, metalwork was produced by hand on a small scale and few examples are to be found in public collections. For a silver coffee and tea service of 1932 in the Bröhan Collection, Berlin, see Bröhan III, 1985, no. 452. In the same collection is a brass double candlestick (Bröhan 1986, no. 15).

Riemerschmid, Richard 1868-1957

Richard Riemerschmid, vom Jugendstil zum Werkbund, Werke und Dokumente, exhibition catalogue, W. Nerdinger ed., Munich Stadtmuseum 1982
Art Nouveau in Munich, exhibition catalogue, Philadelphia Museum of Art, published Philadelphia and Munich 1988

255 Punch-bowl and cover [PLATE 98]

Stoneware, grey body, with relief decoration of rosettes and stylised leaves rising in asymmetrical clusters from a wave-like band at the base of the bowl; the decoration in blue on a grey ground, the interior of bowl and cover glazed grey. The bowl rests on three legs. The body turned in a mould into which the clay for the relief ornament is pressed; on drying, the relief ornament adheres to the body.

MARKS Impressed on the base beneath the glaze 'REINHOLD MERKELBACH' for the firm of R. Merkelbach, Höhr-Grenzhausen, with model number '1768' together with the number '6' (indicating capacity of 6 l) and the letter 'o'.

The bowl designed in 1902, initially with glass liner and lid; the matching stoneware lid designed in 1904. Made by R. Merkelbach, Höhr-Grenzhausen, Rhineland, c.1906-11.

H 30.5 cm, D 27 cm, H of bowl 19.1 cm, H of lid 12.1 cm   1982,5-10,8

Riemerschmid was among the first artists to contribute to the revival of the Westerwald stoneware industry; see also van de Velde, Cat. 293 and 354. This punch-bowl, a popular and traditional form, was one of his earliest designs. This model, with stoneware lid, was advertised in Merkelbach's *Spezialpreisliste* for 'Kunstgewerbliche Gegenstände' of 1905, pl. 82, model no. 1768, as a 'Weinbowle'. It was produced in two sizes, 6 or 11 l (Dry-v. Zezschwitz 1981, 101-2) and was made with matching stoneware cups. It was shown at the Deutsche Kunstgewerbe Ausstellung in Dresden in 1906 (*Kunstgewerbeblatt* 17, 1906, 236, 336), and is illustrated in several contemporary journals between 1904 and 1919. The bowl on its own was sold as a wine cooler. For Riemerschmid's design for the lid, dated 26.1.04 and for full bibliography, see Munich 1982, no. 412. Further examples are to be found in several collections in Germany: e.g. Klinge 1975, no. 751; Cologne 1978, no. 436 (collection W. Sahm, Höhr-Grenzhausen); Bröhan II/1, 1976, no. 527. For further discussion and full references, see B. Dry-v. Zezschwitz in Philadelphia 1988, no. 131.

Early examples to 1905 were executed in grey, celadon green and pink; from 1906 to 1907 the grey-blue combination was introduced and this was replaced with brown from 1911 (Munich 1982, 332). The raised decoration was known as '*Fadenrelief*' (thread relief) because the motifs have raised edges to prevent the colours mingling. For further discussion of the techniques of manufacture, see Wynand, Cat. 332. The foliate decoration combined with the rounded form and tripod feet rely to a greater extent on traditional models than the bold sculptural punch-bowls with abstract decoration created by Albin Müller (Cat. 213) and Paul Wynand (Cat. 332).

For the bowl with optic mould-blown glass lid, as originally designed, see *DK & D* XV, 1904-5, 75, 83. The glass version was shown at the Warenhaus Wertheim in Berlin in 1905 (*DK & D* XVI, 681), together with matching glass cups, and was later exhibited by the Deutsche Werkstätten für Handwerkskunst, Munich (e.g. *DK & D* XXII, 1908, 210). The glass liners, lids and cups were made by the Kristallglasfabrik Benedikt von Poschinger. Riemerschmid was co-founder in 1897 of the Vereinigte Werkstätten in Munich. The Deutsche Werkstätten were formed in 1907 as an amalgamation of the Dresdner Werkstätten, for whom Riemerschmid also worked, and another Munich workshop, the Werkstätten für Wohnungs-Einrichtung.

256 Soup plate   [PLATE 83]

Hard-paste porcelain, the rim with stylised lime-leaf decoration painted in underglaze blue on a white ground, the leaves in pale blue outlined in darker blue, the border with raised blue dots and irregular indentations.

MARKS Meissen factory mark of crossed swords in underglaze blue on the base, with poorly legible impressed number.

Designed by R. Riemerschmid as part of a dinner, tea and coffee service between 1903 and 1905 and made by the Meissen Porcelain Factory, Dresden.

D 24.9 cm, H 3.6 cm   1981,3-10,13

This soup plate is from one of two new services commissioned by Meissen between 1903 and 1905 from outside designers (the other was van de Velde; see Just 1983, 132, and Cat. 294-5). Reimerschmid began to design his service in the summer of 1903; the first trial pieces in porcelain were made early in 1904. In the summer of that year drawings for all pieces were complete and by November the plaster models had been made. After several modifications to both form and decoration the service was announced in October 1905 (Dresden 1989, no. 294). For Riemerschmid's design for the dinner and soup plates, see Munich 1982, no. 383. The design is annotated '*keine grössere Regelmässigkeit. Die äusseren Punkte alle erhöht, jedoch nur so wenig, u. so sanft verlaufend, dass sich nirgends Schmutz festsetzen kann*' ('not to be made more regular [this presumably refers to the indented edge]. The outer dots all raised, but only so slightly and with such a smooth run that the dirt has nowhere to settle').

This service initially received mixed comments when it was shown at the Dresden Exhibition of 1906. It was thought heavy in form and decoration by comparison with the more delicate and traditional Meissen wares (*DK & D* XVII, 1905-6, 266-7) but it had the advantage of being considerably cheaper (*Kunst und Handwerk*, 1906-7, 95). The Meissen factory itself later complained that the designers had not understood the material: Riemerschmid's service would have been more appropriate for rustic majolica and the indenting of the edge was not well designed (Berling 1911, 103). This had already been noted in *The Studio* 40, 1907, 57, with the frivolous comment: 'there is an unlucky slight break in the design which runs along the rims of the dishes and plates, making them look as if they were chipped to begin with. Possibly this is meant to counteract their appearance later on when they actually will have been chipped.' Nevertheless, the service received wide distribution through the Deutsche Werkbund (*Jahrbuch* 1915, 32) and the Dresdner Werkstätten (Just 1983, 132) and remained in production until the 1930s (Munich 1982, 317). A complete service is owned by the Meissen Porcelain Manufactory, while pieces from the

service are to be found in several German collections (see Munich 1982, Franzke 1987 and Wichmann 1985, 115). For further discussion, see Rudoe 1990.

257 Wine glass   [PLATE 96]

Clear free-blown glass with pinched stem.

MARKS None.

Designed in 1900 as part of the 'Riemerschmid' service and made by the Kristallglasfabrik Benedikt von Poschinger, Oberzwieselau near Zwiesel, Bavaria, between 1900 and 1925, when the factory closed.

H 14.8 cm, D of bowl 9.5 cm   1989,1-3,1

For the complete 'Riemerschmid' service, comprising five glasses for champagne, red wine, Bordeaux, Madeira and dessert wine, see Munich 1982, no. 358. This illustration comes from a trade catalogue of the Keller & Reiner gallery in Berlin, who, according to *Velhagen & Klasing's Monatshefte*, September 1903, 128 (with ill.), were the sole retailers of Riemerschmid's glasses. Only one other glass from this service has so far come to light: it is another red-wine glass and was acquired by the Stadtmuseum, Munich in 1988 (Philadelphia 1988, no. 106). Wine glasses from this service were illustrated by the influential critic Hermann Muthesius in an article on 'Neues Ornament' in *DK* 4, 1901, 359.

Many of Riemerschmid's glass designs are still known only from contemporary illustrations in art journals and retailers' catalogues, or from Riemerschmid's surviving designs in the Architektursammlung der Technischen Universität, Munich (Munich 1982, nos 304-10). The working drawing from the Poschinger factory is now in the Kunstmuseum, Düsseldorf, inv.nr.131.Km. (Fig. 26). Prices are given for each glass, either in clear crystal or with gold rim on both foot and bowl.

The Kristallglasfabrik Benedikt von Poschinger is one of several Bavarian glass houses owned by various members of the von Poschinger family. For a brief history of the Poschinger glassworks, see Hilschenz 1973, 104. The property was divided into the Oberzwieselau and Buchenau houses in 1856 by Benedikt von Poschinger (1785-1856), who bequeathed the Oberzwieselau house to his son Benedikt (1812-80), from whom it passed to the latter's son Benedikt Ferdinand (1850-1918).

258 Three glasses   [PLATE 97]

Liqueur glass, champagne cup and champagne flute in clear free-blown glass, the flute with a wavy gold line at the base of the bowl. The two champagne glasses are of extremely thin glass. The liqueur glass is thicker and may be of later manufacture; both rim and foot have been ground.

MARKS None.

Designed *c*.1911 and made by the Kristallglasfabrik Benedikt von Poschinger, Oberzwieselau near Zwiesel, Bavaria. Formerly in Riemerschmid's own possession, by descent to his daughter, Dr Pflederer (1897-1982), from whom they were acquired by the previous owners.

258a Liqueur glass: H 10.8 cm   1987,11-7,1
258b Champagne cup: H 9.9 cm   1987,11-7,2
258c Champagne flute: H 13.7 cm   1987,11-7,3

These three glasses were included in the Riemerschmid exhibition of 1982 together with a white-wine glass, which is a larger version of the liqueur glass (Munich 1982, no. 364). In that catalogue the date was given as *c*.1901. However, among Riemerschmid's designs for glass in the Architektursammlung der Technischen Universität in Munich is a drawing for a seven-piece service dated 'PASING.27.MÄRZ.1911' in Riemerschmid's hand (G110), which shows the liqueur glass as factory no. 141 (Fig. 27). The two champagne glasses do not figure in this drawing, or in any other of Riemerschmid's drawings for glasses, but their bulging profiles and flared bases relate closely to two other designs for different services (G20 and 26), to which the date 1911 has been added, apparently not in Riemerschmid's hand. In the absence of illustrations from the early 1900s of any of these glasses, it is difficult to say whether they are from the same or from different sets. However, in illustrations of the 1950s, i.e. still during Riemerschmid's lifetime, they are shown together: *Innenarchitektur*, 1954, 81; Munich 1958, pl. 25; Thiersch 1953, 67.

A champagne flute, two champagne coupes and two wine glasses of the same shape as the British Museum liqueur glass were acquired by the Museum of Modern Art in New York from Riemerschmid's widow in 1958. For further examples in a private collection, see Philadelphia 1988, no. 107.

Examples of Riemerschmid glasses of different design are held by museums in Munich, Stuttgart, Krefeld (listed in Munich 1982), in Darmstadt (Heller 1982, no. 342), in Zurich (Gysling-Billeter 1975, no. 215), and in the Danske Kunstindustrimuseet, Copenhagen, acquired from the Dresdner Werkstätten in 1906 (Schou-Christensen, 1969, fig. 76c).

Rohde, Johan 1856-1935

Schultz, S., *Johan Rohde Sølv*, Copenhagen 1956
Johan Rohde 1856-1935, maleren, formgiveren, møbeltegneren, exhibition catalogue, Kunstforeningen, Copenhagen 1987
Møller, J., *Georg Jensen, the Danish Silversmith*, Copenhagen 1985, 24-8

259 Sauce boat [PLATE 123]

Silver, hand-raised, with high scroll handle enclosing a disc.

MARKS Stamped on the base with the Jensen factory mark in use from 1919 to *c*.1927 (Møller 1985, 69), the date '1919' and model number '321', and Swedish assay mark and importer's mark 'GAB' for the Guldsmedsaktiebolaget, Stockholm.

Designed and made in 1919 by the firm of Georg Jensen, Copenhagen.

H 15.5 cm, L 19.4 cm   1988,7-4,1

The painter, architect and interior designer Johan Rohde was co-founder in 1891 of the secessionist group, Den Frie Udstilling (the Free Exhibition). Through this group he first met Georg Jensen, who in 1897 exhibited at Den Frie Udstilling the sculpture that had been rejected by the Danish Academy. Both later spent periods in the workshop of the silversmith Mogens Ballin, from which Jensen set up his own workshop in 1906. Rohde's first silver designs, made in 1905 for his own house, were executed by Georg Jensen. He began to collaborate with Jensen in 1908, but it was not until 1917 that he entered into a formal association, which lasted until his death in 1935. During this time Rohde also designed silver for other Copenhagen firms.

Rohde's most successful designs date from around 1920. He is probably best known for his 'acorn-pattern' cutlery of 1916 (Møller, 1985, 26) and his pitcher of 1920 that was considered so in advance of its time that it was not put into production until 1925 (Møller, 27). Like the pitcher, this simple, unde-

corated sauce boat, with its classically inspired handle, marks a significant departure from the Jensen firm's traditional wares with applied floral ornament. To be able to date the piece to the very year of its design is exceptional because Jensen silver does not normally bear date stamps and can only be dated to within ten to fifteen years, by means of the firm's changing trade marks. However, date stamps were used for the five years from 1918 to 1922. An undated example of this sauce boat is held by the Danske Kunstindustrimuseet, Copenhagen (see Gelfer-Jørgensen 1982, pl. 142; Copenhagen 1987, no. 78). See also Schultz 1956, 45.

This sauce boat remained in the possession of the family who acquired it in 1919 until its acquisition by the British Museum in 1988. It has thus escaped the frequent over-polishing of much Jensen silver. It is interesting in this respect to note that Rohde disliked shining silver; he chose Jensen to execute his own silver in 1905 because he liked Jensen's matt finish and his use of oxidisation to enhance relief ornament (Møller 1985, 24). Jensen's matt finish was not always appreciated outside Denmark; one critic wrote: 'Originally Jensen favoured a comparatively dull surface, he may do so still in some cases, but for England, anyhow, the polishing is carried a little further, though rarely beyond what one might call semi-brightness' (*Artwork*, May/August 1925, 257-8).

The sauce boat remained a popular model throughout the 1920s: it was included in Jensen's display at the Paris Exhibition of 1925 and sold in the firm's Paris shop (*Mobilier et Décoration*, February 1925, 13). See also *Die Kunst* 60, 1929, 101.

Rookwood Pottery 1880-1960
See also **Nichols**

Nichols Storer, M., *History of the Cincinnati Music Festivals and of the Rookwood Pottery*, Paris 1919 (privately printed)
Peck, H., *The Book of Rookwood Pottery*, New York 1969
Trapp, K., 'Japanese influence in early Rookwood Pottery', *Antiques*, January 1973, 193-7
Mr. S. G. Burt's Record Book of Ware at Art Museum, 2292 pieces of early Rookwood Pottery in the Cincinnati Art Museum in 1916, The Cincinnati Historical Society 1978
Trapp, K., 'Rookwood and the Japanese mania in Cincinnati', *Cincinnati Historical Society Bulletin* 39, Spring 1981, 51-75
Peck, H., *The Second Book of Rookwood Pottery* (with complete Art Pottery Shape Catalogues nos 1 and 2), New York 1985
See also Kovel 1974, Evans 1987; New York 1986 and Syracuse 1989.

260 Vase [PLATE 44]

Earthenware, thrown, red body coated with slip, with low-relief decoration of two carp swimming amid seaweed, painted in underglaze white slip with incised details. Covered with a transparent rust glaze containing gold flecks. The colour varies in tone according to the thickness of the glaze and the colour of the underlying slip.

MARKS Impressed on the base with the Rookwood Pottery 'RP' and the date-cypher for 1894 (eight flames surrounding the monogram), the shape number '589 D', the letter 'R' indicating red clay and decorator's signature 'A.R.VALENTIEN'.

Decorated by A. R. Valentien in 1894 and made at the Rookwood Pottery, Cincinnati, Ohio.

H 28.6 cm, D 9 cm   1984,7-3,1

Albert Robert Valentien (1862-1925) was Rookwood's chief decorator from 1881 to 1905; he was the first professional decorator to join the pottery, having previously trained at the Cincinnati Art Academy and taught underglaze slip painting at the Coultry commercial pottery in Cincinnati. Valentien visited Europe in 1894 and again in 1899, to prepare the Rookwood Pottery display at the Paris Exhibition of 1900, where he was awarded a gold medal. He left Rookwood in 1905 to settle in San Diego, California, where he ran his own short-lived art pottery from 1910 to 1913 (see Kamerling 1987).

The technique of painting with slip (liquid clay), developed by French potters such as Ernest Chaplet, was introduced to American potters at the Philadelphia exhibition of 1876. The technique was pioneered in America by the Cincinnati potter and rival of Mrs Nichols, Mary Louise McLaughlin. As practised at Rookwood, unfired ceramic forms were painted while still moist with coloured slips or liquid clay; after a first, or biscuit, firing they were dipped in glaze and fired again. The coloured slip grounds were introduced in 1883 and were applied with the aid of an atomizer, so that grounds of different colours could be applied in layers to create subtle gradations (Trapp 1981). For a contemporary description of the process of applying the slip written by William Watts Taylor, manager of the Rookwood Pottery, in 1910, see Kovel 1974, 219-22.

Crystalline glazes were used at Rookwood from the mid 1880s; according to contemporary descriptions 'Tiger Eye' was noted for its 'strange luminosity (*Brush and Pencil* IX, 1902, 358) and its 'striations and sparkling particles of gold' (*Art Journal*, 1897, 344-5). A similar glaze known as 'Goldstone' gave the effect of 'glistening gold particles in aventurine, but rather more limpid [than Tiger Eye]' (*Brush and Pencil* IX, 1902, 358). Since the gold flecks on this vase do not occur in striations and are certainly limpid rather than luminous, the glaze should probably be described as Goldstone. Similar glazes with gold flecks were used by William Burton at Pilkington's Tile and Pottery Company (See Burton, Cat. 30).

The inspiration for the decoration undoubtedly came from one of the Japanese books of illustrations owned by Mrs Nichols. Japanese sourcebooks known to her have been identified and a page from one of them, showing swimming carp, is illustrated in Trapp 1981, 67. From 1887 a Japanese decorator was employed at the pottery. Another example of a vase of this shape, in a larger size, decorated with a dragon, was acquired by the Victoria and Albert Museum from Siegfried Bing in 1900 (inv. no. 1650-1900). An example in the Cooper-Hewitt Museum, New York, was shown at the St Louis Exhibition of 1904 (illustrated in Kovel 1974, 219). The letters following the shape number refer to the sizes: a new shape was normally given the letter C or D; larger versions were then marked A or B, smaller versions E or F.

Rörstrand Porslinsfabrik AB founded 1726

261 Bowl [PLATE 122]

Porcelain, with fluted sides and two handles. Glazed all over in lilac; inside the bowl is a stylised leaf motif painted in deep purple, orange and gold, the handles gilt.

MARKS Printed on the base with Rörstrand factory mark and the designer's name, 'ADELBORG', in deep purplish-brown.

Designed by Louise Adelborg and made by the Rörstrand Porcelain Factory, Lidköping, Sweden, c.1940.

D 17.9 cm (including handles)   1985,10-16,1   Given by Lady Eva Wilson

Louise Adelborg worked at Rörstrand from c.1926 to the late 1950s, specialising in floral designs. For illustrations of her tablewares, see Copenhagen 1954, 31-2; M. Lindgren-Fridell, *Rörstrand of Today*, 1954; London 1959, cat. nos 198-9.

Rosenthal Porzellanmanufaktur founded 1879

Zoellner, A. ed., *Philipp Rosenthal. Sein Leben und sein Porzellan*, Leipzig 1929

Schreiber, H., Honisch, D., Simoneit, F., *Die Rosenthal Story*, Düsseldorf-Vienna 1980

Rosenthal: Hundert Jahre Porzellan, exhibition catalogue, Kestner Museum, Hanover, 1982

262 Cream jug, lidded sugar basin and side plate

[PLATE 84]

Hard-paste porcelain, with moulded decoration in low-relief of cherry branches, the cherries in blue, the leaves in greenish blue, the branches in greenish brown. An overglaze gold outline has been added to the cream jug and sugar basin.

MARKS The base of each piece bears the printed factory mark 'Rosenthal BAVARIA' in use from c.1910 to 1922, together with 'Unterglasur' and 'Pâte sur pâte' in underglaze green. The sugar basin and plate also bear the model name 'DONATELLO' in underglaze green.

The form designed in 1905 by the Porzellanmanufaktur Rosenthal, Selb, Bavaria, under the direction of Philipp Rosenthal (1885-1937), the decoration designed by Julius-Vilhelm Guldbransen c.1910.

262a Jug: H 7.6 cm, W 12.5 cm (with handle)   1982,5-10,6
262b Sugar basin: H 9.1 cm, W 16.1 cm (with handles)   1982,5-10,7
262c Plate: D 20.5 cm   1988,7-5,1

These three pieces form part of the dinner, tea and coffee service known as 'Donatello', factory model no. 250. The service was designed in plain white without relief decoration and such examples were produced between 1905 and 1925 (see Leistikow-Duchardt 1957, pl. 90, 113-14). However, contemporary taste dictated that they should at least have a simple pattern. From c.1910 the 'Donatello' model was produced with four alternative patterns in underglaze relief. The cherries pattern was designed without the gold line that appears on these examples and which has been added later. The other patterns were 'Libellen' (dragonflies), 'Weissdorn' (hawthorn) and 'Alice'. For examples of 'Weissdorn' in the Hessisches Landesmuseum, Darmstadt, see Heller 1982, no. 458; for examples of 'Alice' (a variant of Weissdorn) in the Kunstgewerbemuseum, Cologne, see Beaucamp-Markowsky 1980, no.325; see also Bröhan II/2, 1977, nos 648-50. The factory's use of the term *pâte-sur-pâte* is misleading because the relief decoration is modelled as part of the form rather than built up in layers of slip, as in the *pâte-sur-pâte* technique.

The Donatello service was also produced with a range of patterns other than those in underglaze relief; for a border of underglaze blue triangles, copying a decoration design made by Therese Trethan under Koloman Moser at the Kunstgewerbeschule in Vienna, see Neuwirth 1974b, 267. This pattern on the Donatello model was illustrated in *Keramische Monatshefte* 3, 1906, 34. For examples, see Heller 1982, no. 455. For a coffee set in cobalt blue with gold decoration of *c.*1907, see Hanover 1982, 8. For a coffee and teaset in white with overglaze decoration of green garlands, see Mosel 1971, no. 44. The cherries decoration was also used on other shapes, and the Donatello service with cherries is still in production today.

Guldbransen came to Selb in 1909 from the Royal Copenhagen Porcelain Factory and was the first director of Rosenthal's art department, created in 1910; see Hanover 1989, 9 and no. 11.

A. Leistikow-Duchardt writing in 1957 (p. 114) noted the characteristic feature of this service: the modelling of the handles to follow the line of the body of the vessel, instead of breaking the profile as in traditional designs, and commented, '*wir möchten fast sagen, das Service "Donatello" hat die Klassik dieser Gestaltungsform erreicht.*' ('We might almost say that the "Donatello" service has become a classic example of this type of artistic creation'.)

Roycroft Workshops 1900-38

Shay, F., *Elbert Hubbard of East Aurora*, New York 1926
Brady, N. Hubbard, *The Book of the Roycrofters*, East Aurora 1977 (reprint of 1919 and 1926 Roycroft catalogues)
Hamilton, C. F., *Roycroft Collectibles*, London and San Diego 1980
Stott, M. R., *Rebel with reverence; Elbert Hubbard, a granddaughter's tribute*, 2nd edn, Watkin's Glen, New York 1984
Hamilton, C. F., Turgeon, K. and Rust, R., *History and Renaissance of the Roycroft Movement*, Buffalo and Erie County Historical Society, Buffalo 1984

263 Dish [PLATE 108]

Earthenware, with transfer-printed geometric ornament in deep green and rust red on cream ground, the Roycroft monogram incorporated in the design.

MARKS Printed on the reverse 'BUFFALO POTTERY'.

Designed by the Roycrofters for the Roycroft Inn, East Aurora, New York with decoration adapted from designs by Dard Hunter of *c.*1909-10. Made by the Buffalo Pottery, Buffalo, New York.

L 17.4 cm   1984,10-10,2

The Roycroft Workshops were founded as an Arts and Crafts community in 1900 by the American printer Elbert Hubbard (1856-1915). Initially centred round the Roycroft Press, the community soon expanded its activities to include the manufacture of leather goods, furniture and metalwork. The Roycroft Inn was built in 1903 to accommodate the increasing number of visitors and to house a shop. Following Hubbard's death on board the *Lusitania* in May 1915, the community survived under his son, Elbert, until 1938.

Dard Hunter (1883-1966) is best known as a book designer and printer and as an expert on paper (his books include *Papermaking through Eighteen Centuries*, New York 1930 and *My Life with Paper: An Autobiography*, New York 1958). He also worked in a number of other media, designing windows, lampshades and leaded-glass lighting fixtures for the Roycroft Inn. Hunter went to East Aurora in 1903; inspired by German magazines available at Roycroft, he visited Vienna in 1908, returning

in the summer of 1909 when Karl Kipp had just begun setting up the copper department (see Cat. 264). Hunter and Kipp became friends and both produced Viennese-style designs. Hunter visited Vienna again in 1910, after which he left the Roycrofters and subsequently set up his own school of handicraft.

The Viennese influence is evident in the geometric border decoration of this dish, thus the designs on which it is based were probably made *c.*1908-10, after Hunter's first trip to Vienna and before he left Roycroft. The service was made exclusively for use at the Roycroft Inn and was never sold to the public. For further discussion of Dard Hunter's contribution to Roycroft, see Hamilton, New York 1983, 35-41 and Boston 1987a.

For the Buffalo Pottery, see Altman 1969/87. For a plate from the Roycroft service, see New York 1985, 23, fig. 1.22, and for a cup and saucer, see Bowman 1990, 141, no. 113a-b. Bowman notes that Elbert Hubbard had previous links with the Buffalo Pottery through his former business partners at the Larkin Soap Company, who had founded the Pottery to produce dishes as premiums for soap certificates.

264 Pair of candlesticks [PLATE 108]

Copper, beaten, with two square-section uprights riveted to a square pyramidal base.

MARKS Impressed on the upper surface of the base with the Roycroft monogram.

Designed by Karl Kipp before 1912 and made by the Roycroft Workshops, East Aurora, New York, probably between 1915 and *c.*1926.

H 19.3 cm, W of base 8.4 cm   1987,10-10,1 and 2

The Austrian designer and former banker Karl Kipp joined the Roycrofters in 1908, initially in the bindery, and established the Copper Shop in 1909, leaving in 1911 to form his own company in East Aurora, which he called the Tookay Shop, after his own initials. These candlesticks, known as 'Princess' candlesticks, appear in Tookay Shop advertisements in *The House Beautiful* between October 1912 and February 1913. Kipp rejoined the Roycrofters in 1915. It is not certain whether these candlesticks were designed during his early Roycroft period, before the Tookay Shop interlude of 1911-15; the candlesticks do not appear in the metalwork section of the 1910 Roycroft catalogue (reprinted in Stott 1984, 65-74), but they appear regularly in Roycroft post-1915 catalogues until 1926. For full discussion of an identical pair bearing the mark of the Tookay Shop, see W. Scott Braznell in Boston 1987a, no. 209. The influence of the Wiener Werkstätte on Kipp's designs is also discussed here.

For a general discussion of American Arts and Crafts metalwork, see Bohdan 1979; Volpe and Cathers 1988.

Rozenburg, Koninklijke Porselein- en Aardewerk Fabriek 1883-1917

Rozenburg 1883-1917, Geschiednis van een Haagse fabrik, exhibition catalogue, Gemeentemuseum, The Hague, 1983
J. A. Popper, 'The Rozenburg Factory: an exercise in Anglo-Dutch co-operation', *Journal of the Decorative Arts Society* 7, 1983

265 Teapot [COLOUR PLATE VIII]

'Eggshell' porcelain with very thin walls, cast in a revolving mould, so that the handle and spout are formed in one piece with the four-sided body. The body and eccentrically shaped handle and spout painted on each side in bright underglaze colours with an exotic fish in blue, green, grey and ochre among orange-brown water-weeds on a white ground. There is a small area of restoration to the rim on one side. The lid has a square base which sits proud of the body and rises to a curving peak with central hole.

MARKS On the base, the printed black Rozenburg factory mark without crown in use before 1900; the date cypher for 1899, the decoration designer's monogram and the order number '1307' painted in black.

The shape designed by the architect J. Jurriaan Kok (1861-1919), the decoration designed by the ceramic painter Wilhelmus Petrus Hartgring (1874-1940) and painted by W. P. Hartgring, C. A. Muylwijk and L. de Weij at the Koninklijke Porselein- en Aardewerk Fabriek Rozenburg, The Hague, Holland, in 1899.

H 14.2cm (with lid), 9cm (without lid), w 14.1cm (spout to handle) 1987,3-1,1

According to the factory order books and wages books, order number 1307 was given to the painters' department of the Rozenburg factory between 20 and 27 October 1899 (Rozenburg archive, Gemeentearchief, The Hague, inv. no. 706). The order included a matching set of teapot (model no. 65), sugar bowl (model no. 66) and milk jug (model no. 67). Between 21 October and 3 November, three painters worked on this order: W. P. Hartgring, the designer, who worked for sixteen hours on the order; C. A. Muylwijk, who worked for twenty-six hours and L. de Weij, who worked for sixteen hours (Rozenburg archive, inv. nos 375, 464, 579). Hartgring received the title of 'master' in 1899; Muylwijk had the title 'gezel' (journeyman), while de Weij was a 'pupil' (for the organisation of the painters' department, see The Hague 1983). A sketch for the teapot appears in a small model book in the factory archive (inv. no. 725). The complete service was illustrated in the Catalogue de la Porcelaine Rozenburg of c.1904, 28, where the price for model no. 65, the teapot, is given as D.fl.15. (The above information was kindly supplied by H. Bordewijk of the Gemeentearchief and Marjan Boot of the Gemeentemuseum, both The Hague.)

Rozenburg eggshell porcelains were produced from 1898 until 1914; the earliest piece of eggshell porcelain is a coffee-pot of 1898, model no. 1P, in the Gemeentemuseum, The Hague (The Hague 1983, no. 196), but few other pieces dating from before 1900 are recorded. Thus this teapot is among the earliest documentary pieces. The years 1901-5 represent the peak in production and popularity, during which time the decoration was executed by some sixty painters. Surviving records and objects suggest that the monogram on the base refers to the designer of the decoration rather than the painter: on occasion the designer also executed some or all of the painting, as in the case of this teapot, but the painting was mainly done by a team of painters, without the involvement of the designer (The Hague 1983, 180).

The Rozenburg factory was founded in 1883 and soon became noted for its creative earthenwares. From the early 1890s, under the new directorship of Alexander Vosmaer, experiments were made in the production of high-quality wafer-thin porcelain combined with a new range of bright colours. The first successful eggshell wares, using a bone-china formula, were shown to the Hague Kunstkring (Art Circle) in June 1899. They were not exhibited internationally until the Paris Exhibition of 1900,

where they were widely acclaimed (see, for example, Kunst-gewerbeblatt XII, 1901, 95, with illustrations of similar eccentric shapes opp. pp. 83 and 88). Their success in Paris led to the opening of a Rozenburg shop in the French capital, but the rent proved too high and it did not last long. The German critic Richard Borrmann gave them a significant place alongside the French and Danish porcelains at the Paris exhibition, noting especially the handles and spouts that grew out of the body of the vessel and the flame-like pierced lids (Borrmann 1902, 114-16).

Further accolades followed at Turin in 1902 and at St Louis in 1904. The Studio's commentator on the Dutch section of the Turin exhibition wrote of Rozenburg porcelain, 'What strikes the critic first of all ... is its extreme lightness. Most of the examples exhibited are as thin, transparent and light as a sheet of paper ... but it is open to doubt whether this very want of weight and solidity is not a drawback when the porcelain is in use.' But he nevertheless thought the designs in excellent taste and the colouring original. Rozenburg porcelain was criticised in Holland by the leaders of the abstract movement such as H. P. Berlage, who thought the painting bizarre and not sufficiently related to form (The Studio 26, 1902, 205).

Kok studied architecture at the Polytechnische School in Delft and then became associated with the architect D. P. van Armeijden van Duym, through whom he came into contact with Rozenburg. He joined the factory in 1893 or 1894, becoming art director from June 1894 and managing director from June 1895 until October 1913 (The Hague 1983, 27). He was responsible for the flamboyant forms and made all the models himself (see The Hague 1983, 19, note 98), while a number of designers were responsible for the decoration.

Hartgring joined Rozenburg as an apprentice painter in 1887; he took evening classes at the Academie van Beeldende Kunsten in The Hague in 1890-91 and soon became a master painter, exhibiting under his own name at the exhibition of decorative arts in The Hague in 1896. He left Rozenburg in 1907. From 1931 he left the ceramic industry altogether to work as a painter. His designs are noted for their Japanese inspiration. The decoration in the Japanese taste on this teapot was probably derived from well-known sourcebooks such as Le Japon Artistique (see The Hague 1983, 16). The shape of the main body of the vessel is derived from Chinese vase shapes, but the angular handle and spout, and the curvilinear, wave-like, peaked lid are characteristic of Kok's distinctive forms.

For a comprehensive account of the Rozenburg factory with full reference to the surviving factory archive, see The Hague 1983. The 'Royal' prefix was added to the factory name in December 1900 (The Hague 1983, 67); prior to this date, the factory was known as the Haagsche Porselein- en Kunst-Aardewerk Fabriek Rozenburg. During the 1890s, before the introduction of porcelain, it was known as the Haagsche Plateelbakkerij Rozenburg.

St Petersburg, Imperial Glassworks

founded 1792

There is no monograph on the Imperial Glassworks. Brief factory histories are to be found in Mundt 1973 and Schmitt 1989, but for the most recent and detailed account, see Russian Glass of *the 17th-20th centuries*, exhibition catalogue, the Corning Museum of Glass, Corning, 1990.

266 Tazza [COLOUR PLATE III]

Opaque red crystalline glass, saucer-shaped bowl, mounted in a gilded-bronze stand with four strapwork feet and scroll-shaped handles. The glass is an even deep red colour and the crystals are spread throughout the body. There are two black patches at the edge. Under magnification the crystalline structure resembles myriads of fern leaves, randomly arranged and of different sizes.

MARKS None.

Made at the Imperial Glassworks, St Petersburg, before 1867.

D of bowl 12.6 cm. Total W 14.9 cm, H 5.4 cm   Slade 955   Purchased by Felix Slade at the Paris Universal Exhibition of 1867 and bequeathed with the Slade Collection in 1868

The St Petersburg Glassworks is first documented in 1738; it was renamed the Imperial Glassworks in 1792. From the late eighteenth century it had been the leading glass factory in Russia and during the first half of the nineteenth century was noted for its cut glass, painted glass and a wide range of coloured glass. The influence of historicist trends elsewhere in Europe resulted in Gothic-style wares, followed by Persian-style enamelled glasses (shown at the International Exhibition in London in 1862, Waring 1862, I, pls 42, 51), Renaissance-style engraved glass and glass enamelled with traditional Russian motifs. In addition, there were specialities such as mosaic glass and the purpurine glass, first shown in Paris in 1867 and again in Vienna in 1873, of which this tazza is an example.

The catalogue of the Slade Collection (Nesbitt 1871, 164, no. 955) describes this tazza as: 'A saucer, of opaque red glass, of a very brilliant colour, and full of crystals. It is made with copper, in imitation of the antique porporino, and is a production of the imperial manufactory of St Petersburg, under the direction of the chemist, Leopold Bonafede.'

The Italian mosaic chemists Leopold Bonafede (1833-78) and his elder brother Giustiniano were among the many specialists from Western Europe employed by the factory. Pupils of the celebrated mosaicist Michelangelo Barberi of Rome, they collaborated with him in the studio for Russian mosaic artists established by Barberi in 1846 at the instigation of Tsar Nicholas I, who had sent four Russian artists to Rome to learn the technique of mosaics. The Bonafede brothers were invited to St Petersburg in the early 1850s and worked at the Imperial Glassworks, as chief chemists and as designers, Giustiniano from 1857 to 1866 and Leopold until 1878. They were associated with the founding of the mosaic department at the glassworks, set up to make the mosaics for St Isaac's Cathedral and for which they developed a vast range of opaque colours (Gerspach 1899, 216-17; Petochi et al. 1981, 31 and Corning 1990, 36).

According to the archives of the Imperial Glassworks, Leopold Bonafede invented purpurine glass for the production of special exhibition pieces; this may explain why no example survives in any of the Leningrad collections or in the State Historical Museum, Moscow (information kindly supplied by Tamara Malinina). Yet it is clear from the *Catalogue Spécial de la Section Russe à l'Exposition Universelle de Paris en 1867*, p. 44, Classe 16, no. 111, that the St Petersburg Glassworks' contribution consisted almost entirely of purpurine:

1. Tabernacle en purpurine (ématinon de Pline) orné de bronze	1850r
2. Cassette en purpurine, ornée de bronze	525r
3. Coupes en purpurine, ornées de bronze, la pièce, de	44 à 1025r
4. Coupes en crystal et en aventurine	9 à 46r
5. Plateaux en purpurine, avec bronze	97 à 200r
6. Plateaux en purpurine, taillés	15 à 120r

The Slade tazza is presumably one of the 'coupes' listed as item 3. The prices (in roubles) show that the purpurine glass was considerably more expensive than the crystal or aventurine glass. The 'ématinon de Pline' refers to the opaque red glass mentioned by Pliny, who records that it was called in Greek 'haematinon' or blood-red ware (*Natural History*, XXXVI, LXVII, 198).

The use of the term 'antique porporino' in the Slade catalogue requires explanation. The term 'purpurine' is used by Pliny with reference to colouring matter only and not to describe glass. However, by the second quarter of the eighteenth century, the term 'porporino' was in use in Rome to denote the celebrated 'porporino' or red glass made by Alessio Matteoli for the Vatican mosaic workshop (Petochi et al. 1981, 88). By the nineteenth century it was commonly used to denote red glass, hence Nesbitt's reference to 'antique porporino' rather than 'haematinon'.

Analysis of the red glass (by Mavis Bimson of the British Museum Research Laboratory) has shown it to be a lead-potash glass with crystals of cuprous oxide in a clear glass matrix. The Fabergé workshops also produced a purpurine glass and it has been previously suggested that this tazza was made in the Fabergé workshops (Gros-Galliner 1977-80, 158), but recent investigation has shown that Fabergé purpurine glass is a soda glass and that it was not used until *c.* 1880 (Harding et al. 1989). This article contains a useful account of the history of red glass in Europe; the authors note that opaque red glass continued to be made at the Imperial Glassworks by S. P. Petuchov, who succeeded Leopold Bonafede as chief glaze chemist and who may have supplied Fabergé in the latter part of the nineteenth century.

Sakier, George b.1897

There is no monograph on Sakier, but his designs for industry and the applied arts were widely discussed in contemporary publications (see below). For more recent literature, see Greif 1975, Meikle 1979 and Newhaven 1983.

267-8 Two vases [PLATE 126]

Mould blown glass: 267 light green with six lobes, 268 amber flared rectangular shape with 'skyscraper' outline, slight chips to rim.

MARKS None.

Designed *c.*1930 and made by the Fostoria Glass Company, Moundsville, West Virginia.

267 H 20.2 cm   1988,1-7,1
268 H 20 cm   1989,9-11,1   Given by Fifty/50 Gallery, New York, in memory of the late Ralph Cutler

Sakier trained as an engineer at Columbia University and worked as a commercial illustrator, as art director for *Harper's Bazaar* and as an interior decorator. During the 1920s he directed the Bureau of Design for the American Radiator and Sanitation Company, specialising in luxury bathroom accessories and fittings; see *The Studio* 105, February 1933, 120; see also vol. 123, March 1942, 66-9, for an account of Sakier's work as interior decorator.

Sakier was hired by Fostoria in the late 1920s to design inexpensive glassware for large-scale production. Among his early designs were stemwares with square-shaped ebony-glass bases (*The Studio Yearbook*, 1931, 149), and a square-shaped dinnerware service of 1930 known as 'Mayfair' pattern (Weatherman 1972, 225).

In his own article written in 1933 and entitled 'Primer of Modern Design' (*Arts and Decoration* 40, November 1933, 36-7), Sakier illustrated his bathroom fittings as 'functional modern' and his glassware for Fostoria under the headings 'geometric modern', 'classic modern' and 'romantic modern'. The latter included a lobed bowl while 'classic modern' included a series of cylindrical fluted vases (see also Cheney and Cheney 1936, 221; Newhaven 1983, no. 81; Brooklyn 1986, pl. 8.80). For a hexafoil lobed vase similar to that catalogued here, but with straight instead of curved sides, see McGrain 1982, 81. For the skyscraper vase, see Greif 1975, 181.

Sakier's glassware for Fostoria was included in the Industrial Arts Exposition of 1934 held at the Rockefeller Plaza, New York, cat. nos 459-66. See also *The Studio Yearbook*, 1933, 104 and 110, for illustrations of candlesticks and bowls.

The vases were produced in several colours including amber, rose, green, silver mist and ebony. Green and amber were both discontinued in 1941. Some of Sakier's vase designs remained in production after the war. For Fostoria, see Shelley 1937, Weatherman 1972 and McGrain 1982.

Sèvres, Manufacture Nationale de

founded 1756

The following bibliography relates only to the piece catalogued here and is therefore limited to the period around 1900.

Baumgart, E., *La Manufacture Nationale de Sèvres à l'Exposition Universelle de 1900*, Paris 1900-1

Lechevallier-Chevignard, G., *La Manufacture de Porcelaine de Sèvres*, Paris 1908

Porcelaines de Sèvres au XIX siècle, exhibition catalogue, Musée National de Céramique, Sèvres 1975

Brunet, M. and Préaud, T., *Sèvres des origines à nos jours*, Fribourg 1982

Sèvres de 1850 à nos jours, exhibition catalogue, Le Louvre des Antiquaires, Paris 1983

269 Vase   [PLATE 76]

Hard-paste porcelain (*pâte dure nouvelle*), of square section, with two lugs in the form of vetch tendrils. Covered with crystalline glaze in shades of cream and buff. The crystals occur in patches on the surface of the glaze. Small chip to foot.

MARKS On the base, printed grey factory mark 's 1905' within a triangle.

The shape, known as 'vase de Chevilly', designed by Alexandre Sandier in 1897, the model produced by Henri-Ernest Brécy. Made by the Manufacture Nationale de Sèvres in 1905.

H 23cm   1987,11-2,1

Under the direction of Émile Baumgart (manager from 1891 to 1909) and Alexandre Sandier (art director from 1897 to 1916),

production at Sèvres in the late nineteenth century changed radically. Sandier designed new shapes of simple outline and construction and several new decorative effects were introduced. These were greatly aided by the introduction in 1884 of *pâte dure nouvelle* or *porcelaine nouvelle*, which was fired at a lower temperature and was thus suitable for a much wider range of decorative effects.

According to G. Lechevallier-Chevignard, archivist at the factory, experiments in crystalline glazes had been made at Sèvres as early as 1885, by Charles Lauth (manager from 1879 to 1887), but they were not put into regular production until the mid 1890s and were first exhibited at the Paris Exhibition of 1900 (Lechevallier-Chevignard 1908, 34). For a *vase de Chevilly* with vetch lugs and crystalline glaze, shown at the 1900 exhibition, see Baumgart 1900-1, pl. 32; further *vases de Chevilly* with crystalline glaze but without the lugs are illustrated on pl. 34. Brécy is recorded as producing the model in the Sèvres archives (information supplied by Tamara Préaud).

For comparable pieces in other collections, see Mosel 1971, no. 125, dated 1900; Sèvres 1975, no. 435 (in the Musée Adrien Dubouché, Limoges); Bröhan, II/2, 1977, no. 693, dated 1905; Blanchard and Thauré 1986, no. 54, also dated 1905. A further example is to be found in the Musée National de Céramique, Sèvres, inv. 16062. The same shape was also produced with floral and foliate decoration; see Blanchard and Thauré 1986, no. 16, dated 1898. For examples of Sèvres crystalline glazes dated 1895-8, see Bascou et al. 1988, 197-8 (in the Musée d'Orsay).

Crystalline glazes appeared in the production of many factories in the late nineteenth century, for example at the Copenhagen and the Berlin porcelain factories. The crystals were achieved by adding metal salts to the glaze and delaying the cooling process. In the French, German and Danish examples, the crystals generally occur in patches on the surface of the glaze. For other examples of crystalline glazes in which the crystals occur throughout the glaze, see Burton (Cat. 30) and Rookwood (Cat. 260).

For discussion of *porcelaine nouvelle* see A. Dawson, *French Porcelain. A Catalogue of the British Museum Collection*, London 1994, cat. 192. See also **Doat** (Cat. 80).

Sika, Jutta   1877-1964

There is no monograph on Sika; for biographical details, see Neuwirth, 1974a, 294.

270 Teapot   [PLATE 103]

Hard-paste porcelain, with flat, pierced handles to body and lid; the flat bridge between spout and body is also pierced with a circular hole. Decorated with a band of roses and lines stencilled in yellow.

MARKS Printed on the base in red with the factory mark 'JOS. BÖCK WIEN' in a rectangle.

The shape designed by Sika *c.*1901-2, the decoration designed by Antoinette Krasnik before 1914; made for the Porzellan-Manufaktur Josef Böck, Vienna.

H 16.8cm, max. W 19.2cm (handle to spout)   1981,12-7,1

Sika studied under Koloman Moser at the Kunstgewerbeschule, Vienna, specialising in ceramics. She taught in various applied art schools in Vienna until 1933.

This teapot is from the first of a number of services produced by Böck (see also Cat. 208) and exhibited at the Österreichisches Museum für angewandte Kunst, Vienna, in the early 1900s. It was first produced in undecorated white porcelain (see Neuwirth 1974a, 295 for an undecorated coffee-pot). With its striking combination of curvilinear outline and geometric handles it was a remarkably bold design to put into production at the time, especially as the flat handles are impractical for a teapot and difficult to use.

The Porzellan-Manufaktur Josef Böck was founded in 1898 by Josef Böck as a decorating and distribution organisation. By having the pieces made under contract at other factories, Böck could allow artists and designers to experiment with limited runs. According to one contemporary account the porcelain was made in Bohemia and decorated by the firm's own painters (*Kunstgewerbeblatt*, 1905, 15).

At least five different patterns for this service are recorded, all designed by pupils of Kolo Moser at the Kunstgewerbeschule, Vienna. Many of the original drawings survive in the design archive of the firm of Böck, now in the Museum für angewandte Kunst, Vienna. Some of the drawings are signed, though rarely dated. For the drawing for the pattern on this teapot, signed by Antoinette Krasnik, see Neuwirth 1974b, 443. In the 1905 article, the service is shown both in plain white and with two different patterns: a geometric motif of triangles and a naturalistic floral motif. For a range of patterns in yellow, red and blue, see Neuwirth 1974b, 265-71, nos 153-9. For examples with a pattern of horizontal lines and semicircles, see Heller 1982, no. 372; for examples with overlapping circles in gold on a deep blue ground, see Vienna 1985, 13/5/14; for the same pattern in rust on white, see Franzke 1987, no. 132, with the cups placed to one side of the saucer, as originally designed. Asymmetrically placed cups and saucers from this service appear in Carl Moll's painting 'Breakfast' of 1903, set in a room designed by Hoffmann (Kallir 1986, col. pl. 1).

For contemporary illustrations of this service in the exhibition 'Wiener Kunst im Hause' held by the Wiener Kunstgewerbeverein, see *Das Interieur* 3, 1902, 103 and *Die Kunst* 6, 1902, 132; the Wiener Kunstgewerbeverein was an association of ten graduates of the Kunstgewerbeschule. See also *DK* IX, 1902, 132, 135 and XII, 1904, 240; *Kunstgewerbeblatt*, 1905, 11, 14, 15. A similar service with unpierced handles was exhibited in H. Hirschwald's Hohenzollern-Kunstgewerbehaus, Berlin in 1904 (*DK & D* XV, 1904-5, 178). The service was expensive to produce; the article in *Das Interieur* complained of the high cost of avant-garde artistic wares of this kind. But in general the critics welcomed the initiative of firms such as Böck. The author of a detailed article on the exhibition 'Der Gedeckte Tisch' held in 1905 in the Mährische Gewerbemuseum, Brünn (Moravian Museum, Brno, now Czechoslovakia) described the Sika service as exceptionally original (*Kunstgewerbeblatt*, 1905, 15).

A related service designed by Sika was executed in stoneware by the Wächtersbacher Steingutfabrik on behalf of Böck (Neuwirth 1974b).

Skeaping, John Rattenbury 1901-80

There is no monograph on Skeaping. For biographical details, see Chamot, Farr and Butlin 1964, 644-5; see also Grierson 1930. Skeaping's own writings include *Animal Drawing* (1936),

How to Draw Horses (1941) and his autobiography, *Drawn from Life*, London 1977.

271 Figure of a seated polar bear [PLATE 112]

Earthenware, moulded, with 'Silver Grey' satin glaze.

MARKS Impressed 'J SKEAPING' and printed in blue 'WEDGWOOD ETRURIA ENGLAND MADE IN ENGLAND'.

Designed and first produced in 1927; this example made *c.*1935-9.

H 18 cm, L 24.8 cm   1983,11-4,3

After studying at the Central School and the Royal Academy Schools, Skeaping won the Prix de Rome in 1924, after which he lived in Rome for two years until early 1927. On his return he exhibited in London with Barbara Hepworth, to whom he was briefly married. His first major one-man exhibition was held in Glasgow in 1928. In the 1930s he exhibited with both Hepworth and Henry Moore. He was Professor of Sculpture at the Royal College of Art during the 1950s and is now mainly known for his animal sculptures and drawings.

The Wedgwood animal figures were done soon after his return from Rome and were one of his first commissions. Skeaping was introduced to Wedgwood by Felton Wreford, manager of the factory's London showrooms. Following a visit to Etruria, Wedgwood commissioned Skeaping to model a series of animal studies; he made fourteen models in all, of which ten were put into production, for a fee of £100, in 1927. In his autobiography Skeaping complained at how badly he had been paid, given the success of the figures: 'My next job was for Wedgwood, who commissioned a series of ten animal figures from me for the ridiculous fee of £10 each and no royalties. I was too unbusinesslike to concern myself with such matters in those days. The royalties would, as it turned out, have been worth a fortune, for the figures sold in thousands all over the world, and were reproduced mercilessly by Wedgwood until the moulds were so worn out that the animals were scarcely recognisable. But I was content. . . .' (*Drawn from Life*, 1977, 75).

In 1928-9 the figures were included in the International Exhibition of Ceramic Art held in New York by the American Federation of Arts. Nine of them are listed, with prices, in the catalogue of the Wedgwood exhibition at the Grafton Galleries, London, in April and May 1936, p. 13:

Tiger and Buck	£1 5s. 6d.
Fallow Deer	14s. 6d.
Polar Bear	13s. 6d.
Duiker, Standing	12s. 9d.
Duiker, Lying	8s. 9d.
Sea Lion	15s. 6d.
Bison	16s. 6d.
Kangaroo	12s. 9d.
Monkey	13s. 6d.

The tenth model was a buffalo. They are described as 'figures in moonstone glaze'. The introduction to the catalogue records that 'Moonstone' was introduced eighteen months before (i.e. in 1934). It further states: 'There are now "satin" glazes of a similar durable quality but delicately tinted, such as the "April Green" or "Silver Grey".' This suggests that the satin glazes were introduced *c.*1935-6. The firm's research laboratory developed a number of new glazes from 1933 (see Murray, Cat. 218) under the direction of the glaze chemist, Norman Wilson, who joined the firm as works manager and also designed tableware. Skeaping's models were relatively inexpensive to produce and remained popular throughout the 1930s, in either black basalt or a variety of matt and coloured glazes. This figure was made before 1940 when the factory moved to Barlaston and the new location was incorporated in the factory mark.

For further illustrations and discussion, see Batkin 1982, 188-9, 192-3. For an example of the Fallow Deer group in the Victoria and Albert Museum, given by the artist in 1934, see V & A 1983, xvii. See also Dawson 1984, 147-8, fig. 109.

Slutzky, Naum J. 1894-1965

A monograph on Slutzky was published as this book was going to press and has therefore not been consulted: Rudolph, M., *Naum Slutzky. Meister am Bauhaus, Goldschmied und Designer*, Stuttgart 1990. Biographical details given below are taken from G. Hughes, *Modern Jewelry*, London 1964 and B. Cartlidge, *Twentieth Century Jewelry*, New York 1985. See also Holzhausen 1927 and Lehmann 1931.

272 Decanter   [PLATE 128]

Glass and nickel silver, a green glass bottle mounted in flat riveted strips of nickel, with white-metal stopper. The decanter is improvised from an Italian chianti bottle with the raffia removed; the stopper appears to be made from the end of a bicycle pump.

MARKS None.

Given by the artist probably in 1937 to Margaret Gardiner, from whom the decanter was acquired, and according to whom it was made by Slutzky at the Bauhaus.

H 33.2 cm, W 17.4 cm (with handle)   1984,11-8,1

Born in Kiev, Russia, into a family of goldsmiths, Slutzky studied in Vienna and worked in the Wiener Werkstätte before entering the Bauhaus in Weimar, where he worked in the metal workshop from 1919 to 1923; his spherical copper box of 1920 was engraved with a pattern of segmented circles inspired by the structural theories of Johannes Itten, who directed the metal workshop at that time (Wingler 1981, no. 179). Alongside the metal workshop, which was primarily geared towards the development of everyday articles, was a workshop for precious metals, operated as a private workshop by Slutzky, but discontinued after Moholy-Nagy took over as director in 1923. For examples of Slutzky's strikingly original jewellery made at the Bauhaus in 1922-3, see Gropius 1925, 71-2 and Wingler 1978, 321.

From 1927 to 1933 Slutzky worked as a freelance industrial designer in Hamburg and the city's Museum für Kunst und Gewerbe holds a group of jewellery made by Slutzky during these years (Hughes 1964, pl. 236). Contemporary critics noted the simple, precision-made forms of Slutzky's jewellery, designed to be assembled without solder (Holzhausen 1927) and his use of new materials such as chromium-plated metal combined with forms suitable for modern fashions (Lehmann 1931, references kindly supplied by Rüdiger Joppien). Three pieces of jewellery designed in 1929 were acquired in 1967 by the Victoria and Albert Museum (Bury 1982, 146, Circ.1233, 1244 and 1255.1967) and further pieces are held by Goldsmiths' Hall, London.

Slutzky came to London in 1933, and taught metalwork and engineering at Dartington Hall, Devon, until 1939; after the war he taught at the Central School of Art (1946-50), then at the Royal College of Art (1950-57), where he established the Product and Design Research studios. He was then Head of Industrial Design at Birmingham College of Arts and Crafts (1957-64) and at Ravensbourne College of Art, Bromley (1965). Further examples of Slutzky's metalwork include a biscuit barrel in spun nickel silver acquired by the V & A from the designer in 1935 (Circ.180-1935) and a teapot in brass with chromium finish acquired by the V & A in 1967 (Circ.1232-1967).

Margaret Gardiner formed a collection of British and European twentieth-century art which she gave to Orkney and with it the Pier Arts Centre was founded in 1978. Margaret Gardiner was a friend of many of the artists whose work she collected.

Solon, Marc Louis Emmanuel 1835-1913

There is no monograph on Solon. For biographical details, see Monkhouse, W. Cosmo, 'M. L. Solon', *The Magazine of Art*, 1890, 173-80; Hobson, R. L., 'Memorial Lecture on Mr. M. L. E. Solon', *Transactions of the English Ceramic Society* XIV, 1914-15, 80-95; Mundt 1973, s. v. Solon; London 1976b, 71-6; Atterbury and Batkin 1990.

Solon wrote widely on European ceramic art: his *Art of the Old English Potter* (n.d.) was illustrated with his own etchings. For two articles on *pâte-sur-pâte*, see *The Studio*, 1894, 117ff. and *Art Journal*, March 1901, 74ff. (The *Studio* article was later published in book form by Mintons as *A brief account of pâte sur pâte by M. L. Solon*.)

273 Plaque   [PLATE 77]

Tinted dark green Parian porcelain, with *pâte-sur-pâte* decoration in white on a dark olive-green glazed ground, depicting a seated female with flimsy draperies writing with a quill in a large book held on her knee and supported from below by a cupid, her ink bottle slung from her waist, while a second cupid tears pages from another book. The plaque is mounted in a wooden frame. A paper label on the reverse reads 'Solon plaque' (in a nineteenth-century hand) and in a later hand 'presented by L. Solon to W. Cosmo Monkhouse. Purchased at Christie's 1901', to which is added 'Thos. Boynton'.

MARKS Signed in the *pâte-sur-pâte* on the dais 'L. Solon'.

Designed and executed by M. L. E. Solon in 1884-5.

H 18 cm, W 16.3 cm. Frame: H 25.9 cm, W 23 cm   1920,3-18,16
Bequeathed by Thomas Boynton, who purchased it at Christie's, London, 14 November 1901, lot 21, from the collection of the poet and art critic, W. Cosmo Monkhouse (1840-1901), to whom it was presented by M. L. E. Solon

After training as a graphic artist in Paris, Solon joined the Sèvres manufactory in 1858 as a designer; while there he learnt the *pâte-sur-pâte* process and decorated wares for the dealer Eugène Rousseau, who funded further experiments. Solon's work for Sèvres was shown at the Paris Exhibition of 1867, but the Franco-Prussian war of 1870-71 halted developments and Solon left for England. He was immediately engaged by Minton & Co., where he joined a group of distinguished French ceramists hired by the firm in the second half of the nineteenth century, including the then Art Director, Léon Arnoux.

Solon's success at Minton was due in part to the Minton tinted Parian body, a material far more responsive to the technique than the French hard-paste porcelain and in which he was able to develop a wider range of background colours. The image was built up in successive layers of brush-painted liquid slip, biscuit-fired and then fired with a clear glaze. The relief is usually white and stands out against a coloured background. The colour of the body is visible through the layers in varying degrees, according to the thickness of the relief, which was finely tooled before firing.

Solon also decorated a number of plaques at home; he used Minton materials and had the finished articles fired by Minton's, for which he paid. Solon's manuscript notes of these plaques are still in the possession of his family and this plaque is listed under 'Année 1884-5'. The subject is not legible, but it is clearly annotated 'C. Monkhouse don', i.e. given to C. Monkhouse (information kindly supplied by Bernard Bumpus, 1992). In 1881 Solon was awarded the Society of Arts silver medal for an olive-green *pâte-sur-pâte* tea service (*JSA* 30, 25). Solon produced *pâte-sur-pâte* at Minton, training a number of apprentices, until 1904, when his formal association with the factory ceased. However, he continued to make *pâte-sur-pâte* wares until he went blind, shortly before his death in 1913.

William Cosmo Monkhouse was a civil servant who contributed in his spare time to several literary and art magazines from the 1860s onwards, as well as writing widely on art history and on ceramics, particularly on Chinese porcelain. His book *A History of Chinese Porcelain* was published in 1901. For a sketch portrait of him, see the *Art Journal*, 1892, 197. Monkhouse's collection was sold at Christie's in two parts: paintings and ceramics. The ceramic sale comprised 'Oriental Porcelain and Faience. Old English and Continental Porcelain'. The Solon plaque was the only piece of its kind; it fetched £9 10s., considerably more than any of his eighteenth-century English pieces.

For two further plaques from the Boynton collection, see Hobson 1914-15. Thomas Boynton, FSA, antiquary and collector, was for many years honorary curator of archaeology and ceramics at the Museum of the Yorkshire Philosophical Society in York. His collection of Yorkshire pottery was presented to that museum partly during his lifetime in 1916 and partly after his death in 1920 (see *Catalogue of the Boynton Collection of Yorkshire Pottery presented to Yorkshire Museum*, 1916 and 1920).

Stabler, Harold 1872-1945

There is no monograph on Stabler. For biographical details, see Gere 1975; Anscombe and Gere 1978; Jervis 1984; Culme 1987.

274 Seal-die of the British Museum [PLATE 68]

Ebony, silver and steel, the handle of turned ebony of octagonal section, the domed knop inset with a silver disc engraved 'HAROLD STABLER. LONDON. 1915'. The base fitted with a rectangular steel seal bearing the British Museum crest: the Royal Arms with the words 'BRITISH MUSEUM'.

MARKS As described above.

Designed and made by Harold Stabler in 1915.

H 8 cm, w of seal 2.5 cm   1981,12-10,2   Transferred from British Museum Works Services

After initial training in woodwork and stone-carving at the Kendal School of Art, Stabler became head of metalwork at the Keswick School of Industrial Arts in 1898. He left there in 1902 to work at the Liverpool University Art School and then went to London, where he was head of the John Cass Institute's Art

School from 1907 to 1937. He also taught at the Royal College of Art from 1912 to 1926. After the First World War he became a partner in the Carter, Stabler & Adams pottery at Poole, designed glass for mass-production and produced modern designs for metalwork which had a marked influence on English design of the 1920s and 1930s. In 1936 he was appointed one of the first Designers for Industry by the Royal Society of Arts.

Before the First World War, Stabler made metalwork and jewellery in the Arts & Crafts manner: the Department also holds a silver and cloisonné-enamel pectoral cross made in 1915 in association with his wife Phoebe, a noted enameller (acquired as part of the Hull Grundy Gift in 1978; see C. Gere, in Gere et al. 1984, no. 1171). The seal-die and the cross were made in the same year and illustrate the beginnings of Stabler's move away from the craft revival towards a more simple, geometric style.

Early in 1915 the Trustees of the British Museum decided to modify the armorial bearings of the Museum by removing the Hanoverian escutcheon in the centre (Trustees' Minutes, Standing Committee, 13 February 1915: 3,340). The Trustees' original request to Stabler does not survive, but on 26 April 1915 Stabler sent in an estimate of 13 guineas for two seals, and on 8 May the Trustees 'accepted an estimate from Mr Stabler for preparing two new seals for the sealing of official correspondence' (Standing Committee, 8 May 1915: 3,372). Stabler was asked 'to execute them on steel as you propose, and fix them to ebony hafts' (letter from Assistant Secretary, 13 May 1915). According to the register of incoming correspondence (there are no original letters for this period) Stabler wrote in June to say that he had made the alteration as suggested; he sent the two seals on 11 October. On 12 October the Director, F. G. Kenyon, replied: 'I have received the seals in safety, and am having good impressions of them made to lay before the Trustees, with the seals themselves, at their next meeting. I shall be better able to judge of the seals when I have seen the impressions; but at first sight they look satisfactory.' The Trustees approved the seals on 13 November.

Why the Museum went to Stabler is not known, but the connection may have been made through the Department of Coins and Medals, to whom he would certainly have been known at this time, for in December 1912 Stabler had given to that department one of his own medals (1912,12-8,1, a cast bronze medal of a sow) and in 1916 he won the Royal Numismatic Society competition for a medal commemorating the battle of Jutland (1917,3-1,1).

Stabler's seal was in use until the late 1920s or early 1930s, when the current armorial bearings were introduced.

275 Coffee-pot and cream jug [PLATE 115]

Pewter, cast in several pieces, with a band of ribbed decoration below the spout and on the foot. Both handles are in the form of a flat, curved strip, the handle of the coffee-pot in ebonised wood, with square-shaped wood knop to the lid.

MARKS Stamped on the base of each piece 'HUTTON SHEFFIELD ENGLISH PEWTER SW 1705' and facsimile signature 'Harold Stabler', together with the firm's trade mark, a cluster of crossed arrows.

Designed *c*.1930 and made by the firm of William Hutton & Sons Ltd, Sheffield.

275a Coffee pot: H 15.3 cm   1980,6-14,1
275b Cream jug: H 10.1 cm   1980,6-14,2

The service to which these two pieces belong is an example of Stabler's successful designs for industry and it remained popular for a number of years; it was advertised in *Design for Today* IV, 1936, 150, at which time the coffee-pot, cream jug and sugar bowl together were sold at Heal's for £2 18s. The service was also made in electroplate: see Christie's, London, 27 January 1987, lot 37, a teapot and hot water jug, marked 'W. M. Hutton & Sons Improved Metal Silver Plated'. Stabler designed a service of rather similar shape and proportions which was produced in stainless steel by J. & J. Wiggin, Walsall, Staffordshire, *c.*1936 (Hughes 1967, pl. 144).

Stabler's other successful industrial designs include a coffee-set of *c.*1933 for Carter, Stabler & Adams Pottery (London 1979, 2.131), tiles for London Transport of *c.*1939, heat-resistant glass of *c.*1931 for Chance Brothers, Birmingham (London 1979, 4.141) and a silver teaset of 1935 for Adie Brothers of Birmingham, which was also produced in electroplate; each piece was rectangular and fitted on to a rectangular tray (Birmingham 1973, H. 105; Victoria and Albert Museum 1983, 144-5; for a set with its original tray, see Christie's, London, 27 January 1988, lot 29). Stabler also designed a number of silver presentation pieces in the 1920s and 1930s, in particular for the Goldsmiths' Company (see London 1965, 248-66). Stabler's decorative Chinese-style designs of the late 1920s and early 1930s, often octagonal in form, with curved handles and applied die-stamped ornament (e.g. Victoria and Albert Museum 1983, 114-15, a teaset of 1929-30, and Hughes 1967, pl. 324, a teaset of 1928) gave way from the mid 1930s to pieces in a more streamlined manner with little ornament, such as the Adie Brothers teaset or the centrepiece of 1938-9 for the London, Midland & Scottish Railway Company (in the Victoria and Albert Museum, M.13 and a-1948).

For a detailed account of the early history of W. Hutton & Sons, see Culme 1987. From the early 1900s they supplied Liberty & Co. and then became large-scale producers of flatware. The firm's director, Herbert Hutton, resigned in 1923 (see Hughes 1967, 235) and the goodwill of the company was transferred to James Dixon & Sons, Sheffield, in 1930.

Stevens, Alfred 1817-75

Armstrong, W., *Alfred Stevens. A biographical study*, London 1881

Towndrow, K. R., *Alfred Stevens, architectural sculptor, painter and designer. A biography with new material*, London 1939

Beattie, S., *Alfred Stevens 1817-75*, exhibition catalogue, Victoria and Albert Museum, London 1975

276-7 Two lions [PLATE 26]

Cast iron.

MARKS None.

Designed in 1852 to ornament the former miniature railing outside the main railings of the British Museum.

H 35.1cm. Base: 10.2 × 10.2cm 1983,12-5,1 and 2

The main railings and gates of the British Museum were erected in May 1852; that summer, a miniature railing ornamented with twenty-five of these lions was erected outside the main railings to mark the limits of the Trustees' property. The erection of the low railing is recorded in *The Buildings of the British*

Museum (1914, pl. XII). The lions are clearly visible in nineteenth-century views of the Museum (Fig. 9). Both sets of railings were commissioned by Sydney Smirke (1799-1877), younger brother of Robert Smirke, architect of the British Museum. Sydney Smirke completed the sections left unfinished on his brother's retirement in 1846 and also designed the round Reading Room in 1854.

Smirke was unable to resolve the difficulty of modelling a lion seated on a base one third of its height and the commission was given to Stevens, who was well known for his sculptural metal-work and whose designs for the iron founders Henry Hoole & Co. of Sheffield were highly acclaimed at the Great Exhibition of 1851. According to Mordaunt Crook (1972, 145) Stevens worked from Smirke's drawing of the lion at the foot of the staircase of the Bargello in Florence, while Towndrow records that 'the model was the fine cat of a friend, and Stevens always spoke of the finished work as his "cat"' (Towndrow, 114; for reference to the lions, see also Armstrong, 14). The great railing was cast by John Walker & Co. of York. Since the miniature railing and its lions were put up in the same year as the main railing, it is likely that the same suppliers were used, though they are not specified in the Trustees' Minutes.

The miniature railing was dismantled at the end of 1895 to make room for pavement improvements. Eight of the twenty-five lions were placed in various parts of the Museum, while the remaining seventeen were put into store (British Museum Standing Committee, 8 February 1896, 19874). In 1899 twelve of these were removed to St Paul's Cathedral, together with their connecting lengths of railing, to stand round the Wellington Monument, which Stevens had designed in 1856 (Standing Committee, 11 November 1899, 1029). In 1937 two lions were deposited on loan at the Dorset County Museum in Dorchester (Standing Committee, 3 March 1937, 5354) where they are still on display. Stevens was born in Blandford Forum, Dorset, and the Dorset County Museum has sketches from his early years. One lion is in the Natural History Museum and eight lions are still in the British Museum (at the time of writing: four in the Trustees' Board Room, two in the Department of Medieval and Later Antiquities, one in the Director's Office and one in central administration offices), but the whereabouts of the remaining two is unknown. (I am grateful to Marjorie Caygill and Christopher Date for much of the above information.)

In 1896 Messrs D. Brucciani & Co., a family firm of cast-manufacturers in Covent Garden since 1864, were given permission by the Trustees to supply casts at a price of 7s. 6d. each (Standing Committee, 8 February 1896, 19874). As a result, copies of Stevens's lions can be seen on a number of other London buildings, for example Ely House and the Law Society. They are also to be found outside the City Museum, Leicester and were popular as staircase and fireplace ornaments (see *The Studio Yearbook*, 1906, 100).

Walter Crane greatly admired the formalism of Stevens's lions, comparing it with that of the Assyrian lion-hunt reliefs from Ashurbanipal's palace at Nineveh. In Crane's view the attempted naturalism of modern sculptors resulted in a loss of dignity and character. He deeply lamented the removal of the lions as depriving Londoners of 'perhaps their finest bit of monumental work' (*The Bases of Design*, 1898, 204, with illustration of one of the lions on p. 205).

For an enlarged earthenware copy of Stevens's lion, made by

William Burton at Pilkington's Tile & Pottery Co., see Cat. 30. Earthenware lions derived from the Stevens model were also made by Carter & Co. at Poole, Dorset, in the early 1900s (see Christie's, South Kensington, 7 September 1990, lot 94; Hawkins 1980, 36).

Suetin, Nikolai Mikhailovich 1897-1954

There is no monograph on Suetin. For biographical details, see Oxford and London 1984, Vienna 1988 and Lobanov-Rostovsky 1990.

For Suetin's designs for porcelain, see also Lunacharsky et al. 1927; Lansere 1974; Andreeva 1975; Franzke 1975, 1977 and 1982.

278 Plaque   [PLATE 143; COLOUR PLATE XV]

Hard-paste porcelain, with three-dimensional 'architectonic' relief ornament in the form of a cluster of thin rectangular rods of different lengths placed in the centre and painted in overglaze colours of red, green, black and matt grey on a white glazed ground. The colour is applied to the upper surface of the relief only and to the surrounding area, in abstract lines or blocks, with a matt grey circle to the left. The base is unglazed.

MARKS The base painted in black with 'N. SUETIN' in Cyrillic capitals, 'NO. 173' and the Suprematist logo of a black square within a square.

Designed c.1923-4 and made at the State Porcelain Factory, Petrograd. Since the artist's name is given without the abbreviated prefix 'after the design of' (as on Cat. 34, 279-80, 350), it is possible that the plaque was decorated by the artist himself.

H 22cm, W 20.1cm   1988,6-9,1

Suetin studied under the painter Kasimir Malevich (1878-1935) at the Vitebsk Practical Art Institute from 1918 to 1922, when he moved to Leningrad; he started work at the State Porcelain Factory in 1923, creating new designs and shapes for porcelain. He was involved in experimental art throughout the 1920s. From 1932 to 1954 he was chief artist at the State Porcelain Factory.

The Suprematist movement was begun by Malevich in 1913-15 (see Zhadova 1982). Malevich's most famous work shows a black square on a white ground; hence the logo that appears on porcelain decorated in the style of the Suprematist movement. Suprematism developed into a style based on abstract shapes and pure colours which was adapted to porcelain by Malevich himself, as well as Suetin and another pupil, Ilya Chashnik (see Cat. 34), who worked with Suetin at the State Porcelain Factory from 1923 to 1924.

The two-dimensional Suprematist designs produced by Malevich, Suetin and Chashnik were in many cases put into production in the usual way on pre-revolutionary blanks. The three also experimented with a number of new three-dimensional shapes, many of which seem never to have passed beyond the stage of prototypes. Suetin's architectonic porcelains are derived from the 'architektons' or experimental architectural models made in wood and plaster, conceived by Malevich in collaboration with both Suetin and Chashnik. Suetin's experimentation with architectonic forms in porcelain dates from c.1923 to c.1933. His most familiar architectonic form is an inkwell, designed in 1923-4, with a horizontal instead of vertical cluster of rods, which is known in a handful of examples (e.g. in the

Kunstgewerbemuseum, Cologne; see Beaucamp-Markovsky 1980, no. 381).

This is the only example of this plaque so far known. There are, however, a number of comparable pieces: the closest in conception is a porcelain model for an architectonic relief, published by Zhadova 1982, no. 251, in a private collection in Leningrad. Zhadova dates this piece to the 1930s. Models for architectonic porcelain vases of cylindrical shape with vertical clusters of rectangular rods are published by Andreeva 1975, 263 and pl. 278 (no locations given, and perhaps taken from a contemporary photograph; a further unpublished prototype vase was seen in the reserves of the State Ceramic Museum, Kuskovo, Moscow, by Aileen Dawson in 1982). Andreeva dates these models to c.1933. It is therefore possible that the British Museum plaque belongs to the early 1930s, but it seems closer in conception and use of colour to the inkwell of 1923-4.

279-80 Two small pots   [PLATE 143]

Hard-paste porcelain, painted on each side with a different design in overglaze colours. On one side an abstract pattern of blocks of colour in red, black, blue and ochre; the design on the taller pot incorporates a red disc. On the other side, a design in red, black, grey and beige.

MARKS Hammer, sickle and cogwheel mark of the State Porcelain Factory, Petrograd and the date '1923' painted in overglaze blue (the date is followed by the Russian letter 'g' for 'gorod', or year); 'SUPREMATISM' painted in black Cyrillic capitals with the Suprematist logo of a black square within a black square; 'after the design of N. SUETIN' painted in Cyrillic letters (the word for 'design' is abbreviated); the letter 'A' (an artist's mark) and 'No. 375' also painted in black. The marks are surrounded by areas of green paint, though these do not cover any pre-revolutionary marks.

Painted in 1923, after Suetin's designs, at the State Porcelain Factory, Petrograd.

279 H 3.5cm   1988,4-1,1
280 H 7.6cm   1988,4-1,2

These two pots illustrate the application of two-dimensional Suprematist designs to porcelain. For closely comparable Suprematist designs by Suetin on cups and saucers, see Zhadova 1982, pl. 259. For further discussion, see Lansere, 1974, Andreeva 1975 and Franzke 1977 and 1982.

The shape of the taller pot may be compared to a traditional lidded mustard-pot of which examples are known with propaganda motifs (Lobanov-Rostovsky 1990, no. 82, with illegible Imperial mark) and with Suprematist decoration designed by Chashnik (ibid, no. 151, in the Museum of the Lomonossov Porcelain Factory, formerly the State Porcelain Factory, Leningrad). The porcelain body of the squat pot is much heavier and it may therefore be of post-revolutionary manufacture.

Teague, Walter Dorwin 1883-1960

There is no monograph on Teague. For discussion of his designs for industry and the applied arts, see *Arts and Decoration* 41, October 1934, 44-8; Cheney and Cheney 1936; Meikle 1979; Duncan 1987; and Teague's own book, *Design This Day: The Technique of Order in the Machine Age*, New York 1940.

281 Four glasses   [PLATE 125]

Goblet, dinner wine, champagne and cordial. Clear glass, with vertically ribbed flat-section stems, the bowls and feet free-blown, the stems moulded and polished.

MARKS Acid-etched on the base 'Libbey' in a circle.

Designed in 1939 for the New York World's Fair as part of the 'Embassy' pattern, the design credited jointly to W. D. Teague and E. W. Fuerst. Made by the Libbey Glass Manufacturing Company, Toledo, Ohio, between 1940 and 1941-2.

281a Water goblet: H 22 cm, D of base 8 cm   1988,6-8,1
281b Dinner wine glass: H 17.5 cm, D of base 6.8 cm   1988,6-8,2
281c Champagne glass: H 16.5 cm, w of bowl 9.3 cm   1988,6-8,3
281d Cordial glass: H 17.2 cm, D of base 7 cm   1988,6-8,4

Teague worked initially as an advertising artist from 1908 to 1926, when he visited Europe, where he was much impressed by French modernist design (see *Pencil Points* 18, September 1937, 543). His first industrial design was for Eastman Kodak cameras. In 1932-3 he designed a range of table and ornamental glass for the Corning firm of Steuben (for examples, see Newhaven 1983, nos 8 and 13; Brooklyn 1986, 327, fig. 8.81). Steuben glass remained an expensive status symbol and was promoted as 'severely patrician' by Teague, whereas Libbey glass was advertised as 'well within the reach of the modest income', although using handmade methods in high-quality crystal. According to *Arts and Decoration* 40, November 1933, Libbey glasses ranged in price from $10 a dozen to $25 a dozen.

The 'Embassy' pattern service was designed for the State Dining Room in the Federal Building at the 1939 World's Fair in New York. The original service was engraved with a crest incorporating the American eagle beneath thirteen stars (Duncan 1987, 126); it still survives in the White House (Spillman 1989, 126-7) The service comprised eight stemware sizes: cocktail, sherry, dinner wine, dessert wine, champagne, cordial, goblet and Delmonico. There were also finger bowls and three sizes of tumbler. The specially created columnar stems were unusual because they were the same height for all items. The flattened columns echo George Sakier's 'classic modern' glasses with round-section fluted stems of c.1933-4 (*Arts and Decoration* 40, April 1934, 44).

Teague was design consultant for the Fair while Fuerst was Libbey's in-house designer. After the failure of the Libbey-Nash series in 1935 (see Cat. 220), Libbey was bought up by Owens-Illinois, who employed Edwin W. Fuerst, formerly head of Owens-Illinois' package-design department, to design a new line of crystal called 'Modern American'. The first catalogue of 'Modern American' was printed in 1939. The series, including 'Embassy' pattern, was formally introduced in 1940 but was ended by the restrictions of the war just over a year later. For the Libbey Company and the 'Embassy' service, see Fauster 1979, 119, 247, 397 (illustration of whole service).

Tiffany & Co. founded 1837

Heydt, G. F., *Charles L. Tiffany and the House of Tiffany & Co.*, New York 1893

Purtell, J., *The Tiffany Touch*, New York 1972

Carpenter, C. H. and M. G., *Tiffany Silver*, New York 1978

Safford, F. Gruber and Caccavale, R. Wilford, 'Japanesque silver by Tiffany and Company in the Metropolitan Museum of Art', *Antiques*, October 1987, 808-19

Zapata, J. and Carpenter, C. H., *The Silver of Tiffany & Co. 1850-1987*, exhibition catalogue, Museum of Fine Arts, Boston, 1987

See also Recent Acquisitions, Cat. 351.

282 Ladle   [PLATE 11]

Silver, cast, the handle decorated with classical motifs: on the front a ram's head, satyr's head and stylised bunch of grapes, with engraved owner's monogram 'EL'; on the reverse a palmette. On underside of bowl, a ribbon-tied bunch of grapes and vine leaves.

MARKS Stamped on reverse of stem 'H.H.PATENT 1862 STERLING TIFFANY & CO'.

The design patented in 1862 by Henry Hebbard, flatware manufacturer. Made for Tiffany & Co. between 1862 and 1869.

L 33.1 cm, w of bowl 10.9 cm   1980,10-7,5   Given by Professor and Mrs John Hull Grundy

Tiffany & Co. sold other manufacturers' flatware until 1869, when they began making their own flatware. Before this date, flatware retailed by Tiffany bears both the Tiffany stamp and the maker's stamp. For discussion of Tiffany flatware and illustration of a closely similar mark, see Carpenter 1978, chap. 5 and p. 255. According to Rainwater (1975) Henry Hebbard is listed in New York City directories from 1847 to 1851 as Henry Hebbard & Co. He was later associated with other partners, but continued to obtain patents in his name from c.1853 to 1869.

For a survey of the various types of ladles produced by Tiffany & Co., see Zapata 1989.

283 Waiter   [PLATE 47]

Silver, cast, decorated in the Japanese taste with a dappled frog swimming among water weeds and horizontal waves, implying that the scene is underwater. The surface has been etched away, leaving the weeds and waves in relief on a background which has been punched to give a hammered effect. The background has an overall textured surface within each punch mark. The frog is cast and applied. Where the weeds and waves are applied over the body of the frog, additional parts have been soldered on – e.g. the stem of waterweed over the frog's leg – while two of the horizontal etched waves continue over the body with applied strips.

The frog's black spots are inlaid in copper with a thin black patina which has worn away in parts to reveal the underlying rust-coloured copper. The pupil of the eye is similarly executed in copper with a thin black patina, also partly worn away. The white of the eye is inlaid in gold, with a triangular highlight across the pupil, also in gold. The left corner of the eye is inlaid with copper, surrounded by silver. The toes are inlaid in rust-coloured copper. However, the copper at the corner of the eye bears traces of a crimson-red surface colour. This is also detectable at the lower edges of the toes, especially on the uppermost toe of the front leg. The darker silver areas on the frog's back, surrounding the black spots and extending along the legs, are inlaid in nickel silver. A narrow border of bright silver has been left round each black spot between the black area and the darker nickel inlay.

There are four shallow feet and the rim is raised. On the reverse is the inscription 'Helene Leigh from Mr and Mrs Vanderbilt, 1890'.

MARKS Stamped on the reverse 'TIFFANY & CO / MAKERS / STERLING-SILVER / AND OTHER-METALS', together with the pattern number '5940' for the waiter, the date '1880' and the mounting design number '983'. (Tiffany's Japanese-style wares using a range of applied metals could not accurately be described as sterling, hence the phrase 'and other metals'.)

Designed in 1880 under the direction of Edward C. Moore and made for Tiffany & Co., New York.

W 23.8 cm, L 30.1 cm   1981,3-11,1   Given by Mr and Mrs John Cox

Edward C. Moore (1827-91) was Tiffany's chief designer and director of the firm's silver works from 1868. His own collection (bequeathed to the Metropolitan Museum of Art) was particularly strong in Far Eastern metalwork. Moore's 'Japanese' flatware pattern of 1871 was followed by hollowware designs in

1872. Tiffany & Co. continued to produce silver in the Japanese style until Moore's death in 1891.

The waiter or small tray for visiting cards, in round or square form, was a popular item that lent itself particularly well to Japanese-style ornament and several design drawings for waiters survive in the Tiffany archives. The drawing for this waiter is executed life-size and bears the pattern number 5940, the mounting design number 983 and the date Feb 8 1880 (Fig. 14). The drawing suggests that the nickel-silver inlay on the frog's upper surface was intended to be darker than it appears on this tray, where the inlay has possibly been worn over the years and lost its original hue. It is annotated with details of the coloured metal inlays and with the model number for the frog appliqué:

CAST FROG, GERMAN SILVER NO 6995
    SPOTS, JAP GOLD NO 2
    EYE, FINE GOLD, JAP G.8. SILVER
    RED COPPER
    WHITE, FINE SILVER
    WEEDS ETCHED

These annotations specify the use of two different colours of 'Japanese gold', for the black spots and the eye (whether for the black pupil or the red-coloured copper in the corner is unclear). Analysis has shown that the black spots and pupil are inlaid with copper covered with a thin black patina (Cu_2O, cuprite). Thus it is possible that the term 'Japanese gold' was used by Tiffany to indicate a black inlay. Other drawings in the archive are annotated with the Japanese names *shakudo* and *shibuichi*, blue-black and grey-black copper alloys. It is therefore significant that analysis has also detected platinum in the areas which have the black patina. It is not certain whether the platinum is alloyed with the copper or contained in the surface patina, but if it is in the alloy it suggests that these blackened copper inlays are an adaptation by Tiffany of the Japanese shakudo alloy, with platinum replacing the few per cent gold added to copper in the traditional Japanese recipes. Analysis has also confirmed the silver, gold and red copper inlays, as indicated in the drawing (surface X-ray fluorescence analysis of the inlays was carried out by Susan La Niece of the British Museum Research Laboratory). For an example of Tiffany's adaptation of Japanese alloys, see Sotheby's, New York, 24-27 January 1990, lot 62, a small globular bowl with flared rim, with a swirled pattern of inlaid copper and gold, the neck inscribed 'Gold Silver Shakudo Shibu-Ichi Copper'.

Experiments with polychrome decoration using coloured metal inlays were made by Tiffany from 1875; from 1877 the drawings specify the use of applied motifs and inlays of various alloys. For detailed discussion of the drawings for Tiffany Japanesque silver, see Safford and Caccavale 1987. The dappled frog was a favourite Tiffany Japanese motif and occurs in a different form on a circular waiter in the Metropolitan Museum of Art, New York (illustrated with drawing in Safford and Caccavale op. cit., pl. IV and fig. 8). Here, the frog is model no. 6868 and is annotated 'cast in YM' (yellow metal). Other alloys for the frog are indicated with initials: 'RM' (red metal), 'FG' (fine gold), 'JG' (Japanese gold), 'C' (copper), 'RG' (red gold). The drawing is further annotated 'grass, water and mosquitoes etched' - i.e. the background etched and the decoration left in

relief (both waiter and drawing were shown in an excellent exhibition of Tiffany silver organised by Frances Gruber Safford at the Metropolitan Museum in 1987; no catalogue was published. Tiffany & Co. have presented to the Metropolitan Museum all the existing drawings for the Tiffany silver items in the Museum's collections).

Evidence that the surfaces of Tiffany silver were often originally oxidised (see Cat. 351) is provided by contemporary accounts such as that of the author and critic George Augustus Sala, of Tiffany's display at the Paris Exhibition of 1878: 'Purely of American design and execution is Messrs Tiffany's tea-service in oxidised silver and variously coloured gold, adorned with an exquisite pattern in relief, embodying the apologue of "the Spider and the Fly". I am shown also a teapot, in its way unique, and in which the silver has been oxidised to an inimitably delicate purple hue' (Sala 1880, vol. II, 81; see also Safford and Caccavale).

The drawing for another circular tray in the Metropolitan Museum, with an engraved design of irises, specifies the size of the punch to be used for the hammered effect on the background (Safford and Caccavale, fig. 7). The surfaces were also lightly textured or 'pebbled' within the large punch-marks, but this detail, like the oxidising, is often lost. It is, however, visible on the British Museum tray. The French goldsmith Lucien Falize, writing in 1878, noted that the Americans had been able to study Japanese metalwork two years previously at the Philadelphia Exhibition of 1876 and he welcomed the 'nouvelle palette de l'orfèvre' achieved with coloured inlays, the clever simulation of hand-raised silver and the unpolished surfaces: 'on ne craint plus de poser les doigts sur les surfaces polies, elles ont les fines craquelures de la peau, les nervures de la feuille, les mailles et le tissu de certains fruits . . .' (Gazette des Beaux-Arts XVIII, 2e période, 1878, 123-3). . . The random hammer marks applied by Tiffany craftsmen were often misinterpreted at the time as obtained through hand-raising; ironically it was this belief that made the effect fashionable (Boston 1987b, 15-16, quoting the diary for 1877 of a Tiffany silversmith).

For further discussion of Tiffany silver in the Japanese taste, see Hawley 1976, Carpenter 1978 and New York 1986. See also Ovchinnikov, Cat. 230. For coloured gold jewellery by Tiffany in the Japanese taste, see Gere et al. 1984, cat. nos 1060-66.

The original purchase orders from the nineteenth century do not survive in the Tiffany archive and so it has not been possible to determine which member of the Vanderbilt family ordered this tray.

Tiffany, Louis Comfort 1848-1933

Amaya, M., *Tiffany Glass*, New York 1967

Neustadt, E., *The Lamps of Tiffany*, New York 1970

Koch, R. ed., *Artistic America, Tiffany Glass and Art Nouveau*, New York 1970 (includes reprint in translation of S. Bing, 'Die Kunstgläser von Louis C. Tiffany', *Kunst und Kunsthandwerk* I, 1898, 105-11)

Koch, R., *Louis C. Tiffany's Glass, Bronzes, Lamps*, New York 1971

Koch, R., *Louis C. Tiffany, Rebel in Glass*, 2nd edn, New York 1974

Feldstein, W. and Duncan, A., *The Lamps of Tiffany Studios*, New York and London 1983

284 Vase
[PLATE 109; COLOUR PLATE VII]

Free-blown glass, deep blue, with iridescent surface, inlaid with coloured glass pulled to form a wave-like pattern in gold, greenish gold, purple and turquoise blue. The rim is folded over at the top.

MARKS Etched on the base 'L.C.T. L.602'.

Designed c.1896 and made by L. C. Tiffany's glassworks at Corona, Long Island, New York between c.1896 and 1928.

H 15.6 cm, D 22.1 cm   1980,11-9,1

Louis Comfort Tiffany, the son of Charles Lewis Tiffany (see Cat. 282-3), trained as a painter before turning to interior decoration in 1879. In 1892 he formed the Tiffany Glass and Decorating Company, renamed Tiffany Studios in 1902 and remaining in operation until 1938. It was this part of the enterprise that produced the bronze candlesticks and lamps (see Cat. 286-8). Tiffany's first glass factory at Corona, Long Island was formed in 1893 as the Stourbridge Glass Company with Arthur J. Nash (1849-1934), a former manager of a Webb subsidiary in Stourbridge, England, as manager. It was renamed Tiffany Furnaces in 1902 and continued to operate until 1928 (Cat. 284-5).

Vases with similar decoration are illustrated in a booklet issued by the Tiffany Glass and Decorating Company entitled *Tiffany Favrile Glass* (a copy of the fifth edition, 1896 and 1899, is in the library of the Metropolitan Museum of Art). The trade name 'favrile' was derived from 'fabrile', a seventeenth-century English word meaning 'belonging to a craftsman or his craft'. Tiffany's lustre decoration was initially produced as an attempt to simulate the iridescence caused by natural decay in ancient glass (*Brush and Pencil* IX, no. 3, December 1902, 167-76). The iridescent surface was obtained by applying to the hot glass metallic salts which were absorbed into it to create the lustre, in addition to the coloured glasses which produced the pattern (Klein and Lloyd eds, 1984, 211).

Similar vases were acquired by the Musée des Arts Décoratifs, Paris (Weisberg 1986, pl. 13) and by the Cincinnati Art Museum in 1897 (Koch 1971, 46-9). A vase of almost identical shape and decoration (numbered G2469), but slightly more flared, was included in the collection of Elton John (sold Sotheby's, London, 7 September 1988, lot 617), mounted on a metal stand. The rim of the vase was also folded over at the top, suggesting that the British Museum vase may have been intended for mounting, perhaps as a lamp base (see *The House Beautiful* V, no. 4, March 1899, 179 and no. 5, April 1899, 224).

The complex numbering system of Tiffany glass is difficult to interpret; if the system worked out by Koch (1971, 56) is reliable, then this vase was made in 1899. However, Victor Arwas has noted that numbering is no real indication of the year of production as items were often kept in storage for several years before being numbered and sold (Arwas 1987, 324).

For the role of Siegfried Bing in the promotion of Tiffany glass in Europe, see Weisberg 1986; for further discussion of the reactions to Tiffany glass in Europe, see Schaefer 1962. For further contemporary accounts, see *The Studio* 11, August 1897, 156-65; 14, June 1898, 16-20; 17, June 1899, 39-44 (description of the exhibition of Tiffany glass and metalwork at the Grafton Galleries, London, organised by Bing. See also *The House Beautiful* VII, no. 5, April 1900, listing the different varieties of glass then in production.

285 Vase
[PLATE 109; COLOUR PLATE VII]

Free-blown glass, in the form of a jack-in-the-pulpit flower. Greenish-yellow and pink glass, with heavy base and hollow stem opening out into a flower of undulating glass with stretched edges. The surface is iridescent throughout, giving a lustrous gold effect to the front, while the back is a more silver-green colour.

MARKS Etched on the base 'L C Tiffany-Favrile 9257 G.'.

Designed c.1900 and made by L. C. Tiffany's glassworks at Corona, Long Island, New York between c.1900 and 1928.

H 49.3 cm, D of base 11.9 cm, W of top 26.6 cm   1980,11-8,1

According to Koch 1971, 40, the jack-in-the-pulpit shape was introduced by Thomas Manderson, Tiffany's first master blower.

For discussion of marks and dating, see Cat. 284. If Koch's dating system is reliable, this vase was made in 1912. Several jack-in-the-pulpit vases survive in a variety of colours and with a range of different numbers; see, for example, Christie's, New York, 10 June 1989, lot 244, numbered 5110K, with two variants, lots 248 and 250, numbered 9464A and 4045A.

Jack-in-the-pulpit vases were also made by the Quezal Art Glass and Decorating Company (1901-25), set up as a rival concern by Martin Bach, a former employee of L. C. Tiffany. The Quezal shape is usually more squat and the bases are sometimes decorated with feathering; see, for example, Sotheby's, New York, 16-17 March 1990, lots 523 and 525.

286 Candlestick
[PLATE 109; COLOUR PLATE VII]

Cast and patinated bronze in the form of a stylised tree with four 'roots' in relief running down the 'trunk' and across the base and four 'branches' to hold the shade. The top of the central column has a depression for the candle. The shade is free-blown glass, in swirled colours of green, pale blue and gold, with iridescent surface.

MARKS The bronze base stamped underneath 'TIFFANY STUDIOS NEW YORK 1224' and the engraved number '2954'. The shade etched inside top rim 'L.C.T.'.

Designed c.1900 and made by Tiffany Studios, Corona, Long Island, New York between 1902 and 1918.

Total H 26.1 cm. Base: H 17.8 cm. Shade: H 9.1 cm, W 15.8 cm
1981,7-12,1

According to Koch 1971, 89, the early bronzes were numbered individually (as with the glass) and stamped with the trade mark of the Tiffany Glass and Decorating Company. After 1902 the Tiffany Studios mark was used and the numbering system changed from individual to model numbers. Candlesticks began at 1200. In the Tiffany price list of 1906, model no. 1224 is described as '1 light, cast column, 4-prong shade holder' and sold at $12 (Koch 1971, 180). From 1918 Tiffany Studios retained the vast stock made during the peak years of production and continued in operation until 1938, but no candlesticks were manufactured after 1918.

For a range of candlestick designs, see Koch 1971, 102-7. For the Tiffany green patina, see Koch 1971, 88.

287 Bud candlestick
[PLATE 110; COLOUR PLATE VII]

Cast and patinated bronze, the base with wave-pattern edge and tall, thin stem, the 'bud' formed of green glass blown into a bronze cage (reticulated glass). The stem is made separately and screws into the base. The bud is also a separate piece and contains a removable drip pan and cylinder to hold the candle.

MARKS Stamped on the base 'TIFFANY STUDIOS NEW YORK 8898'. The number is faintly stamped and difficult to read.

Designed c.1900 and made by Tiffany Studios, Corona, Long Island, New York between 1902 and 1918 (see Cat. 286).

H 44.1 cm, D 14.7 cm (base)   1981,7-13,1

Tiffany metalwork received an important international showing in Bing's Art Nouveau exhibition at the Grafton Galleries, London, in 1899. The *Studio* report of this exhibition described the reticulated metalwork with glass bulging through the spaces as an 'ingenious device' creating an 'excellent and homogeneous effect' (vol. 17, 43). For a list of Tiffany objects exhibited in London in 1899, see Koch 1971, 85-8. A similar candlestick is listed as catalogue no. 30: 'Candelabra (one light) in metal with glass blown inside'.

For similar bud candlesticks, including an individually numbered example dating from before 1902, see Koch 1971, 102-3. For a taller version of this candlestick (height 52 cm), see Christie's, New York, 24 March 1990, lot 180.

288 'Spider and web' table lamp

[PLATE 109; COLOUR PLATE VII]

The stand in cast and patinated bronze with 'mushroom pattern' base, resembling the underside of a mushroom. The leaded-glass shade screws on to the stand and has six 'legs' radiating from a finial in the form of the spider's body. The glass 'web' is executed in a geometric pattern with streaked pale-greenish-white glass which changes to yellow and orange in transmitted light. There are three light fittings and the lamp is in working order.

MARKS The base stamped on the underside 'TIFFANY STUDIOS NEW YORK 337'. The shade marked on the interior on one of the ribs with the same Tiffany Studios mark and a poorly legible model number of which only the figure 2 is distinct. The bronze light fittings are stamped 'BRYANT 250W 250V PAT'D JUNE 13 1899', the moulded plastic light switches stamped 'WEBBER'.

Designed before 1906 and made by Tiffany Studios, Corona, Long Island, New York between 1902 and 1918.

Total H 45.5 cm. Base: H 37.7 cm, W 21.9 cm. Shade: H 16.1 cm, D 37.7 cm   1984,7-4,1

Electric lamps with leaded shades were first shown in England at the Grafton Galleries, London, in 1899. The shades were made in many different colours; see, for example, Neustadt 1970, pls 105-6. The Neustadt collection includes stocks of unused glass sheets from the Corona furnaces; the range of colours and types of glass, illustrated in reflected and transmitted light, are fully discussed in Neustadt 1970.

In the Tiffany price list of 1906 this base is described as 'Mushroom, standard, small', price $90 (Koch 1971, 169). Koch also reproduces a price list of 1933 with model numbers, together with original photographs; this lamp is listed as no. 3, the shade is no. 1424 and the price $115 for base and shade.

Tiffany Studios continued until 1938, but in its later years it was mainly a retail organisation for the enormous existing stock of metal and glass, and few new items were produced after the First World War.

Van Briggle Pottery founded 1901

D. Bogue, *The Van Briggle Story*, 1976
S. H. Nelson et al., *A Collector's Guide to Van Briggle Pottery*, Indiana 1986
See also Evans 1987.

289 Vase

[COLOUR PLATE IX]

Earthenware, cast, yellow body with matt blue glaze oversprayed with green, the base also glazed. The angular line of the handles is continued in relief down the body of the vase.

MARKS Impressed on the base with 'VAN BRIGGLE' beneath conjoined 'A's in a rectangle, the date '1902', design number '30' and 'III'.

Designed in 1901 by Artus Van Briggle and made by the Van Briggle Pottery Company, Colorado Springs, in 1902.

H 41.7 cm, max. D 15.3 cm   1984,7-3,2

The Van Briggle Pottery was established in 1901 by Artus Van Briggle (1869-1904), who had been forced by tuberculosis to settle in Colorado in 1899. He had previously worked as a decorator at the Rookwood Pottery in Cincinnati (see Cat. 260) since 1887. From 1893 to 1896 he studied drawing and painting at the Académie Julian in Paris, during which time he became influenced by the matt glazes on oriental ceramics as well as the sculpture of Rodin and the work of the French artist potters. Van Briggle's first matt-glazed wares were made at Rookwood in 1898 and were highly praised at the Paris Exhibition of 1900. After Van Briggle's death in 1904 the Pottery was run by his wife until 1912 and is still active.

A vase of this shape was illustrated in *The Craftsman* IV, September 1903, opp. p. 414, and exhibited at the St Louis Exhibition of 1904 (*Gazette Telegraph*, 1 January 1905, reproduced in Nelson 1986, 28). The vase also appears in a photograph of Van Briggle in his pottery of c.1902 (Bogue, 16 and Nelson, 16) and was illustrated again in *The House Beautiful* XV, February 1904, 137.

The monogram 'AA' was adopted in 1900 by Artus and his fiancée and assistant Anne Gregory, whom he married in 1902. The Roman numeral 'III' indicates the type of clay and the design number '30' was created in 1901. For further discussion of the marks on Van Briggle wares and a catalogue of Van Briggle designs, see Nelson 1986.

Van Briggle's glazes were applied with an atomiser, a second colour often sprayed over the first, as on this vase. According to a contemporary account, the dead glaze was 'a "fat" solution of glass, which, when applied to the biscuit ware, undergoes a devitrification in the second firing, and the result is a finish which seems to possess the depth and softness of velvet ...' (*Brush and Pencil* IX, October 1901, 3-4). For further discussion of the methods of manufacture, see *The Craftsman*, 1903, 415-25.

For the influence of French artist potters on Van Briggle, see Eidelberg 1975.

Van de Velde, Henry Clemens 1863-1957

Osthaus, K. E., *Van de Velde: Leben und Schaffen des Künstlers*, Hagen 1920 (reprinted Berlin 1984)
Kessler, Harry Graf von, *Gesichter und Zeiten*, Berlin 1962
Velde, H. van de, *Geschichte meines Lebens*, Munich 1962
Hammacher, A. M., *Le Monde de Henry van de Velde*, Paris 1967
Huter, K. H., *Henry van de Velde in Weimar*, Berlin 1967
Henry van de Velde 1863-1957, exhibition catalogue, Brussels, L'Ecuyer, 1970
Hesse-Frielinghaus, Herte, *Das Silber Henry van de Veldes im Karl Ernst Osthaus Museum*, Heft 1, Hagen 1976

Pecher, W. D., *Henry van de Velde, das Gesamtwerk, Gestaltung band I*, Munich 1981

Sembach, K.-J., *Henry van de Velde*, London 1989

See also Berlin 1989a (van de Velde's work for Curt Hermann)

See also Recent Acquisitions, Cat. 354.

290 Hair comb   [PLATE 79]

Gold openwork mount riveted to a tortoiseshell comb, the mount hand-cut and pierced. Contained in its original green leather retailer's case with beige velvet inner tray stamped with the van de Velde monogram in gold. The silk lining of the lid is labelled 'Th. Müller Hofjuwelier WEIMAR' with a crown above.

MARKS The gold mount stamped on the reverse with the van de Velde monogram, the maker's monogram 'TM', the gold standard mark '585' used in Germany, and 'DÉPOSÉ'.

Designed in 1899-1900 and made by the firm of Theodor Müller, Weimar.

w of mount 7.9 cm, w of case 11.3 cm   1980,6-15,1

Van de Velde trained as a painter in Antwerp before turning to design in 1892. He designed rooms and furniture in Paris for both Bing's Maison de l'Art Nouveau in 1895 and for Meier-Graefe's La Maison Moderne in 1898, founding in that year his own decorating firm near Brussels. Having received commissions from German clients since 1897, he settled in Berlin in 1900, and went on to design in other fields such as silver and ceramics. After his move to Weimar in 1902, to become artistic adviser to the Duke of Saxe-Weimar and then professor of the new school of applied arts, a number of his silver designs were executed by the court jewellers, Theodor Müller.

Van de Velde's jewellery executed c.1898-1900, before his move to Germany, is generally thought to have been made by his own firm, the Ateliers Société van de Velde, Ixelles, Belgium (Hesse-Frielinghaus 1976, pl.1, and von Hase 1977, nos 517-19, but these three items apparently bear no maker's marks). However, several pieces are recorded which bear, in addition to the artist's monogram, the maker's mark 'TM' conjoined for Theodor Müller, together with the gold and silver standard marks in use in Germany (von Hase nos 527-33, 535, 537-9). That this comb was intended for export is suggested by the appearance of the French design registration mark 'DÉPOSÉ, often used by firms with large-scale export production, to protect their designs: see Cat. 342. The van de Velde pieces, however, do not seem to have been made in large numbers.

An identical comb was exhibited in 1900 at the Salon de la Libre Esthétique in Brussels (see *La revue des Arts Décoratifs*, June 1900, 175). It was also included in an article on jewellery in *Die Kunst* 2, 1899-1900, 10. While the French commentator praised above all the jewels that relied on the sinuous curves of the metal alone, without the addition of gemstones, the writer of the German article found the flat, linear goldwork too severe, preferring the greater relief of the gem-set pieces.

291 Four pieces of silver cutlery   [PLATE 80]

Meat knife, meat fork, fish knife and fish fork, cast in one piece except for the meat knife which has a hollow cast handle and separately applied steel blade. The handle of the meat fork is flat, the handles of the fish cutlery are elliptical in section; all are of asymmetrical shape with engraved curvilinear ornament.

MARKS Each piece stamped with the van de Velde monogram and the Russian silver standard mark '84' (875) in a square.

Designed in 1902 and executed by the firm of Koch & Bergfeld, Bremen. Part of a large group of van de Velde's silver owned by the first French ambassador in Moscow after the First World War (sold Galerie W. Ketterer, Munich, 15 November 1980, lots 925-49).

291a Meat knife: L 24.8 cm   1980,12-8,1
291b Meat fork: L 22 cm   1980,12-8,2
291c Fish knife: L 20.6 cm   1980,12-8,3
291d Fish fork: L 17.8 cm   1980,12-8,4

The design for the dessert knife, fork and spoon dated c.1902 is in the van de Velde archive, Brussels, E.N.S.A.A.V., inv. 4101 (illustrated in Houston 1976, no. 490). For van de Velde's own comments on the design of cutlery, and his dislike of the manufacture of spoons and forks in two parts when modern machinery was capable of making them in one, see his lecture 'Der neue Stil', 1906 (reprinted in Curjel 1955, 156-68).

This cutlery was designed in the autumn of 1902 as part of a table service of 355 pieces commissioned from van de Velde by the State of Weimar as a gift for the Grand Duke of Saxe-Weimar on the occasion of his wedding in 1902. According to Huter 1967 (259, note 73), no silversmith in Saxe-Weimar was capable of executing such varied work and so the service was executed initially by Koch & Bergfeld of Bremen, who produced the service until the autumn of 1903; and indeed two knives acquired at the Dresden Exhibition of 1906 by the Stuttgart Museum bear their maker's mark (inv. nos 6,201-2; information kindly supplied by Heike Schröder). Huter further states that from 1903 the Weimar court silversmiths Theodor Müller built a workshop and brought in craftsmen to carry out van de Velde's designs for silver. But cutlery required special machinery and although it is frequently stated that cutlery of this pattern was made by Müller of Weimar, no examples bearing the maker's mark (as distinct from retailer's name) of Müller have been located. It seems most likely that the cutlery continued to be manufactured by Koch & Bergfeld in Bremen, with Müller acting as sole retailer. Among the factory archives of Koch & Bergfeld are four order books for cutlery with several quotations for cutlery supplied to Müller, after van de Velde's designs (information supplied by A. Löhr). Löhr has also noted the retailer's wish to disguise factory-made goods by insisting that they should be supplied without the manufacturer's marks and model numbers, but with the retailer's name (Bremen 1981, 20). Thus the factories themselves owned punches with the retailers' names.

For examples from the service in the Karl Ernst Osthaus Museum, Hagen, including the meat and fish cutlery, see Hesse-Frielinghaus 1976, figs 13, 15 and Brussels 1977, no. 227. The Hagen pieces are engraved with the monogram of Karl Ernst Osthaus, the industrialist for whom van de Velde built the Folkwang Museum in Hagen in 1900-2. The service was also owned by a number of other friends and clients of van de Velde, including the artist Curt Hermann (information kindly supplied by Luke Hermann) and Herbert Esche at Chemnitz, for whom van de Velde worked between 1899 and 1906. Pieces belonging to Esche also bear his monogram (the author has seen examples acquired from Esche's son in the possession of K. Barlow Decorative Arts Ltd in 1987).

For examples in other collections, see Gysling-Billeter 1975, no. 276 (thirteen pieces formerly owned by Nele van de Velde, now in the Kunstgewerbemuseum, Zurich); Wichmann 1985, 154; Franzke 1987, no. 45 with the monogram of Riccarda Buschmann; Germanisches Nationalmuseum, Nuremberg,

Anzeiger, 1971/2, 192-3, also with Buschmann monogram. Pieces are also owned by the Kunstindustrimuseet, Oslo, the Museum für Kunst und Gewerbe, Hamburg and the Rijksmuseum Kröller-Muller, Otterlo. Most of these examples bear the '800' silver standard mark used in Germany, and the van de Velde monogram. The examples catalogued here may have been made in the higher standard for use in Russia. See Cat. 14 and 296 for examples of German cutlery made in a higher-grade silver for export.

292 Sauce boat [PLATE 80]

Silver, hand-raised, the interior gilded, the handle extending in one piece from the rim and body. The base of the handle ends in a 'whiplash' motif across the lower body.

MARKS Stamped on the base 'TH.MULLER' with the van de Velde monogram, the German State crown-and-crescent assay mark for silver and the Russian silver standard mark '84' (875).

Designed c.1902-3 and made by the firm of Theodor Müller, Weimar. Formerly owned by the French ambassador to Moscow after the First World War (see Cat. 291 and Galerie W. Ketterer, 15 November 1980, lot 946).

L 22.3 cm, H 10.4 cm   1982,3-2,1

This sauce boat may also belong to the Duke of Weimar's service, see Osthaus 1920, 142, where it is illustrated with the cutlery. See also Brussels 1970, 91, no. 171c. Contrary to traditional methods, in which the handle would be made separately and soldered on, the flowing lines of van de Velde's design are here uninterrupted.

293 Vase [PLATE 82; COLOUR PLATE X]

Salt-glazed stoneware, buff body, cast, the rim incised with three parallel lines and extending to form two handles that merge with the body, which has a ridge below the shoulders. The exterior covered with a deep purplish-red glaze turning to brilliant blue round the lower part. The glaze has dropped down below the ridge and has pulled away from the other mouldings so that the profile is always highlighted. The blue effect is an optical illusion caused by phase separation, in which the glass within the glaze scatters a blue light. The interior glazed green. The glaze is of *sang-de-boeuf* type fired in a reducing atmosphere and then re-oxidised.

MARKS Impressed on the base with the van de Velde monogram and the factory model number '2043'.

Designed for the Düsseldorf exhibition of 1902 and made by the firm of Reinhold Hanke, Höhr-Grenzhausen, Rhineland.

H 23.1 cm, max. W 17.4 cm   1986,11-2,1

In December 1900 the Westerwald district council in Montabaur approached the Ministry of Trade in Berlin to ask if they would arrange for van de Velde to collaborate in the much-needed revival of the stoneware industry. After the disastrous participation in the Paris Exhibition of that year, where traditional historicist wares had been shown, it had become clear that the Westerwald was no longer in touch with current artistic trends. Although many artists eventually contributed to the modernisation of the stoneware industry, van de Velde was the first to be selected through official channels. The initial response in Berlin was negative, for modern trends were still regarded with reserve, but later the Ministry agreed. Van de Velde's first designs were divided in early 1902 between all the factories in the Westerwald capable of producing them in order that they should be ready

for the Düsseldorf exhibition in the summer; van de Velde himself oversaw the production (Dry-v. Zezschwitz 1981, 64-5).

Van de Velde's stoneware designs were his first ceramic designs. They broke with tradition both in form and decoration. While Merkelbach and other Höhr-Grenzhausen firms produced them in traditional Westerwald greys and blues, van de Velde's association with the firm of Reinhold Hanke resulted in the first examples of Rhenish stoneware to use *sang-de-boeuf* glazes, thereby bringing the stoneware industry into line with international taste. August Hanke, Reinhold's son and the firm's chemist and technician, had been developing copper-based glazes influenced by those of the French ceramists Delaherche and Dalpayrat, whose work he had admired at the Paris Exhibition of 1900. Hanke's experimental glazes were expensive and risky; there were often huge losses in the firing and the glazes were frequently unsuccessful. Successful pieces, such as this vase, could be very striking.

For contemporary illustrations of this vase in a room designed by van de Velde for the Deutsch-Nationalen Kunstausstellung in Düsseldorf, see *Kunst und Kunsthandwerk*, 1902, 540, 545; *Die Kunst*, 8, 1902, 37 and *DK* VI, 1902, 37. In these interiors, carefully arranged by van de Velde himself, three or four vases are prominently placed. By contrast, the factory display in the same exhibition shows van de Velde's art pottery stacked cheek by jowl with traditional relief-moulded beer jugs (Dry-v. Zezschwitz 1981, pls 9, 21). For further discussion of the Düsseldorf display, see Rudoe 1990.

For other examples of this model in private collections, see Düsseldorf 1974, no. 280, with rust-red glaze all over; Brussels 1977, no. 501; Cologne 1978, no. 245. In the latter the glaze has never been reduced and is a greenish-buff colour. A similar effect is to be seen on an example acquired by the Kunstindustrimuseet, Copenhagen in 1907. For an example in the Museum für Kunst und Gewerbe, Hamburg, given by K. E. Osthaus in 1902, see Spielmann 1977, pl. VII (inv. no. 1902.445). The colours are similar to the British Museum vase, but the glaze is uneven at the base. The Hamburg vase is incised 'Hanke'. Van de Velde's designs for R. Hanke do not always bear a factory mark, but the connection between artist and manufacturer is well documented; after the autumn of 1902, certain of van de Velde's designs were produced by Hanke exclusively, enabling van de Velde to insist on his pieces being impressed with his monogram. Osthaus' vase must therefore be among the earliest examples produced by Hanke, before the autumn of 1902, and may have been acquired at the Düsseldorf exhibition of that year. In her discussion of the marks on van de Velde stoneware, Beate Dry-v. Zezschwitz notes a Merkelbach vase with the designer's signature impressed on the side; the assumption is that firms other than Hanke did not use the van de Velde monogram (Dry-v. Zeschwitz 1981, 64-8). For examples of van de Velde's other models for stoneware, see Mosel 1971, no. 2; Franzke 1987, nos 183-4; Höhr-Grenzhausen 1986, nos 174-81.

Van de Velde also designed table and ornamental wares in the traditional Westerwald manner with relief decoration in blue and grey. These items were sold as cheaper versions of the 'art' wares with their expensive glazes (see Recent Acquisitions, Cat. 354). Sometimes the same forms appear with patterned decoration. An example of the British Museum vase with two-tone decoration also designed by van de Velde is illustrated by Pecher 1981, 188, who gives no source or date, but the illustration appears to be taken from a Hanke catalogue. A number of similar designs were later produced by van de Velde's pupils.

294 Gravy boat   [PLATE 81]

Hard-paste porcelain, cast, the vessel, handle and base formed in a single thick-walled piece, with bold diagonal line from handle to base. A band of underglaze blue decoration on a white ground encircles the rim.

MARKS Impressed on the base with the van de Velde monogram in a square shield and the number '38'; the Meissen crossed-swords mark and the number '14' in underglaze blue.

Designed in 1903-4 and made by the Porzellanmanufaktur Meissen, Dresden.

H 13.2 cm, W 27.3 cm   1988,1-10,1

In 1903 Meissen commissioned a tea and dinner service from van de Velde, and from Riemerschmid (see Cat. 256), in an attempt to introduce an outstanding new range intended for general production. But van de Velde had not designed for porcelain before and had little understanding of its technical requirements. The service took two years to develop, during which time the Meissen modeller Otto Stange had to spend seventeen weeks with van de Velde in Weimar. In July 1903 Stange wrote to the Meissen factory that *der Herr Professor arbeitet eben das erste Mal für Porzellan, es ist somit nicht jeder Griff allemal der Richtige* ('as it is only the first time that the Professor has worked with porcelain, he does not always get it right straight away'; Beaucamp-Markowsky 1980, no. 148, quoting Just 1972, 16). The first models were developed early in 1903, but suggestions for the decoration came only at the end of the year. Van de Velde insisted that his models bear his signet.

The service, known as 'Peitschenhieb' because of the whiplash border motif on the plates and dishes (see Cat. 295), was shown at the third Deutsche Kunstgewerbe-Ausstellung in Dresden in 1906 and was widely illustrated in contemporary periodicals; see, for example, *Die Kunst* 16, 1907, 62. Doubts were voiced straight away by the German critic L. Gmelin: *van de Velde hat es nicht verstanden, der Feinheit des materials gerecht zu werden* ('van de Velde has not understood how to do justice to the delicacy of the material'; *Kunst und Handwerk* 59, 1906-7, 80, 95). These doubts were echoed by H. Singer in *The Studio* 40, 1907, 57: 'it is all van de Velde and not a bit porcelain. The ornamentation is in no way adapted to the material, it would do as well for a book cover, or a piece of furniture.' The factory's own reservations surface in the official bicentennial publication of 1910 which presents an apology for the 'by no means brilliant results' achieved by 'renowned industrial artists' on the grounds that china as a material is difficult to master. The van de Velde service is described as more suitable for production in metal (Berling 1911, 103, with illustration of tea service). By 1911, when K. E. Osthaus acquired the service for a travelling exhibition of the Deutsche Werkbund, the factory expressed its clear disapproval of the choice as representative of modern Meissen production (Beaucamp-Markowsky 1980, no. 148, quoting Just 1972, 6).

The service was produced with underglaze blue or matt burnished gold decoration. The gold decoration was no longer included in the *Malereimusterliste* of 1913; the blue decoration still appears in the 1930 list (Dresden 1989, no. 293), but it is very doubtful whether it was still produced at that date. The service was expensive and since it did not sell widely, attempts were made to make it look more like traditional Meissen porcelain by adding painted flower sprays in areas left blank in van de Velde's design; a tureen with gold decoration and multi-coloured flowers on the lid was in the possession of K. Barlow Decorative Arts Ltd, London, in 1987 (see Rudoe 1990, fig. 12). The original design for the tureens was with plain lids, but examples are known with lids bearing the whiplash motif used for the plates (Walcha 1981, pl. 80).

Pieces from this service are to be found in a number of European collections; for example: the Kunstgewerbemuseum, Zurich (Gysling-Billeter 1975, no. 295); Die neue Sammlung, Munich (Wichmann 1985, 114 and 1988, 57 and 121); the Kunstgewerbemuseum, Cologne (Beaucamp-Markowsky, nos 148-9); the Bröhan collection, Berlin (Bröhan II/2, 1977, no. 449); the Kunstgewerbemuseum, Berlin (Just 1983, pl. 91); the Kaiser Wilhelm Museum, Krefeld (Düsseldorf 1974, no. 305) and the Masowische Museum, Plock, Poland (Makus 1987, fig. 3). See also Habsburg, Feldman, Geneva, 14 November 1988, lot 64/63: a large part-dinner service comprising several other shapes such as eggcups, butter dishes and an hors-d'oeuvre platter. For further discussion, see Rudoe 1990.

295 Dessert plate   [PLATE 81]

Hard-paste porcelain, decorated with a whiplash motif moulded in low-relief and painted in underglaze blue, the rim pierced.

MARKS Impressed on the base with the van de Velde monogram in a square, with the numbers '22', '2' and '89'; Meissen crossed-swords mark in underglaze blue.

Designed in 1903-4 and made by the Porzellanmanufaktur Meissen, Dresden.

D 21.8 cm   1981,12-9,1

See Cat. 294 for discussion of the whole service. For two of van de Velde's studies for this plate in the Archives Henry van de Velde, Brussels, E.N.S.A.A.V., inv. 1253-4, see Houston 1976, no. 491. Each drawing is labelled 'Kgl. Porzellan-Manufactur Meissen' with the figures 'I' and 'IV'. They both vary from the plates as executed: neither has the pattern of squares within the whiplash motif.

This plate is unusual in having a pierced rim which appears to be a combination of two van de Velde designs. In addition to the painted whiplash motif, he also designed a plain white border pattern comprising the same moulded relief whiplash and a pierced motif filling the rest of the rim (Just 1983, pl. 90). Along the edge of the pierced motif is a row of pierced slashes, as on the British Museum plate. According to Just, the pierced model was too expensive to produce and was rejected by both designer and manufacturer. In view of the cost of the pierced work, the factory may have decided to retain just the simple pierced slashes on some pieces, which were then painted as usual.

A modification which appears to be the factory's own is to be found on a plate in the Hessisches Landesmuseum, Darmstadt, where the whiplash motif in blue is combined with a chequerboard pattern in gold filling the rest of the border (Heller 1982, no. 406).

Vereinigte Silberwaren-Fabriken, Düsseldorf founded 1887, closed before 1967

296 Set of twelve fish knives and forks [PLATE 88]

Silver, stamped and hand-finished, with a ribbon motif round the stem and foliate motifs on the reverse, the blades of the knives engraved with a swirling pattern, the forks engraved with a 'crab leg' motif. The owner's initials 'JPS' engraved on the handles. Contained in the original green cloth-covered case with cream velvet interior and decorative paper band on the lid. An upper removable tray holds the first six pairs. On a silk ribbon inside the lid, the retailer's name 'S & M Benzen, KGL HOFJUVELERER, Amagertorv. 18, KJOBENHAVN.' and the royal crown.

MARKS Each handle stamped 'S & M BENZEN' with royal crown, '830 S' for the silver standard, Copenhagen town mark with date, and assayer's mark. One knife is dated '1903', three are dated '1904', three '1905', one '1906' and four '1907'. The twelve forks are dated '1903', '1904', '1905', and '1907', each date occurring on three forks. Items dated '1903' bear the assayer's mark 'SG' for Simon Groth, assayer 1863-1904. The rest bear the assayer's mark 'CFH' for C. F. Heise, assayer 1904-32, except for the three knives dated '1904', which were assayed while Groth was still assayer.

Designed and made by the Vereinigte Silberwaren-Fabriken, AG, Düsseldorf, c.1901, for export to Denmark and retailed by S. & M. Benzen, Copenhagen, between 1903 and 1907.

L of knives 22 cm, L of forks 18.7 cm. Knives 1981,7-11,1-12 (in date order); forks 1981,7-11,13-24 (in date order).

For a fish knife and fork of this design stamped with German assay marks and '800' silver standard mark, together with the factory mark of the Vereinigte Silberwaren-Fabriken, Düsseldorf, see Solingen 1979, no. 102, an example formerly in the possession of Friedrich August III (1865-1932) and bearing his monogram.

As with the Behrens cutlery designed for the Düsseldorf firm of F. Bahner, this service was made for export to Denmark in the higher 830 silver standard (see Cat. 14). The Vereinigte Silberwaren-Fabriken was in fact an offshoot of the Bahner family firm. It was founded in 1887 as the Silberwarenfabrik Gebrüder Bahner by Anton junior and Wilhelm (sons of Anton Bahner the elder), and in 1901 became the Vereinigte Silberwaren-Fabriken Bahner AG, Düsseldorf.

Voysey, Charles Francis Annesley 1857-1941

There is a vast body of contemporary literature on Voysey; full references are to be found in the most recent publications listed below. Early articles relating to items catalogued here are cited in the relevant entries.

Gebhard, D., *Charles F. A. Voysey, Architect*, Los Angeles 1975

Symonds, J., *Catalogue of Drawings by C. F. A. Voysey in the Drawings Collection of the Royal Institute of British Architects*, Farnborough 1976

C. F. A. Voysey: architect and designer 1857-1941, exhibition catalogue, Royal Pavilion Art Gallery and Museum, Brighton, 1978, J. Brandon-Jones et al.

Simpson, D., *C. F. A. Voysey – an architect of individuality*, London 1979

297 Bell pull [PLATE 64]

Brass and textile. At each end, a saw-pierced openwork brass mount, each with a different design of birds on flowering branches. The textile

band of woven silk (weft) and silk or cotton (warp) with a repeating vertical pattern of addorsed birds perched in stylised trees, the upper branches of which contain three tulip-like flowers. The pattern repeats seven times with variations in the top and bottom motifs, and a larger area of plain cloth at the upper end. The original colours are now much faded, but appear to have been red for the birds, yellow for the flowers and white for the trees. The background colour, revealed on the reverse, where the textile was folded over to attach the brass ends, was turquoise *jaspé* (i.e. varying in colour along its length), with mixed bright blue and grey threads. The backing textile is a similar long strip sewn at the edges, of a paler blue, with mixed turquoise, grey and cream threads. The bell-pull is stiffened with an interlining of paper or glue-stiffened textile. The technique is tabby tabby lampas for the main textile and extended tabby for the backing textile.

MARKS None.

Designed c.1899-1901 for the architect's own house, The Orchard, Chorleywood, Hertfordshire. The brass ends probably made by the firm of Thomas Elsley & Co., Portland Metalworks, London, the textile band probably hand-woven in a small workshop. Subsequently in the collection of Voysey's son C. Cowles-Voysey and remaining in Voysey family possession until its acquisition by the British Museum.

Total L 129 cm (with mounts), L of textile 114 cm, w of textile 10 cm, w of mounts 14 cm 1982,3-1,1

The contemporary term for the weave used in the bell-pull was 'tissue'; it was woven on a loom with jacquard attachment. Hero Granger-Taylor (to whom I owe the technical description) has suggested that in view of the areas without pattern at top and bottom, and the non-repeating motif at each end of the pattern, this length of cloth was woven to be cut vertically into identical strips for bell-pulls. It would not have been practical to have woven only one strip and so the width of the cloth probably comprised six or seven strips.

The Victoria and Albert museum holds an identical bell-pull (but lacking the brass mounts), similarly faded, given in 1970 (T.268-1970) and thought by the donor to have come from The Orchard, although it does not have a family provenance.

Most of Voysey's textile designs were produced by the firm of Alexander Morton & Company, who made a number of textiles with similar motifs of paired birds among foliage, a recurring theme in Voysey's work of the 1890s (for example, *The Studio* 18, October 1899, 38 and Brighton 1978, D24, a wool tissue of 1902). But the technique of the bell-pull is not one that was used much by Morton and it is more likely that the bell-pulls were specially woven in a small workshop such as that of Edmund Hunter (1866-1937) at Haslemere from 1902 to 1908 and then at Letchworth (I am grateful to Linda Parry for this suggestion and for information about the V & A bell-pull). For further discussion of Voysey's textiles, see Parry 1988.

Voysey's use of cut-out silhouette work for brass mounts was derived from the brass door furniture for the Houses of Parliament designed by Pugin, whom Voysey greatly admired (Brighton 1978, 132-3). For examples of Voysey's brass door hinges with cut-out bird motifs made by Thomas Elsley & Co., see *The Studio* 18, 1899, 44.

For The Orchard, see *The Studio* 1901, 181-94; *Architectural Review*, 1901, 32-8.

298 Fire shovel and tongs [PLATE 65]

Cast brass, leaf-shaped shovel, the tongs with leaf-shaped terminals, both with ball knop at end for suspension and rivets incorporated as part of the design.

MARKS None.

Designed c.1898-1901 and made by the firm of Thomas Elsley & Co., Portland Metalworks, London.

298a Shovel: L 63 cm, W 14.1 cm   1982,5-12,1
298b Tongs: L 66 cm, w of terminals 3.4 cm   1982,5-12,2

The earliest contemporary illustration of these fire-irons is apparently in 1901, when they were shown resting on the fender in the dining-room and study of Voysey's own house, The Orchard, Chorleywood, Hertfordshire: see *The Studio*, Special Summer Number, 1901, 190, 192. The shovel and tongs were also used at Moor Crag, Windermere, built for J. W. Buckley in 1898 (see Brighton 1978, 134, E8), but it is not known whether they were first designed for this house or for Voysey's.

The complete set of fire-irons comprised shovel, tongs and poker. There was also a stand for all three pieces formed of a shaft on four feet surmounted by a copper sphere with a central flange having notches from which the irons were hung. At the top was a brass figure of an eagle. The irons with stand were included in the Arts & Crafts Exhibition Society's exhibition of 1903, held at the New Gallery, London. The set cost £4 15s. and was executed by Thomas Elsley & Co. (Arts & Crafts Exhibition Society, *Catalogue of the Seventh Exhibition*, 1903, 151, no. 394u). For contemporary illustrations, see *The Studio*, 1903, 28, 35 and *Der Moderne Stil*, 1903, pl. 64. For a complete set with stand, formerly in the Handley-Read collection and now in the Cecil Higgins Art Gallery, Bedford, see London 1972, 101, E114-117. See also Pevsner 1968, 144.

The fire-irons were used repeatedly in Voysey's later interiors, for example Garden Corner, Chelsea, designed for E. J. Horniman in 1906-7. Here, figures of eagles were placed at each corner of the four-poster bed, in Voysey's words 'to drive away bad spirits' (Simpson 1979, 125).

299 Pen tray

[PLATE 65]

Brass, handmade of one piece of metal, cut and folded. The sides decorated with a pierced heart, a scroll at each end.

MARKS None.

Designed c.1901-3 and made by H. J. L. J. Massé.

L 26.5 cm, W 5.5 cm, H 4.2 cm   1980,5-8,1

The pen tray was included in the Arts & Crafts Exhibition Society's exhibition of 1903; see *The Studio*, 28, 1903, 28; according to the exhibition catalogue (151, no. 394 hh) the pen tray cost 10s. and was made by H. J. L. J. Massé.

Henri Jean Louis Joseph Massé, metalworker, joined the Art Workers' Guild in 1888, becoming Assistant Secretary in 1889. He wrote a series of guides to the cathedrals of England and France, a history of the Art Workers' Guild (1934) and several books on pewter: *Pewter Plate, a Historical and Descriptive Handbook* (1904), *Chats on Old Pewter* (1911) and *The Pewter Collector. A Guide to English Pewter* (1921).

For another pen tray, see Brighton 1978, 135, E9, where reference is made to an exhibition of Voysey's work at the Batsford Gallery, London, in 1931: the catalogue of this exhibition noted that the pen tray could be made by children, as it was of one piece of metal which could be cut by hand, and needed no soldering.

Although the pen tray does not appear to be illustrated before 1903, it is likely that it was designed for Voysey's own house a year or two earlier.

300 Inkwell

[PLATE 65]

Beaten brass, double inkwell of rectangular form, flaring out towards the base, the wells fitted with domed hinged lids having a scrolling thumb-piece formed of a strip of brass in one piece with the lid.

MARKS Stamped on the base with the monogram 'JB C°' and model number '672'.

Designed c.1901-3 and made by Jesson, Birkett & Co., Birmingham, between 1904 and 1910.

L 25 cm, W 15 cm, H 7.8 cm   1988,6-6,1

The double inkwell was exhibited alongside the pen tray (see Cat. 299) at the Arts & Crafts Exhibition Society's exhibition of 1903; it was made by Rathbone & Company and cost £1 12s. 6d. with stand (*Catalogue of the Seventh Exhibition*, 1903, 151, 394 gg). For contemporary illustrations, see *The Studio* 28, 1903, 28 and *Kunst & Kunsthandwerk* VI, 1903, 73. It is likely that both inkwell and pen tray were designed at the same time for Voysey's own house. Items illustrated in contemporary views of The Orchard were often used in Voysey's later houses.

This design was also used for a single inkwell, see Brighton 1978, E7 (private collection); for an example of the double version with its own stand in the form of a pen tray, see London 1986, no. 141.

The inkwell was initially produced by the Birmingham arts and crafts metalworking business of R. LL. B. Rathbone, part of which was taken over by the Faulkner Bronze Company in 1902; the latter was reconstituted as Jesson, Birkett & Co., in 1904. This new company took over more of Rathbone's business, but was liquidated in 1910. This inkwell can therefore be dated securely to 1904-10. For the history of the various Birmingham workshops, see Birmingham 1984, 113.

301 Four pieces of cutlery

[PLATE 66]

Electroplate, forged, comprising meat knife, fish knife, jam spoon and dessert knife, the meat and dessert knives with bone handles stained green, the jam spoon with applied rat's tail on the reverse of the bowl.

MARKS Stamped indistinctly on the blade of the meat knife 'KOOYSIRA 3 OXFORD' (?).

Designed c.1907 and made probably by the firm of Charles William Fletcher, Sheffield. This group belonged to Voysey himself and subsequently to his son C. Cowles-Voysey and then to the latter's physician, Dr Joan Slack, who acquired much of the Voysey estate.

301a Meat knife: L 23.4 cm   1982,2-5,1
301b Fish knife: L 17.6 cm   1982,2-5,2
301c Jam spoon: L 14.4 cm   1982,2-5,3
301d Dessert knife: L 17.9 cm   1982,2-5,4

According to Pevsner (1940, repr. 1968, 144 and 151, pl. 25) this cutlery was designed in 1907 and indeed the service does not appear to be illustrated in contemporary sources before this date; see, for example, *The Studio Yearbook*, 1908, B216 and *Art Chronicle*, November 1909, 38. However, the service has more recently been described as designed c.1902; see Brighton 1978, 135, E11, where it is stated that pieces from the service were exhibited at the Baillie gallery in 1903; reference is also made to *Kunst & Kunsthandwerk* VI, 1903, 96, which discusses the Arts & Crafts exhibition of 1903, but does not mention or illustrate the cutlery.

For examples stamped with the maker's mark 'C.W.F.' for C. W. Fletcher of Sheffield, see London 1952, S14 and Brighton 1978, 135, E11.

302 Pair of fire-dogs [PLATE 64]

Cast and wrought iron, cast upright stem with leaf-shaped terminal decorated in low relief with birds in branches, set on three scrolling feet in wrought iron.

MARKS None.

Designed c.1906-7, maker unknown.

H 52 cm, L 19.6 cm (base)   1982,11-4,1 and 2

For examples of these fire-dogs in use at Garden Corner, Chelsea, where Voysey redesigned the interior in 1906-7, see *The Studio* XLII, 1907-8, 19; the same illustration appeared in *Kunst & Kunsthandwerk* III, 1909, 87, in an article entitled 'Neuere Arbeiten von C. F. A. Voysey', suggesting that the fire-dogs were designed for Garden Corner, which was owned by E. J. Horniman of the tea family.

The manufacturer of these fire-dogs is not recorded, though the Falkirk Iron Company is known to have executed some of Voysey's ironwork (for example, an iron fireplace; see *The Furnisher* I, January 1900, 108).

Wagenfeld, Wilhelm 1900-90

Wilhelm Wagenfeld, exhibition catalogue, Die Neue Sammlung des Bayerischen National-Museums, Munich 1939

Industrieware von Wilhelm Wagenfeld: Künstlerische Mitarbeit in der Industrie 1930-1960, exhibition catalogue, Kunstgewerbemuseum, Zurich 1960

Wilhelm Wagenfeld, 50 Jahre Mitarbeit in Fabriken, exhibition catalogue, Kunstgewerbemuseum, Cologne, 1973

Schöne Form gute Ware: Wilhelm Wagenfeld zum 80 Geburtstag, exhibition catalogue, Württembergisches Landesmuseum, Stuttgart 1980

Täglich in der Hand: Industrieformen von Wilhelm Wagenfeld aus 6 Jahrzehnten, exhibition catalogue, Bremer Landesmuseum, Bremen 1987, eds B. Manske and G. Scholz

Wilhelm Wagenfeld-Glasdesign. Objekte aus der Sammlung Günther, Berlin, exhibition catalogue, Freunde der Glaskunst Richard Süssmuth e. V., Immenhausen 1988

Wilhelm Wagenfeld, Kunst in Gebrauch, exhibition catalogue, Kunsthistorisches Institut der Universität Bonn, Bonn, 1988

303 Teapot [PLATE 136]

Clear fireproof glass, with glass infuser; mould-blown body, free-blown spout and pressed glass lid and infuser.

MARKS Acid-etched on the base with factory mark in use until 1945: 'SCHOTT & GEN. JENA' in a circle with four corners; on the lid, the trade mark 'Durax'.

Designed between 1930 and 1931 and made by Schott & Genossen Jenaer Glaswerke, Jena, Thuringia, Germany, before 1945.

H 11.1 cm, D 15.3 cm. Strainer: H 8.8 cm, D of rim 5.7 cm   1980,12-9,1

Wagenfeld trained initially as a goldsmith in Bremen and at the Zeichenakademie, Hanau. He joined the Bauhaus Metal Workshop in 1923 and then taught at the Bauhaus from 1926 to 1931. From 1931 to 1939 he worked for Schott Glaswerke on a freelance basis, and at the same time made designs for the Vereinigte Lausitze Glaswerke (see Cat. 307-8), where he was Art Director from 1935 to 1947, and for Fürstenberg porcelain (see Cat. 305-6). Wagenfeld is one of the few Bauhaus designers to have established continued involvement with industry,

designing mass-produced objects according to modernist ideals of simplicity.

Schott Glaswerke was founded in 1884 by Otto Schott, specialising initially in optical and scientific glass. Domestic glassware was introduced by Otto's son, Dr Erich Schott, in the 1920s. Erich Schott first met Wagenfeld in 1922, when Wagenfeld gave a lecture on the Bauhaus in Jena. As a result Schott asked him to collaborate on the design of domestic glassware. Erich Schott also engaged another Bauhaus artist, Gerhard Marcks (see Cat. 154). The round profiles of Wagenfeld's tea service were adapted to a more square, angular outline by Heinrich Löffelhardt in the 1950s, but Wagenfeld's original model is still in production. For Schott, see *Schott Information*, 3/1984 (*100 Years of Schott—100 Years of innovation*) and Immenhausen 1988.

For a contemporary illustration of this teapot in an article by Wagenfeld on Jenaer glass, see *Die Form*, 6 Jahrgang, Heft 12, December 1931, 461-4. See also *Die Schaulade*, 8 Jahrgang, Heft 3/4, February 1932, 198-9, where Wagenfeld notes that the teapot was blown in an iron mould, while the spout was free-blown and therefore always variable, hence differences in contemporary illustrations: for example, the spouts can be less curved (*Design for Today* III, October 1935, 408). For more recent literature, see Cologne 1973, no. 61; Bremen 1987, nos 41-3.

304 Pair of cups and saucers [PLATE 136]

Clear fireproof glass, mould-blown.

MARKS Acid-etched on the base 'Jenaer Glas' with the model name 'Teho' (i.e. *Teetasse hoch*) and the factory mark used for domestic glassware prior to 1945: a circle contained in a pentagon.

Designed between 1930 and 1934 and made by Schott & Genossen Jenaer Glaswerke, Jena, Thuringia, Germany, before 1945.

H of cup 4.5 cm, D 9.7 cm, D of saucer 16.8 cm   1981,3-10,1 and 2

For discussion of this service, see Cat. 303.

305-6 Coffee-pot and covered tureen [PLATE 136]

Hard-paste porcelain, glazed white.

MARKS On the base of each, an 'F' in underglaze blue for the Porzellanmanufaktur Fürstenberg and impressed model number '639/5' on the coffee-pot and '639/4' on the tureen.

Designed in 1934 and made by the Porzellanmanufaktur Fürstenberg, Weser, Niedersachsen, Germany.

305 Coffee-pot: H 24.5 cm, D 13.3 cm   1981,3-10,3
306 Tureen: 13.7 cm, D 22.6 cm (including handles)   1981,6-11,1

For discussion and illustrations of Wagenfeld's designs for Fürstenberg, from the 1930s to the 1970s, see Düsseldorf 1970. See also Cologne 1973, 78 and Bremen 1987, nos 130-31.

307 Vase [PLATE 135]

Free-blown steel-blue glass with thin walls, the rim wheel-cut.

MARKS None.

Designed in 1937 and made by the Vereinigte Lausitze Glaswerke AG, Weisswasser, northern Bohemia.

H 20.2 cm, D 23.9 cm   1982,12-3,3

For a contemporary illustration of this shape, see *Deutsche Warenkunde* 1939, Werkstoffgruppe C, Blatt 26; see also

Cologne 1973, no. 143. This vase was produced in eight different sizes from 7 to 34 cm high. From 1945 to c.1960 this series of vases was produced by VEB Oberlausitzer Glaswerke, Weisswasser (Dresden 1987, no. 120).

From 1935, as part of a large-scale reorganisation, VLG began to pay attention to the artistic design of its products. In that year Wagenfeld was invited to Weisswasser as artistic director at the request of Karl Mey, chairman of the firm's supervisory board. Wagenfeld had his own design studio, overseeing all aspects of production. He also designed the firm's trade catalogues and registered trade logo (see Cat. 308). For VLG, see Immenhausen 1988, 10-12 and Dresden 1987.

Wagenfeld worked for VLG until 1947. In 1950 he designed a modified version of this shape in thicker glass for the glassworks of the Württembergische Metallwarenfabrik in Geislingen. Like the earlier model it was produced in several sizes in a deep green described as tourmaline-coloured, see *Innenarchitektur* 11, 1954, 40; Cologne 1973, no. 438 and Bremen 1987, no. 186.

308 Stacking set of containers and vessels, 'Kubus-Geschirr' [PLATE 135]

Clear pressed glass, comprising ten separate refrigerator storage containers, designed for stacking with interchangeable lids: seven boxes with half and quarter sizes of square or oblong shape and three jars with pouring lips and handles, all with air vents. The lids consist of one large square lid which fits both deep and shallow containers, two oblong lids and four small square lids which fit both boxes and jars.

MARKS Most pieces bear impressed rhomboid mark of VLG, used without initials for pressed glass (see Dresden 1987, mark no. 21).

Designed in 1938 and made by the Kamenz Glassworks of Vereinigte Lausitzer Glaswerke AG, Weisswasser, northern Bohemia. The measurements given below are as follows: length × width × height. They all vary slightly within a millimetre or two, but have been standardised so that the relationships in size are obvious.

308a Large square deep box 18 × 18 × 9 cm   1981,12-4,1
308b Large square shallow box 18 × 18 × 5 cm   Lid: 18 × 18 cm 1981,12-4,2
308c Oblong deep box 18 × 9 × 9 cm   Lid: 18 × 9 cm   1981,12-4,3
308d-e Oblong shallow boxes 18 × 9 × 5 cm   1981,12-4,4-5
308f-g Small square shallow boxes 9 × 9 × 5 cm   Lid: 9 × 9 cm 1981,12-4,6-7
308h Tall square jar 9 × 9 × 16.4 cm   1981,12-4,8
308i-j Small square jars 9 × 9 × 9 cm   1981,12-4,9-10

For a contemporary illustration, see Deutsche Warenkunde 1939, Blatt 1176-7. See also Löffelhardt 1949, 59-61; Zurich 1960, 14; Stuttgart 1968, no. 358; Cologne 1973, no. 291; Bröhan III, 1985, no. 576; Bremen 1987, nos 72-4, together with Wagenfeld's sketches, nos 70-71. A letter written to Wagenfeld by Karl Mey, chairman of the supervisory board of VLG, in September 1939, suggests that 'Kubus-Geschirr' was not yet widely available: 'The photographs you sent me of your new refrigerator vessels are so much admired here at Osram that everyone is asking if they can buy them already. You seem to have succeeded extraordinarily well. I believe you have taken a really new direction with Kubus-Geschirr which will be of immense value to VLG. Certainly great success is in store for you with such use of pressed glass' (Bremen 1987, 33).

Although Wagenfeld's 'Kubus-Geschirr' was perceived as innovatory in Germany, Ray Notley has noted that similar stacking glassware was already being made in America by the Jeannette Glass Company, Jeannette, Pennsylvania: a refrigerator set of stacking rectangles and cubes (with tall models for tea and coffee) was advertised in the company's 1938 catalogue under the title 'Jadeite Kitchenware'.

Wedgwood, Josiah & Sons founded 1759

See also **Follot**; **Goupy**; **Lessore**; **Murray**; **Powell, A. H.**; **Skeaping**

There is a vast body of literature on Wedgwood; the publications listed below deal specifically with nineteenth and twentieth-century material.

Batkin, M., *Wedgwood Ceramics 1846-1959*, London 1982
Dawson, A., *Masterpieces of Wedgwood in the British Museum*, London 1984
Wedgwood in London, exhibition catalogue, Josiah Wedgwood & Sons Ltd, Barlaston and London, 1984

309 Pilgrim flask [PLATES 17-18]

Earthenware, with incised slip decoration (sgraffito) in cream, red-brown and black slips, with gilded highlights. On one side a profile Egyptian head in cream with black and gold details and on the other a scarab in cream, bordered with lotus flowers and buds in buff, black and gold. The neck is decorated with scarabs and lotus flowers, and has a firing crack on one side. The handles are outlined in gold.

MARKS Impressed 'WEDGWOOD 4' and indistinct date-letters, probably 'HRF' for 1877.

Made at the Wedgwood factory, Etruria, Staffordshire; the flask made in 1877 and decorated perhaps a year or so later.

H 29 cm   1983,11-4,2

The Wedgwood factory archive contains a description of c. 1878 of a closely similar vase; the description occurs as an entry in the 'F' Pattern Book of 1875-97 for 'Queensware fancies with gold': 'F 453, Red Pilgrim Vase scraffito [sic] with peg tap border round front and back. Handles traced in gilt and gold lines Egyptian Heads front and back.' The vase under discussion does not have an Egyptian head on both sides, but otherwise the description corresponds, if one accepts the 'peg tap' border as the lotus flowers and buds (reference kindly supplied by Sharon Gater, who has suggested that the pattern-book entry may be slightly erroneous, as it seems unlikely that two such similar vases would have been produced at around the same time).

No designer or decorator is given, but the decoration may be tentatively attributed to Albert Toft on the basis of a closely comparable sgraffito plaque decorated with a similar Egyptian head which is, most exceptionally, signed and dated on the front 'A. A. Toft 1879' (Fig. 7a and b, in the collection of the late Dr Leonard Rakow in the USA who has kindly supplied the photographs). The signed Toft plaque was noted by Hugh Tait after the publication of Aileen Dawson's book in 1984, where the flask is attributed to Rhead (Dawson 1984, 144, fig. 105). A. A. Toft (1862-1949) joined the Wedgwood factory in 1877 as a trainee modeller with his father, Charles Toft (1831-1909), who was appointed principal modeller in that year. In 1881 Albert left to study in London, returning briefly to Wedgwood before opening his own studio as a sculptor in London. In 1877, when the flask itself was made, Albert would have been a young boy of fifteen. Maureen Batkin has therefore suggested that this and similar pieces were decorated by A. A. Toft, F. Rhead and others under the direction of Charles Toft, who was noted for his inlaid wares (letter from M. Batkin of 21 August 1984). It is possible that the elder Toft kept the flask in store and that it was decorated by his son a year or two after manufacture. One thing is clear: the signed plaque demonstrates that by 1879 Albert Toft was a highly competent decorator.

The border of this flask, known as 'Isis', was also used on the plaque decorated by Thomas Allen (Cat. 310). Maureen Batkin has suggested that the design for the Egyptian head may have been taken from W. Theed's sculpture 'Africa' designed for the Albert Memorial, the central figure of which embodies Egypt (an engraving of the sculpture was published in the *Art Journal*, 1872, opp. p. 28).

For a flask of the same shape with Japanese-style decoration, see Batkin 1982, pl. 133.

I am grateful to Sharon Gater for her help with this entry.

310 Wall plaque [PLATE 19]

Creamware, painted in bright colours with a partly draped Nubian lady holding a fan in one hand and juggling with three oranges in the other. Behind her is a screen and a massive stone head with cacti and shrubs. The border is decorated with a band of lotus flowers and buds.

MARKS Signed on the front beneath the screen 'T. Allen. 1878'. Impressed on the base 'WEDGWOOD' with date-letters 'GHF' for 1877 and the letter 'R'.

Designed in 1878 at the Wedgwood factory, Etruria, Staffordshire, the decoration designed and executed by Thomas Allen (1831-1915).

D 38.5cm 1983,6-2,1

After an early training in the potteries, Allen won a National Art Training Scholarship in London in 1852 for two years, returning to Stoke to work for Minton until late 1875 or early 1876, when he joined Wedgwood. He was appointed Wedgwood's Art Director in 1878, a post he held until his partial retirement in 1898. His work received its first international showing at the Paris Exhibition of 1878, including a similar wall plaque with a classical scene of a paintress decorating a vase (*Art Journal* 1878, 54). Examples of Allen's painted wares were also shown by Wedgwood at the Society of Arts exhibition of Modern English Pottery held in 1882 (*JSA* 30, 770 and 920).

Egyptian motifs are here interpreted very freely: the Cobra head-dress suggests Egyptian royalty, but the figure wears no jewellery, while the diaphanous draperies and the posture are not at all Egyptian but modelled rather on the subtle eroticism favoured by artists such as Leighton or Poynter. For further discussion, see Dawson 1984, 142-3, col. pl. 15b.

The Wedgwood factory owns a number of original drawings by Allen, while his journal is to be found in the Wedgwood archive at the University of Keele. For Allen, see Haggar 1966 and 1968; Rockwell 1983; Batkin 1982, 60-61, pls 135-43 and 203-10.

311 Teapot [PLATE 44]

Majolica (lead-glazed earthenware), cast in two-piece mould, with relief decoration in the Japanese taste of chrysanthemums and flowering branches, painted in brightly coloured glazes over an opaque white glaze ('Argenta' ware), the chrysanthemums in turquoise blue and the flowering branches in blue, pink, yellow and brown. The knop to the lid in the form of a seated female figure in crimson-purple hooded cloak and blue skirt. The handle, spout and rims of pot and lid outlined in rust.

MARKS The base impressed 'WEDGWOOD' with date code 'SNO' for 1886 (this can also be read as 'ONS' for 1890 in the subsequent cycle of year-letters) and the letter 'F'; painted red number '9'.

Made at Wedgwood, Etruria, Staffordshire, probably in 1886.

H 16.3cm 1909,12-1,479 Given by Mr and Mrs Isaac Falke

Wedgwood had produced highly modelled and brightly coloured earthenware known as majolica since the 1860s (see also Minton, Cat. 196). From 1878 new shapes and designs with decoration on a light ground were marketed under the trade name 'Argenta' (Batkin 1982, 34). Many of the 'Argenta'-ware patterns on pale grounds exploited the taste for Japanese-style ornament of the 1870s and 80s. The pattern that appears on this teapot is not recorded among the 'Argenta'-ware patterns in the Wedgwood factory archive; Sharon Gater has therefore suggested that it may have been a traditional pattern used on earlier creamwares and terracottas which was later modified for use on majolica. Closely similar, though not identical, 'Argenta'-ware patterns include 'Palm', registered in 1879 and 'Fan', registered in 1881 (see Batkin 1982, 48, pl. 89 and 35, col. pl. XXXVII) and St Louis (Batkin, 49, pl. 95). For further discussion of Wedgwood 'Argenta' wares, see Karmason and Stacke 1989, 81-2.

The teapot shape was introduced in the first half of the nineteenth century and appeared in the Great Exhibition of 1851 (*Art Journal Illustrated Catalogue*, 14).

Worcester Porcelain, Chamberlain & Co.
1788-1852
See also Worcester Royal Porcelain Company

Godden, G. A., *Chamberlain-Worcester Porcelain 1788-1852*, London 1982

312 Inkstand [PLATE 4]

Bone china, enamelled and gilded, in the form of the tomb of King John in Worcester Cathedral. The lid bears the recumbent figure of the king, flanked by two bishops. The base, in the form of the tomb chest, contains three cavities for inkwells, and a pen tray. Only one inkwell survives. The base is gold, the shields red and gold on a green ground; the lid is black, with the relief in several colours: the king's robes in red, green and gold, the bishops' robes in blue lined with white. The lid has old repairs with rivets and the figure has at some stage come off the lid, resulting in loss of glaze at the join. Inside the lid is the transfer-printed inscription: 'Representation of the Tomb of/King John/ in the Cathedral Church of/Worcester;/where he was interred according/to the instructions/ contained in his will./This Monarch was born in 1165./He signed Magna Charta/in the presence of the barons of/England 15 June 1215./ Died 19th Oct 1216.'

MARKS Painted in red inside the lid and on the base: 'Chamberlain & Co./Worcester./155 New Bond Street/& No. 1 Coventry Street/London.'

Made by Chamberlain & Co., Worcester Porcelain, c.1840-44.

H 12.7cm, L 21.8cm 1987,6-9,1 Given by the Hon. Mrs Mary Anna Marten

Although Chamberlain had owned the porcelain works since 1788, the company was not known as Chamberlain & Co. until 1840, when the two rival Worcester firms of Flight, Barr & Barr and Chamberlain were united as Chamberlain & Co. with London retail premises at 155 New Bond Street (run by Chamberlain's since 1816) and 1 Coventry Street (formerly owned by Flight, Barr & Barr). Both addresses appear on the inkstand. The Coventry Street shop was sold in December 1844, so the inkstand was presumably made prior to this date. The Bond Street shop was sold in 1845. The united company was not successful and by 1851, when Walter Chamberlain retired, no member of the Chamberlain family was left in the firm. From 1852, the works were run by Kerr & Binns until 1862, when the firm became known as the Worcester Royal Porcelain Company.

This is among the more elaborate of the popular novelty inkstands produced by the factory in the mid-nineteenth century. It was based on a famous local monument, situated then and now in the Chancel of Worcester Cathedral. The effigy of King John (d. 1216) was made in 1232. In 1529 the effigy and lid were placed on top of a new tomb chest, which despite its late date, was still in the Gothic style.

Surviving accounts show that the inkstand was in production by 1841, but the reason for its introduction at this date is unclear. There is no obvious commemorative association, since it post-dates both the anniversary of the King's death in 1216 and the installation of the effigy in 1232, while it predates the programme of restoration of Worcester Cathedral begun in 1857. It is nevertheless of considerable antiquarian interest not only because it is very accurately modelled, but also because it depicts the effigy with its original colours, traces of which were still visible in the nineteenth century, until 1873 when the monument was gilded. In 1914 Canon J. M. Wilson exposed the gilding as erroneous (and it has since been removed), with particular reference to C. A. Stothard's coloured plate of the effigy, published in 1817 in *The Monumental Effigies of Great Britain* (opp. p. 15). The plate is annotated 'drawn in 1813'. According to Stothard's description the King wears a 'dalmatic of crimson lined with green, the neck and cuffs edged with a gold and jewelled border; his tunic is yellow, or cloth of gold; he is girt with a belt; on his hands are jewelled gloves, a ring on the middle finger of his right hand ... He wears red hose, golden spurs, his feet have on them black shoes, and rest upon a lion.' The colours are accurately represented on the inkstand, apart from a few minor details. Stothard has slightly misunderstood the King's robes in that the green folds represent the lining of a gold mantle worn over the red dalmatic (Wilson 1914, 497). As further evidence that the original colours were visible in the first half of the nineteenth century, Wilson cites a number of other pre-1873 descriptions of the effigy and, significantly, discusses in detail Chamberlain's porcelain inkstand, then in the Worcester Museum (now the Dyson Perrins Museum).

A drawing for the inkstand is preserved in the Worcester factory drawing book (Godden 1982, fig. 312); it was made in plain white as well as richly decorated. A decorated version cost 4 guineas in 1841; similar tombs with covers altered to form a paperweight sold in 1843 for 4 guineas for a decorated tomb and 2 guineas for a 'stone colour' tomb (Godden 1982, 251-2). Few other examples are known: in addition to the coloured version described by Wilson in 1914, the Dyson Perrins Museum also owns a verion in Parian porcelain. For an ivory glazed tomb inkstand with Kerr & Binns marks (1852-62), see Phillips, Son & Neale, 19 July 1989, lot. 182. The inkstand continued to be produced by the Worcester Royal Porcelain Company after 1862, with an alternative version as a casket (Sandon 1973, 6).

Worcester Royal Porcelain Company Ltd
established 1862

Binns, R. W., *Catalogue of a Collection of Worcester Porcelain in the Museum at the Royal Porcelain Works*, Worcester 1882
Binns, R. W., *Worcester China, A Record of the Work of Forty-five Years, 1852-1897*, London 1897
Sandon, H., *Royal Worcester Porcelain from 1862 to the Present Day*, London 1973
Dawson, A., 'Worcester porcelain and the Aesthetic style', *Antique Dealer & Collector's Guide*, August 1982

313-14 Pair of vases   [PLATE 43]

Soft-paste porcelain ('Ivory Porcelain'), of flat, octagonal shape, decorated on both sides in low relief with scenes depicting the making of silk in rich colours of green, brown, purple, pink, turquoise grey and a dull red, with details picked out in gold. The first vase (313) shows, on one side, the harvesting of mulberry leaves, and on the other the cultivation of silkworms; the second (314) shows the feeding of silkworms and the spinning of silk.

MARKS Standard Royal Worcester red printed mark (Godden 1964, no. 4349) and standard impressed mark (Godden 4350) on the base of each, together with '76' for 1876 beneath the printed mark on the vase depicting silkworms (314). The other vase has no date beneath the mark, but is incised with the shape number '283'.

Designed in 1872 by James Hadley (1837-1903), Worcester's chief modeller, for the Universal Exhibition in Vienna of 1873, and made by the Worcester Royal Porcelain Company Ltd in 1876.

H 26.5 cm
313 1979,10-5,1
314 1979,10-5,2

Following the exhibition of Japanese art objects in London in 1862 and in Paris in 1867, R. W. Binns, artistic director of the Royal Worcester factory, built up his own collection of Far Eastern ceramics to inspire the factory workers. Japanese-style wares were first exhibited by Worcester in London in 1872 (*Art Journal Illustrated Catalogue of the International Exhibition of 1872*, 59). In the same year a Japanese mission visiting Great Britain came to the factory and made detailed notes of the materials and manufacturing processes, to the immense satisfaction of R. W. Binns (Binns 1897, 49-50).

The body known as 'Ivory Porcelain' was invented in 1856 and first shown at the 1862 Exhibition (Binns 1882). In his 1882 catalogue Binns notes the introduction in 1872 of bronzed and coloured golds for use on 'Ivory Porcelain'. This combination was widely praised at Vienna's Universal Exhibition of 1873; the *Illustrated London News* reported that 'the most striking, because the most novel, are those made of ivory porcelain enriched with gold, bronze and colours in imitation of the Japanese style (28 June 1873, quoted in *A Guide to the Royal Porcelain Works*, Worcester, 1878, 77).

One of the silkworm vases, depicting the harvesting of mulberry leaves, is illustrated in the *Art Journal* report of the 1873 Vienna Exhibition (*Art Journal* 1873, 181); the report describes 'many vases of various shapes designed by Hadley: an octagon pair decorated with the story of the silkworm in bronze and gold ...' (p. 277). A version of this model is also illustrated in Binns's 1882 catalogue of the Worcester Porcelain Works, 174. The decorator is not recorded, but the chief decorators at this period were E. Béjot and James Callowhill. James Hadley worked at Worcester from 1852 until 1875. For full discussion of the silkworm vases and the Japanese source of inspiration for the silk-making scenes, see Dawson 1982.

For a pair of pilgrim-flask vases also modelled by Hadley, with relief Japanese-style scenes showing the making of pottery, see Aslin, 1969, pl. 103 (acquired by the Victoria and Albert Museum from the 1872 London Exhibition). A similar pair dated 1875 was sold at Sotheby's, New York, 21 April 1989, lot 140; other versions of the pilgrim-flask vases are illustrated in Binns 1882, 174; Godden, 1961a, pl. 59 and Sandon 1973, pl. 65. See also Phillips, London, 30 November 1988, lot 420, for a pair of pilgrim vases with different Japanese-style scenes and a design registration code for 1878. Similar wares were still being exhibited in 1882 at the Society of Arts exhibition of Modern English Pottery (JSA 30, 1882, 771, 921-2).

315 Teapot [PLATE 46]

Bone china, of square shape, with pagoda knop to lid matching conical feet. The handle in the form of a scaled dragon whose mouth forms the spout and whose tail curls round the side of the teapot. The body decorated with flying birds and flower sprays in low relief painted in pink, blue, green and brown on a yellow ground, the knop, dragon handle and feet glazed in bronze.

MARKS Impressed Worcester factory mark on the base with applied stamped design registration mark for 18 January 1872, parcel 6.

Designed and modelled by James Hadley and decorated by James Callowhill at the Worcester Royal Porcelain Company Ltd, between 1872 and c.1882.

H 19.5cm   1980,3-1,1

Worcester porcelains incorporating a variety of Chinese and Japanese motifs, often combined in the same object, were exhibited in London in 1872, at Vienna in 1873 (see Cat. 314), Paris 1878 (Art Journal, 1878, 7 and 193) and at the Society of Arts Exhibition of Modern English Pottery in London in 1882 (JSA 30, 1882, 771). Here the list of exhibits includes a 'Jug, dragon handle' (no. 14) and a 'Japanese kettle' (no. 34). R. W. Binns's 1882 catalogue of porcelain in the factory's own museum lists as no. 1842 a 'Square Kettle, with dragon handle, decorated with bronze and gold in Japanese style, designed and modelled by Hadley, decorated by Callowhill' (Binns 1882, 168; the kettle is illustrated in Binns's later publication of 1897, opp. p. 48; in this example, in the Dyson Perrins Museum, Worcester, the decoration is in pink, orange, purple and green on a mottled buff ground, the handle in bronze). The 'Japanese kettle' was shape no. 254, introduced in 1872 (Sandon 1973, pl. 63, 174). The kettle was part of a set of square-shaped tea-ware; Sandon also illustrates a milk jug, teacup and saucer. For a teapot, hot water pot, milk jug, sugar bowl and matching tray with decoration executed in gilt and bronze on a white ground, see London, Fine Art Society, 1990, no. 23 (although this teaset was included in an exhibition of Christopher Dresser's work, there is no evidence that it was designed by Dresser). The service was made in a number of other colour schemes; a kettle with decoration in white and gold on a blue ground, the handle in bronze-coloured glaze, is held by the National Museum of Wales, Cardiff (inv. no. A.30.153, acquired in 1922).

A series of complimentary contemporary reports was printed at the back of the Guide to the Worcester Porcelain Works (see Cat. 314), but the critics were not unanimous in their praise: the Official Report of the Vienna Exhibition of 1873 noted that

the originality of English artists and their 'preference for that which is extraordinary and bizarre, must at times, it is self-evident, lead to uncertainty and error. This is the only explanation to be found for the unlovely angular imitations of the forms of some Japanese and Chinese vessels and knick-knacks by Mintons, but still more by the Worcester Manufactory, upon which, however, an amount of industry appears to have been expended which was really worthy of a better cause.'

The square shape with dragon handle is inspired by Chinese eighteenth-century models.

Wright, Frank Lloyd 1869-1959

Hitchcock, H.R., In the Nature of materials: The Buildings of Frank Lloyd Wright 1887-1914, New York 1942 (reprinted 1973)
John Lloyd Wright, My Father Who Is on Earth, New York 1946
Frank Lloyd Wright, the Early Work, New York, Horizon Press, 1968
Manson, G.C., Frank Lloyd Wright to 1910, New York 1958
Hanks, D.A., The Decorative Designs of Frank Lloyd Wright, New York 1979
Spencer, B.A. ed., The Prairie School Tradition, New York 1979

316 'Weed-holder' (or vase) [PLATE 107]

Sheet copper, hand-wrought in the form of a tapering square-section shaft set on a pyramidal base. At the junction of base and shaft is a short square section with an indented motif of an oval within a square on each side set at a 45-degree angle to shaft and base.

MARKS None.

Designed between 1893 and 1899 and made in the workshops of the coppersmith James A. Miller and Brother, Chicago.

H 73.7cm, w of base 10.6cm   1985,5-5,1

Wright's tall copper vases were inspired by his love of long, spindly weeds or dried grasses; they were described as weed-holders by his son: 'Not satisfied with the bric-a-brac of the day, Father designed his own. The copper weed-holders . . . are his early creations. Father liked weeds' (J.L. Wright 1946, 24). Frank Lloyd Wright himself, writing about his respect for sheet metal as a medium in 1928, described his first meeting with James Miller some thirty years before: 'At that time I designed some sheet copper bowls, slender flower holders and such things, for him' (Architectural Record 64, October 1928, 334-5).

It is generally accepted that the weed-holders date from after 1893, when Wright began to practise independently. Contemporary photographs show them to have been in use by 1899 in the house which Wright designed for himself at Oak Park, near Chicago. An early article on the architect's house and studio in The House Beautiful 7, no. 1, December 1899, includes a photograph of weed-holder of this form in the draughting-room. A description of the Oak Park studio in the Architectural Record for June 1900 observed 'some very interesting vessels and flower-holders of sheet copper of Mr Wright's design, always filled with masses of summer bloom or trophies of autumn fields and woods according to the season'. There are a number of other undated photographs of Wright's studio showing the weed-holders in situ, sometimes filled with grasses (see Hanks 1979, pl. 27) or on their own, as in a photograph in the Metropolitan Museum of Art, New York (Fig. 29), Department of Prints and Drawings, Henry Fuermann collection, 1985.1005.17, dating probably from after 1903. I am grateful to David Kiehl for bringing this to my attention. A photograph included in the 1902 exhibition of the Chicago Architectural Club showed a pair of weed-holders with a cube chair and a statue of the architect's son; the photograph was captioned 'Individual Flower Holder. Made by James A. Miller' (Hanks 1979, pl. 141; the same illustration is erroneously dated 1889 in *Frank Lloyd Wright, the Early Work*).

Weed-holders of this design were used in other Wright houses of the period; for example, in 1903 in the dining-room of the Susan Lawrence Dana House, Springfield, Illinois (*Frank Lloyd Wright, the Early Work*, 36). Weed-holders were also used at Taliesin III, Spring Green, Wisconsin, the house which Wright built for himself in 1911 (Hanks 1979, pl. 155).

A number of examples survive in public and private collections, though the provenance is not always known, one of the problems being that it is not clear whether the weed-holders were custom-made for Wright's houses or whether they were made for stock. Two examples are said to come from Oak Park (Hanks 1979, 70; Sotheby's, New York, 1-2 December 1989, lot 667, from the collection of the architect's son). A third comes from Falling Water, Bear Run, Pennsylvania, built for Edgar Kauffmann senior in the 1930s (Princeton 1972, no. 84). A fourth and fifth are in the Frank Lloyd Wright Foundation at Taliesin West, Scottsdale, Arizona (Hanks 1979, 70). An unprovenanced pair was acquired by the Metropolitan Museum of Art in 1985 and a single example by the Museum of the Carnegie Institute, Pittsburgh, in the same year (Carnegie Institute 1985, 214). Further saleroom examples include Christie's, New York, 6 June 1988, lot 116; see also London 1985, no. 1.

The Miller workshops executed two other Wright designs in copper, an urn and a lamp, see Princeton 1972, cat. nos 86-7. Wright made further designs for copper objects, apparently not executed, including another tapering vase with pyramidal base and large circular knop (Hanks, pl. 55, drawing in Taliesin archives). For the history of J. Miller & Brothers, see Hanks 1979, 212-13.

317 Plate [PLATE 107]

Hard-paste porcelain, with printed decoration of overlapping circles in red, yellow, green and ochre on a white ground.

MARKS Printed on the reverse in pink 'K WAKABAYASHICO TOKYO YOKOHAMA' with the Wakabayashico company monogram and '1961'.

Designed c.1922 for the Imperial Hotel, Tokyo, Japan and made by the Wakabayashico Porcelain Company, Tokyo after 1961.

D 20.5 cm 1984,10-10,1

The geometric design of overlapping circles recalls Wright's stained-glass windows for the Avery Coonley Playhouse, Riverside, Illinois of 1912 (Hanks 1979, col. pl. 10) and the murals at Midway Gardens, Chicago of 1914 (Hanks 1979, pl. 125). Wright's designs at this period were strongly influenced by his visit to Europe in 1909-10. It has been noted that the decoration of this service is closely related to one of the patterns that appears on Jutta Sika's tea and coffee set of 1901-2 (see Cat. 270) with asymmetrically placed circles (London 1985, no. 40).

The Imperial Hotel was built between 1915 and 1922, and demolished in 1968. The porcelain service remained in produc-

tion, with modifications, until the 1960s. Further pieces are illustrated in Hanks 1979, col. pl. 13. The service was reissued in 1984 by Noritake, Japan, and was marketed by Heinz & Company, Illinois, USA (examples in the Art Gallery and Museum, Brighton, and in the Victoria and Albert Museum).

Wright, Russel 1904-76

Hennessey, W.J., *Russel Wright: American designer*, Gallery Association of New York State, Cambridge, Mass., 1983

Kerr, A., *Russel Wright Dinnerware: Designs for the American table*, Paducah, Ky., 1985

318 Pancake and corn set [PLATE 124]

Chromium-plated brass, comprising butter can, salt and pepper pot, on tray with deep blue glass base.

MARKS Can and shakers stamped 'CHASE USA' with Sagittarius trade mark used by the Chase Company.

Designed before 1934 and made by the Chase Brass & Copper Company, Waterbury, Connecticut.

Can: H 13 cm. Pots: H 4.6 cm and 3 cm. Tray: D 15.3 cm
1988,1-9,1a-d

Russel Wright trained as a theatrical designer with Norman Bel Geddes (see Cat. 113) in the 1920s before setting up his own studio for the design of furniture and other household products for retail sale in aluminium, chrome, ceramics and wood. Following the success of his aluminium wares and his participation in the Metropolitan Museum's Third International Exhibition of Contemporary Industrial Art in 1930-31 (cat. nos 423-6), Wright received a consulting commission from the Chase Brass & Copper Company.

The Chase Company introduced its chromium line in about 1930. Chrome was then becoming fashionable as a sleek new 'machine age' material, especially during the Depression years, when it was widely used as a substitute for silver. The Metropolitan Museum's exhibition of industrial art contained a large group of German metalwork designed by Marianne Brandt at the Bauhaus, by Wilhelm Wagenfeld and by Wolfgang von Wersin and others. Much of Chase's chromium line seems indebted to Bauhaus theories and the German metalwork shown in New York may also have influenced Chase's choice of designers, among whom were two designers of German origin: Walter von Nessen (who left Berlin for America in 1923) and Albert Reimann (see Cat. 254).

Wright's corn set was included in the Industrial Arts Exposition held at the Rockefeller Plaza, New York, in 1934 (see *Arts and Decoration* 41, May 1934, 49) and is illustrated, with other designs by Wright, in the Chase Company's 1936-7 catalogue (reprinted 1978, ed. G. Koch, p. 22, no. 28003). The accompanying text reads: 'This amusing four-piece set designed by Russel Wright in polished chromium will add sparkle and color to any table setting. Deep blue glass forms the bottom of the tray. The pitcher may be used for syrup, drawn butter, cream, French dressing, or chocolate sauce for ice-cream. The spheres will hold salt and pepper, powdered sugar and other condiments.' The price for the set was $4, the pitcher only $2 and the spheres $1. There was also a larger sugar sphere and a sphere pitcher with Bakelite handle (p. 14, nos 90078 and 90079), but the pitcher is not credited to Wright and may be the firm's own addition. The production of the Chase chromium line ceased in 1942.

For further discussion, including Wright's chromium designs for his own studio, see *Creative Art* 9, 1931, 475-82; Hennessey 26-7; Kerr 29-30 and Brooklyn 1986, 326.

319-25 Group of 'American Modern' dinnerware

[COLOUR PLATE XVI]

Earthenware, cast, comprising pitcher and dinner plate in 'Seafoam' glaze, celery dish in 'Chartreuse' glaze, salt and pepper shakers in 'Granite Grey' and 'White', cream jug in 'Coral', gravy boat and saucer in 'Cedar Green', carafe in 'Granite Grey'. The 'Granite Grey', 'Cedar Green' and 'Coral' glazes are mottled.

MARKS On base of most pieces impressed facsimile signature 'Russel Wright' and 'MFG. BY STEUBENVILLE'.

Designed in 1937 and produced by Steubenville Pottery, East Liverpool, Ohio, from 1939 to c.1959.

319 Pitcher: H 26.7 cm   1988,1-17,1   Given by Antony Griffiths
320 Plate: D 25.6 cm   1988,1-16,1   Given by David Kiehl
321 Celery dish: L 33.5 cm   1988,1-18,1   Given by Judy Rudoe
322 Shakers: H 5.2 cm   1988,1-18,2a and b   Given by Judy Rudoe
323 Cream jug: L 18.4 cm   1989,1-8,3
324 Gravy boat: L 26.3 cm; saucer: L 27.6 cm   1989,1-8,2 and 2a
325 Carafe: H 16.2 cm   1989,1-8,1

The designs for 'American Modern' were completed in 1937, but it took Wright two years to find a factory willing to undertake production. In order to overcome an initial lack of response, Wright mounted a huge advertising campaign, using his theatrical background to promote the service with radio interviews, appearances in stores, lectures and so on. Within two years the factory was unable to keep up with demand and over the next twenty years more than eighty million pieces of 'American Modern' dinnerware were produced, making it one of the most popular mass-produced patterns for informal dinnerware ever sold and the standard present for young brides in the early 1940s.

Its success lay not only in its unprecedented asymmetrical organic shapes but also in its equally unconventional colours, subtle and original shades which customers were encouraged to mix and match as desired. Wright worked with ceramic engineers at Alfred University, New York, to develop the glazes, which were very different from the bright primary colours used in Frederick Hurten Rhead's 'Fiestaware', another informal service. In his use of soft shapes without rims or hard angles, Wright was among the first to make the shift from Bauhaus-inspired geometries to more complex, biomorphic forms and himself acknowledged his esteem for the Surrealists (Hennessey, 38). For similar concern with organic form, see Eva Zeisel's 'Town and Country' dinnerware (Cat. 333-5).

For further discussion, see Greif 1975, 172-3; Hennessey, 37-44; Kerr, 34-44, Brooklyn 1986, 62.

Wright found that his simple and austere style was no longer appreciated in the 1950s. He closed his design office in 1958 and became an environmental consultant for developing countries and then for the National Parks Service (*Industrial Design* 23, March/April 1976, 46-51).

326-7 Butter dish and wine carafe

[COLOUR PLATE XVI]

High-fired earthenware, cast, the butter dish in the form of a shallow tray and domed lid with pinched-in grips glazed in 'Sugar White'; the wine carafe with tall neck-cum-handle through which the vessel is filled, the spout at the base of the neck, in 'Charcoal'.

MARKS The butter dish printed on the base in brown 'IROQUOIS CASUAL CHINA by Russel Wright U.S.A'; the carafe unmarked.

Designed in 1946 as part of the 'Casual China' range made by the Iroquois China Company, Syracuse, New York, 1946-c.1965.

326 Butter dish: L 20 cm, H 7 cm   1988,1-17,2   Given by Antony Griffiths
327 Wine carafe: H 25.3 cm   1989,7-10,1   Given by David Kiehl

Like 'American Modern', 'Casual China' comprised inventive shapes with exciting colours, but in general the shapes are less exaggerated, being designed for easy stacking and resistance to damage. Russel Wright and his wife were pictured in 'china-breaking' sessions to show how durable it was (Hennessey, 8) and this feature became a significant selling-point. Some of the shapes were redesigned in the 1950s, but the pinch-grips are characteristic of the original designs. For further discussion, see Hennessey, 55, 58-9; Kerr, 45-57.

Württembergische Metallwarenfabrik
founded 1880

Art Nouveau Domestic Metalwork from the Württembergische Metallwarenfabrik: The English Catalogue 1906, with introduction by G. Dry, Antique Collectors Club, Woodbridge 1988

328 Flower pot

[PLATE 93]

Copper and brass, the pot in copper with brass handles and applied ornament.

MARKS Stamped on the base with the ostrich trade mark of the Württembergische Metallwarenfabrik in a lozenge (mark in use 1880-1925) and the model number '100'.

Designed and made by the Württembergische Metallwarenfabrik, Geislingen, near Ulm, c.1906.

H 34.2 cm, W 37.6 cm   1980,5-10,1

The Württembergische Metallwarenfabrik (WMF) was founded as Daniel Straub in 1853 and became known as the Württembergische Metallwarenfabrik in 1880, following the merger of Straub & Schweizer of Geislingen and A. Ritter & Co. of Esslingen. The factory's main production was of metal and electroplated household wares, but they also made electrotype reproductions of historical metalware. From the late nineteenth century to the First World War the WMF art studio was run by the sculptor Albert Mayer with a staff of anonymous designers, modellers and craftsmen, who were required to turn out designs in the prevailing style, whether historical or modern. WMF frequently adapted models by artists such as Albin Müller at Darmstadt (see Cat. 211, a pair of candlesticks), in order to create a recognisable company style. But occasionally, as in the case of this flower pot, models of striking originality were produced.

This flower pot is included in a WMF English export catalogue of 1906 in the surviving factory archive as model no. 4068 E; the description reads 'antique copper, antique brass handles and mountings', suggesting that the surfaces may originally have been patinated. (I am grateful to Graham Dry for checking all the catalogues at the WMF factory in Geislingen.) It should be noted that there were a number of catalogues in circulation at this date, for the German market as well as English export versions, but each catalogue usually represents a selection of current production only; thus this flower pot does not appear in other English export catalogues of 1906 (for example, the catalogue reprinted in 1988).

329 Frame [PLATE 93]

Pewter, cast, with surface patina of oxidised silver, containing a mirror glass. A stand has been fitted to the reverse and two square supports soldered to one side on which the frame rests.

MARKS None.

Designed originally as a tray with wood centre c.1905-6 by the Württembergische Metallwarenfabrik, Geislingen, near Ulm, and converted at a later date for use as a mirror, possibly by the firm of Albert Köhler & Cie, Vienna.

L 52 cm, W 28 cm   1983,11-5,1

The identical design occurs in an English export catalogue of 1906 issued by the 'Wurtemberg [sic] Electro Plate Co., 91 Fore Street, London EC' as model no. 84, a tray with oak centre and silver-plated mount (WMF 1906 catalogue, reprinted 1988, 181). The tray as advertised was executed in two sizes, 15 and 20 in (38 and 51 cm) long, with silver-plated mount in 'old Silver' finish or bright finish. The tray is illustrated vertically rather than horizontally, which may have suggested the later conversion to a mirror. An undated German WMF catalogue includes a much elongated, narrower version, 47 cm (18½ in) long, model no. 184, in 'oxidised silver plate'.

WMF wares were usually made of silver-plated Britannia metal, a lightweight alloy of tin, antimony and copper. The metal used and the surface finish were normally indicated by a system of letters stamped on the reverse (WMF 1906 catalogue, reprinted 1988, xlix-l). An example of the 15-in tray in a private collection bears the WMF trade mark, with the letter 'B' for Britannia metal, the percentage '10' indicating the thickness of the silver-plating and 'OX' for oxidised. Analysis of the British Museum example (by Susan La Niece of the British Museum Research Laboratory) has shown that it is made of pewter with an unusually high lead content for pewter of this period: 73% tin, 21% lead, 4% antimony and 2% copper. It has a thin plating of silver, tarnished and then polished so that the blackened areas remain in the lower parts of the relief but are polished off the higher areas, which are left in a matt finish.

For another frame of this design, also assembled as a mirror with added supports, see Darmstadt 1976, Bd 4, no. 16. The catalogue entry attributes the design to Behrens by analogy with the leatherwork panels and benches which Behrens designed for the Hamburger Halle at the Turin Exhibition of 1902 (Spielmann et al. 1979, no. 104a-d). However, Graham Dry has noted the use of sweeping curves to form a group of elongated triangles together with small adjacent squares in ornament designed by Albin Müller, for example in a wine coaster designed by Müller for WMF (DK 1905, 322 and WMF 1906 catalogue, reprinted 1988, 153). WMF internal designs frequently borrowed motifs from other designers, in this case from either Behrens or Müller. The frame mentioned above bears the mark 'AK & Cie', for Albert Köhler & Cie, Vienna, a metalware factory which was taken over by WMF after 1900 and which served as a WMF repairs factory after 1918. Thus it is possible either that the British Museum 'mirror' was also assembled by the WMF-owned firm of Köhler in Vienna and that both conversions were done as 'repairs' after 1918, or that the frame was made by Köhler after a WMF design, given that the alloy is not one known to have been used by WMF. (For these suggestions and for information about Köhler, I am indebted to Graham Dry.)

It should be recorded that much of the silver and pewter sold in the early part of this century by Liberty's in London, probably mostly imported from Germany, was oxidised, not only to show up the pattern, but also to overcome the cleaning problem (Bury 1977, 23; see also Liberty 1904). The continued popularity of such wares is illustrated by a report on the British Industries Fair of 1915 at which William Hutton & Sons Ltd of Sheffield showed oxidised silver-plate, specifically to meet the demand for goods that were not being imported from Germany during the war: 'they showed some oxidised silverware of beautiful French-grey finish, and lacquered to prevent tarnishing; thus the various articles only required dusting with a soft damp cloth to preserve their original freshness' (quoted in Culme 1987, I, 249).

Wynand, Paul 1879-1956

There is no monograph on Wynand. For biographical details, see Cologne 1978; Dry-v. Zezschwitz 1981, 42, note 12; Bonn 1987 and Kunsthandwerk Aktuell 4, March 1987, 4-7 (published by Merkelbach & Goebel, Höhr-Grenzhausen).

330 Jug [PLATE 99]

Salt-glazed stoneware with pewter lid. Grey-buff body with rich chocolate-coloured 'Kölnisch braun' ('Cologne brown') glaze with vertical rows of circular bosses surrounded by raised beading, the rows divided by raised ribs. The glaze has pulled away from the raised areas, leaving the beading and ribs in the body colour.

MARKS Impressed on the base with model number '2199' and 'R. MERKELBACH GRENZHAUSEN', the factory mark in use c.1903/4 to 1916 (Dry-v. Zezschwitz 1981, 31).

Designed c.1909 and made by the firm of R. Merkelbach, Höhr-Grenzhausen, Rhineland, Germany.

H 35 cm   1988,1-15,1

Paul Wynand studied initially in Berlin before returning to his native town of Elberfeld, where he attended the Kunstgewerbeschule from 1900 to 1903. He studied briefly with Rodin in Paris in 1904 and then taught at the Kunstgewerbeschule in Elberfeld, from 1904 to 1905, before taking over from Ernst Barlach as teacher at the Keramische Fachschule, Höhr, from 1905 to 1909. From 1909 to 1911 he worked in Rome and then returned to Berlin as a freelance sculptor. He supplied designs for Merkelbach between 1908 and 1912; often only sketchily outlined, these designs were translated into ceramic forms by the modeller Carl Mehlem (1885-1976) and won for Merkelbach a gold medal at the Brussels Exhibition of 1910 (Dry-v. Zezschwitz in Kunsthandwerk Aktuell 4, March 1987). Wynand was one of a number of local artists whose collaboration with the factory modellers encouraged the introduction of new models on a very large scale.

Model no. 2199 is credited to Wynand in the Merkelbach catalogue of 1912 (pl. 11) and a closely related design for a globular jug with the same decoration, model no. 2179, is illustrated in Die Kunst XXVI, 1911-12, 521.

Most of Wynand's stoneware designs were made by Merkelbach, but he also made designs for Gerz which were shown in an exhibition of Westerwald stoneware at the Landesgewerbemuseum, Stuttgart in 1912 (Sprechsaal 45, 1912).

331 Jug [PLATE 99]

Salt-glazed stoneware with pewter lid, bulbous form, the handle continuing the sloping line of the rim and spout. Grey body with relief decoration of beaded roundels increasing in size towards the base and two large roundels with spiral ornament on either side of the neck. The relief is in cobalt-blue clay which turns a rich black beneath the 'braun geflammt' or speckled brown glaze.

MARKS Impressed on the base with the model number '2110' and 'R. MERKELBACH GRENZHAUSEN' in a circle, the factory mark in use from 1900 (Dry-v.Zezschwitz 1981, 31).

Designed c.1909 and made by the firm of R. Merkelbach, Höhr-Grenzhausen, Rhineland, Germany.

H 24.4 cm, D of body 19.3 cm   1988,7-3,1

This model is illustrated in *Die Kunst* 22, 1909/10, 461; *The Studio Yearbook*, 1910, 200 and 1912, 176. For another example of model 2110 with further bibliography, see Bröhan II/1, 1976, no. 532. The flat lid echoing the sloping line of the rim is unusual and was probably designed specially by Wynand. Riemerschmid also designed special lids to match his unusual shapes, but most models by other designers were fitted with a range of standard domed lids. For the beer tankard that matches this jug, see *Kunsthandwerk Aktuell* 4, March 1987, 6.

For discussion of the relief decoration, see Cat. 332. The 'braun geflammt' glaze was achieved by adding oxygen at the end of the firing.

332 Punch-bowl with lid [PLATE 99]

Salt-glazed stoneware, grey body, bulbous form with three square-sided legs and relief decoration comprising five cartouches with spiral ornament and beading, a band of similar ornament round the neck, beading outlining the lid and feet, and a series of bosses round the base of the bowl. The lid with hollowed-out pinch-grip. The relief decoration is in cobalt blue which turns black when covered with the glaze, in this case a speckled 'braun geflammt' glaze.

MARKS Impressed on the base with model number '2117', 'R. MERKELBACH GRENZHAUSEN', the factory mark in use from c. 1903/4 to 1916, and the letters 'DB WB' within a 'G' within a square.

Designed in 1909 and made by the firm of R. Merkelbach, Höhr-Grenzhausen, Rhineland, Germany after 1914.

H 25.6 cm (with lid), 22.4 cm (without lid), D 29.4 cm   1989,1-4,1

This punch-bowl was among the prize-winning designs for the student-art competition (Wettbewerb für Studentenkunst) held in the Landesgewerbemuseum, Stuttgart in 1909 (Lüthgen 1909, 9). The competition was organised by the museum's director, G.E. Pazaurek. Wynand won third prize jointly with Merkelbach, Albin Müller's stonewares won first prize and the second prize was awarded to glass. Later in 1909 the punch-bowl was included in an exhibition of stoneware organised by the industrialist and collector K.E. Osthaus at the Deutsches Museum für Kunst im Handel und Gewerbe (German Museum for Art in Trade and Industry) in Hagen (Hagen 1984, 53, 73). It was almost certainly exhibited as new work at the Brussels Exhibition of 1910, at which Merkelbach received a gold medal (see Cat. 330), though Hanke received a higher award, the Diploma of Honour.

The model catalogued here combines modernist form with Biedermeier-revival decoration in the jewel-like reliefs. Similar decoration with recurring spirals was a feature of the Munich style at this period; much of the Westerwald stoneware was destined for the Bavarian market and some of it seems to have been designed with this in mind. This model was among several sold through the Deutsche Werkstätten shop in Munich.

From the mid 1870s relief decoration in the Westerwald began to be formed in the mould rather than applied. This enabled new models to be produced more cheaply and in greater numbers. A plaster mould was made from the original model and was hollowed out to receive the relief decoration in cobalt blue. The piece was then thrown within this mould. After drying, the piece would shrink and detach itself from the mould, with the relief decoration attached and ready for glazing (Dry-v. Zezschwitz 1989, 286).

This example bears the mark of the Dürerbund-Werkbund-Genossenschaft, a trade association set up in 1912 between the Werkbund (founded in 1907) and the Dürerbund (an earlier reform movement of the 1890s). It was based in Dresden-Hellerau and its aim was to promote household articles of good design, which were functional, artistic and well made, by preparing a compendium or illustrated price list, the 'Deutsches Warenbuch', which comprised articles that represented value for money and had the approval of both organisations. It was intended that the objects should be featured in a nationwide chain of shops, but the success of the first issue was marred by its delayed publication in 1915 owing to the outbreak of war. In that year the association comprised 160 of the most reputable specialist dealers. The trade mark 'DB WB G' was designed by the architect and designer Fritz Hellmuth Ehmcke in 1914. For further examples with this trade mark, see Bröhan II/1, 1976, no. 534 and Bonn 1987, no. 231. For further discussion of Wynand's contribution to the revival of the stoneware industry, see Rudoe 1990.

Zeisel, Eva b.1906

Eva Zeisel: Designer for Industry, exhibition catalogue, Musée des Arts Décoratifs, Montreal 1984

Eva Zeisel: Designerin für die Industrie, exhibition catalogue, Keramik-Museum, Schloss Ziegelberg, Mettlach 1989

See also Recent Acquisitions, Cat. 357-60.

333-5 Teapot, salt and pepper shakers, and lidded bean pot [PLATE 127; COLOUR PLATE XVI]

Earthenware, cast. The teapot is of asymmetrical ovoid form with pale orange glaze; the upper surface slopes at an angle and the lid is placed off centre. The handle is moulded to fit the thumb. The salt and pepper shakers are in the form of zoomorphic sculptures, moulded to fit the hand; the larger example is glazed in a turquoise blue, the smaller in buff. The bean pot is glazed turquoise blue.

MARKS None.

Designed in 1945-6 as part of the 'Town and Country' dinner service and made by Red Wing Pottery, Red Wing, Minnesota, USA.

333 Teapot: L 29.3 cm, H 11.7 cm   1989,1-7,1
334 Salt and pepper shakers: H 11.3 and 7.5 cm   1989,1-7,2 and 3
335 Bean pot: H 20.9 cm, D 22.2 cm   1989,11-4,1   Given by Antony Griffiths

Zeisel was born in Budapest, where she studied briefly at the Royal Academy of Art and was apprenticed to the Hungarian potters' guild before setting up her own pottery in 1925. She then worked for the Kispester Pottery in Budapest, joining the Schramberger Majolika Fabrik in the Black Forest, Germany, in 1928. There she produced geometric designs of great inventiveness and individuality. From 1930 to 1931 she worked in Berlin, leaving in 1932 for the Soviet Union, where she worked initially for the Lomonossov factory in Leningrad and then for the Dulevo factory near Moscow.

In 1939 Zeisel settled in New York, where she taught ceramic design at the Pratt Institute, Brooklyn, but it was her formal porcelain 'Museum Service' designed c.1942-5 for the Museum of Modern Art and made by Castleton China that brought her widespread recognition. As a result she received the commission from Red Wing for an informal, inexpensive earthenware service named 'Town and Country' after the popular magazine. It was intended to be humorous, even eccentric: the shapes are more asymmetrical than Russel Wright's 'American Modern' service (see Cat. 319-25), the lids could be in a different colour from the body of the vessel, while the salt and pepper shakers were photographed by the artist to suggest a mother and children or a whole family of friendly creatures (Montreal 1984, 39-40, fig. 58). The large and small forms were thus intended to be used together. The service was produced from 1947. For further discussion and bibliography, see the essay by Martin Eidelberg in Montreal 1984.

Unattributed

336 Plate

[PLATE 129]

Earthenware, turned, white body, with stencilled pattern in matt red glaze on a matt black ground.

MARKS Impressed on the base '2864' with an unidentified production mark.

Designer and manufacturer unknown, probably German, c.1925-30.

D 19.3 cm   1988,1-13,1

A similar plate has previously been attributed to Lissitzky (see Berlin 1977, 1/644); it bears on the reverse a similar mark, which has been identified as the monogram 'EL', and the numbers '1923' and '5/20', the first being interpreted as a date. However, the reading of the mark as 'EL' is not convincing and the design bears little relation to Lissitzky's work of the early 1920s. It is more likely that this plate was made by one of the many German factories producing stencilled decoration in the late 1920s and early 1930s. Designs of this type are illustrated regularly in the German trade journal *Die Schaulade* during these years.

Appendix: Recent Acquisitions

The following is a list of acquisitions made in 1990, after research for the catalogue was completed.

Adamovich, Mikhail 1884-1947

See Cat. 2.

337 Plate   [COLOUR PLATE XII]

Porcelain, painted overglaze with the slogan 'Kapital'. A red worker tramples 'Kapital' underfoot, thereby releasing the dynamic forces of industry for the benefit of the workers. In the background, a factory in red with billowing chimneys, the smoke interspersed with flashes of yellow and black. The plate has a scalloped edge.

MARKS Imperial Porcelain Factory mark of Nicholas II, 1901, printed in underglaze green; State Porcelain Factory mark and date '1921' painted in overglaze blue.

Decorated at the State Porcelain Factory, Petrograd, in 1921, after a design by Adamovich.

D 24.8 cm 1990,5-6,1 Purchased with the aid of the National Art-Collections Fund

For a plate with the same subject, also dated 1921 but painted in red and black only, see Lobanov-Rostovsky 1990, pl. 1.

Behrens, Peter 1869-1940

See Cat. 11-17.

338 Wine glass   [PLATE 95; COLOUR PLATE VI]

Free-blown, with clear glass bowl and red glass hollow stem.

MARKS None.

Designed in 1901 for the dining-room of Behrens' house in the artists' colony at Darmstadt and made by the Rheinische Glashütten, Köln-Ehrenfeld.

H 15.3 cm 1990,4-7,1

Behrens' own service was exhibited in his house as part of the exhibition 'Ein Dokument Deutscher Kunst', held at the colony in 1901 (see Koch 1902, 369; *Die Kunst* 6, 1901-2, 24 and *Innendekoration*, 1902, 24). Other services were probably made to order. Glasses from this service are to be found in German collections such as the Kunstgewerbemuseum in Cologne, the Badisches Landesmuseum, Karlsruhe, and the Stadtmuseum, Munich.

339 Four tiles   [PLATE 87]

Earthenware, with a spiral motif in deep brown on a buff ground.

MARKS Impressed mark of the Villeroy & Boch factory on the reverse.

Designed *c.*1904 and made by Villeroy & Boch, Mettlach.

16.7 × 16.7 cm 1990,4-8,1-4

Floor tiles of this pattern were used in a number of buildings in Düsseldorf and Nuremberg, where Behrens was working at this period. Contemporary photographs of the tiles *in situ* show that the floors were made up of alternating spiral patterns in brown on buff (as on these tiles) or reversed, in buff on brown, with border tiles of a different design. For illustrations of original floors and examples of the border tiles, see Nuremberg 1980, 263 and 265; see also *Anzeiger des Germanisches Nationalmuseums Nürnberg*, 1981, 110, and Ulmer 1990, no. 12.

Chekhonin, Sergei 1878-1936

See Cat. 35.

340 Plate   [PLATE 139]

Porcelain, painted overglaze with the slogan in black 'A Komsomol [Youth Communist League] through Lenin's studies into the ranks of the Russian Communist party'. In the centre the letters 'KNM' within a red star and a red and gold flag, surrounded by the letters 'CCCR' with floral sprays in many colours.

MARKS Imperial Porcelain Factory mark of Nicholas II, 1899, printed in underglaze green; Lomonossov factory mark and date '1925' painted in overglaze blue.

Decorated at the Lomonossov Porcelain Factory (formerly State Porcelain Factory), Leningrad, in 1925, probably after a design by Chekhonin.

D 31.3 cm, H 4.6 cm 1990,5-6,2 Purchased with the aid of the National Art-Collections Fund

341 Plate   [PLATE 139]

Porcelain, painted overglaze with stylised border pattern of flowers and leaves in red, yellow, blue, green, grey, black and purple, with gilded borders.

MARKS Imperial Porcelain Factory mark of Alexander II, 1893, printed in underglaze green; State Porcelain Factory mark and date '1918' painted in overglaze blue.

Decorated at the State Porcelain Factory, Petrograd, after a design by Chekhonin.

D 24.3 cm   1990,5-6,6   Given by the British Museum Society

The stylised border pattern of flowers and leaves is a bold modernisation of traditional motifs. For a similar plate dated 1921, see Lobanov-Rostovsky 1990, pl. 116.

Fahrner, Theodor, Gold- und Silberwaren-Fabrik 1855-1979

342 Pendant [PLATE 102]

Silver, set with garnets and pearls, the border in white enamel scattered with gold stars let into the enamel.

MARKS Stamped on the reverse with the monogram 'TF' in a circle, the silver standard mark '935' and 'DÉPOSÉ'.

Made by the firm of Theodor Fahrner, Pforzheim, c.1910-13.

W 3.5 cm   1990,6-8,1

For a pendant with similar decoration in the Schmuckmuseum, Pforzheim, see von Hase 1977, 194, no. 146, and Pforzheim 1990, no. 1.135. The French design registration mark, 'DÉPOSÉ' was often used by Pforzheim firms with large-scale export production: see also Cat. 290.

Girschfeld, Natalya worked at the State Porcelain Factory, Petrograd, 1919-22

343 Plate [COLOUR PLATE XII]

Porcelain, painted overglaze with the slogan 'Petrograd 1921' in the centre in black and gold, surrounded by ears of wheat, the border with floral motifs in thick gold leaf and blue.

MARKS Imperial Porcelain Factory mark of Nicholas II, 1896, printed in underglaze green; special State Porcelain Factory mark designed by Chekhonin with hammer and sickle and the slogan 'for the benefit of the starving 1921' painted in gold; artist's initials 'NG' painted in gold.

Designed and painted at the State Porcelain Factory, Petrograd, by N. Girschfeld, as one of twenty-three elaborate pieces made to raise money for the Volga region famine victims in 1921.

D 35.8 cm, H 5.8 cm   1990,5-6,3   Purchased with the aid of the National Art-Collections Fund

The series of twenty-three pieces, each of different design by a number of different artists and each bearing the special gold factory mark, was intended for sale at auction, but the auction never took place and so a number of pieces remained at the Factory (Moscow 1962, 97). Published examples include a plate with a design by Shchekotikhina-Pototskaya (Andreeva 1975, 158, and Oxford and London 1984, 34, no. 216) and a dish with a design by Vilde (Lansere 1974, pl. 27; Andreeva 1975, 182; Oxford and London, no. 256), both in the Museum of the Lomonossov Porcelain Factory, Leningrad. For a vase by Lebedeva, see Lansere 1974, pl. 31 (no location given). For another example of the design by Vilde, see Lobanov-Rostovsky 1990, pl. 55, but this has the ordinary blue factory mark, so is presumably a duplicate of the original. For a dish initialled by the artist N. A. Kulikova, after a design by Chekhonin, see Oxford and London 1984, 43, no. 146 (lent by M. P. and T. M. Danilov, Moscow). Three further pieces from the series are held by the State Museum of Ceramics at Kuskovo: a dish with the inscription in German 'The Proletariat of all lands unite', a plate with a design by Adamovich and a plate with a mother and children against a background of burning settlements, by Chekhonin (Moscow 1962, 97).

Lalique, René attributed

See Cat. 140.

344 Ceiling light [PLATE 118]

Cast glass and brass, formed of five panels of opalescent glass set in a five-sided frame.

MARKS None.

H 16.9 cm, max. W 42.7 cm   1990,10-20,1   Given by David and Geoffrey Bindman

According to the donors, the light was purchased by their mother at the Lalique shop in Paris in 1929. However, it does not appear in F. Marcilhac's recently published Catalogue raisonné of Lalique's glassware (1989) and Félix Marcilhac has suggested that it is more likely to be by the firm of M. E. Sabino, Paris, specialists in light fittings.

Lebedeva, Maria Vasilievna 1895-1942

345 Plate [COLOUR PLATE XIII]

Porcelain, painted overglaze with folk-tale image of an evil genie bearing away the old order, the genie and floral border in black, orange and purple.

MARKS Imperial Porcelain Factory mark of Nicholas II, 1914, printed in underglaze green; State Porcelain Factory mark and date '1923'; artist's mark, the monogram 'MV' with a swan ('lebedev' is the Russian word for 'swan'), all painted in overglaze blue.

Designed and painted at the State Porcelain Factory, Petrograd, in 1923 by M. Lebedeva, whose signature appears on the front.

D 36.6 cm, H 5.4 cm   1990,5-6,4   Purchased with the aid of the National Art-Collections Fund

This plate, signed by the artist, appears to be the only recorded version of this subject.

Marcks, Gerhard 1889-1981

See Cat. 154.

346-8 Three figures [PLATE 101]

Porcelain, in the form of a falcon on a perch, a lynx eating and a striding lioness, the lioness glazed white, the others painted with underglaze colours of browns and greens.

MARKS All three with impressed factory mark of a running fox and 'Schwarzburger Werkstätten für Porzellankunst', together with impressed model numbers, the falcon '1004', the lynx '1007' and the lioness '1020'; the lioness incised on the upper surface 'Gerh. Marks' (sic).

Designed in 1909-10 and made by the Schwarzburger Werkstätten für Porzellankunst, Unterweissbach, Thuringia, Germany.

346 Falcon: H 24 cm   347 Lynx: L 30.1 cm   348 Lioness: L 44 cm, H 23.5 cm   1990,4-6,1-3

These are Marcks' earliest sculptural works and represent three out of the four models that he made for the Schwarzburger Werkstätten; the fourth model was a mask of a cat, but no example of this has been recorded. The Schwarzburger Werkstätten were founded in 1908 by the ceramic artist Max Adolf Pfeiffer (1875-1957) and directed by him until 1913 (see Scherf 1980, 405-6 and Wendl 1984, 100-5); the four models are illustrated in the *Kat. Schwarzburger Werkstätten für Porzellankunst, Max Adolf Pfeiffer GmbH*, Unterweissbach 1912, pls 34-5. Few surviving examples are recorded. For a falcon and a lioness in the Thüringer Museum, Eisenach, see Rudolstadt 1983, nos 32 and 34; for a lynx and a lioness in the Staatliche Museen Heidecksburg, Rudolstadt, see Rudolstadt 1983, no. 33 and Scherf 1984, pl. 349 (references kindly supplied by Graham Dry). The lioness seems only to have been made in white; the lynx and falcon were offered in both white and coloured glazes (a white lynx is held by the Württembergisches Landesmuseum, Stuttgart).

Powell, James & Sons, Whitefriars Glass Works 1834-1980

See Cat. 234-43.

349 Decanter and five matching glasses [PLATE 57]

Champagne glass, port glass, liqueur glass, tumbler and extra large tumbler. The glasses engraved with a single band of holly, the decanter engraved with a spiral band of holly round the whole body.

MARKS None.

Purchased by the family of the donors from James Powell & Sons, Whitefriars Glass Works, London, between 1891 and 1912.

349a H of decanter 21.8 cm (without stopper), 27.2 cm (with stopper); H of glasses in the order in which they are listed above: **b** 11.2 cm, **c** 10.8 cm, **d** 7.9 cm, **e** 12.4 cm, **f** 15.9 cm 1990,10-19,1-6   Given by Mr and Mrs R. Le G. Hetherington

The original bills from Powell & Sons dating from 1891 to 1912 are still in the possession of the donors and indicate that the service originally comprised twelve or more glasses of each size, which were added to and replaced as needed. The survival of the original bills is of special significance in that Powell & Sons' glass was never marked and the table-glass patterns often remained in production over decades. The holly-pattern glasses are illustrated in a Powell & Sons catalogue of c.1880 in the Powell archive, but the decanter, with its spiralling holly branch, has not previously been recorded as a Powell & Sons design.

Shchekotikhina-Pototskaya, Alexandra 1892-1967

350 Plate [PLATE 140]

Porcelain, painted overglaze with the slogans 'Petrograd' and 'Uritsky Square', with Commissar Uritsky crossing Palace Square, renamed Uritsky Square after the latter's assassination in 1918.

MARKS Imperial Porcelain Factory mark of Nicholas II, 1912, printed in underglaze green; State Porcelain Factory mark and date '1922', painter's initials 'EY' and 'after the design of Shchekotikhina', factory number 'N-322/11', all painted in overglaze blue.

Decorated at the State Porcelain Factory, Petrograd, in 1922 by Ekaterina Yakimovskaya, after the design of Shchekotikhina-Pototskaya.

D 23.7 cm   1990,5-6,7   Given by the British Museum Society

For further information about the assassination of Mosei Uritsky, see Sotheby's, London, 30 November 1990, lot 197. Uritsky Square is again known as Palace Square today. This was a popular design and many other examples are recorded: for example, Gollerbach and Farmakovski 1924, 67; Andreeva 1975, 167; Venice and Biella 1978, no. 97 (in the Russian Museum of Applied Art, Moscow); Lobanov-Rostovsky 1990, pl. 36.

Tiffany & Co.

See Cat. 282-3.

351 Tankard [PLATE 50]

Silver and oxidised silver, in the Japanese taste, decorated with applied silver motifs of figures, bamboo and other plants, the background oxidised to a deep grey-black colour. The handle with classical-style palmettes.

MARKS Stamped on the base 'TIFFANY & CO. MAKERS STERLING SILVER', with the shape number '2834'.

Made by Tiffany & Co., New York, c.1874-6.

H 10.2 cm   1990,10-17,1

The original design drawing for this tankard (Fig. 16) survives in the Tiffany archive in New York; shape number 2834 was put into production between 1870 and 1874, while the decoration was designed on 15 December 1874 (indicated by the decoration number '296' on the drawing). This is an early example of Tiffany silver in the Japanese taste, hence the combination of Japanese and classical-style motifs, and an exceptional survival of an original oxidised silver surface, intended to imitate Japanese *shakudo* grounds.

Timorev, Vasilii 1870-1942

352 Dish [PLATE 137]

Porcelain, painted overglaze with the slogan 'From heroic military deeds to labour heroic deeds and from labour heroic deeds to military heroic deeds'. Workers in military uniform at an anvil and above them the Polish eagle and a second slogan 'the Poland of the rich landlords', referring to the war against Poland at the end of the Russian civil war. The central scene in shades of green, brown, grey, rust, and the eagle in purple; the inscription in reddish-brown.

MARKS Imperial Porcelain Factory mark of Alexander III, 1892, printed in underglaze green; State Porcelain Factory mark and date '1920' with artist's symbol of V. Timorev painted in overglaze blue.

Designed and painted at the State Porcelain Factory, Petrograd, in July 1920 by Vasilii Timorev, whose signature appears on the front with the date '20.VI'.

D 36.8 cm, H 6.9 cm   1990,5-6,5   Purchased with the aid of the National Art-Collections Fund

353 Plate [PLATE 138]

Porcelain, painted overglaze in pale colours with a soldier, worker and peasant facing an obelisk rising from the ruins of the old order, bordered with a wreath of oak and laurel. The obelisk bears the dates '1917-22'. Painted to commemorate the fifth anniversary of the October Revolution.

MARKS Imperial Porcelain Factory mark of Nicholas II, 1906, printed in underglaze green; State Porcelain Factory mark and date 'November

1922'; artist's symbol of V. Timorev; the Cyrillic initials 'G.O' and letter 'N' with two strokes through it, all painted in overglaze blue.

Designed and painted at the State Porcelain Factory, Petrograd, in November 1922 by Vasilii Timorev, whose signature appears on the front with the date '22.IX'.

D 36.6 cm, H 5.7 cm   1990,5-6,8

These two large pieces, signed by the artist, appear to be the only recorded examples of these subjects. For two further large dishes by Timorev with commemorative subject-matter, see Lobanov-Rostovsky 1990, pls 44 and 45. One of these also bears on the reverse the unidentified Cyrillic initials 'G.O' in overglaze blue and the letter 'N' with two strokes through it.

Van de Velde, Henry   1863-1957

See Cat. 290-95.

354 Jug   [PLATE 82]

Salt-glazed stoneware, buff body, with incised and painted curvilinear decoration in blue on a grey ground, with pewter lid also designed by van de Velde.

MARKS Impressed with artist's monogram on the base.

Designed in 1902 and made by the firm of R. Hanke, Höhr-Grenzhausen, Rhineland, Germany.

H 31.2 cm   1990,7-11,1

This is an example of van de Velde's stoneware designs executed in the traditional Westerwald colours of blue and grey and intended as a cheaper range of art wares to complement the very expensive experimental wares with *sang-de-boeuf* glazes (see Cat. 293).

Venini & Co.   founded 1921

355 Vase   [PLATE 128]

Free-blown pale green glass.

MARKS None.

Designed in 1921 by Vittorio Zecchin and made by Vetri Soffiati Muranese Cappelin-Venini & Co. *c.*1921-5.

H 22.1 cm   1991,1-8,1

This vase was designed as part of a series of vases for the newly founded firm of Cappelin-Venini in Murano. The series was exhibited at the Salon d'Automne in Paris in 1922, at the International Exhibition in Monza in 1923, at the Venice Biennale in 1924 and at the Paris Exhibition of 1925. This particular model, known as 'Veronese', became one of the firm's classic designs of the 1920s. It was known as 'Veronese' because it was inspired by a vase of the same shape depicted in Paolo Veronese's *Annunciation* from the Scuola dei Mercanti, *c.* 1581. The painting has been in the Gallerie dell' Accademia in Venice (inv. no. 260) since 1807.

Paolo Venini (b.1895), a Milanese lawyer, and Giacomo Cappelin (1887-1968), a Venetian antique dealer, founded the Vetri Soffiati Muranese Cappelin-Venini & Co in 1921. The designer, Vittorio Zecchin (1878-1947), a distinguished Muranese painter, decorator and glass designer, was appointed artistic and technical director. Zecchin's purist shapes in pastel colours with no external decoration were in startling contrast to traditional highly decorated Venetian glass. See Deboni 1990, 35, for a group of Zecchin's designs of the 1920s.

Vilde, Rudolf   1868-?1942

356 Plate   [PLATE 141]

Porcelain, painted overglaze with the slogan in black 'Knowledge in your head means food in your belly'. In the centre, the tools of reading and writing on top of a hammer and sickle, in black, grey, buff and red, with green borders.

MARKS Imperial Porcelain Factory mark of Alexander II (date rubbed), printed in underglaze green; State Porcelain Factory mark and date '1920' painted in overglaze blue.

Decorated at the State Porcelain Factory, Petrograd, in 1920, after a design by R. Vilde.

D 22.1 cm   1990,5-6,9   Given by the British Museum Society

For a cup and saucer designed by Vilde with similar emblems but a different inscription, see Gollerbach and Farmakovski 1924, 59; according to a booklet published by the Order of Lenin State History Museum, Moscow, *Porcelain in the early years after the October Revolution*, no. 8, this cup and saucer was made in 1921 to the order of the State Publishing House, whose name appears on the cup.

357 Plate   [PLATE 141]

Porcelain, painted overglaze with the slogan 'Rossiya 1917-1921' in black and red. In the centre, a hammer and sickle enclosing a spray of flowers in blue, yellow, purple, grey and black. The slogan celebrates the first five years of the Revolution; the USSR was not formed until 1922.

MARKS Imperial Porcelain Factory mark of Nicholas II, 1912, printed in underglaze green; State Porcelain Factory mark and date '1921' painted in overglaze blue.

Decorated at the State Porcelain Factory, Petrograd, in 1921, after a design by R. Vilde.

D 23.4 cm   1990,5-6,10

For a similar plate, see Lobanov-Rostovsky 1990, pl. 49.

Zeisel, Eva   b. 1906

See Cat. 333-5.

358-61 Five pieces of earthenware
[PLATE 127; COLOUR PLATE XVI]

Handleless jug with rust-coloured glaze, designed to be held by the rim; cream jug with plum-coloured glaze; pair of cruets with stoppers in lime green and bronze glazes; mustard pot in green glaze with combined stopper and scoop, hollow cast, the firing hole closed off with a button at the top.

MARKS None.

Designed in 1946 as part of the 'Town & Country' service and made by the Red Wing Pottery, Red Wing, Minnesota, USA.

358 Handleless jug: H 14.7 cm   1990,12-2,1
359 Cream jug: H 12.2 cm   1990,12-2,2
360 Cruets: H 13.3 cm   1990,12-2,3a (green) and 3b (bronze)
361 Mustard pot: H 15 cm   1990,12-2,4

Bibliography

The publications that follow are referred to in abbreviated form in the catalogue entries. Monographs and articles listed in full under each heading are not repeated here unless they are referred to in abbreviated form elsewhere. Periodicals are abbreviated as follows:

A & D: Art et Décoration
DK: Dekorative Kunst
DK & D: Deutsche Kunst und Dekoration
JSA: Journal of the Society of Arts (from 1908, *JRSA: Journal of the Royal Society of Arts*)

Abeler, J. 1977. *Meister der Uhrmacherkunst*, Wuppertal

d'Albis, J. and **Romanet, C.** 1980. *La Porcelaine de Limoges*, Paris

Altman, S. and **V.** 1969 and 1987. *The Book of Buffalo Pottery*, Westchester

Andreeva, L. 1975. *Soviet Porcelain 1920-1930*, Moscow

Anscombe, I. and **Gere, C.** *Arts & Crafts in Britain and America*, London

Arwas, V. 1987. *Glass, Art Nouveau to Art Deco*, London

Aslin, E. 1969. *The Aesthetic Movement*, London

Aslin, E. 1973. *French Exhibition Pieces 1844-78*, Victoria and Albert Museum, London

Atterbury, P. 1976. 'Minton Maiolica. The revival of sixteenth- and seventeenth-century earthenwares', *Connoisseur*, August, 305-8

Atterbury, P. ed. 1989. *The Parian Phenomenon*, Shepton Beauchamp

Atterbury, P. and **Batkin, M.** 1990. *The Dictionary of Minton*, Woodbridge

Baranova, O. 1983. *Kuskovo*, Leningrad

Barber, E. A. 1909. *The Pottery and Porcelain of the United States*, New York (reprinted 1976)

Barnett, R. D. and **Faulkner, M.** 1962. *The Sculptures of Assurnasirpal II, Tiglath-Pileser II, Esarhaddon, from the Central and South-West Palaces at Nimrud*, British Museum, London

Barrelet, J. 1953. *La verrerie en France de l'époque gallo-romaine à nos jours*, Paris

Bascou et al. 1988. **Bascou, M., Massé, M.-M., Thiébaut, P.,** *Catalogue sommaire illustré des arts décoratifs*, Musée d'Orsay, Paris

Batkin, M. 1982. *Wedgwood Ceramics 1846-1959*, London

Bauscher, Gebr. 1980. *100 Jahre Bauscher. 100 Jahre Hotelporzellan*, Porzellanfabrik Gebrüder Bauscher, Weiden

Bayer, H. et al. 1975. **H. Bayer, W. Gropius** and **I. Gropius** eds, *Bauhaus 1919-1928*. London (first published New York 1938, to accompany an exhibition held at the Museum of Modern Art)

Beaucamp-Markowsky, B. 1980. *Kataloge des Kunstgewerbemuseums Köln. Band VI. Porzellan*, Cologne

Bergerat, E. 1878. *Les Chefs-d'oeuvre d'art à l'exposition universelle 1878*, Paris

Berling, K. 1911. *Festschrift zur 200 jährigen Jubelfreier der ältesten europäischen Porzellanmanufaktur Meissen 1910*, Leipzig

Berning, M., Weisser, M. and **Zippelius, A.** 1984. *Steingutfabrik und Kunsttöpferei Franz Anton Mehlem in Bonn und Steingutfabrik Villeroy & Boch, Bonn*, Cologne

Bickerton, L. M. 1986. *Eighteenth Century English Drinking Glasses*, 2nd edn, Woodbridge

Billcliffe, R. and **Vergo, P.** 1977. 'Charles Rennie Mackintosh and the Austrian Art Revival', *Burlington Magazine* CXIX, November, 739-44

Blanchard, H. and **Thauré, M.** 1986. *La Collection de Sèvres du Musée des Beaux-Arts de Saintes 1890-1910*, Saintes

Bloch-Dermant, J. 1974. *L'Art du Verre en France 1860-1914*, Lausanne

Bloch-Dermant, J. 1983. *Le verre en France d'Émile Gallé à nos jours*, Osny

Bohdan, C. 1979. 'Arts and Crafts Copperware', *American Antiques*, March-April, 108-15

Bornfleth, E. 1985. *Glas, Gewerbemuseum Nürnberg*, Nuremberg

Borrmann, R. 1902. *Moderne Keramik*, Leipzig n.d. (1902)

Bouilhet, T. 1941. *L'orfèvrerie française au XXe siècle*, Paris

Bowman, L. Greene. 1990. *American Arts & Crafts: Virtue in Design. A catalogue of the Palersky/Evans Collection and Related Works at the Los Angeles County Museum of Art*, Los Angeles

Boyer, J. 1928. 'La Pâte de Verre hier et aujourd'hui', *La Nature*, 15 January, 62-4

Brandt, F. R. 1985. *Late 19th and Early 20th Century Decorative Arts. The Sydney and Frances Lewis Collection in the Virginia Museum of Fine Arts, Richmond*, Richmond

Bröhan, K. H. II/I, 1976. *Kunst der Jahrhundertwende und der zwanziger Jahre. Sammlung Karl H. Bröhan. Berlin. Band II. Kunsthandwerk. Jugendstil, Werkbund, Art Deco. Teil 1, Glas, Holz, Keramik*, Berlin

Bröhan, K. H. II/2, 1977. Ibid., *Teil 2, Metall, Porzellan*, Berlin

Bröhan, K. H. III, 1985. *Kunst der 20er und 30er Jahre. Sammlung Karl H. Bröhan. Berlin. Band III. Gemälde, Skulpturen, Kunsthandwerk, Industriedesign*, Berlin

Bröhan, K. H. ed. 1986. *Neuerwerbungen für das Bröhan-Museum Berlin*, Berlin

Bromhead, C. N. 1952. 'What was Murrhine?', *Antiquity* XXVI, June, 65-70

Burgers, C. 1972. 'De Nederlandsche tentoonstelling van decoratieve Kunst in het Museum van Kunstnijverheid te Kopenhagen', *Antiek*, 7 Jg, no.1, 9ff.

Burty, P. 1869. *Chefs d'oeuvre of the Industrial Arts*, London

Bury, S. 1966. 'The lengthening shadow of Rundells', *Connoisseur* 161, February, March, April, 79-84, 152-8, 218-22

Bury, S. 1971. *Victorian Electroplate*, London

Bury, S. 1977. 'New light on the Liberty metalwork venture', *Bulletin of the Decorative Arts Society 1890-1940*, no. 1, 14-27

Bury, S. 1982. *Jewellery Gallery Summary Catalogue*, Victoria and Albert Museum

Bush, D. J. 1975. *The Streamlined Decade*, New York

Campbell, L. 1986. 'A Model Patron: Bassett-Lowke, Mackintosh and Behrens', *Journal of the Decorative Arts Society* 10, 1-9

Carnegie Institute 1985. *Museum of Art, Carnegie Institute, Collection Handbook*, Pittsburgh

Carrington, J. B. and Hughes, G. R. 1926. *The Plate of the Worshipful Company of Goldsmiths*, Oxford

Chamot, M., Farr, D., and Butlin M. 1964. *The modern British paintings, drawings and sculptures*, 2 vols, London, Tate Gallery

Cheney, S. and M. C. 1936. *Art and the Machine: an Account of Industrial Design in 20th Century America*, New York

Collins, M. 1987. *Towards Post-Modernism: Design since 1851*, London

Cooke, F. 1986. *Twentieth Century Design: Glass*, London

Coysh, A. W. 1976. *British Art Pottery*, London

Crisp Jones, K. ed. 1981. *The Silversmiths of Birmingham and their Marks 1750-1980*, London

Cross, A. J. 1980. *Pilkington's Royal Lancastrian Pottery and Tiles*, London

Culme, J. 1977. *Nineteenth Century Silver*, London

Culme, J. 1987. *The Directory of Gold & Silversmiths, Jewellers and Allied Traders 1838-1914*, Woodbridge

Curjel, H. 1955. *Henry van de Velde: Zum neuen Stil, aus seinen Schriften ausgewählt und eingeleitet von Hans Curjel*, Munich

Dawson, A. 1984. *Masterpieces of Wedgwood in the British Museum*, London

Dawson, A. 1986. 'Pieces for Presentation', *Ceramics* 11, February/March, 71-6

Dawson, A. Forthcoming. *Catalogue of French Porcelain in the British Museum*, London

Deboni, F. 1990. *Venini Glas*, Basel

Dillon, E. 1907. *Glass*, London

Dowling, H. G. 1935. *A Survey of British Industrial Arts*, Benfleet

Drexler, A. and Daniel, G. 1959. *Introduction to Twentieth Century Design from the collection of the Museum of Modern Art, New York*, New York

Dry, G. 1989. 'Nietzsche-Verehrung. Jugendstil aus München und Nürnberg', *Antiquitäten-Zeitung* 22/1989, 654-5

Dry-v. Zezschwitz, B. 1981. *R. Merkelbach, Grenzhausen und München, Nachdruck der Specialpreisliste 1905* (Westerwälder Steinzeug des Jugendstils I), Munich

Dry-v. Zezschwitz, B. 1982. *Rosskopf & Gerz, Steinzeugfabrik, Höhr im Westerwald 1901-1914* (Westerwälder Steinzeug des Jugendstils IV, reprint of 1914 catalogue), Munich

Dry-v. Zezschwitz, B. 1989. 'Westerwälder Steinzeug des 19 Jahrhunderts', in *Historismus. Angewandte Kunst im 19 Jahrhundert. Band 2*, Staatliche Kunstsammlungen, Kassel, 285-304

Duncan, A. 1987. *American Art Deco*, New York

Eidelberg, M. 1975. 'American Ceramics and International Styles 1876-1916', *Aspects of the Arts and Crafts Movement in America*, Record of the Art Museum of Princeton University, 34, 13-19

Eidelberg, E. ed. 1987. *From our Native Clay: Art Pottery from the collections of the American Ceramic Arts Society*, New York (published in conjunction with an exhibition at Christie's, New York)

Evans, P. 1987. *Art Pottery of the United States*, New York

Falk, F. 1985. *Europäische Schmuck, Vom Historismus zum Jugendstil*, Schmuckmuseum Pforzheim, Königsbach-Stein

Fauster, C. U. 1979. *Libbey Glass since 1918*, Toledo

Field, S. and Bonney, S. R. 1925. *The Chemical Colouring of Metals*, London

Fishlock, D. 1962. *Metal Colouring*, Teddington

Franzke, I. 1975. 'Zum Dekorationsstil russisches Porzellan im ersten Jahrzehnt nach der Oktober-Revolution', *Jahrbuch der Staatlichen Kunstammlungen in Baden-Württemberg*, Band 12, 195-204

Franzke, I. 1977. 'Russisches Porzellan mit Suprematistischem Dekor im Badisches Landesmuseum Karlsruhe', *Keramos*, Heft 78, October, 23-30

Franzke, I. 1982. 'Die Suprematisten und russisches Porzellan der zwanziger Jahre', *Pantheon* 11, Jg. XL, 92-8

Franzke, I. 1987. *Jugendstil*, Badisches Landesmuseum, Karlsruhe, Bestandskatalog

Gelfer-Jørgensen, M. 1982. *Dansk Kunsthåndwerk fra 1850 til for tid*, Copenhagen

Gent, P. M. van. 1937. 'De Leerdamsche Glasindustrie' in *Leerdam door de eeuwen heen*, Leerdam

Gere, C. 1975. *European and American Jewellery 1830-1914*, London

Gere, C. et al. 1984. C. Gere, J. Rudoe, H. Tait and T. Wilson, *The Art of the Jeweller: A Catalogue of the Hull Grundy Gift to the British Museum*, 2 vols, London

Gerspach, E. 1899. *La Mosaïque*, Paris

Godden, G. 1961a. *Victorian Porcelain*, London

Godden, G. 1961b. 'Pilkington's Royal Lancastrian Pottery', *Apollo*, October, 97-9

Godden, G. 1964. *Encyclopaedia of British Pottery and Porcelain Marks*, London

Gollerbach, E. 1922. *La Porcelaine de la Manufacture d'État*, Moscow

Gollerbach, E. and Farmakovski, M. 1924. *La Porcelaine d'Art Russe*, Leningrad

Grassimuseum, 1980. *Museum des Kunsthandwerks. Kunsthandwerk im Grassimuseum von 1790-1930*, Leipzig

Gray, R. 1981. 'The Pilkington Tile & Pottery Company: Some Early Designs', *Transactions of the English Ceramic Circle* 11, Parts 1-3, 1981-3, 173-86

Greif, M. *Depression Modern: The Thirties Style in America*, New York

Grierson, J. 1930. 'The New Generation in Sculpture', *Apollo* XII, July-December, 347-51

Gropius, W. 1925. *Neue Arbeiten der Bauhauswerkstätten*, Passau (new edn ed. H. Wingler, Mainz and Berlin, 1981)

Gros-Galliner, G. 1977-80. '19th century foreign glass', *Bulletin de L'Association Internationale pour l'Histoire du Verre* 8, 153-65

Grzesiak, A. 1987. *Die Burg auf den Grassimessen*, Leipzig

Gunnis, R. n.d. (1964). *Dictionary of British Sculptors 1660-1851*, revised edn, London

Gysling-Billeter, E. 1975. *Objekte des Jugendstils aus der Sammlung des Kunstgewerbemuseums Zürich*, Bern

Haggar, R. 1966 and 1968. 'Thomas Allen', *Proceedings of the Wedgwood Society* 6, 61-8 and 'Thomas Allen - a further note', ibid. 7, 186-9

Halén, W. 1990. *Christopher Dresser*, Oxford

Harden, D. and **Loewenthal, A. I.** 1949. 'Vasa Murrina', *Journal of Roman Studies* XXXIX, 31-7

Harding, R. et. al. 1989. **R. Harding, S. Hornytzkyj** and **A. R. Date**, 'The composition of an opaque red glass used by Fabergé', *The Journal of Gemmology* 21, no. 5, January, 275-87

Hartlaub, G. F. 1931. *Das Ewige Handwerk im Kunstgewerbe der Gegenwart*, Berlin

Hartmann, J. B. 1979. *Antike Motive bei Thorwaldsen*, Tübingen

Hase, U. von. 1977. *Schmuck in Deutschland und Österreich 1895-1914*, Munich

Haslam, M. 1975. *English Art Pottery*, Woodbridge

Hauschild, J. 1987. 'Ferne Welten - Hohe Klassen: Verpackung des Jugendstils', *Weltkunst*, 57 Jg, no. 15, 1 August, 2038-41

Hawley, H. 1976. 'Tiffany's silver in the Japanese taste', *Bulletin of the Cleveland Museum of Art*, October, 236-52

Heller, C. B. 1982. *Kataloge des Hessischen Landesmuseums Nr.12. Jugendstil, Kunst um 1900*, Darmstadt

Heppe, K. B. 1988. *Die Düsseldorfer Goldschmiedekunst von 1596 bis 1918*, Düsseldorf

Heskett, J. 1986. *Design in Germany 1870-1918*, London

Hilschenz, H. 1973. *Das Glas des Jugendstils: Katalog der Sammlung Hentrich im Kunstmuseum Düsseldorf*, Munich

Hilschenz-Mlynek, H. and **Ricke, H.** 1985. *Glas. Historismus, Jugendstil, Art Deco. Band 1, Frankreich. Die Sammlung Hentrich im Kunstmuseum Düsseldorf*, Munich

Hirzel, S. 1953. *Kunsthandwerk und Manufaktur in Deutschland seit 1945*, Berlin

Holzhausen, W. 1927. 'Neue Fassungen von Slutzky', *Das Kunstblatt*, 11 Jg, 436-9

Hughes, G. 1967. *Modern Silver throughout the world 1880-1967*, London

Jackson, B. H. ed. 1950. *Recollections of Thomas Graham Jackson 1835-1924*, London

Janda, A. 1959. 'Bauhaus Keramik', *Kunstmuseen der DDR: Mitteilungen und Berichte*, Band II, Leipzig, 83ff.

Jarchow, M. 1984. *Die Staatliche Porzellanmanufaktur Berlin (KPM) 1918-1938*, PhD dissertation, Hamburg

Jarchow, M. 1988. *Berliner Porzellan im 20.Jahrhundert*, Berlin

Jedding, H. 1981. *Meissener Porzellan des 19.und 20.Jahrhunderts*, Munich

Jervis, S. 1983. *High Victorian Design*, Woodbridge

Jervis, S. 1984. *The Penguin Dictionary of Design and Designers*, London

Jewitt, L. 1883. *The Ceramic Art of Great Britain*, 2nd edn (reprinted Poole 1985)

Jones, J. 1989. 'Designers and the Minton China Works', *The Antique Collector*, June, 155-60

Joppien, R. 1984. 'Die Hannoversche Keksfabrik Hermann Bahlsen auf der Werkbund-Ausstellung', *Der Westdeutsche Impuls 1900-1914. Kunst und Umweltgestaltung im Industriegebiet: Die Deutsche Werkbund-Ausstellung Cöln*, exhibition catalogue, Kölnische Kunstverein, 216-26

Just, J. 1983. *Meissener Jugendstil Porzellan*, Leipzig

Kallir, J. 1986. *Viennese Design and the Wiener Werkstätte*, London

Kamerling, B. 1987. 'Anna and Albert Valentien: The Arts & Crafts Movement in San Diego', *Arts & Crafts Quarterly* I, issue 14, July

Karmason, M. G. and **Stacke, J. B.** 1989. *Majolica*, New York

Katz, S. 1978. *Plastics, Design and Materials*, London

Killinger, T. 1986. *Die Entwicklung der Glashüttenindustrie zwischen Arber und Rachel von den Anfängen bis heute*, Frauenau (typescript publication by author)

Klein, D. and **Lloyd, W.** 1984. *The History of Glass*, London

Kley-Blekxtoon, A van der. 1984. *Leerdam Glas 1878-1930*, Lochem

Klinge, E. 1975 and 1978. *Kataloge des Hetjens-Museums Düsseldorf. Deutsche Keramik des 20.Jahrhunderts*, I (A-K) and II (L-Z), Düsseldorf

Koch, A. 1902. *Ein Dokument Deutscher Kunst 1901. Grossherzog Ernst Ludwig und die Ausstellung der Künstler-Kolonie in Darmstadt von Mai bis Oktober 1901*, Darmstadt (reprinted Stuttgart 1989 as *Die Ausstellung der Darmstädter Künstlerkolonie*)

Koch, G. L. ed. 1978. *Chase Chrome*, Stamford, Connecticut (reprint of Chase catalogue for 1936-7)

Koehler, V. A. 1987. *American Art Pottery*, Cooper-Hewitt Museum, New York (Goodman Collection)

Köllmann, E. and **Jarchow, M.** 1987. *Berliner Porzellan 1763-1963*, 2 vols, Munich

Kovel, R. and **T.** 1974. *The Kovels' Collector's Guide to American Art Pottery*, New York

Krekel-Aalberse, A. 1989. *Art Nouveau & Art Deco Silver*, London

Lamm, C. J. 1929-30. *Mittelalterliche Gläser und Steinschnittarbeiten aus dem nahen Osten*, 2 vols, Berlin

Lansere, A. K. 1974. *Soviet Porcelain. The Artistry of the Lomonossov Porcelain Factory*, Leningrad

Lehmann, E. 1931. 'Gerät und Schmuck von Naum Slutzky', *Der Kreis* VII, 4 Jg, December, 713-14

Leidelmeijer, F. and **Van der Cingel, D.** 1983. *Art nouveau en art deco in Nederland*, Amsterdam

Leistikow-Duchardt, A. 1957. *Die Entwicklung eines neuen Stiles im Porzellan. Eine Betrachtung über die neuzeitliche Porzellankunst in Europa seit 1860*, Heidelberg

Léon, P. 1927. *Exposition Internationale des Arts Décoratifs et Industriels Modernes, 1925. Rapport Général. v. Accessoires du Mobilier*, Paris

Lethaby, W. R. 1932. *P. Webb and his Work*, London

Lianda, N. 1980. 'Sergei Chekhonin and the New Soviet Porcelain', *Soviet Union/Union Soviétique* 7, Parts 1-2, 157-69

Liberty, A. Lasenby. 1904. 'Pewter and the Revival of its use', *Journal of the Society of Arts* 52, 626-40

Lobanov-Rostovsky, N. 1990. *Revolutionary Ceramics: Soviet Porcelain 1919-1927*, New York

Löffelhardt, H. 1949. *Wie Wohnen. Hausrat aus Keramik, Glas, Holz*, Stuttgart

Lueg, G. 1989. *Design im 20. Jahrhundert*, Museum für Angewandte Kunst, Cologne

Lukomski, G. 1924. *Russisches Porzellan 1744-1923*, Berlin

Lunacharsky, A. V. et al. 1927. *Sovietski Farfor*, Moscow

Lüthgen, G. E. 1909. *Deutsches Steinzeug, behandelt im Anschluss an den Wettbewerb für Studentenkunst Stuttgart 1909*, reprinted Munich 1981 (Westerwälder Steinzeug des Jugendstils III, with introduction by B. Dry-v. Zezschwitz)

Makus, H. 1987. 'Jugendstil in Polen: das Masowische Museum in Plock', *Weltkunst*, Jg 15, no. 15, 1 August, 2034-7

Maryon, H. 1954. *Metalwork and Enamelling*, London

McCarthy, F. 1981. *The Simple Life. C. R. Ashbee in the Cotswolds*, London

McGrain, P. ed. 1982. *Fostoria, the Popular Years*, Frederick, Maryland

Meikle, J. L. 1979. *Twentieth Century Limited: Industrial Design in America 1925-1939*, Philadelphia

Moeller, G. 1984. 'Peter Behrens und die Düsseldorfer Kunstgewerbeschule 1903-1907', *Der westdeutsche Impuls 1900-1914. Düsseldorf. Eine Grossstadt auf dem Weg in die Moderne*, exhibition catalogue, Kunstmuseum Düsseldorf, 33-52

Møller, J. E. R. 1985. *Georg Jensen, The Danish Silversmith*, Copenhagen

Mordaunt Crook, J. 1972. *The British Museum, a case-study in architectural politics*, London

Morris, B. 1978. *Victorian Table Glass and Ornaments*, London

Morris, B. 1989. *Liberty Design 1874-1914*, London

Morris, B. 1989a. 'Aesthetic and Arts and Crafts Glass', *The Decorative Arts in the Victorian Period*, Occasional Paper (New Series) XII, The Society of Antiquaries, London, ed. S. M. Wright

Mosel, C. 1971. *Bilderkataloge des Kestner-Museums Hannover, XI. Kunsthandwerk im Umbruch, Jugendstil und zwanziger Jahre*, Hanover

Mundt, B. 1973/1983. *Historismus: Kunsthandwerk und Industrie im Zeitalter der Weltausstellungen, Kataloge des Kunstgewerbemuseums Berlin*, Band VII, Berlin

Mundt, B. 1981. *Historismus: Kunstgewerbe zwischen Biedermeier und Jugendstil*, Berlin

Muthesius, H. 1905. *Das Englische Haus*, London

Nachtlicht, L. 1904. *Deutsches Kunstgewerbe, St. Louis 1904*, Berlin

Nauhaus, W. 1981. *Die Burg Giebichenstein*, Leipzig

Naylor, G. 1971. *The Arts & Crafts Movement*, London

Naylor, G. 1985. *The Bauhaus Reassessed*, London

Nesbitt, A. 1871. *Catalogue of the Collection of Glass formed by Felix Slade Esq., F.S.A.*, London

Neuwirth, W. 1973. *Das Glas des Jugendstils. Sammlung des Österreichisches Museums für angewandte Kunst, Wien*, Munich

Neuwirth, W. 1974a. *Wiener Keramik*, Vienna

Neuwirth, W. 1974b. *Österreichische Keramik des Jugendstils: Sammlung des Österreichischen Museum für angewandte Kunst*, Vienna

Neuwirth, W. 1976/7. *Lexikon der Wiener Gold- und Silberschmiede*, Vienna

Neuwirth, W. 1984. *Wiener Werkstätte - Avantgarde, Art Deco, Industrial Design*, Vienna

Neuwirth, W. 1985. *Die Schutzmarken der Wiener Werkstätte, Band 1: Rosenmarke und Wortmarke*, Vienna

Nichols, G. Ward. 1878. *Pottery: How it is made, its Shape and Decoration*, New York

Nikiforova, L. 1973. *Russian Porcelain in the Hermitage Collection*, Leningrad

Parry, L. 1988. *Textiles of the Arts & Crafts Movement*, London

Passarge, W. 1937. *Deutsche Werkkunst der Gegenwart*, 2nd edn, Berlin (1st edn 1936)

Pazaurek, G. E. n.d. (1901). *Moderne Gläser*, Leipzig

Pazaurek, G. E. 1925. *Kunstgläser der Gegenwart*, Leipzig

Pazaurek, G. E. and Spiegl, W. 1983. *Glas des 20. Jahrhunderts*, Munich (an amalgamation of Pazaurek's publications of 1901 and 1925, with a mixture of original and recent illustrations)

Pelka, O. 1924. *Keramik der Neuzeit*, Leipzig

Pelka, O. 1925. *Deutsche Keramik 1900-1925*, Reutlingen (reprinted Munich 1984)

Perry, Mrs A. F. 1881. 'Decorative Pottery of Cincinnati', *Harper's New Monthly Magazine* 62, May, 834-45

Pese, C. 1980. 'Das Nürnberger Kunsthandwerk des Jugendstils', *Peter Behrens und Nürnberg*, exhibition catalogue, Germanisches Nationalmuseum, Nuremberg, 169-72

Petochi, D. et al. 1981. D. Petochi, M. Alfieri and M. G. Branchetti, *I Mosaici Minuti Romani dei Secoli XVIII e XIX*, Rome

Pevsner, N. 1940. 'C. F. A. Voysey', *Elseviers Maandschrift*, May (reprinted in Pevsner 1968)

Pevsner, N. 1950. *Ch. R. Mackintosh*, Milan (one of series entitled *Architetti del Movimento Moderno*, reprinted in Pevsner 1968)

Pevsner, N. 1968. *Studies in Art, Architecture and Design*, London (includes reprints of Pevsner's articles on Voysey and Mackintosh of 1940 and 1950)

Pfleiderer, W. 1924. *Die Form ohne Ornament*, Stuttgart

Pica, V. 1902-3. *L'arte decorativa all'Esposizione di Torino*, Bergamo

Polak, A. 1962. *Modern Glass*, London

Polak, A. 1967. 'Background to Gallé', *Annales du 4ᵉ Congrès International d'Étude Historique du Verre, Ravenne-Venise, 13-20 mai 1967*, Association Internationale pour L'Histoire du Verre, Liège, 206-13

Quenioux, G. 1925. *Les Arts Décoratifs Modernes*, Paris

Rago, D. 1987. 'Good-Better-Best', *Arts & Crafts Quarterly* 1, issue 2, January, 6-7

Rainwater, D. T. 1975. *Encyclopaedia of American Silver Manufacturers*, New York

Reade, J. 1983. *Assyrian Sculpture*, British Museum, London

Reineking von Bock, G. 1979. *Keramik des 20. Jahrhunderts in Deutschland*, Munich

Revi, A. C. 1967. *Nineteenth Century Glass*, New York

Rochowanski, L. W. 1923. *Wiener Keramik*, Vienna

Rockwell, D. 1983. 'The Artistry of Thomas Allen', *Proceedings of the 28th Annual Wedgwood Seminar, held at the Museum of Fine Arts, St. Petersburg, Florida, March 21-26, 1983*, 137-51

Rückert, R. 1982. *Die Glassammlung des Bayerischen Nationalmuseums München*, 2 vols, Munich

Rudoe, J. 1987. 'Lady Layard's jewellery and the Assyrian style in nineteenth century jewellery design', *Austen Henry Layard tra l'Oriente e Venezia*, International Symposium in Venice,

1983, papers edited by F. M. Fales and B. Hickey, Rome, 213-26

Rudoe, J. 1989. 'Assyrian-style jewellery: a forgotten chapter in the history of Backes & Strauss, London', *The Antique Collector*, April, 42-8

Rudoe, J. 1990. 'Aspects of design reform in the German ceramic industry around 1900, as illustrated by the British Museum collection', *Journal of the Decorative Arts Society* 14, 24-33

Rutherford, J. and Beddoe, S. 1986. *Art Nouveau, Art Deco, The Twenties, The Thirties and Post-war Design. The Ceramic, Glass and Metalwork Collections at Brighton Museum*, Brighton

Safford, F. Gruber and Caccavale, R. Wilford. 1987. 'Japanesque silver by Tiffany and Company in the Metropolitan Museum of Art', *Antiques*, October, 808-19

Sala, G. 1880. *Paris Herself Again in 1878-9*, 2 vols, London

Sänger, R. 1984. 'Massenfabrikation in Silber - Bemerkungen zur Tafelgeräte- und Besteckindustrie im rheinisch-westfälischen Raum', *Der westdeutsche Impuls 1900-1914. Die Margarethenhöhe. Das Schöne und die Ware*, exhibition catalogue, Museum Folkwang, Essen

Sauzay, A. 1868. *La Verrerie*, Paris

Schack von Wittenau, C. 1971. *Glas zwischen Kunsthandwerk und Industrie-Design*, PhD thesis, Cologne

Schaeffer, H. 1962. 'Tiffany's fame in Europe', *The Art Bulletin* 44, December, 309-28

Scheffler, W. 1966. *Kataloge des Kunstgewerbemuseums Berlin, Band II, Werke um 1900*, Berlin

Scheidig, W. 1967. *Crafts of the Weimar Bauhaus*, London (first published in German as *Bauhaus Weimar 1919-1924. Werkstattarbeiten*, Leipzig and Munich)

Scherf, W. 1980. *Thüringer Porzellan*, Leipzig

Schmidt, P. 1975. 'Die Zeit des Zeitlosen: Zu einigen Entstehungsbedingungen moderner Gebrauchsformen, dargestellt am Beispiel "Arzberg 1382" von Hermann Gretsch', *Jahrbuch der Staatlichen Kunstsammlungen in Baden-Württemberg*, Band 12, 213-24

Schmitt, E. 1989. *Glas - Kunst - Handwerk 1870-1945. Glassammlung Silzer* (Leihgabe der Deutschen Bank im Augustinermuseum Freiburg im Breisgau), Freiburg

Schmoranz, G. 1899. *Altorientalische Glas-Gefässe*, Vienna and London

Schou-Christensen, J. 1969. 'Glaskunst omkring år 1900', *Kunstindustrimuseets Virksomhed*, Copenhagen, 161-82

Schweiger, W. 1982. *Wiener Werkstätte. Kunst und Handwerk 1903-1922*, Vienna (English edn, New York 1984)

Sekler, E. 1968. 'Mackintosh and Vienna', *Architectural Review* 144, 455-6

Seyfert, I. 1988. *Die Glashütte der Bayerischen Waldes*, Regen

Shelley, L. D. 1937. *Modern Fine Glass*, New York

Shin, C. and D. 1971. *The Illustrated Guide to Victorian Parian China*, London

Snowman, A. K. 1979. *Carl Fabergé*, London

Solodkoff, A. von. 1981. *Russian Silver*, Fribourg

Sparrow, W. Shaw. 1904. *The British Home of Today*, London

Sparrow, W. Shaw. 1909. *Hints on House Furnishing*, London

Spielmann, H. 1977. *Räume und Meisterwerke der Jugendstil-Sammlung*, Museum für Kunst und Gewerbe, Hamburg

Spielmann, H. et al. 1979. *Kataloge des Museums für Kunst und Gewerbe Hamburg. v. Die Jugendstil-Sammlung. Band I: Künstler A-F*, Hamburg

Spillman, J. Shadel. 1989. *White House Glassware: Two Centuries of Presidential Entertaining*, White House Historical Association, Washington

Tait, H. 1985. 'Exciting *Pâte-sur-Pâte* Find in the British Museum', *Ars Ceramica* No. 2, 16-17

Taylor, D. 1987. 'Keith Murray' in R. Dodsworth ed., *British Glass between the wars*, exhibition catalogue, Broadfield House Glass Museum, Kingswinford

Thiersch, H. 1953. *Wir fingen einfach an. Richard Riemerschmid zum 85. Geburtstag*, Munich

Thorpe, W. A. 1929. *A History of English and Irish Glass*, London

Thorpe, W. A. 1935. *English Glass*, London

Towndrow, K. R. *Alfred Stevens, architectural sculptor, painter and designer. A biography with new material*, London

Ulmer, R. 1990. *Museum der Künstlerkolonie, Darmstadt. Katalog*, Darmstadt n.d. (1990)

Vainker, S. J. 1991. *Chinese Pottery and Porcelain from Prehistory to the Present*, British Museum, London

Victoria and Albert Museum 1983. *British Art & Design 1900-1960*, London

Victoria and Albert Museum 1987. *Art & Design in Europe and America 1800-1900*, London

Volpe, T. and Cathers, B. 1988. *Treasures of the American Arts & Crafts Movement 1890-1920*, London

Wakefield, H. et al. 1961-2. H. Wakefield, E. Aslin, B. Morris and S. Bury, 'British Decorative Arts of the late Nineteenth Century in the Nordenfjeldske Kunstindustrimuseum', *Nordenfjeldske Kunstindustrimuseum Årbok*, Trondheim, 37-106

Wakefield, H. 1982. *Nineteenth Century British Glass*, London

Walcha, O. 1981. *Meissen Porcelain*, London (first published Dresden 1973)

Waring, J. B. 1862. *Masterpieces of Industrial Art and Sculpture at the International Exhibition of 1862*, 3 vols, London

Wasch, K. 1924 and 1927. *Glas en Kristal*, Rotterdam

Weatherman, H. M. 1972. *Fostoria: Its First Fifty Years*, Springfield

Weber, O. 1977. 'Das Gewerbemuseum in Darmstadt' in G. Bott ed., *Von Morris zum Bauhaus*, Hanau, 185-216

Weisberg, G. P. 1978. 'Gérard, Dufraissex & Abbot: The Manufactory of Art Nouveau Bing Porcelains in Limoges, France', *Connoisseur* 197, February, 125-9

Weisberg, G. P. 1986. *Art Nouveau Bing: Paris Style 1900*, New York

Wendl, M. 1984. *Altes Thüringer Porzellan*, Rudolstadt

Wichmann, H. 1985. *Industrial Design, Unikate, Serienerzeugnisse. Die Neue Sammlung. Ein neuer Museumstyp des 20. Jahrhunderts*, Munich

Wichmann, H. 1986. *Neu Donationen und Neu-Erwerbungen 1982/3, Die Neue Sammlung*, Munich

Wichmann, H. 1988. *Neu Donationen und Neu-Erwerbungen 1984/5, Die Neue Sammlung*, Munich

Wichmann, H. 1989. *Neu Donationen und Neu-Erwerbungen 1986/7, Die Neue Sammlung*, Munich

Wichmann, S. 1981. *Japonisme: The Japanese influence on Western Art since 1858*, London

Williams-Thomas, R. S. 1983. *The Crystal Years: Stevens & Williams Ltd*, Brierley Hill

Wilson, Canon J. M. 1914. 'Was the Effigy of King John in

Worcester Cathedral originally coloured, or gilt?', *Associated Architectural Societies Reports* XXXII, Part II, 485-98

Wingler, H. M. 1969. *The Bauhaus*, Cambridge, Mass. (first published in German, Cologne 1962)

Wingler, H. M. 1978. As above, paperback edn

Wingler, H. M. 1981. *Bauhaus-Archiv Museum für Gestaltung: Sammlungs-Katalog*, Berlin

Zapata, J. 1989. 'Tiffany Ladles for Every Course', *Silver*, January-February, 14-21

Zhadova, L. A. 1982. *Malevich*, London.

Exhibition Catalogues

Amsterdam 1985. Stedelijk Museum. *Industry and Design in the Netherlands 1850-1950*

Berlin 1972. Kunstgewerbemuseum. *20er Jahre Neuerwerbungen*, B. Mundt

Berlin 1977. Neuern National Galerie, Akademie der Künste and Grossen Orangerie des Schlosses Charlottenburg. *Tendenzen der Zwanziger Jahre*

Berlin 1978. International Design Zentrum. *Industriekultur, Peter Behrens und die AEG 1907-1914*, T. Buddensieg et al.

Berlin 1989. Bauhaus-Archiv Museum. *Keramik und Bauhaus*

Berlin 1989a. Berlin Museum. *Curt Hermann 1854-1929. Ein Maler der Moderne in Berlin*

Birmingham 1973. City Museum and Art Gallery. *Birmingham Gold and Silver 1773-1973*

Birmingham 1984. City Museum and Art Gallery. *By Hammer and by Hand. The Arts & Crafts Movement in Birmingham*, ed. A. Crawford

Bonn 1987. Rheinisches Landesmuseum. *Westerwälder Steinzeug: Die Neue Ära 1900-1930, Jugendstil und Werkbund*, J. Erlebach and J. Schimanski, published Düsseldorf

Bonn 1988. Kunsthistorisches Institut der Universität Bonn. *Wilhelm Wagenfeld. Kunst im Gebrauch*

Boston 1987a. Museum of Fine Arts. *The Art that is Life: The Arts & Crafts Movement in America 1875-1920*, ed. W. Kaplan

Boston 1987b. Museum of Fine Arts. *The Silver of Tiffany & Co. 1850-1987*, C. H. Carpenter Jr. and J. Zapata

Bremen 1981. Bremer Landesmuseum (Focke Museum). *Bremer Silber von den Anfängen bis zum Jugendstil*, A. Löhr

Brooklyn 1986. The Brooklyn Museum. *The Machine Age in America*

Brussels 1977. Palais des Beaux-Arts. *Jugendstil*

Brussels 1988. Musées Royaux des Beaux-Arts. *Bauhaus 1919-1933. Le Bauhaus dans les collections de la République Démocratique Allemande*

Cheltenham 1988. Cheltenham Art Gallery and Museum. *The Guild of Handicraft 1888-1988*, A. Carruthers and F. Johnson

Cologne 1974. Kunstgewerbemuseum. *Französische Keramik zwischen 1850 und 1910* (Sammlung Maria und Hans-Jörgen Heuser, Hamburg), Munich

Cologne 1976. Kunstgewerbemuseum. *Sammlung Giorgio Silzer. Kunsthandwerk vom Jugendstil bis zum Art Deco*

Cologne 1978. Kunstgewerbemuseum. *Meister der deutschen Keramik 1900-1950*, G. Reineking von Bock

Cologne 1984. Kölnischer Kunstverein. *Der westdeutsche Impuls 1900-1914. Kunst und Umweltgestaltung im Industriegebiet: Die Deutsche Werkbund-Ausstellung Cöln*

Copenhagen 1954. Kunstindustrimuseet. *Rörstrand*

Corning 1987. Corning Museum of Glass. *Glass of the Caesars*, Milan

Darmstadt 1901. Künstlerkolonie. *Hauptkatalog. Die Ausstellung der Künstlerkolonie, Darmstadt 1901*, ed. J. Olbrich

Darmstadt 1904. Künstlerkolonie. *Ausstellung der Künstlerkolonie*

Darmstadt 1962. Hessisches Landesmuseum. *Jugendstil. Sammlung K. A. Citroen, Amsterdam*

Darmstadt 1976. Kunsthalle. *Ein Dokument Deutscher Kunst 1901-1976*, 5 vols, Darmstadt

Dresden 1987. Museum für Kunsthandwerk Schloss Pillnitz. *Lausitzer Glas. Geschichte und Gegenwart*, G. Haase (organised by the VEB Kombinat Lausitzer Glas Weisswasser and the Staatlichen Kunstsammlungen Dresden)

Dresden 1989. Porzellansammlung Dresden. *Meissener Blaumalerei aus drei Jahrhunderten*, ed. K.-P. Arnold and V. Diefenbach, Leipzig (exhibition also held in Hamburg, Museum für Kunst und Gewerbe)

Düsseldorf 1970. Hetjens-Museum. *Fürstenberg Porzellan, Tradition und Gegenwart*

Düsseldorf 1974. Hetjens-Museum. *Europäische Keramik des Jugendstils, Art Nouveau, Modern Style*, B. Hakenjos and E. Klinge

Düsseldorf 1978. Kunstmuseum. *Ilja Tschashnik*

Düsseldorf 1984. Kunstmuseum. *Der westdeutsche Impuls 1900-1914. Kunst und Umweltgestaltung im Industriegebiet. Düsseldorf. Eine Grossstadt auf dem Weg in die Moderne*

Edinburgh 1983. Royal Museum of Scotland. *Vienna 1900. Vienna, Scotland and the European avant-garde*

Essen 1984. Museum Folkwang. *Der westdeutsche Impuls 1900-1914. Kunst und Umweltgestaltung im Industriegebiet. Die Margarethenhöhe. Das Schöne und die Ware*

Flensburg 1972. Museum Flensburg. *Stilwende um 1900*

Glasgow 1984. Art Gallery & Museum, Kelvingrove. *The Glasgow Style 1890-1920*

Hagen 1984. Karl Ernst Osthaus Museum. *Der westdeutsche Impuls 1900-1914. Kunst und Umweltgestaltung im Industriegebiet. Die Folkwang-Idee des Karl Ernst Osthaus*

Hamburg 1977. Museum für Kunst und Gewerbe. *Hohe Kunst zwischen Biedermeier und Jugendstil: Historismus in Hamburg und Norddeutschland*, H. Jedding et al.

Hamburg 1989. See Dresden 1989

Hamilton, New York 1983. Gallery Association of New York. *Arts & Crafts in New York State*, C. L. Ludwig

Hanover 1982. Kestner Museum. *Rosenthal: Hundert Jahre Porzellan*

Hohenberg 1989. Museum der Deutschen Porzellanindustrie. *175 Jahre Hutschenreuther. Ein Beitrag zum Firmenjubiläum 1814-1989*, ed. W. Siemen

Höhr-Grenzhausen 1986. Keramikmuseum Westerwald. *Reinhold und August Hanke, Westerwälder Steinzeug, Historismus–Jugendstil*. H. Reinhold et al.

Houston 1976. Institute for the Arts, Rice University. *Art Nouveau Belgium France*, Y. Brunhammer et al.

Karlsruhe 1979. Badisches Landesmuseum. *Karlsruher Majolika*

Kassel 1968. Staatliche Kunstsammlungen. *Jugendstilsammlung Dr. Gerhard P. Woeckel München*, G. P. Woeckel

Kingswinford 1987. Broadfield House Glass Museum. *British Glass between the wars*, ed. R. Dodsworth

Kommern 1980. Museum für Volkskunde. *Porzellan- und*

Steingutfabrik Wessel, Bonn-Poppelsdorf, Katalog 2 zur Ausstellung Volkskunst im Wandel, M. Weisser

Leeuwarden 1986. Museum het Princessehof. *Amstelhoek 1897-1910,* J. D. van Dam and A. Hidding

Leipzig 1928. Grassimuseum. *Europäisches Kunstgewerbe. Bericht über die Ausstellung Europäisches Kunstgewerbe 1927*

Leipzig 1989. Museum des Kunsthandwerks, Grassimuseum. *Die Glassammlung des Kunstmuseums Düsseldorf. Eine Auswahl,* H. Ricke, Düsseldorf

London 1952. Victoria and Albert Museum. *Victorian & Edwardian Decorative Arts*

London 1959. Victoria and Albert Museum. *Three Centuries of Swedish Pottery*

London 1965. Goldsmiths' Hall. *The Worshipful Company of Goldsmiths as Patrons of their Craft 1919-53*

London 1968. British Museum. *Masterpieces of Glass,* ed. H. Tait

London 1968. Royal Academy. *50 Years Bauhaus* (see Stuttgart 1968)

London 1971. Victoria and Albert Museum. *Victorian Church Art*

London 1972. Royal Academy. *Victorian and Edwardian Decorative Art. The Handley-Read Collection*

London 1975. Victoria and Albert Museum. *Liberty's 1875-1975*

London 1976a. Hayward Gallery. *The Arts of Islam*

London 1976b. Victoria and Albert Museum. *Minton 1798-1910,* E. Aslin and P. Atterbury

London 1979. Hayward Gallery. *Thirties. British art and design before the war*

London 1981. The Fine Art Society. *Architect-Designers, Pugin to Mackintosh*

London 1983. Liberty & Company. *Liberty Style,* V. Arwas

London 1985. Fischer Fine Art. *Frank Lloyd Wright: Architectural Drawings and Decorative Art*

London 1986. Fischer Fine Art. *Truth, Beauty and Design. Victorian, Edwardian and Later Decorative Art*

London 1989a. The Fine Art Society. *Spring 1989*

London 1989b. Victoria and Albert Museum. *Scandinavia. Ceramics and Glass in the Twentieth Century,* J. Hawkins Opie

London 1990. The Fine Art Society. *Christopher Dresser 1834-1904*

Manchester 1982. City Art Gallery. *A catalogue of the Lancastrian Pottery at Manchester City Art Galleries,* R. Gray and D. Clarke

Manchester 1986. Whitworth Art Gallery. *Reflections of Venice: The Influence of Venetian Glass in Victorian England 1840-1900*

Miami 1988. The Wolfsonian Foundation. *Stile Floreale: The Cult of Nature in Italian Design,* G. Weisberg

Minneapolis 1971. The Minneapolis Institute of Arts. *The World of Art Deco,* B. Hillier

Moscow 1962. State Ceramic Museum, Kuskovo. *Soviet Artistic Porcelain 1918-1923,* ed. B. I. Alekseev

Munich 1958. Die neue Sammlung. *Geformtes Glas aus Vergangenheit und Gegenwart*

Munich 1972. Haus der Kunst. *Weltkulturen und moderne Kunst,* ed. S. Wichmann

Munich 1979. Museum Villa Stuck. *Silber des Jugendstils*

Munich 1986. Kunsthalle. *Fabergé, Hofjuwelier der Zaren,* G. von Habsburg

Newhaven 1983. Yale University Art Gallery. *At Home in Manhattan. Modern Decorative Arts, 1925 to the Depression,* K. Davies

New York 1978. Cooper-Hewitt Museum. *Vienna Moderne 1898-1918* (organised by the Sarah Campbell Blaffer Gallery, Houston), New York

New York 1985. Whitney Museum of American Art. *High Styles: Twentieth Century American Design*

New York 1986. The Metropolitan Museum of Art. *In Pursuit of Beauty. Americans and the Aesthetic Movement*

New York 1987. American Ceramic Arts Society. *From our Native Clay: Art Pottery from the collections of the American Ceramic Society,* ed. M. Eidelberg

Nuremberg 1980. Germanisches Nationalmuseum. *Peter Behrens und Nürnberg,* ed. P. Schuster

Oxford and **London** 1984. Museum of Modern Art, Oxford and Crafts Council, London. *Art into Production: Soviet Ceramics and Textiles*

Paris 1966. Musée des Arts Décoratifs. *Les Années 25, Art Deco/Bauhaus/Stijl/Esprit Nouveau*

Paris 1976. Musée des Arts Décoratifs. *Cinquantenaire de l'exposition de 1925,* Y. Brunhammer et al.

Paris 1988. Grand Palais. *Le Japonisme,* Réunion des Musées Nationaux

Pforzheim 1990. Schmuckmuseum. *Theodor Fahrner, Schmuck zwischen Avantgarde und Tradition. Jugendstil. Art Deco. Fünfziger Jahre,* U. von Hase-Schmundt, C. Weber and I. Becker

Philadelphia 1978. Philadelphia Museum of Art. *The Second Empire: Art in France under Napoleon III*

Philadelphia 1988. Philadelphia Museum of Art. *Art Nouveau in Munich,* published Philadelphia and Munich, ed. K. Hiesinger

Princeton 1972. Art Museum, Princeton University. *The Arts & Crafts Movement in America,* ed. R. J. Clark

Rudolstadt 1983. Staatliche Museen Heidecksburg. *Schwarzburger Werkstätten für Porzellankunst Unterweissbach und Rudolstadt-Volkstedt 1909-1949*

Solingen 1979. Deutsches Klingenmuseum. *Bestecke des Jugendstils,* R. Sänger, Cologne

Stuttgart 1924. Deutsche Werkbund. *Die Form ohne Ornament,* ed. W. Pfleiderer

Stuttgart 1968. Württembergischer Kunstverein. *50 Jahre Bauhaus* (reissued in an abridged form as *Bauhaus* by the Institut für Auslandsbeziehungen, Stuttgart, 1975)

Stuttgart 1975. See above

Syracuse 1989. Everson Museum of Art. *Fragile Blossoms, Enduring Earth. The Japanese influence on American Ceramics,* B. Stone Perry

Utrecht 1976. Nederlands Goud-, Zilver- en Klokkenmuseum. *Klokken, zilver, sieraden uit de Nederlandse Art Nouveau en Art Deco*

Venice 1982. Palazzo Ducale Museo Correr. *Mille anni di arte del vetro a Venezia,* ed. R. Barovier Mentasti et al.

Venice & Biella 1988. (Location not given) *La Rivoluzione in salotto, Porcellane Sovietiche 1917-1930,* published Milan

Vicenza 1982. Museo Civico di Palazzo Chierati. *Antonio Salviati e la rinascimenta ottocentesca del vetro artistico veneziano,* R. Barovier Mentasti

Vienna 1973. Österreichisches Museum für angewandte Kunst. *150 Jahre Lobmeyr, 1823-1973*

Vienna 1982. Österreichisches Museum für angewandte Kunst. *Meissener Porzellan von 1710 bis zur Gegenwart*

Vienna 1985. Historisches Museum. *Traum und Wirklichkeit, Wien um 1870-1930*

Vienna 1988. Österreichisches Museum für angewandte Kunst. *Kunst und Revolution. Russische und Sowjetische Kunst 1910-1932*

Zons 1978. Kreismuseum. *Zinn des Jugendstils*, Schriften des Rheinischen Museumamtes 8

List of Periodicals

The following contemporary periodicals were found to be of particular use in the preparation of this catalogue and are cited frequently in the text. Some of them are extremely rare and so the libraries in which they were consulted are also given. Otherwise, complete or partial runs are available in the Victoria and Albert Museum Library or the British Library. The dates given are those available in the above libraries; no periodical research has been undertaken. For availability in other UK libraries, see *British Union - Catalogue of Periodicals*, 4 vols, London 1955.

Abbreviation of sources

V & A: Victoria and Albert Museum Library

BL: British Library

BAD: Bibliothèque des Arts Décoratifs, Paris

MMA: Metropolitan Museum of Art, New York

The Architectural Review. London. BL, V & A: 1896ff.

L'Art Décoratif, Paris. V & A: 1900-13

L'Art Décoratif pour tous, Paris. BAD: 1902-4

Art et Décoration, Paris. BL: 1897-1938, 1939ff.; V & A: 1897-1939, 1946ff.

The Art Journal, London. BL, V & A: 1849-1912

L'Art Vivant, Paris. BL: 1925ff.; V & A: 1925-39

Arts and Decoration, New York. MMA: 1910-42

Brush and Pencil, Chicago. V & A: 1897-1907

The Craftsman, Eastwood, New York. V & A: 1901-7; MMA: 1901-16

Creative Art, New York. MMA: October 1927-May 1923

Dekorative Kunst, Munich, 1897-1929, continued as *Das Schöne Heim* 1929-42 (first series also issued with slight variations as part 2 of *Die Kunst*). BL: 1897-1901; V & A: 1897-1936, 1940

Design for Today, London. BL, V & A: 1933-6

Deutsche Kunst und Dekoration, Darmstadt. V & A: 1897-1933 (from 1934, absorbed by *Die Kunst*)

Les Échos des Industries d'Art, Paris, 1925-9, continued from 1931 as *Les Échos d'Art*. BAD

Die Form, Bonn and Berlin. BL: 1925-32. V & A: 1925ff.

Furniture Gazette, London. BL (Colindale): 1872-97; V & A: 1873-94

Gazette des Beaux-Arts, Paris. BL, V & A: 1859ff.

The House Beautiful, Chicago, MMA: 1896ff.

Innen-Dekoration, Darmstadt. From 1900 published in Stuttgart. BL: 1891, 1902-3, 1910-24, 1928-9, 1933; V & A: 1894, 1908-40

Das Interieur, Vienna. V & A: 1900-1904, 1907-9, 1911-12

Journal of the Society of Arts, London. BL, V & A: 1852ff. (continued from 1908 as *Journal of the Royal Society of Arts*)

Keramic Studio, Syracuse, New York. V & A: 1902-23; MMA: 1899-1924

Keramische Monatshefte, Halle. V & A: 1901

Keramische Rundschau, Coburg, 1893-1927, continued as *Keramische Rundschau und Kunstkeramik 1928-43*. V & A: 1927

Die Kunst, Munich. BL: parts only from 1899; V & A: 1928ff. (first series to 1929 published in two parts annually, the second part being a revised version of *Dekorative Kunst*)

Kunst und Gewerbe, Weimar 1867-87, Nuremberg 1867-98. BL: 1867-98; V & A: 1874-87

Kunst und Handwerk, Munich. V & A: 1889-1907

Kunst und Kunsthandwerk, Vienna. V & A: 1898-1921

Kunstgewerbeblatt, Leipzig. BL: 1885-1917; V & A: 1885-1916

The Magazine of Art, London. BL, V & A: 1878-1904

Mobilier et Décoration, Sèvres. V & A: 1931-40, 1946-74; BAD: 1922-39

Der Moderne Stil, Stuttgart. V & A: 1899-1905

Nyt Tidsskrift for Kunstindustrie, Copenhagen. V & A: 1928-47; Kunstindustrimuseum, Copenhagen

Onze Kunst, Antwerp. BL: 1902-29; V & A: 1902-3, 1915-20 (from 1855 to 1902 known as *Tijdschrift voor Kunsten*; BL and V & A 1855-1902)

The Pottery Gazette, London. BL (Colindale): 1879ff.; V & A: 1879-1970

La Revue des Arts Décoratifs, Paris. BL: 1880-1902; V & A: 1880-1902

Die Schaulade, Nuremberg. 1921-32. Germanisches Nationalmuseum, Nuremberg

The Studio, London. BL, V & A: 1893ff.

Velhagen und Klasings Monatshefte, Leipzig. V & A: 1903-7

Werkbund Jahrbuch, Jena. V & A: 1912-15

Addenda

to Cat. 1-361

I am indebted to Imogen Loke for checking the design registration marks discussed in many of the following entries.

26 Marianne Brandt teapot

For a more recent account of Brandt's work see *Die Metallwerkstatt am Bauhaus*, exhibition catalogue, Bauhaus-Archiv, Berlin, 1992. Brandt joined the Metal Workshop as a designer; she did not train as a goldsmith and most of her designs were executed by other members of the Metal Workshop.

27 Brocard mosque lamp

For a vase in the form of a mosque lamp, together with underdish, signed and dated 1874, see Christie's, New York, 12 December 1992, lot 339.

28 Brouwer vase

For a vase of identical design, acquired by the Museo Internazionale delle Ceramiche, Faenza, as a gift from the manufactory, see G. Cefariello Grosso, *Ceramiche del 'Modern Style'*, Museo Internazionale delle Ceramiche, Faenza, 1992, cat. no. 83, dated *c.* 1901-10.

40 Clichy engraved glass tazza

The ornament is derived in the first instance from engraved rock-crystal vessels of the sixteenth and seventeenth centuries, produced in Milan and Prague for the courts of Europe. Several such vessels entered the French Royal collections and would have been familiar to the Clichy engravers. For examples with similar engraved scrolls, see H. Tait, *Catalogue of the Waddesdon Bequest in the British Museum, III. The Curiosities*, nos 39-40 and fig. 347 (a bowl from the Sloane collection). These rock-crystal vessels also inspired German glass engravers of the eighteenth century.

83-94 Dresser metalwork

Many of these pieces bear design registration marks. In theory, the mark stamped on the object should correspond to both a description and a representation in the records of registered designs held at the Public Record Office, but sometimes the wrong numbers were stamped on the objects. This means that although the brief listing in the Registers of Ornamental Designs confirms that Hukin & Heath registered designs on that day (the listings rarely give detailed descriptions of the object registered), the actual design itself, contained in separate volumes of Representations of Ornamental Designs, may differ from the object.

83 Register BT 51/12, Representation book BT 50/29. Design corresponds exactly to object.

84 and 85 Register BT 44/4. Representation book BT 43/44 illustrates variants of both kettle designs, together with two cruet sets, design nos 321184-7, one of which is a version of Cat. 86.

86 This cruet set is wrongly stamped. Register BT 44/4 includes an entry for 9 October 1878, no. 327395, but there is no corresponding design in the Representation books. However, a squatter version of this cruet set appears in Representation book BT 43/44, in the group of designs nos 321184-7, mentioned above, registered on 6 May 1878.

87 Entered on 9 October 1878 (not 8 October; the stamp on the object is unclear), design no. 327395 (see above, Cat. 86), but there is no corresponding representation.

88 Register BT 44/4, design no. 352892. The corresponding design in Representation book BT 43/47 illustrates the more common version of this tureen with knop handle; the ladle is barely visible inside the tureen. A design for another version of this tureen, made of silver and wood, without a lid but with glass liner, appears later in Representation book BT 43/49 and is listed in Register BT 44/5 under 11 July 1881, parcel 11, design no. 366971.

89 Incorrectly stamped; the entries for 9 May 1881 list and illustrate three items registered by Hukin & Heath, design nos 364883-5, a spoon and two decanters, but no letter-rack.

94 Register BT 44/5, Representation book BT 43/55. Design corresponds exactly.

111 C.T. & G. Fox silver caster

For earlier examples of Chinese-style silver by this firm, see Sotheby's, New York, 28 October 1992, lot 254, a lidded jug with dragon handle, hallmarked 1851.

120 Grueby vase

For an example of this model fitted with a Tiffany leaded-glass shade, see Christie's, New York, 8 December 1990, lot 186.

136 Köpping liqueur glass

For a cartoon strip on the subject of Köpping's ornamental glasses, published in the satirical paper *Lustige Blätter* in 1898, see C. Schack, *Die Glaskunst*, Munich 1976, fig. 42, p. 142. An elderly professor buys one of Köpping's fragile and expensive glasses, but as he leaves the shop (holding the glass unwrapped!), he is overcome by a violent sneeze, the force of which shatters his precious glass.

169 Martinware figure of kneeling Hercules

This figure is almost certainly based on a small Italian Renaissance bronze of a kneeling man with a shell, attributed to the workshop of Severo da Ravenna (*fl.* 1475-1500), bequeathed to Birmingham City Museum and Art Gallery (inv. no. P82'47) in 1949 by F.J. Nettlefold, who inherited his father's distinguished collection of Martinware pottery. Presumably Nettlefold senior possessed this bronze by 1904, when the Martinware figure was made.

226 Olbrich candlestick

Advertised in the *Mode/Katalog* 1903/4 issued by the Warenhaus Wertheim, Berlin. The page is titled 'Moderne Zinngefässe'; the candlestick is described as 'modelliert von Professor Olbrich' and is the only piece credited to a designer, see S. Gronert, 'Das Schöne und die Ware — Zur Produktion von Gebrauchsgegenständen und Waren', in Essen 1984, 127.

234-5 Powell glasses designed by Webb and Jackson

See J. Rudoe and H. Coutts, 'The table glass designs of Philip Webb and T.G. Jackson for James Powell & Sons, Whitefriars Glassworks', *Journal of the Decorative Arts Society, 16: Historicism in Europe 1830-1880*, 1992, 24-41.

236 Powell tazza

Jeanette Hayhurst has drawn my attention to a description of this tazza in *The Collector's Magazine* XXVIII, vol. III, April 1905, 115-17, in an article on 'Modern glass for collectors' which illustrates and describes six pieces of Powell glass. The tazza is shown next to a goblet with cobweb threaded work and is described as 'an illustration of another kind of thread ornamentation producing a most curious and interesting effect. The thread in this instance is in the first place so fine, and afterwards so completely incorporated into the metal, which is then shaped so that the thread becomes scarcely more than a hazy shadow, that it is difficult to realise that such marking can be produced by the simple addition of a thin thread of precisely the same material at a certain stage. Such, however, are some of the possibilities of glassmaking.' If the description of a 'hazy shadow' refers to the matt areas within the trailed green pattern, this suggests that they were achieved during the shaping and not by etching.

266 St Petersburg purpurine glass tazza

The Walters Art Gallery, Baltimore, has a pair of Russian purpurine glass dishes mounted in gilt bronze, acquired in 1947 (47.415, 416). They have been attributed to St Petersburg.

273 Solon plaque

For detailed discussion of Solon's *pâte-sur-pâte*, see B. Bumpus, *Pâte-sur-pâte. The art of ceramic relief decoration, 1849-1922*, London 1992.

283 and 351 Tiffany Japanesque silver

For further discussion of oxidised silver by Tiffany and others, see J. Rudoe, 'Oxidised silver in the nineteenth century: the documentary evidence', in S. La Niece and P. Craddock (eds), *Metal Plating and Patination*, Oxford 1993, 161-70.

309 Wedgwood pilgrim flask

Bernard Bumpus has suggested that this flask was shown at the Paris Exhibition of 1878 and that the design may be by Frederick Rhead with decoration executed by Henry Till. For a description that corresponds closely to this flask, see *The Society of Arts. Artisan Reports on the Paris Universal Exhibition of 1878*, London 1879, 90. Other reports refer to Egyptian-style bottles designed by Rhead with sgraffito decoration by Till, e.g. *The Pottery and Glass Trades Review* 1, 1877-8, 223. In addition to the reference from the Wedgwood factory archive already quoted, there is apparently a second reference to this flask in a 'miscellaneous' estimate book, which mentions payment to Rhead (references kindly supplied by B. Bumpus, whose forthcoming article in *Ars Ceramica* will discuss this in greater detail).

311 Wedgwood teapot

For a Wedgwood toilet service with similar, though not identical, decoration in the Japanese taste, see *The Silber & Fleming Glass & China Book*, n.d. (*c.* 1890), Wordsworth Editions 1990, 60-61.

312 Worcester porcelain inkwell

This model was produced as late as 1876, see Christie's, London, 20 February 1992, lot 353, with date-code for 1876. Other coloured examples are at Preston Manor, Brighton (reg. no. 325171) and at Norwich Castle Museum. See also Christie's, London, 10 October 1988, lot 405. For the restoration and colouring of the tomb in the late nineteenth century, see John Physick in *Church Monuments* II, 1987, 53-4.

315 Worcester porcelain teapot

Design registration mark corresponds to the Registers in the Public Record Office, design no. 259801. It was registered in plain white.

317 Frank Lloyd Wright plate

Noritake had already reissued the service in the 1960s, see Christie's, New York, 14 December 1991, lots 42-3, and Christie's, New York, 6 June 1992, lots 47-8, all marked 'NORITAKE NIPPON TOKI KAISHA JAPAN', with various dates between 1962 and 1968. The pieces in Brighton dated 1984 are presumably a later reissue.

Recent Bibliography

Note on the Plates

The following is a selection of books published since the first edition of this catalogue went to press, which are of especial relevance to the items catalogued here and which are not cited in the list of acquisitions 1991-3.

Bröhan, K.H. (ed.). 1990. *Kunst vom Jugendstil zur Moderne (1889-1939). Sammlung Karl H. Bröhan, Berlin, Band IV, Metallkunst*, Berlin

Bröhan, T. (ed.). 1992. *Glas-Kunst der Moderne von Josef Hoffmann bis Wilhelm Wagenfeld*, Munich

Gere, C. and **Whiteway, M.** 1993. *Nineteenth Century Design from Pugin to Mackintosh*, London

Kardon, J. (ed.). 1993. *The Ideal Home 1900-1920. The History of Twentieth-Century American Craft*, New York

Hajdamach, C.R. 1991. *British Glass 1800-1914*, Woodbridge

Hoffmeister, B. and **Joppien, R.** 1991. *Europäischer Jugendstil*, exhibition catalogue, Museum für Kunst und Gewerbe, Hamburg

Ellis, A.J. 1992. *Rookwood Pottery. The Glorious Gamble*, New York

Montgomery, S. 1993. *The Ceramics of William H. Grueby*, Lambertville, New Jersey

Mundt, B. 1991. *Produkt Design 1900-1990. Eine Auswahl. Bildführer zur neuen Sammlung im Kunstgewerbemuseum*, Berlin

Sellner, C. 1992. *Gläserner Jugendstil aus Bayern*, Grafenau

Sembach, K.J. and **Schulte, B.** (eds). 1992. *Henry van de Velde. Ein europäische Künstler in seiner Zeit*, Cologne

The dates given in each caption refer to the date when the object was designed. Where precise dates of manufacture are known which differ from the design date they are also given. Whenever possible the names of the designer, then manufacturer, are given.

PLATE I

W. Burges, Barkentin & Krall, 1877-8 (Cat. 29)

PLATE II

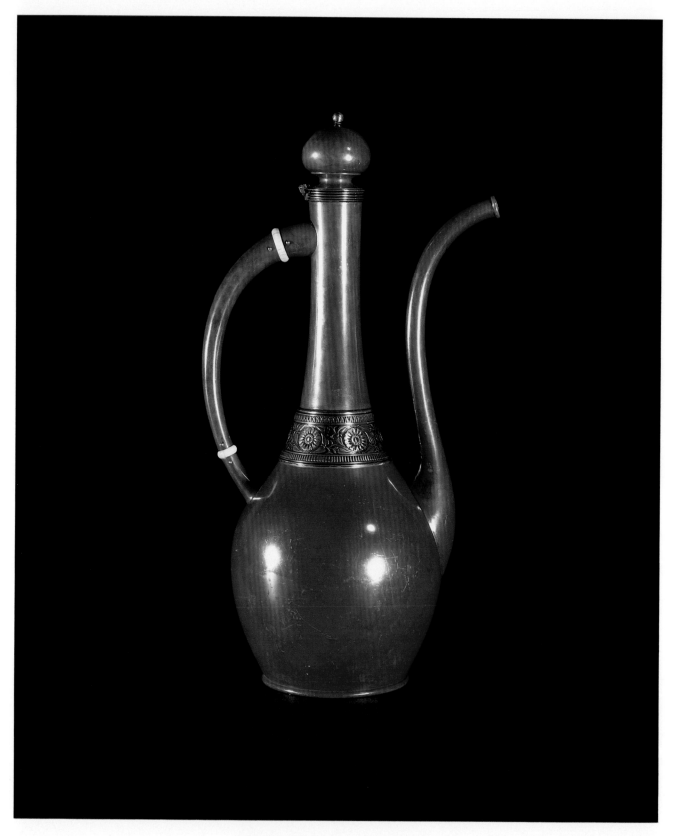

Gorham Manufacturing Co., 1882 (Cat. 115)

PLATE III

St Petersburg Imperial Glassworks, 1867 (Cat. 266)

P. R. de F. D'Humy, 1878
(back row, left to right: Cat. 71, 62, 73, 59, 61, 67; front row: 68, 65, 64)

PLATE IV

W. Crane, Pilkington's Tile & Pottery Co., 1906 (Cat. 56)

PLATE V

W. De Morgan, Orange House Pottery, 1880 (Cat. 78)

B. Moore, 1902 and later
(left to right: Cat. 203, 200, 204, 199, 206, 205, 201)

PLATE VI

Left to right: J. Powell & Sons, 1870 (Cat. 235);
K. Köpping, *c.*1898 (Cat. 136); O. Prutscher, *c.*1907 (Cat. 245); P. Behrens, 1901 (Cat. 338)

Left: W. Burton, Pilkington's Tile & Pottery Co., 1899-1900 (Cat. 30)
Right: C. Dresser, Linthorpe Pottery, *c.*1867-80 (Cat. 102)

PLATE VII

Martin Brothers, 1889-1907 (front row: Cat. 193, 194, 189, 187, 188, 190;
back row: 195, 186, 192, 191, 185)

L. C. Tiffany, c.1896-1906 (Cat. 284, 285, 286, 287, 288)

PLATE VIII

Rozenburg Porcelain Factory, 1899 (Cat. 265)

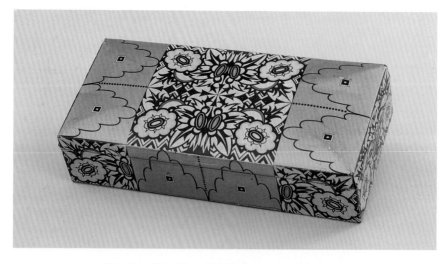

E. J. Margold, Bahlsens Keksfabrik, 1914-15 (Cat. 156)

PLATE IX

A. Van Briggle, 1902 (Cat. 289)

PLATE X

H. van de Velde, Steinzeugfabrik R. Hanke, 1902 (Cat. 293)

PLATE XI

C. R. Mackintosh, 1919 (Cat. 151)

PLATE XII

N. Girschfeld, State Porcelain Factory, Petrograd, 1921 (Cat. 343)

M. Adamovich, State Porcelain Factory, Petrograd, 1921 (Cat. 337)   M. Adamovich, State Porcelain Factory, Petrograd, 1922 (Cat. 2)

PLATE XIII

M. Lebedeva, State Porcelain Factory, Petrograd, 1923 (Cat. 345)

PLATE XIV

C. Lebeau, Leerdam, 1924-5 (Cat. 141)

PLATE XV

M. Brandt, 1924 (Cat. 26)

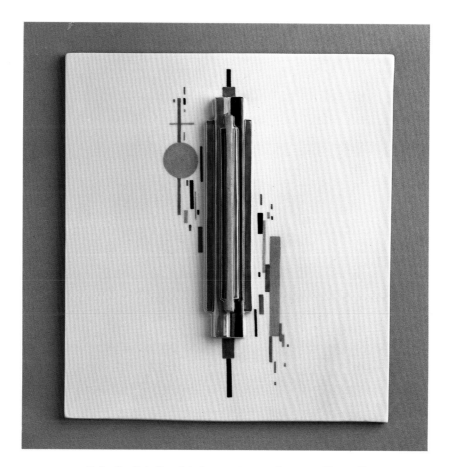

N. Suetin, State Porcelain Factory, Petrograd, 1923-4 (Cat. 278)

PLATE XVI

Russel Wright, Steubenville Pottery, 1939, and Iroquois China Co., 1946 (Cat. 319-27)

E. Zeisel, Red Wing Pottery, 1946 (Cat. 333-5, 358-61)

The black and white plates are classified in groups of related material, arranged as far as possible in a chronological sequence. Comparative material is shown alongside the relevant catalogue number; for full details see the list of figures on page 289.

PLATE I   GOTHIC REVIVAL : A. W. N. PUGIN

A. W. N. Pugin, Minton & Co., designed before 1852, made 1856 (Cat. 247)

Fig. 1 Watercolour design for Cat. 247   Fig. 2 Watercolour design for Cat. 247

A. W. N. Pugin, Minton & Co., before 1849 (Cat. 246)

PLATE 3

GOTHIC REVIVAL: E. W. GODWIN

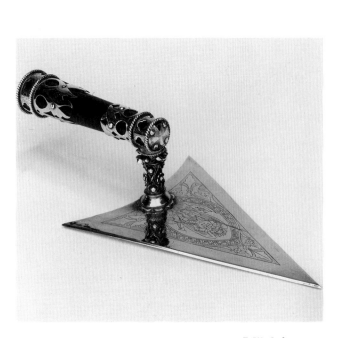

E. W. Godwin, Birmingham, 1861 (Cat. 114)

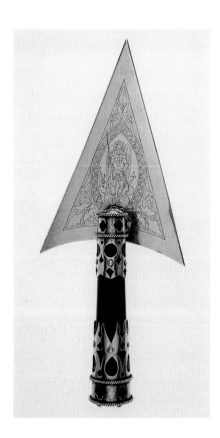

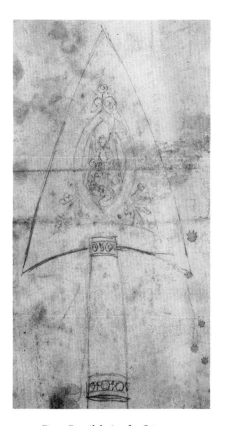

Fig. 3 Pencil design for Cat. 114

Castle Hedingham Pottery, c. 1865-1901 (Cat. 33, 31, 32)

Representation of the Tomb of
King John
in the Cathedral Church of
Worcester,
where he was interred according
to the instructions
contained in his Will.
His Monarch was born in 1165.
He signed Magna Charta
in the presence of the Barons of
England 15 June 1215.
Died 19th Oct 1216.

Worcester Porcelain, Chamberlain & Co.,
c. 1840-44, and inscription inside lid
(Cat. 312)

PLATE 5   GOTHIC REVIVAL : WILLIAM BURGES

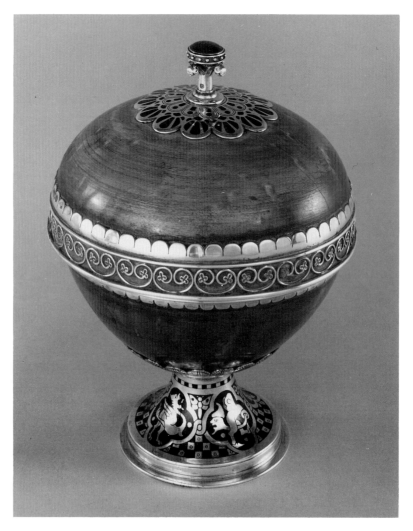

W. Burges, Barkentin & Krall, 1877-8 (Cat. 29)

Cat. 29 : enamel roundel inside cover

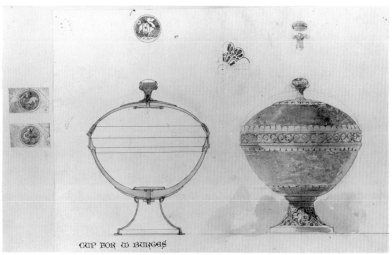

Fig. 4 Watercolour design for Cat. 29

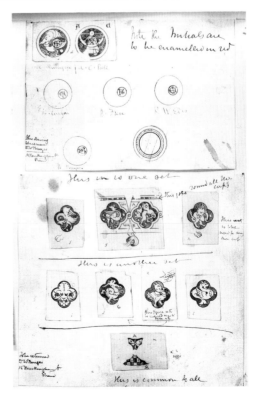

W. Burges, Barkentin & Krall, 1877-8
(Cat. 29)

Centre Cat. 29 : inscription round rim of base

Above Cat. 29 : enamel roundel inside base

Right Fig. 5 Watercolour designs for the
enamelled quatrefoils on Cat. 29 (upper
row)

PLATE 7   MID-NINETEENTH-CENTURY GLASS

Cristalleries de Clichy, 1862 (Cat. 40)

Fig. 6 Illustration from *Art Journal Illustrated Catalogue*, 1862

J. F. Christy, Stangate Glass Works, *c.*1845-50 (Cat. 39)

Bohemian, mid-19th century (Cat. 25)

PLATE 9   CLASSICAL REVIVAL

P. Ipsens Enke Terracotta-Fabrik, Copenhagen, *c.*1875 (Cat. 128)

P. Ipsens Enke Terracotta-Fabrik, Copenhagen, *c.*1875 (Cat. 128)

PLATE II

CLASSICAL REVIVAL

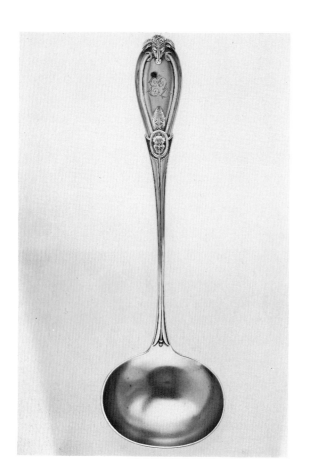

Tiffany & Co., 1862-9 (Cat. 282)

Gorham Manufacturing Co., 1882 (Cat. 116)

W. T. Copeland & Sons Ltd, *c.*1868 (Cat. 43)

PLATE 13

ASSYRIAN REVIVAL

W. T. Copeland & Sons Ltd, *c.*1868 (Cat. 44)

W. T. Copeland & Sons Ltd, *c.*1868, made 1893 (Cat. 45)

W. T. Copeland & Sons Ltd, 1882 (Cat. 46-7)

W. T. Copeland & Sons Ltd, 1882 (Cat. 48)

PLATE 15

ASSYRIAN REVIVAL

Hunt & Roskell, 1852-3 (Cat. 127)

Cat 127: inscription inside lid

Hunt & Roskell, 1852-3 (Cat. 127)

PLATE 17

EGYPTIAN REVIVAL

J. Wedgwood & Sons (A. A. Toft), 1877 (Cat. 309)

J. Wedgwood & Sons (A. A. Toft), 1877 (Cat. 309)

Fig. 7a Wedgwood plaque, signed A. A. Toft, 1879
Fig. 7b Wedgwood plaque, signed A. A. Toft, 1879 (detail)

PLATE 19

EGYPTIAN REVIVAL

J. Wedgwood & Sons (T. Allen), 1878 (Cat. 310)

Minton & Co., before 1862, made before 1873 (Cat. 196)

Gorham Manufacturing Co., 1882 (Cat. 115)

PLATE 21

ISLAMIC REVIVAL

P.-J. Brocard, 1867 (Cat. 27)

J.-T. Deck, *c.* 1861 - 78 (Cat. 57)

PLATE 23

WILLIAM DE MORGAN

W. De Morgan, Orange House Pottery, 1880 (Cat. 78)

Fig. 8 Watercolour design for Cat. 78

W. Crane, Maw & Co., 1889 (Cat. 55)   W. De Morgan, Sands End Pottery, c. 1890 (Cat. 79)

PLATE 25
WALTER CRANE

W. Crane, Pilkington's Tile & Pottery Co., 1906 (Cat. 56)

W. Burton, Pilkington's Tile & Pottery Co., 1899-1900 (Cat. 30)

A. Stevens, 1852 (Cat. 276-7)

Fig. 9 View of the former railing outside the British Museum, showing Stevens's lions

PLATE 27

BERNARD MOORE

B. Moore, 1902 (Cat. 200, 199, 201)

B. Moore, 1902 (Cat. 204)

B. Moore, c. 1930 (Cat. 206)

B. Moore, *c.* 1904 - 5 (Cat. 205)

B. Moore, 1902 (Cat. 203, 202)

PLATE 29

CHRISTOPHER DRESSER

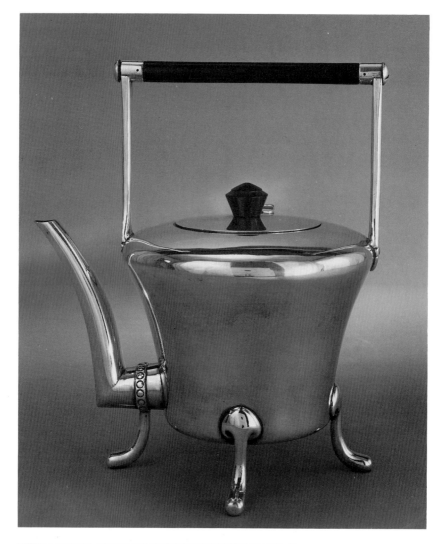

C. Dresser, Hukin & Heath, 1878 (Cat. 84)

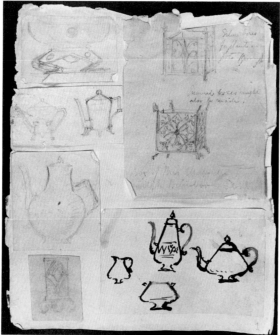

Fig. 10 Pencil design for a kettle similar to Cat. 84

C. Dresser, Elkington & Co., 1885 (Cat. 83)

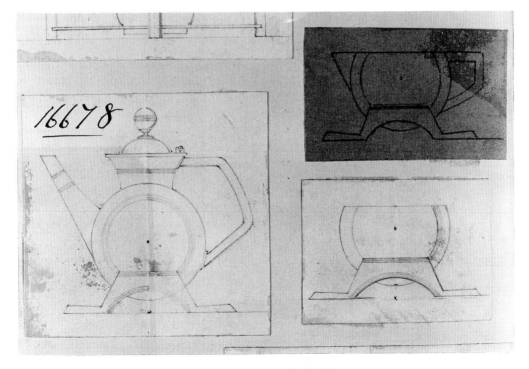

Fig. 11 Pencil design for Cat. 83

PLATE 31

CHRISTOPHER DRESSER

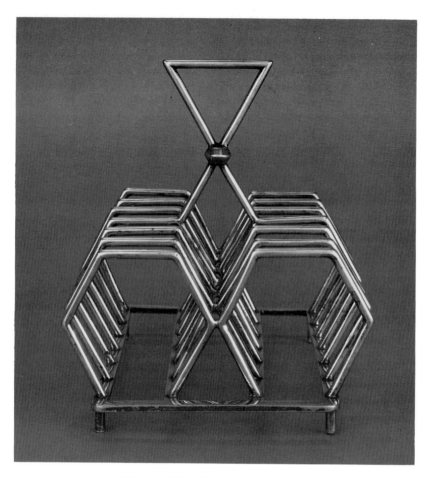

C. Dresser, J. Dixon & Sons, *c.* 1885 (Cat. 93)

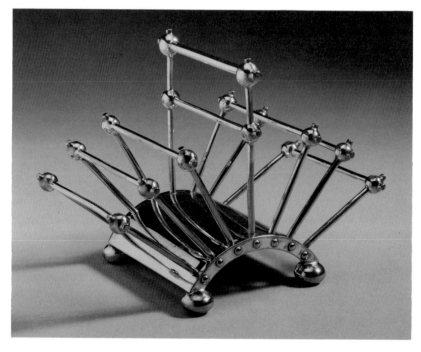

C. Dresser, Hukin & Heath, 1881 (Cat. 89)

C. Dresser, J. Dixon & Sons, 1880 (Cat. 91)

C. Dresser, J. Dixon & Sons, *c.* 1885 (Cat. 92)

PLATE 33   CHRISTOPHER DRESSER

C. Dresser, Hukin & Heath, 1880 (Cat. 88)

C. Dresser, Hukin & Heath, 1878 (Cat. 85)

PLATE 35   CHRISTOPHER DRESSER

C. Dresser, Hukin & Heath, 1878 (Cat. 86)

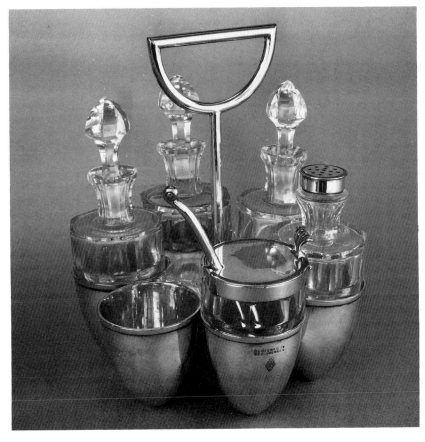

C. Dresser, Hukin & Heath, 1878 (Cat. 87)

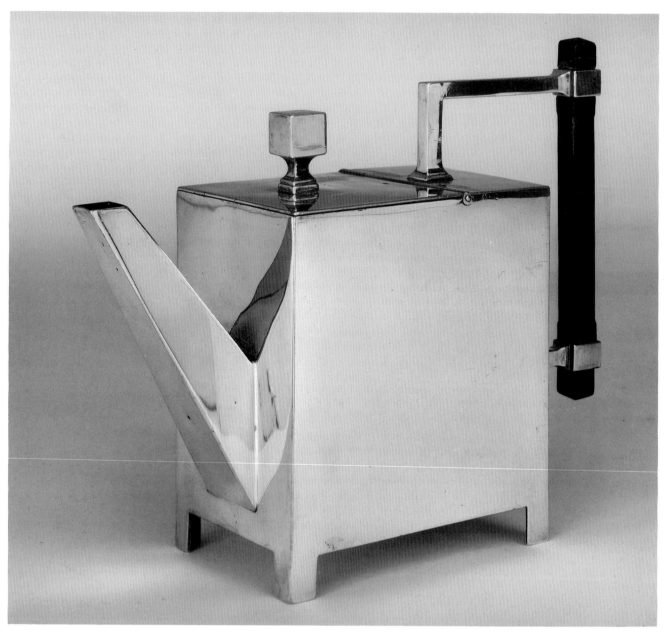

C. Dresser, J. Dixon & Sons, *c.* 1878-9 (Cat. 90)

C. Dresser, Perry Son & Co., 1883 (Cat. 94)

C. Dresser, Benham & Froud, c.1885 (Cat. 95)

PLATE 37

CHRISTOPHER DRESSER

C. Dresser, Linthorpe Art Pottery, 1879-80 (Cat. 97)

C. Dresser, Linthorpe Art Pottery, 1879-80 (Cat. 98)

C. Dresser, Linthorpe Art Pottery, 1879-80 (Cat. 99)

C. Dresser, Linthorpe Art Pottery, 1880-81 (Cat. 100)

C. Dresser, Thomas Johnson, 1879-80, made 1881 (Cat. 82); Linthorpe Art Pottery, 1879-80 (Cat. 96)

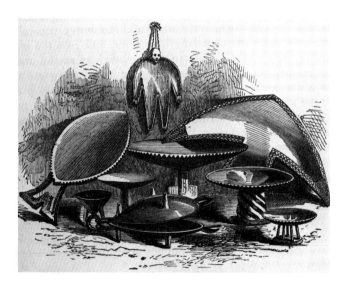

Fig. 12 Group of Fiji ritual drinking vessels

C. Dresser, Linthorpe Art Pottery, 1879-80 (Cat. 96)

PLATE 39

CHRISTOPHER DRESSER

C. Dresser, Linthorpe Art Pottery,
*c.*1879-80 (Cat. 103)

C. Dresser, Linthorpe Art Pottery, *c.*1879-80 (Cat. 101)

C. Dresser, Linthorpe Art Pottery, *c.*1867, made *c.*1879-82 (Cat. 102)

C. Dresser, Old Hall Earthenware Co., 1884 (Cat. 104)

PLATE 41   CHRISTOPHER DRESSER

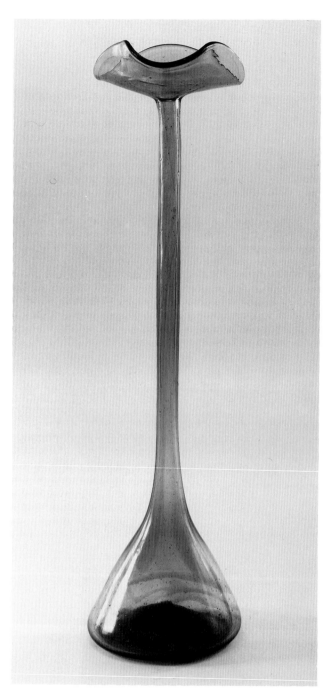

C. Dresser, J. Couper & Sons, *c.* 1880-90 (Cat. 105)

C. Dresser, J. Couper & Sons, *c.* 1880-90 (Cat. 106)

C. Dresser, J. Couper & Sons, c. 1880-90 (Cat. 107)

Commondale Brick, Pipe & Pottery Co., 1880-82 (Cat. 41-2)

PLATE 43 THE AESTHETIC MOVEMENT AND JAPANESE TASTE

Worcester Royal Porcelain Co., 1873, made 1876 (Cat. 313)

Worcester Royal Porcelain Co., 1873, made 1876 (Cat. 314)

J. Wedgwood & Sons, 1886 (Cat. 311)

Rookwood Pottery, 1894 (Cat. 260)

PLATE 45   THE AESTHETIC MOVEMENT AND JAPANESE TASTE

M. L. Nichols, *c.*1880 (Cat. 221)

Fig. 13 Related vase decorated by M. L. Nichols,
before 1881, Cincinnati Art Museum

Worcester Royal Porcelain Co., 1872 (Cat. 315)

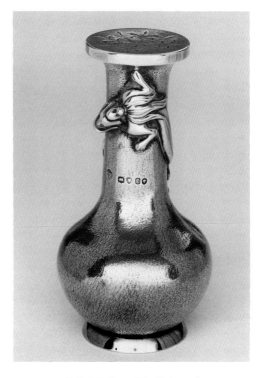

C. T. & G. Fox, 1861 (Cat. 111)

PLATE 47   THE AESTHETIC MOVEMENT AND JAPANESE TASTE

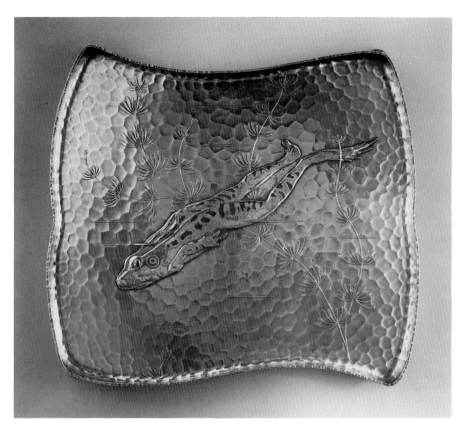

Tiffany & Co., 1880 (Cat. 283)

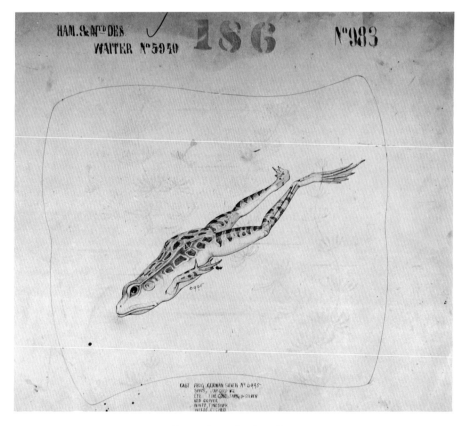

Fig. 14 Design for Cat. 283

P. Ovchinnikov, 1882 (Cat. 230)

P. Ovchinnikov, 1882 (Cat. 230)

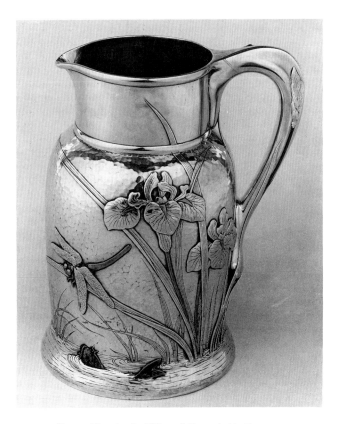

Fig. 15 Silver jug by Tiffany & Co. copied in Cat. 230,
Musée d'Orsay, Paris

PLATE 49   THE AESTHETIC MOVEMENT AND JAPANESE TASTE

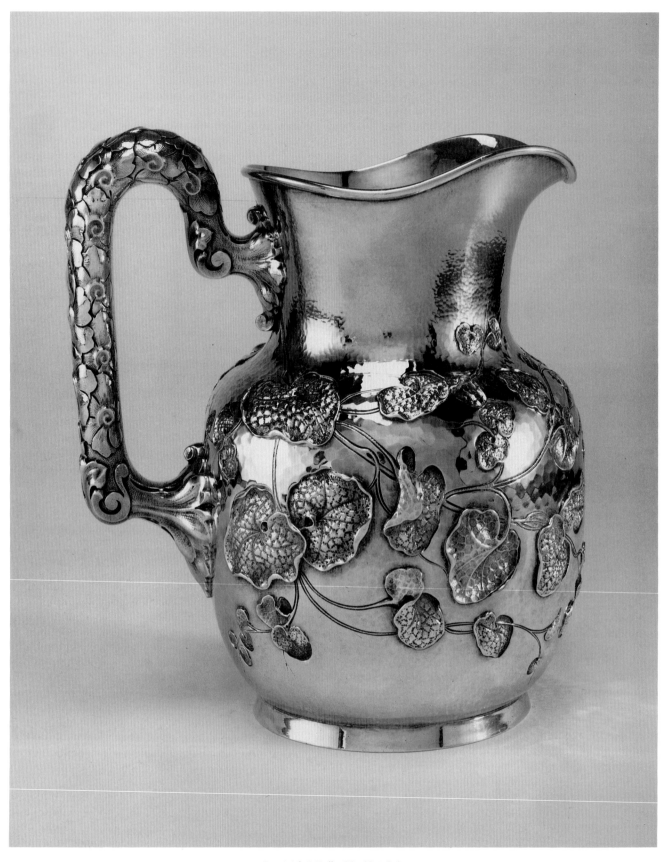

Dominick & Haff, 1883 (Cat. 81)

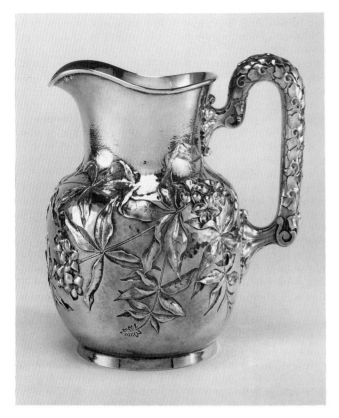

Dominick & Haff, 1883 (Cat. 81)

Tiffany & Co., 1874 (Cat. 351)

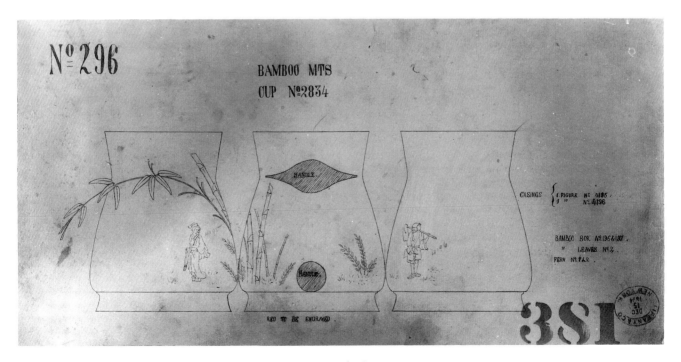

Fig. 16 Design for Cat. 351

PLATE 51   MARTINWARE

R. W. Martin, *c.*1885-90 (Cat. 162)

Martin Brothers, 1902 (Cat. 170)

Martin Brothers, *c.* 1882-7 (Cat. 160a, 159, 161, 158, 160b)

Martin Brothers, 1880-1904 (Cat. 163, 166, 171, 164-5, 170 (face jug), 168, 169, 167)

PLATE 53

MARTINWARE

Martin Brothers, 1879-96 (Cat. 173a and b, 174, 172, 175, 176)

Martin Brothers, 1883-1900 (Cat. 177a and b, 182, 181, 180, 179, 178, 183)

Martin Brothers, 1889-1907 (front row: Cat. 193, 194, 189, 187, 188, 190;
back row: Cat. 195, 186, 192, 191, 185)

Martin Brothers, 1898 (Cat. 184)

PLATE 55

P. R. DE F. D'HUMY

P. R. de F. D'Humy, 1878 (Cat. 59, 61, 60)

P. R. de F. D'Humy, 1878 (Cat. 62, 67, 63)

P. R. de F. D'Humy, 1878 (Cat. 75)

P. R. de F. D'Humy, 1878 (Cat. 70, 66, 72, 73, 71, 69, 74)

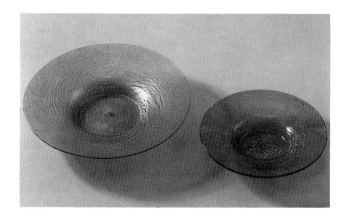

P. R. de F. D'Humy, 1878 (Cat. 68, 65)

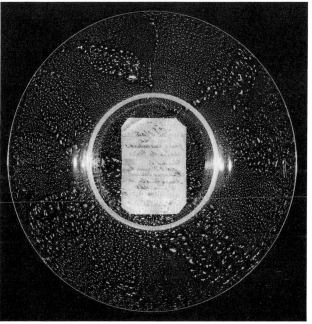

P. R. de F. D'Humy, 1878 (Cat. 64)

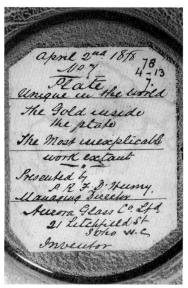

Cat. 68 : label on base

PLATE 57

J. POWELL & SONS

J. Powell & Sons, before 1891 (Cat. 349)

P. Webb, J. Powell & Sons, *c.* 1860 (Cat. 234)

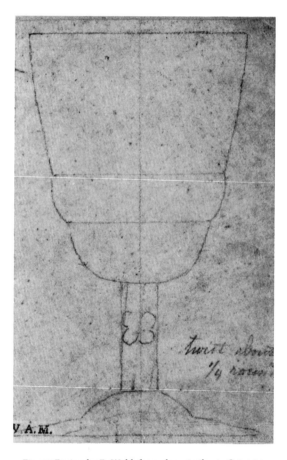

Fig. 17 Design by P. Webb for a glass similar to Cat. 234

T. G. Jackson, J. Powell & Sons, 1870 (Cat. 235)

Fig. 18 Factory working drawing for Cat. 234-5

PLATE 59

J. POWELL & SONS

H. J. Powell, J. Powell & Sons, before 1902 (Cat. 236)

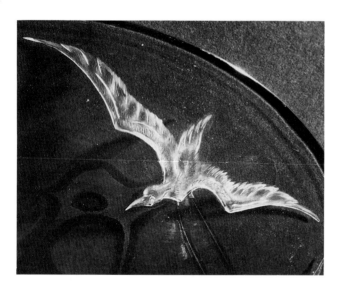 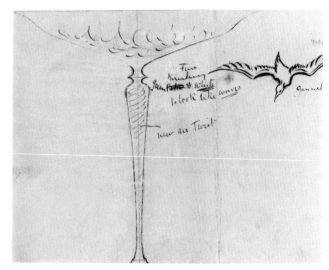

Cat. 236: detail

Fig. 19 Sketch for Cat. 236

H. J. Powell, J. Powell & Sons, before 1906 (Cat. 237)

H. J. Powell, J. Powell & Sons, c. 1900 (Cat. 238)

J. Powell & Sons, before 1923 (Cat. 241); before 1905 (Cat. 239)

PLATE 61   J. POWELL & SONS

J. Powell & Sons, before 1923 (Cat. 240)

J. Powell & Sons, 1883-94 (Cat. 242)

Fig. 20 Design for cut version of candlestick Cat. 240

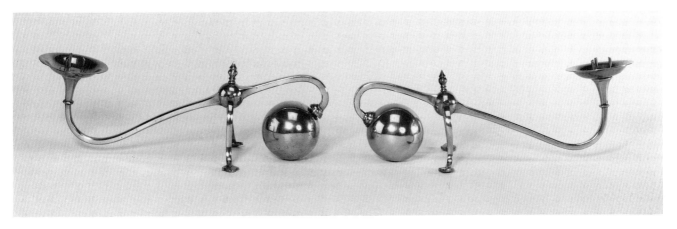

W. A. S. Benson, before 1887 (Cat. 19)

W. A. S. Benson, before 1898 (Cat. 21)

W. A. S. Benson, c.1880-90 (Cat. 20)

PLATE 63   W. A. S. BENSON

W. A. S. Benson, *c.* 1890 (Cat. 22)

W. A. S. Benson, *c.* 1900 (Cat. 23)

C. F. A. Voysey, *c.*1899-1901 (Cat. 297)

C. F. A. Voysey, *c.* 1906-7 (Cat. 302)

Cat. 297: detail

PLATE 65

C. F. A. VOYSEY

C. F. A. Voysey, Jesson Birkett & Co., *c.*1901-3, made 1904-10 (Cat. 300)

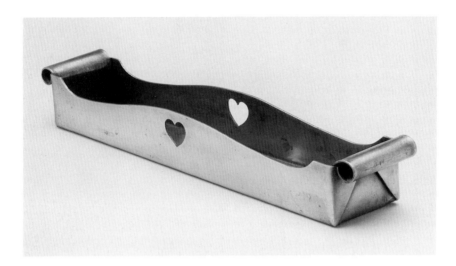

C. F. A. Voysey, *c.*1901-3 (Cat. 299)

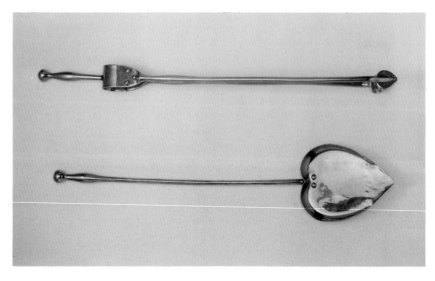

C. F. A. Voysey, Thomas Elsley & Co., *c.*1898-1901 (Cat. 298)

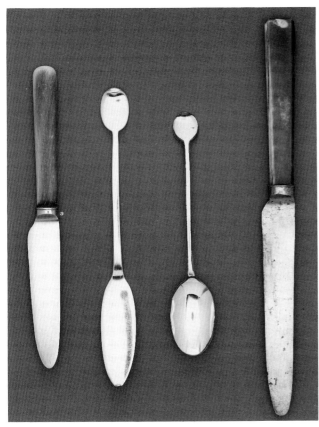

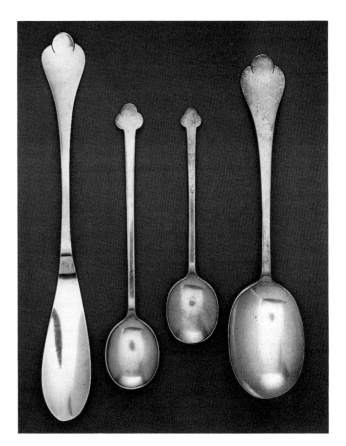

C. F. A. Voysey, *c.* 1907 (Cat. 301)

C. R. Mackintosh, *c.* 1905 (Cat. 150)

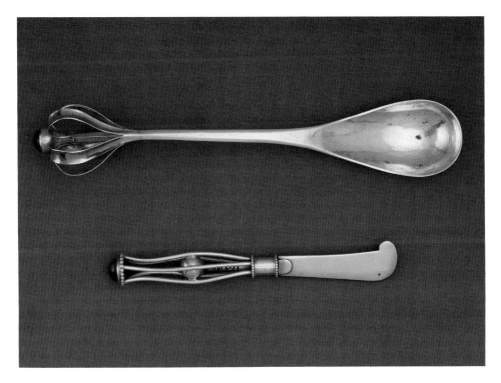

C. R. Ashbee, Guild of Handicraft, before 1902, made 1905 (Cat. 5, above);
c. 1897-1900, made 1900 (Cat. 4, below)

PLATE 67

ENGLISH ARTS AND CRAFTS

A. H. Powell, 1926 (Cat. 233)

Hart & Huyshe, Guild of Handicraft, *c.*1920 (Cat. 121)

G. Marks, 1902 (Cat. 157)

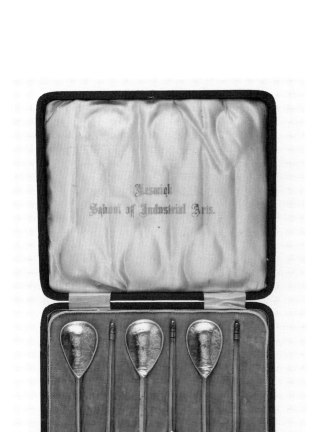

Keswick School of Industrial Arts, 1917 (Cat. 132)

H. Stabler, 1915 (Cat. 274)

PLATE 69   OMAR RAMSDEN AND ALWYN CARR

O. Ramsden, 1934 (Cat. 252); Ramsden & Carr, 1915 (Cat. 250)

Cat. 252: detail of enamel roundel
inside bowl

Cat. 250: detail of enamel roundel
inside bowl

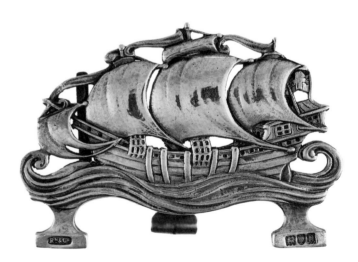

Above Ramsden & Carr, 1908 (Cat. 249)

Left O. Ramsden, 1926 (Cat. 251)

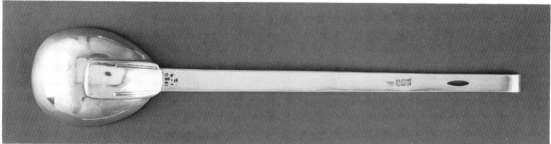

C. R. Mackintosh, 1902 (Cat. 147)

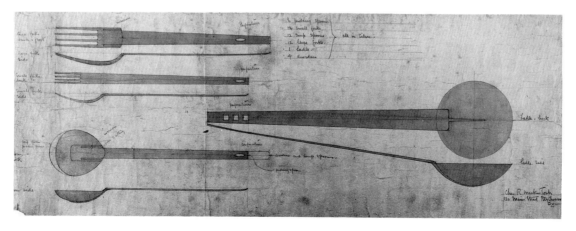

Fig. 21 Pencil and wash design for Cat. 147

PLATE 71

CHARLES RENNIE MACKINTOSH

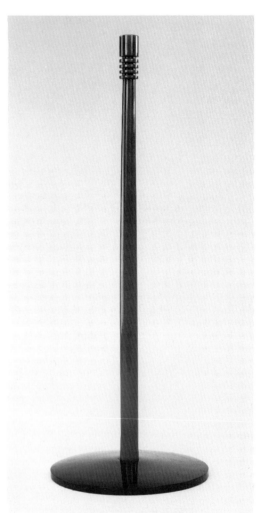

C. R. Mackintosh, 1904 (Cat. 148-9)

C. R. Mackintosh, c. 1917 (Cat. 152)

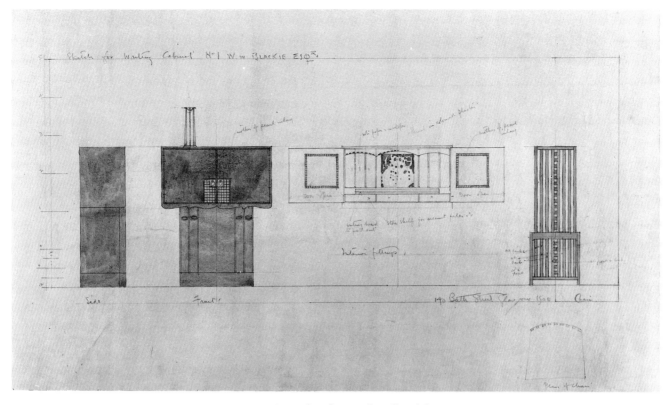

Fig. 22 Design for cabinet and candlestick for
Walter Blackie (Cat. 148)

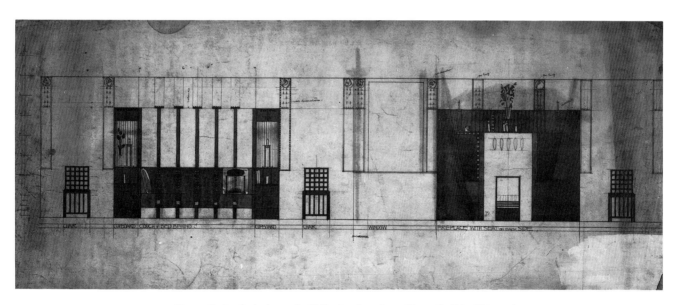

Fig. 23 Design for bedroom for Katherine Cranston with candlesticks (Cat. 149)
on the cupboard flanking the bed

PLATE 73   CHARLES RENNIE MACKINTOSH

C. R. Mackintosh, 1919 (Cat. 151)

Fig. 24 View of the guest bedroom at 78 Derngate with Cat. 151 on fireplace, reflected in the mirror

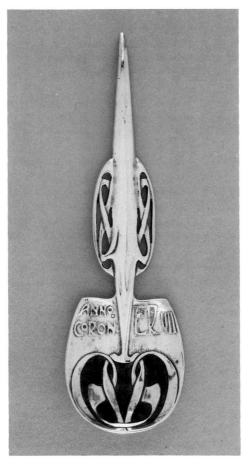

A. Knox, Liberty & Co., 1901 (Cat. 133)

A. Knox, W. H. Haseler for Liberty & Co., 1903 (Cat. 134)

PLATE 75

ART NOUVEAU : MINTON

Minton & Co., 1898 (Cat. 197)

M. Dufrène, Maison de l'Art Moderne, *c.*1902-3 (Cat. 108)

G. de Feure, Maison de l'Art Nouveau, 1901-2 (Cat. 58)

Sèvres, 1897, made 1905 (Cat. 269)

PLATE 77

PÂTE-SUR-PÂTE

T. Doat, Sèvres, 1895-7 (Cat. 80)

M. L. E. Solon, Minton & Co., *c.* 1880 (Cat. 273)

J. W. Eisenlöffel, 1902 (Cat. 109)

PLATE 79   ART NOUVEAU: HOLLAND AND BELGIUM

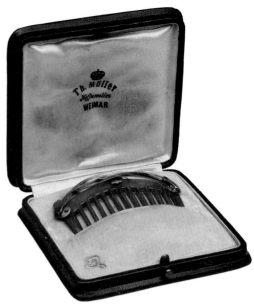

H. van de Velde, T. Müller, 1899-1900 (Cat. 290)

J. M. van Kempen & Sons, 1904 (Cat. 131)

W. C. Brouwer, c. 1900-1901, made 1902 (Cat. 28)

H. van de Velde, T. Müller, *c.* 1902-3 (Cat. 292)

H. van de Velde, Koch & Bergfeld, 1902 (Cat. 291)

PLATE 81   HENRY VAN DE VELDE

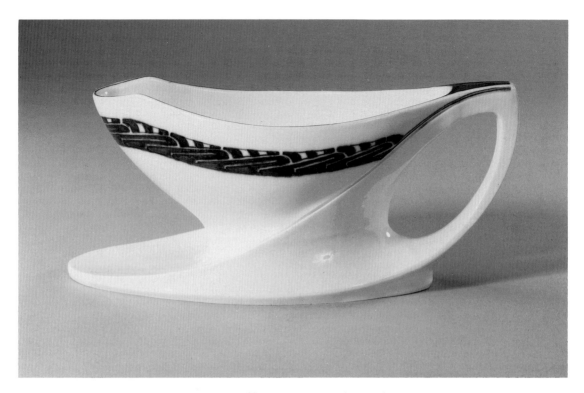

H. van de Velde, Meissen, 1903-4 (Cat. 294)

H. van de Velde, Meissen, 1903-4 (Cat. 295)

H. van de Velde, R. Hanke, 1902 (Cat. 354)

H. van de Velde, R. Hanke, 1902 (Cat. 293)

PLATE 83   ART NOUVEAU : GERMANY

R. Hentschel, Meissen, 1901 (Cat. 122)

H. Christiansen, Krautheim & Adelberg, *c.* 1903 (Cat. 38)

R. Riemerschmid, Meissen, 1903-5 (Cat. 256)

Rosenthal, 1905, decoration 1910 (Cat. 262)

W. Magnussen, J. Uffrecht & Co., 1901 (Cat. 153)

PLATE 85

PETER BEHRENS

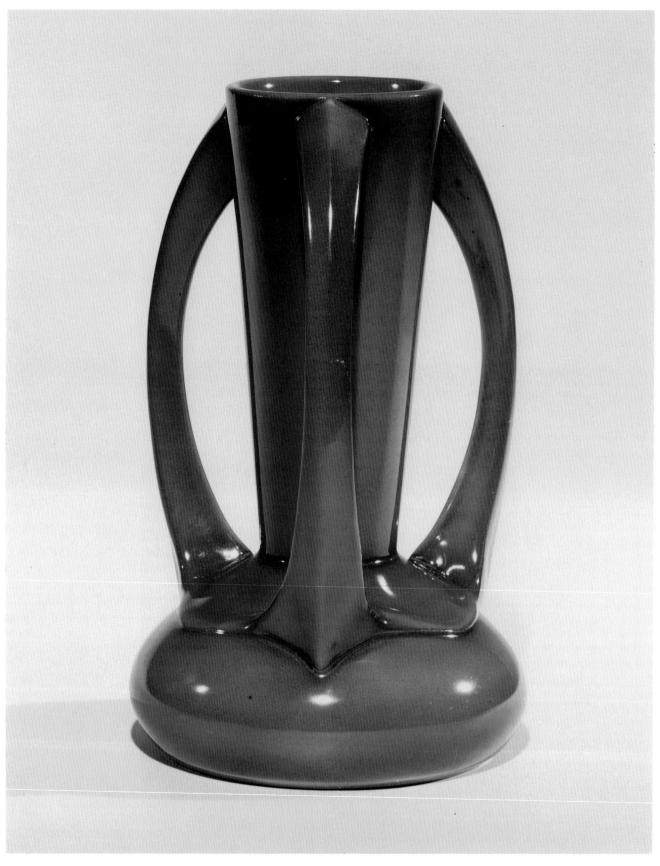

P. Behrens, F. A. Mehlem, 1900-1901 (Cat. 12)

P. Behrens, Gebrüder Bauscher, 1901 (Cat. 11)

P. Behrens, Nuremberg Master-classes, Krautheim & Adelberg, 1901 (Cat. 17)

PLATE 87   PETER BEHRENS AND MAX LAEUGER

P. Behrens, Villeroy & Boch, c.1904 (Cat. 339)

M. Laeuger, Tonwerke Kandern, c.1900 (Cat. 138)

Above P. Behrens, Franz Bahner, 1903, made 1916-17 (Cat. 14)

Below, left and right Vereinigte Silberwaren-Fabriken Düsseldorf, *c.*1901, made 1903-7 (Cat. 296)

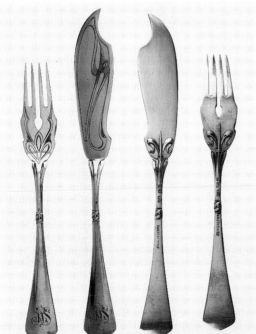

PLATE 89   ART NOUVEAU : GERMANY

H. Christiansen, P. Bruckmann & Söhne, *c.*1901 (Cat. 37)

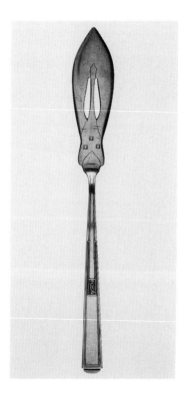

J. M. Olbrich, Christofle & Cie,
*c.*1900-1901 (Cat. 224)

J. M. Olbrich, Clarfeld & Springmeyer, 1901, made 1904 (Cat. 225)

J. M. Olbrich, Robert Macco, *c.*1902-3 (Cat. 228)

J. M. Olbrich, Villeroy & Boch, 1903, with later
decoration attributed to B. Mauder (Cat. 229)

Fig. 25 Design for Cat. 229

PLATE 91   J. M. OLBRICH

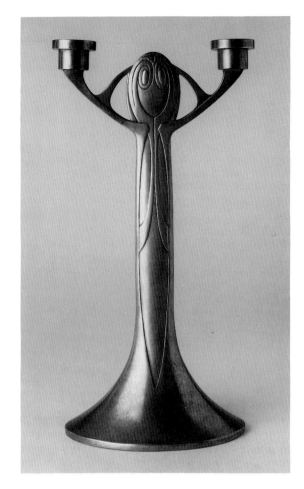

J. M. Olbrich, E. Hueck, *c.* 1901-2 (Cat. 226)

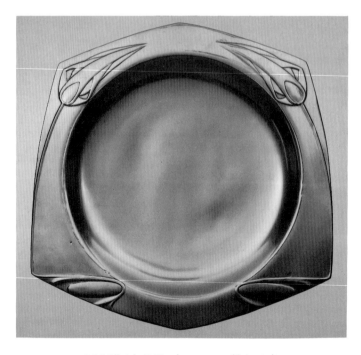

J. M. Olbrich, E. Hueck, *c.* 1903-4 (Cat. 227)

A. Müller, E. Hueck, 1903-4 (Cat. 209)

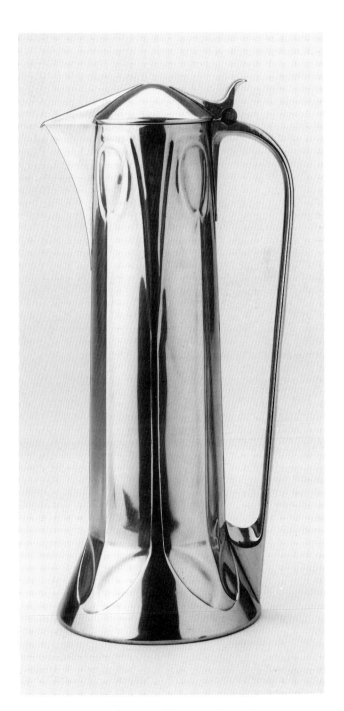

A. Müller, E. Hueck, 1903-4 (Cat. 210)

PLATE 93   WÜRTTEMBERGISCHE METALLWARENFABRIK

A. Müller, Württembergische Metallwarenfabrik, *c.*1904-5 (Cat. 211)

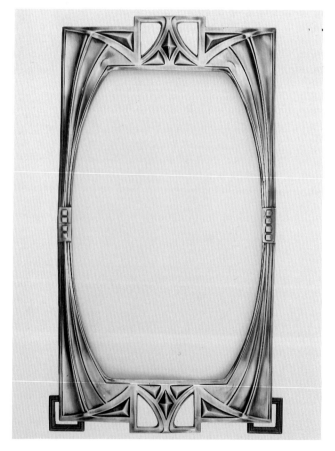

Württembergische Metallwarenfabrik, *c.*1905-6 (Cat. 328)   Württembergische Metallwarenfabrik, *c.*1905-6 (Cat. 329)

P. Behrens, AEG, 1908-9 (Cat. 15)

P. Behrens, AEG, 1910, produced after 1926 (Cat. 16)

PLATE 95

ART NOUVEAU : GERMANY

K. Köpping, Fachschule Ilmenau, c.1898 (Cat. 136)

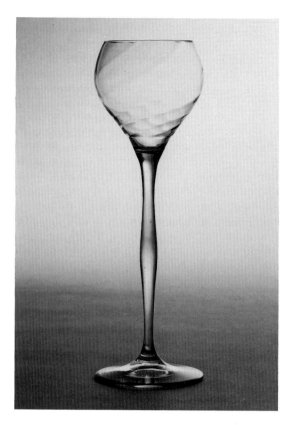

H. Christiansen, Theresienthaler Krystallglasfabrik,
1900-1901 (Cat. 36)

P. Behrens, Rheinische Glashütten, 1901 (Cat. 338)

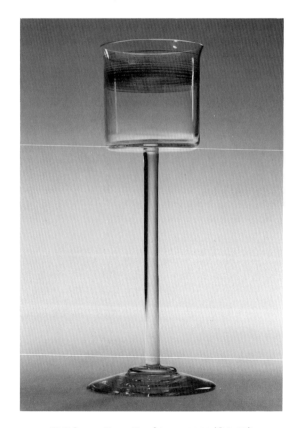

P. Behrens, B. von Poschinger, 1902 (Cat. 13)

R. Riemerschmid, B. von Poschinger, 1900 (Cat. 257)

Fig. 26 Factory working drawing for Cat. 257

PLATE 97

RICHARD RIEMERSCHMID

R. Riemerschmid, B. von Poschinger, *c.*1911 (Cat. 258)

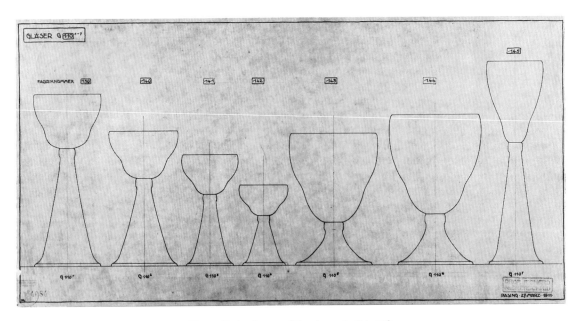

Fig. 27 Design for one of the glasses in Cat. 258

R. Riemerschmid, R. Merkelbach, 1902/4 (Cat. 255)

A. Müller, S. P. Gerz, c. 1910 (Cat. 213)

PLATE 99

GERMAN STONEWARE

P. Wynand, R. Merkelbach, 1909 (Cat. 332)

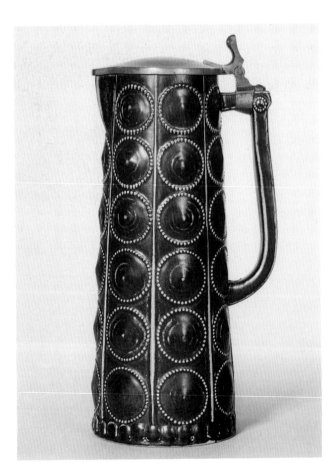

P. Wynand, R. Merkelbach, c.1909 (Cat. 330)

P. Wynand, R. Merkelbach, c.1909 (Cat. 331)

C. Krause, R. Merkelbach, *c.*1912-15 (Cat. 137)

A. Müller, R. Merkelbach, *c.*1910 (Cat. 212)

PLATE 101   GERHARD MARCKS

G. Marcks, Schwarzburger Werkstätten, 1909-10 (Cat. 346-8)

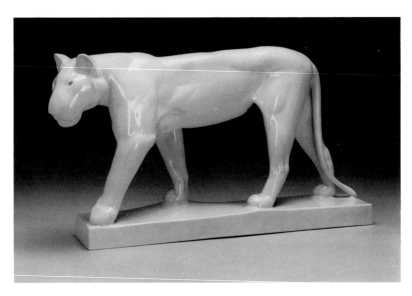

G. Marcks, Schwarzburger Werkstätten, 1909-10 (Cat. 348)

G. A. Jensen, 1910 (Cat. 129)

Cat. 129: detail of label on case

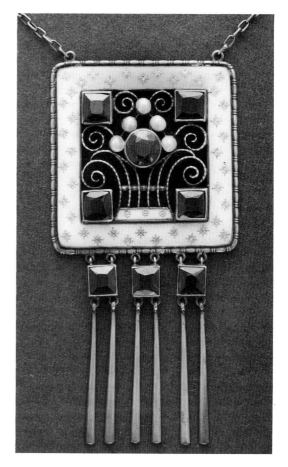

T. Fahrner, c.1910-13 (Cat. 342)

PLATE 103   ART NOUVEAU : AUSTRIA

K. Moser, 1899-1900 (Cat. 207)

J. Sika (shape), A. Krasnik (decoration), Josef Böck, c. 1901-2 (Cat. 270)

K. Moser pupils, Vienna, Josef Böck, c. 1901-2 (Cat. 208)

J. Hoffmann, Wiener Werkstätte, 1909-11 (Cat. 125)

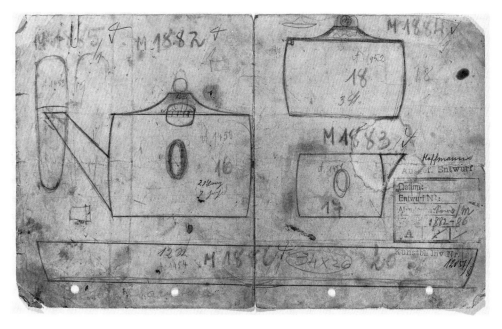

Fig. 28 Design for Cat. 125

PLATE 105

JOSEF HOFFMANN AND THE WIENER WERKSTÄTTE

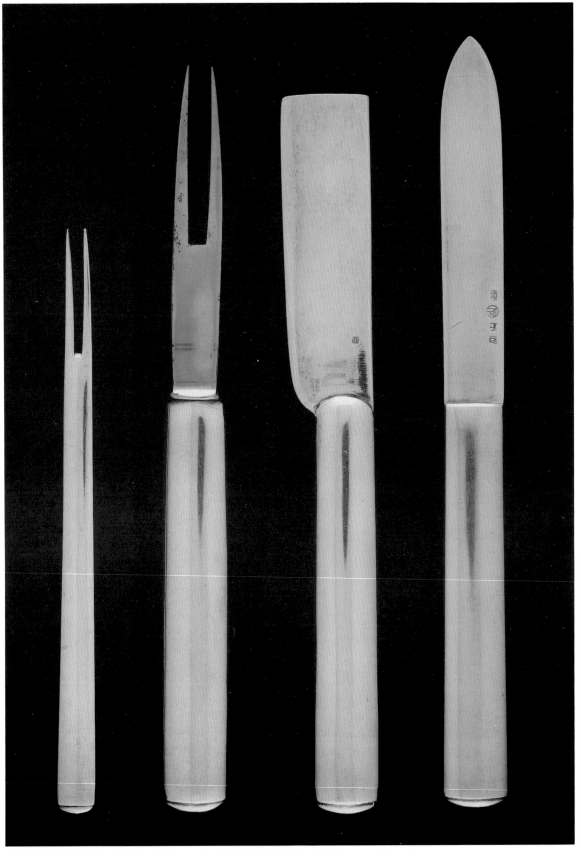

J. Hoffmann, Wiener Werkstätte, 1906 (Cat. 124)

J. Lötz Witwe (?), *c.* 1914-20 (Cat. 146)

M. Powolny, J. & L. Lobmeyr, *c.* 1914 (Cat. 244)

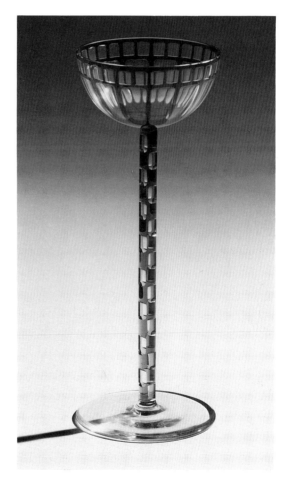

J. Hoffmann, Wiener Werkstätte, *c.* 1905 (Cat. 123)

O. Prutscher, Meyr's Neffe, *c.* 1907 (Cat. 245)

PLATE 107

FRANK LLOYD WRIGHT

Frank Lloyd Wright, Wakabayashico Porcelain Co., *c.*1922,
made after 1961 (Cat. 317)

Frank Lloyd Wright, James A. Miller, 1893-9 (Cat. 316)

Fig. 29 Photograph of Wright's studio, with a weed-holder
on the desk

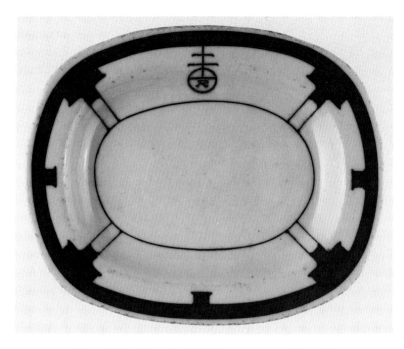

Roycroft Workshops, Buffalo Pottery, *c.*1909-10 (Cat. 263)

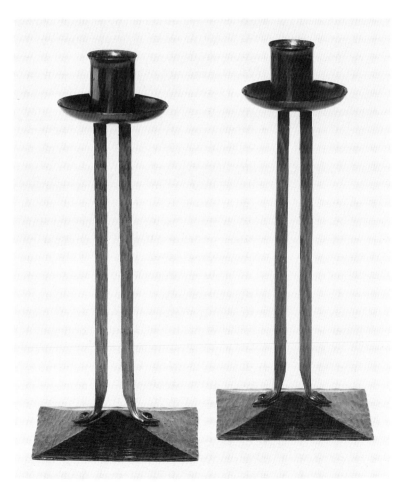

K. Kipp, Roycroft Workshops, before 1912 (Cat. 264)

PLATE 109

LOUIS COMFORT TIFFANY

L. C. Tiffany, c. 1900 (Cat. 285)

L. C. Tiffany, before 1906 (Cat. 288)

L. C. Tiffany, c. 1906 (Cat. 286)

L. C. Tiffany, c. 1896 (Cat. 284)

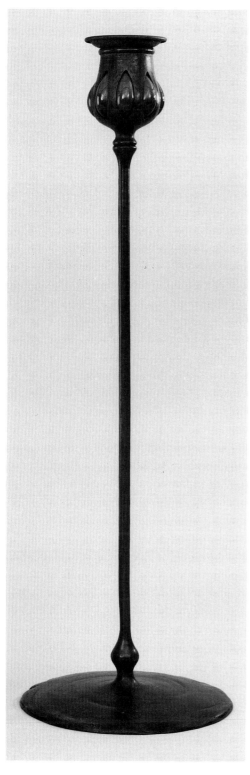

L. C. Tiffany, *c.* 1900 (Cat. 287)

Grueby Pottery, *c.* 1897-8 (Cat. 120)

PLATE III

ENGLAND: WEDGWOOD, 1920S

T. Lessore, c. 1920-24 (Cat. 142)

T. Lessore, c. 1920-24 (Cat. 143)

M. Goupy, J. Wedgwood & Sons, before 1915, made 1924 (Cat. 117)

J. R. Skeaping, J. Wedgwood & Sons, *c*.1926-7, made *c*.1935-9 (Cat. 271)

P. Follot, J. Wedgwood & Sons, 1912-13, made 1921 (Cat. 110)

PLATE 113   KEITH MURRAY

K. Murray, J. Wedgwood & Sons, 1933 (Cat. 218)

K. Murray, J. Wedgwood & Sons, 1933 (Cat. 219)

K. Murray, Stevens & Williams, 1933 (Cat. 215)

K. Murray, Stevens & Williams, 1939 (Cat. 217)

K. Murray, Stevens & Williams, 1933 (Cat. 216)

PLATE 115

ENGLAND: 1930S

H. Stabler, W. Hutton & Sons, *c.* 1930 (Cat. 275)

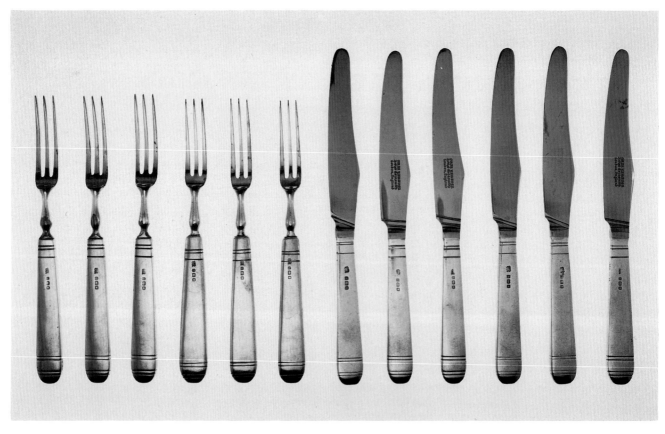

O. Ramsden, 1935-6 (Cat. 253)

Gray-Stan Studio, 1926-36 (Cat. 118)

J. Powell & Sons, c.1930 (Cat. 243)

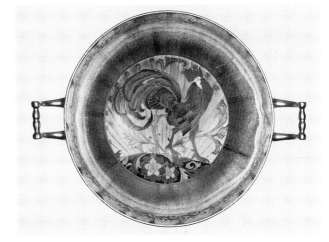

Minton & Co., 1925 (Cat. 198)

PLATE 117   FRANCE: 1920S

J. G. Argy-Rousseau, 1921 (Cat. 3)   Cat. 3: original Liberty & Co. box

R. Lalique, 1920 (Cat. 140)

R. Lalique (or M. E. Sabino), before 1929 (Cat. 344)

J. Puiforcat, 1929 (Cat. 248)

PLATE 119 HOLLAND: LEERDAM GLASS, 1920S-1930S

A. D. Copier, Leerdam, 1926-7 (Cat. 51)

A. D. Copier, Leerdam, 1930 (Cat. 53)

C. de Lorm, Leerdam, 1920-23 (Cat. 77)

A. D. Copier, Leerdam, 1923-4 (Cat. 50)

A. D. Copier, Leerdam, c.1936 (Cat. 54)

A. D. Copier, Leerdam, 1927 (Cat. 52)

PLATE 121

SCANDINAVIA : JACOB BANG

J. Bang, Holmegaard, 1928 (Cat. 6-8)

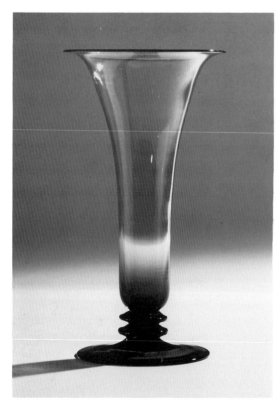

J. Bang, Holmegaard, c. 1928 (Cat. 9)

J. Bang, Holmegaard, 1928 (Cat. 10)

Royal Copenhagen Porcelain Factory, after 1922 (Cat. 49)

A. Aalto, Iittala, 1936, made c. 1981 (Cat. 1)

Rörstrand (Louise Adelberg), c. 1940 (Cat. 261)

PLATE 123

SCANDINAVIA : G. JENSEN

J. Rohde, G. Jensen, 1919 (Cat. 259)

H. Nielsen, G. Jensen, 1930, made 1933-44 (Cat. 223)

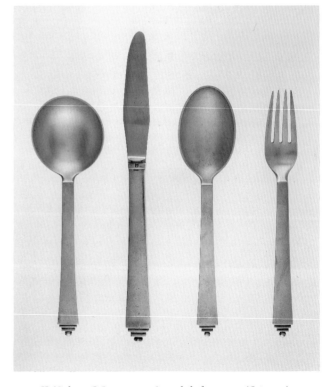

H. Nielsen, G. Jensen, 1926, made before 1934 (Cat. 222)

P. Müller-Munk, Revere Copper & Brass Co., 1935 (Cat. 214)

Russel Wright, Chase Brass & Copper Co., before 1934 (Cat. 318)

PLATE 125

AMERICA: 1930S

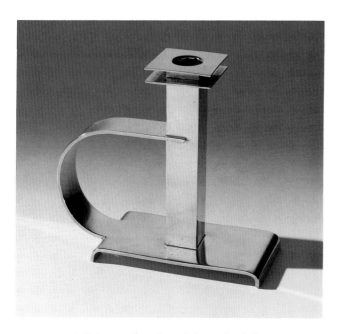

A. Reimann, Chase Brass & Copper Co., before
1931 (Cat. 254)

N. Bel Geddes, Revere Copper & Brass Co., 1934
(Cat. 113)

W. D. Teague and E. W. Fuerst, Libbey Glass Co., 1939 (Cat. 281)

A. D. Nash, Libbey Glass Co., 1931-2 (Cat. 220)

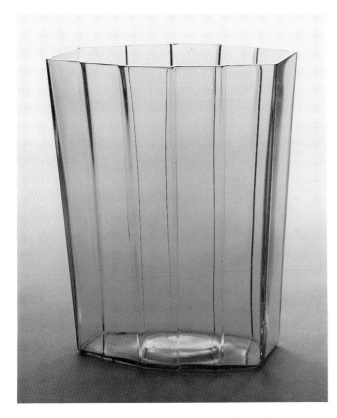

G. Sakier, Fostoria Glass Co., c. 1930 (Cat. 268)

G. Sakier, Fostoria Glass Co., c. 1930 (Cat. 267)

PLATE 127

AMERICA: EVA ZEISEL, 1940S

E. Zeisel, Red Wing Pottery, 1946 (back row: Cat. 335, 358, 333; front row: Cat. 360, 359, 334, 361)

E. Zeisel, Red Wing Pottery, 1946 (Cat. 361)

J. Hoffmann, *c.*1923 (Cat. 126)

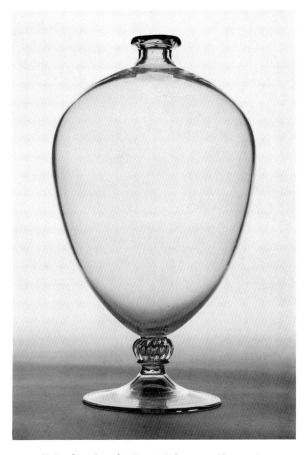

V. Zecchin, Cappelin-Venini & Co., 1921 (Cat. 355)

Poschinger'sche Krystallglasfabrik, *c.*1920-30 (Cat. 232)

N. Slutzky, before 1937 (Cat. 272)

PLATE 129 GERMANY: CERAMICS

Unattributed, probably German, *c.* 1925-30 (Cat. 336)

E. J. Margold, Ludwig Wessel AG, after 1911 (Cat. 155)

M. Laeuger, 1924 (Cat. 139)

L. König, Majolika-Manufaktur Karlsruhe, 1922 (Cat. 135)

Majolika-Manufaktur Karlsruhe, c. 1930-33 (Cat. 130)

PLATE 131

BAUHAUS

M. Brandt, 1924 (Cat. 26)

Cat. 26: strainer

O. Lindig, Majolika-Manufaktur Karlsruhe, before 1929, made 1929-62 (Cat. 144)

O. Lindig and T. Bogler, Majolika-Manufaktur Karlsruhe, before 1923,
made 1929-62 (Cat. 145)

T. Bogler, Steingut-Fabriken Velten-Vordamm, 1925-6 (Cat. 24)

PLATE 133   GERMANY: 1920S-1930S

M. Friedländer, Berlin Porcelain Factory, 1929, decoration T. Petri 1931 (Cat. 112)

T. Petri, Berlin Porcelain Factory, 1931/8 (Cat. 231)

H. Gretsch, Arzberg, 1931 (Cat. 119)

G. Marcks, Schott & Genossen, 1925-30, made 1930-39 (Cat. 154)

PLATE 135   WILHELM WAGENFELD

W. Wagenfeld, Vereinigte Lausitzer Glaswerke, 1937 (Cat. 307)

W. Wagenfeld, Vereinigte Lausitzer Glaswerke, 1938 (Cat. 308)

W. Wagenfeld, Schott & Genossen, 1930-34, made before 1945 (Cat. 303-4)

W. Wagenfeld, Fürstenberg, 1934 (Cat. 305-6)

PLATE 137   RUSSIAN REVOLUTIONARY PORCELAIN

V. Timorev, State Porcelain Factory, Petrograd, 1920 (Cat. 352)

V. Timorev, State Porcelain Factory, Petrograd, 1922 (Cat. 353)

PLATE 139

S. Chekhonin, Lomonossov Porcelain Factory, Leningrad, 1925 (Cat. 340)

S. Chekhonin, State Porcelain Factory, Petrograd, 1918 (Cat. 341)

S. Chekhonin, State Porcelain Factory, Petrograd, 1920 (Cat. 35)

A. Shchekotikhina-Pototskaya, State Porcelain Factory, Petrograd, 1922 (Cat. 350)

V. P. Belkin, State Porcelain Factory, Petrograd, 1919 (Cat. 18)

PLATE 141   RUSSIAN REVOLUTIONARY PORCELAIN

R. Vilde, State Porcelain Factory, Petrograd, 1920 (Cat. 356)

R. Vilde, State Porcelain Factory, Petrograd, 1921 (Cat. 357)

I. G. Chashnik, State Porcelain Factory, Petrograd, 1923 (Cat. 34)

PLATE 143

RUSSIAN REVOLUTIONARY PORCELAIN

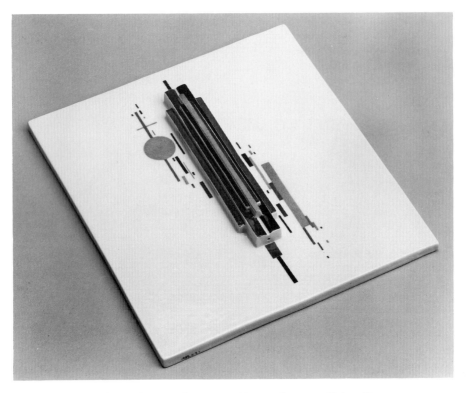

N. Suetin, State Porcelain Factory, Petrograd, 1923-4 (Cat. 278)

N. Suetin, State Porcelain Factory, Petrograd, 1923 (Cat. 279-80)

List of Comparative Illustrations

The comparative illustrations are listed here in order of their appearance in the plates, not in order of catalogue entries

Figs 1 and 2 (plate 1) Pugin, Cat. 247. Two watercolour drawings from the Minton factory archive, from a group of related designs, many of which are signed by Pugin, with the date 1850 or 1851. Design no. s13 shows the border motif on the tazza, while design no. s15 shows the central rosette. Royal Doulton.

Fig. 3 (plate 3) Godwin, Cat. 114. E. W. Godwin's design for the presentation trowel awarded to the Mayor of Northampton in 1861. Contained amongst Godwin's designs for Northampton Town Hall. Victoria and Albert Museum, Department of Prints and Drawings, E.598-1963. Given by the artist's son, Edward Godwin.

Fig. 4 (plate 5) Burges, Cat. 29. Burges's water-colour design for the cup in section and elevation, showing the enamelled rosette at the top and the camel medallion inside the lid. RIBA Drawings Collection, Burges albums, 'Orfèvrerie Domestique', p. 16.

Fig. 5 (plate 6) Burges, Cat. 29. Burges's water-colour designs for the enamelled quatrefoils on his own cup and on those for his friends. RIBA Drawings Collection, Burges albums, 'Orfèvrerie Domestique', p. 15.

Fig. 6 (plate 7) Cristalleries de Clichy, Cat. 40. Illustration from the *Art Journal Illustrated Catalogue of the International Exhibition of 1862*, p. 213, showing engraved glass exhibited by the Cristalleries de Clichy, including Cat. 40.

Figs 7a and b (plate 18) Wedgwood, Cat. 309. Wedgwood earthenware sgraffito plaque with an Egyptian head, signed A. A. Toft and dated 1879. Formerly in the collection of the late Dr Leonard Rakow.

Fig. 8 (plate 24) De Morgan, Cat. 78. William De Morgan's water-colour design for a closely similar dish with deer and trees. Victoria and Albert Museum, Department of Prints and Drawings, E.1218-1917. Bequeathed by Evelyn De Morgan.

Fig. 9 (plate 26) Stevens, Cat. 276-7. View of the former miniature railing outside the main railing of the British Museum, showing Stevens's lions *in situ*. Enlarged detail from an old postcard of the museum, made before the railing was dismantled in 1895. British Museum Archive. Given by Christopher Date.

Fig. 10 (plate 29) Dresser, Cat. 84. Pencil design for a kettle with angled spout and claw feet, from Dresser's sketchbook. Ipswich Museum, MS R.1972-72, p. 1. Given by Capt. C. A. Orchard in 1972.

Fig. 11 (plate 30) Dresser, Cat. 83. Pencil design for this teaset from the Elkington Pattern Book, Volume 2. Birmingham Public Library, Archive Department, ref. no. ZZ323 (660631), p. 329.

Fig. 12 (plate 38) Dresser, Cat. 82 and 96. Group of Fiji ritual drinking vessels including a male figure dish, from T. Williams, *Fiji and the Fijians*, London 1850, 60.

Fig. 13 (plate 45) Nichols. Cat. 221. Glazed earthenware vase decorated with a dragon in relief, with free-standing leg. Cincinnati Art Museum, 1881.43; H. 25 in. Gift of the Women's Art Museum Association.

Fig. 14 (plate 47) Tiffany & Co., Cat. 283. Hammering and mounting design for this waiter of 8 February 1880, indicating the different coloured alloys to be used. Courtesy of the Tiffany Archives, New York.

Fig. 15 (plate 48) Ovchinnikov, Cat. 230. Silver jug by Tiffany & Co. with applied coloured metals, copied by Ovchinnikov in silver-gilt. Musée d'Orsay, Paris, inv. no. OAO 1042; H. 22 cm. Photo Musées Nationaux.

Fig. 16 (plate 49) Tiffany & Co., Cat. 351. Design drawing for this tankard of 15 December 1874. Courtesy of the Tiffany Archives, New York.

Fig. 17 (plate 57) Powell, Cat. 234. Philip Webb's design for a similar wine glass, *c.*1860. Victoria and Albert Museum, Department of Prints and Drawings, E327-1944. Given by Miss Dorothy Walker.

Fig. 18 (plate 58) Powell, Cat. 234-5. Working factory drawing for six drinking glasses designed by Philip Webb and T. G. Jackson. Museum of London, Powell Archive.

Fig. 19 (plate 59) Powell, Cat. 236. Harry Powell's sketch for this tazza and for one of the gannets, from his source notebook, 1901-2. Museum of London, Powell Archive, ref. 80.547/3251/1.

Fig. 20 (plate 61) Powell, Cat. 240. Design for a cut-glass candlestick of similar shape and dimensions, number 0 2923, from the Special Designs Book of 1906-13. Museum of London, Powell Archive.

Fig. 21 (plate 70) Mackintosh, Cat. 147. Mackintosh's pencil and wash design for the silver cutlery made for Francis and Jessie Newbery. University of Glasgow, Mackintosh Collection, Q(b)7.

Fig. 22 (plate 72) Mackintosh, Cat. 148. Mackintosh's sketch for a writing cabinet for Walter Blackie at the Hill House, with a 'Hill House' candlestick placed on top of the cabinet. Dated 1904. Pencil and wash. University of Glasgow, Mackintosh Collection, M(e)5.

Fig. 23 (plate 72) Mackintosh, Cat. 149. Mackintosh's sketch for the Blue Bedroom for Katherine Cranston at Hous'hill, with two 'Hous'hill' candlesticks placed in the alcoves above the bedside cupboards. Pencil and wash. University of Glasgow, Mackintosh Collection, M(f)8.

Fig. 24 (plate 73) Mackintosh, Cat. 151. View of the guest bedroom at 78 Derngate, Northampton, with the clock *in situ* on the fireplace, seen reflected in the mirror. University of Glasgow, Mackintosh Collection, G(h)19.

Fig. 25 (plate 90) Olbrich, Cat. 229. Olbrich's 'Design for a simple wash service', signed and dated 21 November 1903, showing his pattern of triangles. Kunstbibliothek Berlin, inv. no. 12099.

Fig. 26 (plate 96) Riemerschmid, Cat. 257. Factory working drawing for the 'Riemerschmid' table glass service from the Kristallglasfabrik B. Von Poschinger. Kunstmuseum Düsseldorf, Inv. no. 131km. Photo Landesbildstelle Rhineland.

Fig. 27 (plate 97) Riemerschmid, Cat. 258. Riemerschmid's design for a glass service, G110, dated 1911. Architektursammlung der Technischen Universität, Munich.

Fig. 28 (plate 104) Hoffmann, Cat. 125. Hoffmann's designs for this coffee service, design nos 1882-4. Österreichisches Museum für angewandte Kunst, Vienna, Wiener Werkstätte archive, inv. no. 12051/8.

Fig. 29 (plate 107) Wright, Cat. 316. Contemporary photograph (after 1903) of Frank Lloyd Wright's studio at Oak Park, showing a weed-holder *in situ*. The Metropolitan Museum of Art, Department of Prints, 1981.1005.17. Henry Fuermann Collection. Gift of Hermann G. Pundt PhD and the Edward Pearce Casey Fund.

Index of Marks, Monograms and Signatures

This index includes all manufacturers', importers' and retailers' marks, designers' signatures, stamps and monograms that are photographically reproducible, with the exception of those that form an integral part of the description of an object and which are therefore illustrated with the object, e.g. original boxes (Cat. 3, 129), original lables (Cat. 68) and inscriptions (Cat. 27, 29, 312). The marks are illustrated in catalogue order and each is identified with its catalogue number and the name of the designer or manufacturer. In those cases where the same mark appears on more than one object, the clearest mark is shown and identified by its catalogue number, while the catalogue numbers of the other pieces with same mark are listed in brackets. If the mark required appears on a catalogue number given in brackets and thus not in numerical sequence, the reader is referred to the catalogue headings or the general index, which list other items by the same firm or designer. The reader should also be aware that some objects have more than one mark photograph. Where variant marks of the same firm occur on different objects, cross-references to the relevant catalogue numbers are given.

N.B. Russian porcelain. All these pieces bear the mark of the State Porcelain Factory, Petrograd (Leningrad from 1925). Examples of this mark are shown under Cat. 34 and Cat. 35, which also illustrates the obliterated Imperial Porcelain Factory mark. For examples of Imperial Porcelain Factory marks, see Cat. 34, 345, 350 and 353. All artists' marks and signatures are illustrated under the relevant catalogue numbers.

1 Alvar Aalto

3 G. Argy-Rousseau

4 C. R. Ashbee, with London hallmarks

5 Guild of Handicraft Ltd, with London hallmarks

11 Peter Behrens

12 Steingutfabrik und Kunsttöpferei Franz Anton Mehlem

14 Copenhagen assay marks and retailer's initials 'BJ'

17 Nürnberger Handwerkskunst Bayerisches Gewerbemuseum; Krautheim & Adelberg (see Cat. 38 for variant)

19 (20) W. A. S. Benson

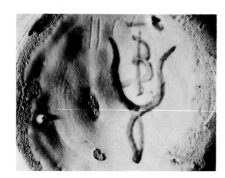

23 (21, 22) W. A. S. Benson

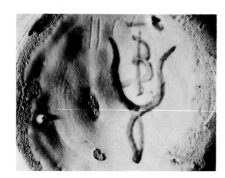

24 Theodor Bogler

27 P.-J. Brocard. See also plate 21

28 W.C. Brouwer and M. B. Bruyn

29 Jes Barkentin for Barkentin & Krall

32 E. Bingham senior, Castle Hedingham Pottery

33 E. W. Bingham, Castle Hedingham Pottery

34 'Suprematism' with Suprematist logo; State Porcelain Factory, 1923; Imperial Porcelain Factory, Nicholas II 1906; 'after the design of Ilya Chashnik'

35 State Porcelain Factory, 1920; Obliterated Imperial Porcelain Factory mark

37 Bruckmann & Söhne (eagle), with German assay marks; M. T. Wetzlar (retailer)

38 Krautheim & Adelberg (see also 17); Louis Noack (retailer)

39 J. F. Christy

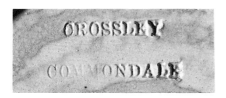

41 Commondale Pottery

42 Commondale Pottery

46-7 (43-5, 48) W. T. Copeland & Sons

44 A. Hays

45 (43-4) A. Jarvis

49 Royal Copenhagen Porcelain Factory

50 (51-4) A. D. Copier, Leerdam serial glass signet

53 Signet of the Vereniging van Nederlandse Wijnhandelaren

55 Walter Crane

56 Walter Crane (left); R. Joyce (right); Pilkington's Tile and Pottery Co. (centre)

57 Théodore Deck

58 Georges de Feure; Art Nouveau Bing

77 C. de Lorm, Leerdam serial glass signet

79 W. De Morgan & Co.; Joe Juster

80 Taxile Doat; Sèvres, 1897 (see 269 for variant)

81 Dominick & Haff

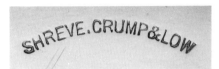

81 Shreve, Crump & Low (retailer)

82 Thomas Johnson

83 Elkington & Co.

84 (85-9) Hukin & Heath, with design registration mark for 6 May 1878

92 Christopher Dresser, facsimile signature; J. Dixon & Sons

93 (90-91) J. Dixon & Sons

94 'Dr. Dresser's design' with design registration mark for 30 October 1883

94 R. Perry & Son

103 (97, 99, 100-102) Henry Tooth

103 (96-102) Linthorpe Art Pottery

104 Christopher Dresser, printed facsimile signature on Old Hall earthenware

105 (107) Liberty & Co. Clutha trademark incorporating Dresser's name, with matt words and flower (left)

105 James Couper & Sons' Clutha trademark (right)

106 Liberty & Co. Clutha trademark, with matt background (left); James Couper & Sons' Clutha trademark (right)

108 La Maison Moderne

109 J. Eisenlöffel

111 G. Fox for C. T. & G. Fox, with London hallmarks

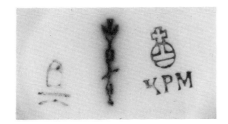

112 Kunstgewerbeschule Halle (left); Staatliche Porzellanmanufaktur (sceptre and orb), see also 231

113 (214) Revere Copper & Brass Co.

115 (116) Gorham Manufacturing Co.

117 (110, 271) Wedgwood

118 Gray-Stan

119 Porzellanfabrik Arzberg

120 Grueby Pottery

121 Hart & Huyshe

124 (123) Monogram FK-KF; Wiener Werkstätte

125 (123, 124) Wiener Werkstätte rose trademark; Josef Hoffmann

125 Otto Prutscher

127 J. S. Hunt for Hunt & Roskell

127 Alfred Brown

128 P. Ipsens Enke

129 G. Jensen. See 222-3 and 259 for variants

131 Van Kempen en Zonen, with The Hague assay mark and date-letter

132 Keswick School of Industrial Arts, with Chester hallmarks

133 Liberty & Co., with Birmingham hallmarks

134c W. H. Haseler 'Solkets' trademark

135 Ludwig König; Majolika-Manufaktur, Karlsruhe (see 144 for variant)

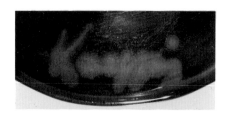

136 Karl Köpping

137 (212, 330, 332) R. Merkelbach (see 331 for variant); C. Krause

138 Max Laeuger, Tonwerke Kandern

139 Max Laeuger

140 R. Lalique (moulded)

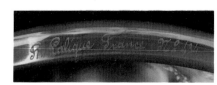

140 R. Lalique (etched)

141 C. Lebeau, Leerdam serial glass signet

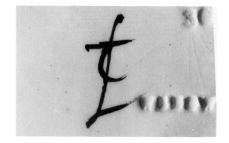

142 (143) Thérèse Lessore

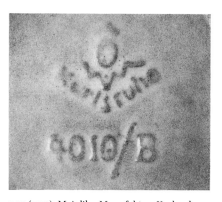

144 (145) Majolika-Manufaktur, Karlsruhe. See also 135

147 (148-9) D. W. Hislop, with Glasgow hallmarks

150 Miss Cranston's Tea-rooms

153 J. Uffrecht & Co.; Walter Magnussen

154 Schott & Genossen, Jenaer Glas. See also 303-4

155 E. Margold; L. Wessel AG

156 Bahlsens Keksfabrik

157 Gilbert Marks

157 Gilbert Marks, with London hallmarks for 1902

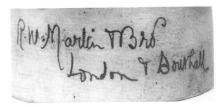

161 (173-4, 177-8) R. W. Martin & Bros

166 (158) R. W. Martin Sᶜ

172 (159, 176) R. W. Martin

175 (160, 179-83, 186-95) Martin Bros

185 (184) Martin Brothers

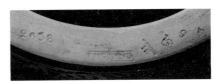

197 Minton & Co., with date symbol for 1898

198 Minton & Co.

205 Bernard Moore

206 (199) Bernard Moore

208 Pupils of Kolo Moser, at the Kunstgewerbeschule Vienna

209 Albin Müller (in relief)

209 (226) Eduard Hueck (in relief). See 210 for variant

210 Albin Müller (impressed); Eduard Hueck (impressed)

213 S. P. Gerz

215 (216-17) Keith Murray; Stevens & Williams

218 (219) Keith Murray; Wedgwood

220 (281) Libbey Glass Manufacturing Co.

222d G. Jensen; 'GS' for G. Stockwell & Co. Ltd., with London import marks

222a,b,c G. Jensen; 'G. J. L^D'. for G. Jensen & Co. Ltd., with London import marks

223 H. Nielsen; G. Jensen

224 Christofle

225 Clarfeld & Springmayer

226 Eduard Hueck. See 210 for variant

226 (224, 227) J. Olbrich

229 Villeroy & Boch. See also 339

230 Ovchinnikov, with Moscow assay marks

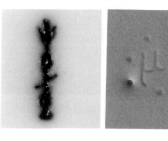

231 Staatliche Porzellanmanufaktur, Berlin, with Greek year letter *mu*

233 Alfred Powell

244 J. & L. Lobmeyr

248 Jean Puiforcat

248 M. Beer & Son Ltd., with London import marks

250 (249) Ramsden & Carr

252 (251, 253) Omar Ramsden

254 A. Reimann

254 (318) Chase Brass & Copper Company

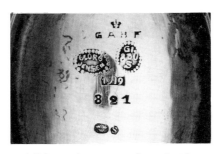

259 G. Jensen (see 129, 222 for variants); Guldsmedsaktiebolaget (importer) with Swedish assay marks

260 Rookwood Pottery; A. R. Valentien

261 Rörstrand Porcelain Factory; Louise Adelborg

262 Porzellanmanufaktur Rosenthal

263 Buffalo Pottery

264 Roycroft Workshops

265 Rozenburg porcelain factory, with date cypher for 1899; monogram of W. P. Hartgring

269 Sèvres. See 80 for variant

270 Porzellanmanufaktur J. Böck

271 J. Skeaping

273 M. L. E. Solon

275 W. Hutton & Sons Ltd; Harold Stabler

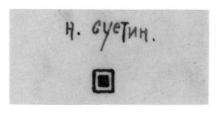

278 N. Suetin, with Suprematist logo

279 'Suprematism' with Suprematist logo; State Porcelain Factory, 1923; 'after the design of N. Suetin'

280 'Suprematism' with Suprematist logo; State Porcelain Factory, 1923; 'after the design of N. Suetin'

282 Henry Hebbard; Tiffany & Co.

283 Tiffany & Co. See 351 for variant

284 L. C. Tiffany

285 L. C. Tiffany

286 (287-88) Tiffany Studios

289 Artus & Anne Van Briggle

290 H. van de Velde; T. Müller (see 292 for variant)

292　T. Müller. See 290 for variant

292 (291)　H. van de Velde

293 (354)　H. van de Velde

294 (295)　H. van de Velde

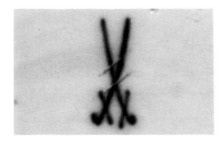

294 (122, 256, 295)　Porzellanmanufaktur Meissen

296　Copenhagen assay marks; S. & M. Benzen, retailers

300　Jesson, Birkett & Co.

303　Schott & Genossen, Jenaer Glaswerke. See 154 for variant

304　Schott & Genossen, Jenaer Glaswerke

305 (306)　Porzellanmanufaktur Fürstenberg

308　Vereinigte Lausitzer Glaswerke

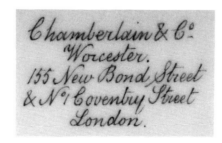

312　Worcester Porcelain, Chamberlain & Co.

314　Worcester Royal Porcelain Co. Ltd.

315　Worcester Royal Porcelain Co. Ltd. with design registration mark for 18 January 1872

317　K. Wakabayashico Porcelain Co.

320 (319, 321-5)　Russel Wright; Steubenville Pottery

326 Iroquois China Co.; Russel Wright

328 Württembergische Metallwarenfabrik

331 R. Merkelbach. See 137 for variant

332 Dürerbund-Werkbund-Genossenschaft

336 Unidentified

339 Villeroy & Boch. See 229 for variant

342 Theodor Fahrner

343 State Porcelain Factory special famine mark 1921; Natalya Girschfeld

345 Maria Lebedeva, signature

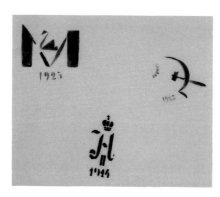

345 Maria Lebedeva, monogram; State Porcelain Factory, 1923; Imperial Porcelain Factory, Nicholas II 1914

347 (346, 348) Schwarzburger Werkstätten für Porzellankunst

348 Gerhard Marcks

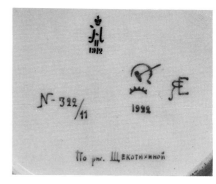

350 Imperial Porcelain Factory, Nicholas II 1912; State Porcelain Factory, 1922; Ekaterina Yakimovskaya, monogram; 'after the design of Shchekotikhina-Pototskaya'

351 Tiffany & Co. See 283 for variant

352 Vasilii Timorev, signature

353 Vasilii Timorev, signature

353 (352) State Porcelain Factory; Imperial
Porcelain Factory, Nicholas II 1906; Vasilii
Timorev, artist's mark (trefoil); unidentified
initials G.O.

Acquisitions 1991-1993

The following are short entries for acquisitions made since the first edition of this catalogue went to press. Illustrations of selected objects can be found on Plates 144-7 (pp. 324-7).

Albertus, Gundorph 1887-1970

For a brief biography, see *Georg Jensen Silversmithy*, exhibition catalogue, Renwick Gallery, Washington 1980.

362 Eight pieces of cutlery

Stainless steel, comprising dinner knife and fork, luncheon knife and fork, dinner, dessert and tea spoons, and a butter knife.

MARKS The knife blades each stamped 'GEORG JENSEN DENMARK' and 'STAINLESS STEEL RAADVAD'.

Designed in 1941 as part of the 'Mitra' service and made by G. Jensen, Copenhagen.

362a-b Knives: L 23cm and 20.3cm   1991,12-5,1-2
362c-d Forks: L 18.8cm and 17.5cm   1991,12-5,3-4
362e-g Spoons: L 19cm, 17.7cm and 13cm   1991,12-5,5-7
362h Butter knife: L 16.2cm   1991,12-5,8
Given by Sir David and Lady Wilson, who acquired them in the early 1950s

Gundorph Albertus trained as a sculptor; he worked at Jensen as a chaser and from 1926 to 1954 as the company's assistant director. This cutlery service was originally conceived in silver, with the title 'Mermaid', but with the restrictions of the war years it was made in stainless steel instead, under the name 'Mitra', and became the company's first stainless steel cutlery pattern; it is still in production. In 1985, a new version was produced in silver-plate under the original name, 'Mermaid'.

Baccarat, Cristalleries de founded 1764

Curtis, J.-L., *Baccarat*, London 1992
Sautot, D., *Baccarat, une histoire. 1764...*, Paris 1993

363 Ewer   [PLATE 146]

Glass, free-blown, with ovoid body and narrow neck expanding into a grotesque sea-monster's mask, its open mouth forming the spout. Decorated with wheel-engraved ornament over the entire upper part to suggest the monster's face and scaly body, which terminates in entwined tails wreathed with delicate ivy tendrils at the base of the ewer. The lower part of the ewer is left partly clear. The foot is also engraved with ivy tendrils. The high handle has a protruding point at the base.

MARKS None.

Made by the Cristalleries de Baccarat, Lorraine, for the Paris Exposition Universelle of 1878.

H 31.9cm   1991,7-2,1

This highly original zoomorphic neo-Mannerist ewer is a virtuoso piece of wheel-engraving and is unlike anything else produced at the time by other firms specialising in engraved glass, either in France or in England. Only two other versions of this model are recorded: one in the Musée des Arts Décoratifs, Paris, presented by Baccarat after the 1878 Exhibition, the other acquired by the museum at Lieberec, Czechoslovakia, in 1882 (where it was seen in 1987 by Jean-Luc Olivié of the Musée des Arts Décoratifs, Paris). Both examples are unpublished. The Paris version differs slightly in that the lip at the top is pulled up to a high peak. Probably a few versions were made for the Paris Exhibition and the best one given to the Musée des Arts Décoratifs. For an illustration of the British Museum version, see *Journal of Glass Studies* 35, 1993, 124.

The Museum of the Cristalleries de Baccarat in Paris holds an earlier version of this model, made for the Paris Exhibition of 1867 (illustrated in Sautot 1993, 53). It has the same inventive shape, with a high lip which is pierced to form the spout, but the engraved decoration comprises formal arabesques and grotesque ornament. There is no suggestion of a monster's head or body. This earlier version is also illustrated in Philadelphia 1978, cat. no. IV-21, where it is erroneously associated with the Paris Exhibition of 1855.

Bang, Jacob Eiler 1900-65

See Cat. 6-10.

364 Vase   [PLATE 147]

Glass, with wheel-engraved pattern of rows of wheat-ears curving alternately to the left or to the right and running to the edge of the vase.

MARKS Signed in diamond-point on the base 'H.G. 115 Jacob Bang Runemalm. 1936'.

The shape designed by Jacob Bang, with engraving executed by Elving Runemalm, and made at Holmegaards Glasvaerk, Naestved, Denmark, in 1936.

H 18.8cm   1992,6-12,1

Elving Runemalm, a glass engraver at the Orrefors factory in Sweden, worked at Holmegaard from the beginning of 1934 to 1939 and made many designs in conjunction with Bang. They are always signed with the two artists' names, a working number and the date. The Holmegaard factory archives contain a working list of the designs made by Runemalm with a sketch of each engraving; this vase appears as no. 115, with production number 6659/190, the number 190 referring to the engraving, which could be used on other shapes. Conversely, the same shape was used for a number of different engraved patterns; the shape of this vase may be earlier than 1936 and it was among the most popular (information kindly supplied by Mogens Schlüter).

This shape with the wheat-ears pattern was illustrated in *The Studio*, April 1937, 206. For a recent illustration of this vase, see *Journal of Glass Studies* 35, 1993, 129. For other vases designed jointly by Bang and Runemalm, see Lassen and Schlüter 1987, 26-7, pls 50, 65-6.

Barbédienne, Ferdinand 1810-92

There is no monograph on Barbédienne. For biographical details, see Mundt 1973.

365 Pair of candlesticks   [PLATE 145]

Gilt-bronze two-branch candlesticks decorated in champlevé enamel with stylised floral and geometric motifs in imitation of Chinese *cloisonné*. Double chains hang in a loop from the top of each candlestick to the branches at the side. The candle-holders are removable. The gilding is slightly worn at the tops.

MARKS Stamped on the foot 'BARBEDIENNE PARIS'.

Made by the firm of Ferdinand Barbédienne, Paris, c.1872-3.

H 34.5cm   1994,1-10,1 and 2

The firm of Barbédienne, established in Paris for the production of bronzes by 1847, specialised in reproductions of ancient metalwork, *champlevé* enamel bronzes and damascened or inlaid metalwork. They exhibited *champlevé* enamel bronzes in the Chinese taste at the London Exhibition of 1872 (*Art Journal Illustrated Catalogue*, 1872, 61) and at Vienna in 1873 (*Art Journal*, 1873, 325).

Unlike Elkington in Birmingham and the rival firm of Christofle in Paris, who produced *cloisonné* enamels, Barbédienne preferred the *champlevé* enamel technique, which they first exhibited in London in 1862, when the Victoria and Albert Museum acquired a large gilt-bronze vase and tripod with champlevé enamel in the Byzantine style (see Victoria and Albert Museum 1987, 112-13).

These candlesticks are a characteristic example of nineteenth-century eclecticism in their inspiration from both oriental and classical sources: the enamel motifs are partly Chinese in inspiration, albeit closer to illustrations of Chinese motifs in Owen Jones' *Grammar of Ornament* (1856) than to any direct Chinese prototype, while the looped chains are derived from Roman bronze lamps.

Behrens, Peter 1869-1940

See Cat. 11-17 and 338-9.

366 Wine glass   [PLATE 146]

Clear glass, free-blown, with tulip-shaped bowl and stem that expands to a ridge in the centre. The stem is made in two parts and joined at the centre.

MARKS None.

Designed in 1899 as part of a twelve-piece service for the Münchener Jahresausstellung im Glaspalast and made by the Kristallglasfabrik Benedikt von Poschinger, Oberzwieselau, Bavaria.

H 20.5cm   1992,5-12,1

Behrens' original drawing for this service describes this glass as a 'Römerkelch' or rummer; the drawing survives in the Kunstmuseum, Düsseldorf (see C. Sellner, *Gläserne Jugendstil aus Bayern*, Grafenau 1992, pl. 88). The design of this service dates from Behrens' early years in Munich; remarkable for its simplicity, it was the first 'artist's' service produced by Poschinger and was also Behrens' first set of table glasses. It was displayed as part of his dining room ensemble for the Munich Glaspalast exhibition (Nuremberg 1980, 37, pl. 2). For contemporary illustrations, see *Dekorative Kunst* 3, 1899-1900, 18-19, and *Art et Décoration* 10, 1901, 132, amongst glassware displayed at the Maison Moderne in Paris. The exclusive distribution rights were held by Keller & Reiner, Berlin.

For illustrations of other glasses from this service, see Darmstadt 1976, Band 4, cat. no. 15; Nuremberg 1980, no. 69; Philadelphia 1988, cat. no. 11 (with extensive bibliography); Ulmer 1990, cat. no. 14.

367 Fork

Silver, cast, with linear relief ornament. The back of the handle is left plain in the centre to take engraved initials.

MARKS Stamped on the reverse of the handle with manufacturer's name, 'RÜCKERT', and mark (an 'R' with a wheel), and the silver standard marks '800', a crown and a crescent.

Designed in 1901 as part of a service of cutlery for Behrens' own house at the Darmstadt artists' colony, for the exhibition *Ein Dokument Deutscher Kunst*, held in 1901. Made by the firm of M.J. Rückert, Mainz.

L 21.7cm   1992,7-12,1

The cutlery was shown on the table in Behrens' dining room, together with the table glasses with red stems (see Cat. 338) and the porcelain dinnerware with linear decoration (see Cat. 11 and 368). For a complete set, comprising dinner, breakfast, fish cutlery, servers, etc., from the dowry ordered from Behrens in 1902 by Emilie Reif for her daughter, see Nuremberg 1980, cat. no. 170. This fork is the dinner fork. Several other pieces from this service are to be found in museums in Germany, for example the Hessisches Landesmuseum, Darmstadt (Heller 1982, cat. no. 9) and the Museum der Künstlerkolonie, Darmstadt (Ulmer 1990, cat. no. 4). For contemporary illustrations of the service, see Koch 1902, 368; *Die Kunst* 6, 1901-2, 25. For the most recent discussion, in the context of the German cutlery industry, see Sänger 1991, no. 9.

368 Cup, saucer and plate

Hard-paste porcelain, glazed white with overglaze printed decoration in red. The cup of octagonal shape with incurved sides and linear pattern, the saucer and plate both completely flat, octagonal, with shallow rim, the saucer with red border only, the plate with a much more elaborate pattern.

MARKS On the base of each item artist's monogram 'PB' and 'GESCHÜTZT' printed in overglaze red, see mark for Cat. 11.

Designed in 1900-1901 and made by the Porzellanfabrik Gebrüder Bauscher, Weiden, Oberpfalz, Upper Bavaria.

368a Cup: H 7 cm, D of saucer 15.8 cm 1993,10-12,3 and 3a
368b Plate: D 17 cm 1993,10-12,4

The cup and matching saucer belong to the service that Behrens designed for his own house at the Darmstadt artists' colony (see Cat. 11), which formed part of the 1901 exhibition *Ein Dokument Deutscher Kunst*. Behrens' service was decorated with the same pattern but in pale grey, not red (See Ulmer 1990, cat. no. 5). The plate is from a different service, using the same shapes, but with a denser pattern; examples of this alternative pattern are to be found in the Hessisches Landesmuseum, see Nuremberg 1980, no. 65, and Heller 1982, cat. no. 14.

Borgen, A. & Co. London 1869-79

There is no recent literature on this Danish firm of retailers, who had premises in London from 1869 to 1879. For contemporary accounts, see *The English Woman's Domestic Magazine*, 1 March 1869, 140-42 and *Art Journal*, 1870, 267-70, and 1873, 377.

369 Two soup plates

Earthenware (creamware), with transfer-printed and hand-painted decoration in the Japanese taste. On one plate (369a), a group of shrimps set asymetrically in shades of salmon pink with black outlines; on the other (369b) an asymmetrical group of mussels in shades of grey-black. In both groups the objects are arranged at different angles and cast shadows which are naturalistically depicted. The plate with mussels has a chip on the rim and has been restored.

MARKS Both plates impressed 'WEDGWOOD' with impressed date letters for 1868 (369a) and 1871 (369b) with a special printed backstamp incorporating the Prince of Wales' feathers and motto, with 'Royal Danish Galleries, 142 New Bond Street, A. Borgen & Co.' and 'Designed and painted by Léonce Goutard and Pierre Mallet', all in capital letters, and 'TRADE MARK' (see Batkin 1982, 227).

Designed and painted by Pierre Mallet and Léonce Goutard on Wedgwood blanks for A. Borgen & Co.'s Royal Danish Galleries, London, *c.*1873.

D 24.3 cm 1993,5-6,1-2

A description of Messrs Borgen & Co.'s Royal Danish Galleries published in *Art Journal*, 1873, 377, advertises a new line of ornamental and table ceramics painted by two French artists, Léonce Goutard and Pierre Mallet, 'whose services have been exclusively secured by Messrs Borgen'. This would explain the special registered backstamp. Little is known of the artists involved or how they came to work for Borgen. Pierre Mallet (d. 1898) worked as a ceramic painter in Paris until 1870, when he fled to London following the Paris Commune and turned to engraving. Léonce Goutard is recorded in the 1860s as a lithographic artist specialising in birds (J. Adhémar, *Inventaire du fonds français après 1800*, Bibliothèque Nationale, Paris 1955).

These two plates are from a series of tablewares (Batkin 1982, pl. 197) clearly inspired by Félix Bracquemond's well-known 'service Rousseau' of 1866-7. Commissioned by F.E. Rousseau

and decorated with Bracquemond's designs in the manner of Hokusai, the 'service Rousseau' was shown to great acclaim at the Paris Exhibition of 1867. For a full account of the service, see J.P. Bouillon et al., *Art, industrie et Japonisme. Le service 'Rousseau'*, exhibition catalogue, Musée d'Orsay, Paris 1988. Borgen's service was no doubt intended as a cheaper version of the celebrated French service, with the cachet of two French artists.

Brownfield, William & Son 1850-91

Jewitt, L., *Ceramic Art of Great Britain*, London 1878 and 1883, 472-6
Rhead, G.W. and F.A., *Staffordshire Pots and Potters*, 1906

370 Pair of vases [PLATE 145]

Earthenware, moulded, of square shape with relief decoration of parallel horizontal ridges down each side and a vertical panel in the centre with irises; at each side are stylised elephant-head handles containing fixed loops. The upper part has a cylindrical top and base and is set on a footed 'stand' with four scrolls at the junction. Glazed all over in deep yellow.

MARKS Each vase impressed on the base with the factory name 'BROWNFIELD', together with factory numbers 7/77, 122. A different design registration mark is applied in relief to the base of each vase, (a) 22 May 1877, parcel 5, and (b) 30 October 1872 or 1880, parcel 9.

Made by W. Brownfield & Son, Corbridge, Staffordshire; the design registered on 1 December 1875, parcel 2.

H 27.2 cm 1991,6-13,1-2

The shape of these vases derives from the ancient Chinese *zong*, a ritual jade carving in which a squared section encloses a cylinder. From the fourteenth century onwards such jades were reproduced in other materials, and it is likely that these earthenware vases were inspired by Chinese porcelain reproductions in *blanc-de-chine* or celadon of the ancient jade carvings. The elephant-head handles are derived from other Chinese porcelains, as is the idea of setting the vessel on a stand. Western copies of Chinese vessels on stands, by Minton for example, were, like these vases, made in one piece, though the 'stands' were often glazed brown to imitate the Chinese lacquer originals. Other versions of these Brownfield vases were made with the 'stand' glazed brown and the upper part yellow.

Incorrect design registration marks have been applied to both vases. In one case, the factory simply used the wrong stamp, but in the other, the stamp does not correspond to a registered design at all. The mark for 22 May 1877, parcel 5, that appears on one of these vases corresponds to three different registered designs by Brownfield & Son (nos 310359-61), described as two flower holders and a biscuit box. The other mark, for 30 October 1872 or 1880, does not relate to any entry in the Design Registration volumes at the Public Record Office. The vases with brown-glazed bases referred to above (in the possession of Michael Whiteway in 1991) also bear an incorrect mark, for 30 October 1875. Again, Brownfield do not appear to have registered any design on this date. However, the volumes of Representations of Registered Designs show that the design for these vases was registered on 1 December 1875, registration no. 296475, described as a flower vase (I am grateful to Imogen Loke for checking the Registers at the Public Record Office).

Brownfield & Son was a large Staffordshire concern making a wide range of table and ornamental wares. Relief-moulded earthenware or majolica was one of their specialities. For a toilet service in the Chinese style, see Jewitt 1883, 476.

Cantagalli, Figli di Giuseppe 1878-1954

'Cantagalli' in *Dizionario Biografico degli Italiani* XVIII, Rome 1975
Conti, G., *Maioliche Cantagalli in donazione al Bargello*, Museo Nazionale del Bargello, Florence, 1982
Conti, G. and Grosso, G.C., *La Maiolica Cantagalli*, Rome 1990

371 Tile   [PLATE 145]

Tin-glazed earthenware, enamelled in relief on a white ground with flowers and leaves in blue, turquoise and red in the Iznik manner.

MARKS Impressed in relief on the reverse 'CANTAGALLI FIRENZE'.

Designed by Ulisse Cantagalli and made by the factory of Figli di Giuseppe Cantagalli, Florence, c.1880-1900.

23.7 × 23.7 cm   1993,7-14,1

The Cantagalli factory, traditionally in existence since the fifteenth century, was run by Giuseppe Cantagalli until his death in 1878, when the factory was taken over and transformed by his two sons, Ulisse (1839-1902) and Romeo. The factory won a gold medal at the Milan Exhibition of 1881 and is perhaps best known for its production of Renaissance-style ceramics, as well as direct copies of celebrated pieces of Renaissance maiolica in collections in Italy, England and elsewhere.

From about 1880, Ulisse Cantagalli also revived the techniques of Iznik pottery. He would certainly have known the collection of Iznik pottery in the Musée de Cluny, published in 1883, which had already inspired Théodore Deck (see Cat. 57 and 382), as well as examples seen during his travels in the Middle East. For a full account of Cantagalli's Iznik-style ceramics, see M.V. Fontana,'L'imitazione europea della ceramica ottomana di Iznik. La fabbrica ottocentesca fiorentina "Figli di G. Cantagalli"', in U. Marazzi (ed.), *La Conoscenza dell'Asia e dell'Africa in Italia nei secoli XVIII e XIX*', vol. I, part II, Istituto Universitario Orientale, Naples 1984, 727-47; this article illustrates a number of comparable Iznik-style tile designs by Cantagalli, together with their Iznik prototypes, e.g. pls XXXIX-XLIII. Cantagalli ceramics are rarely dated. The production of Iznik-style ceramics continued after Ulisse's death into the early twentieth century. For illustrations from a trade catalogue of c.1906 with several comparable tiles, see Conti and Grosso 1990, 93-5.

Christiansen, Hans 1866-1945

See Cat. 36-8.

372 Wine glass   [PLATE 146]

Clear glass, free-blown, with stencilled gold stylised rose motifs round the bowl; beneath one of the roses is the artist's monogram, 'HC', also in gold, as part of the design. The rims of both bowl and foot are gilded.

MARKS None.

Designed c.1903 and made probably by the Theresienthaler Krystallglasfabrik, Zwiesel, Bavaria.

H 25 cm   1992,6-11,1

This is the large white wine glass from an eleven-piece service; it is the largest piece. The rose motif was designed by Christiansen initially as part of the decoration of his house at the Darmstadt artists' colony, built in 1901. He later adapted the motif for furniture and other items. In the case of this glass service, he also designed the shapes of the glasses. Glasses from this service are owned by several museums in Germany, for example the Museum der Künstlerkolonie, Darmstadt (Ulmer 1990, cat. no. 66), the Mittelrheinisches Landesmuseum, Mainz (*Abteilungskatalog* I, *Jugendstil Glas*, *Sammlung H.R. Gruber*, Mainz 1976, cat. no. 217) and the Badisches Landesmuseum, Karlsruhe (Franzke 1987, cat. no. 89). See also Schack von Wittenau 1971, 231ff, for an example in the collection of the Theresienthal factory, and Zimmerman-Degen 1981, 99, fig. 205.

Colonna, Edouard 1862-1948

Eidelberg, M., *E. Colonna*, exhibition catalogue, The Dayton Art Institute, Dayton, Ohio, 1983

373 Pendant and chain

Gold, hand-raised and chased, of curvilinear form, comprising an upper winged element, decorated with *ombré* or shaded enamel in salmon pink, with a blister pearl below. The pendant hangs on its original machine-made gold chain. There is slight loss to the enamel.

MARKS Stamped on the reverse of the lower pendant 'COLONNA'. Both pendant and chain stamped with Paris 18 ct gold standard mark, the chain with maker's mark, a lozenge with the initials 'ANSB', for Art Nouveau Siegfried Bing.

Designed c.1898-1900 and made for Siegfried Bing's Maison de l'Art Nouveau, Paris.

L of whole pendant 8.8 cm   1991,7-1,1
Acquired from Dr Audrey Baker, grand-daughter of Harry Powell, director of James Powell & Sons, Whitefriars Glassworks, of London. According to Dr Baker the pendant was originally owned by her grandmother.

Colonna was one of the major designers for Bing's Maison de l'Art Nouveau. From 1898 to 1900 he designed furniture, metalwork and ceramics. The ceramics were made in Limoges, but the furniture and metalwork were produced in Bing's own workshops. In the case of this pendant and chain, the machine-made chain was presumably bought in and stamped with Bing's mark. There is no doubt that Colonna's bold curvilinear forms owe a significant debt to van de Velde, who had worked for Bing before Colonna's arrival.

Harry Powell may have purchased the pendant for his wife either directly from Bing in Paris or at the Turin Exhibition of 1902. For the earliest contemporary illustration of a pendant of this design, see Pica 1902, 143, where it is shown amongst the objects from the Maison de l'Art Nouveau at the Turin Exhibition. Powell & Sons were represented at the Turin Exhibition (see Cat. 236). For another pendant of the same design, see Eidelberg 1983, 43, fig. E. For further examples of Colonna's jewellery, see Eidelberg, op. cit., and Weisberg 1986, 150 and 194 (in the Musée des Arts Décoratifs, Paris). Examples are also held by the Museum für Kunst und Gewerbe, Cologne, and by museums in Hamburg and Karlsruhe. Colonna's jewels were widely illustrated in contemporary publications, for example *Die Kunst* 2, 1899-1900, 14-15, 104, 420-25; R. Rücklin, *Das Schmuckbuch*, 1901, pls 171-2, and H. Vever, *La bijouterie française au XIXe siècle*, vol. 3, Paris 1908.

374 Plate

Hard-paste porcelain, with moulded decoration, glazed white. In the centre an impressed curvilinear motif and round the edge a relief motif glazed in celadon green.

MARKS Printed in underglaze green on the reverse 'L'Art Nouveau Paris', with '89-7' painted in overglaze red.

Designed c.1899-1900 as part of the Canton service and made by the Limoges factory of Gérard, Dufraissex & Abbott for Siegfried Bing's Maison de l'Art Nouveau, Paris, before 1903, when the latter closed down.

D 21.5cm   1992,6-13,1

The Canton service was the second complete dinner set commissioned by Bing (the first was decorated with designs by Edouard Vuillard: Weisberg 1986, col. pls 17-19) and the first designed for him by Colonna. According to Weisberg, Colonna's preliminary drawings were sent to Limoges; experimental pieces were created with gold, pink and green borders, but Bing finally approved only the green, as on this plate. The Canton service was widely demanded and collected, and even used as tableware in Gustav Stickley's Craftsman restaurants in the United States (Weisberg 1986, 188-90). The name 'Canton' must have been chosen to draw attention to the underglaze impressed pattern of a type often found in Chinese ceramics.

For a coffee pot in the Musée des Arts Décoratifs, Paris, see Weisberg 1986, pl. 192, and also pls 193-4 for an oval platter and similar plate in a private collection. For the Limoges manufactory see Cat. 58.

Copeland, W.T. & Sons Ltd founded 1847

375 Bust of 'Clytie'   [PLATE 144]

Parian porcelain, bust of 'Clytie' set on a circular plinth.

MARKS The bust impressed at the back 'COPELAND O 81', the plinth impressed 'C. DELPECH. RED.T 1863 ART UNION OF LONDON'.

Modelled by C. Delpech in 1855 and made by W.T. Copeland & Sons Ltd, Stoke-on-Trent, in 1881.

H 33.7cm   1991,6-12,1

Busts of Clytie from a model by C. Delpech were executed by Copeland as prizes for the Art Union of London from 1855 onwards, in two sizes, 22-inch and 13-inch (this is the 13-inch model). The plinth is not of the same date as the bust. This is not uncommon; the factory held stocks of plinths that were used indiscriminately. The moulds were renewed about every twenty years. The detail on this example is good, suggesting that it came from a relatively new mould. For further discussion, see Atterbury and Batkin 1990, 135 and fig. 610. Busts of Clytie were included in Copeland catalogues until at least 1900. They were also produced in Parian porcelain by a number of other factories.

For the Art Unions, see Atterbury and Batkin, 26-39.

The Roman marble bust of Clytie was one of the most celebrated of the classical sculptures that entered the British Museum with the collection of Charles Townley in 1805. It was much copied in Rome in the late eighteenth century, before it was brought to London, and throughout the nineteenth century. For the most recent discussion of the bust and its identity, see S. Walker, 'Clytie — a false woman?' in M. Jones (ed.), Why Fakes Matter: Essays on problems of authenticity, London 1992, 32-40.

Copier, Andries Dirk 1901-91

See Cat. 50-54.

376 Water goblet

Smoky-topaz glass, the pear-shaped bowl free-blown, the stem and foot moulded and then cut to produce ten facets.

MARKS Acid-etched on the base with the Copier/Leerdam serial glass signet in use from 1924 to c.1945, see mark for Cat. 50.

Designed in 1926-7 as part of the 'Peer' (pear) service and made by the NV Glasfabriek Leerdam, Holland, between 1927 and c.1945.

H 12.4cm   1994,1-12,1   Given by Judy Rudoe

For discussion of the 'Peer' service, see Cat. 51.

377 Bowl

Dark green glass, the bowl free-blown, the foot moulded and cut to produce eight facets.

MARKS As above.

Designed in 1927 and made by the NV Glasfabriek Leerdam, Holland, between 1927 and c.1945.

H 4.5cm, D 12.3cm   1994,1-12,2   Given by Judy Rudoe

Dalpayrat, Pierre Adrien 1844-1910

There is no monograph on Dalpayrat; for biographical details, see Cologne 1974, 150-51, and Du Second Empire à l'Art Nouveau. La création céramique dans les musées du Nord-Pas-de-Calais, exhibition catalogue, Saint-Amand-les-Eaux, published Lille, 1986, 60.

378 Vase

Stoneware, square-section body drawn into a narrow square-section neck, with deep red sang-de-boeuf glaze speckled with green.

MARKS Incised on the base 'Dalpayrat'.

Made in the factory of Pierre Adrien Dalpayrat, Bourg-la-Reine, near Paris, between 1892 and 1910.

H 16.3cm   1991,6-11,1

Dalpayrat established his stoneware factory in 1889, with the sculptor Alphonse Voisin-Delacroix. From 1892 he produced copper-red glazes. French artist potters were among the first to experiment with copper-red glazes inspired by Chinese ceramics; stonewares with copper-red glazes were shown to great acclaim by Auguste Delaherche at the Paris Exhibition of 1889.

Dawson, Nelson 1859-1942 and Edith 1862-1928

The Studio 22, 1901, 169-75
Dawson, Mrs N., Enamels, London 1906
Dawson, N., Goldsmiths' and Silversmiths' Work, London 1907
Bickerdike, R. (née Dawson), 'The Dawsons: an equal partnership of artists', Apollo, November 1988, 320-25
Bury, S., Jewellery 1789-1910. The International Era, vol. 2, Woodbridge 1991, 634-5

379 Waist-buckle

Silver, oxidised, of square form, containing a central cloisonné enamel plaque with a motif of four leaves in translucent mauve on a deep purple ground, with green dots in the spaces. Four applied silver leaf motifs at each corner. The reverse fitted with two silver attachment loops; in addition there are two separate silver loops for sewing to a fabric belt to clasp the buckle. Attached to the buckle is an old price tag, £4 14s. 6d.

MARKS Incised on the reverse of the silver frame with a letter 'D'.

Designed and made by Nelson and Edith Dawson, London, c.1900. The buckle was formerly in the collection of Celia Larner (sold Christie's, London, 9 October 1992, lot 102), who acquired it from Charles Handley-Read, who had in turn bought it from Nelson and Edith Dawson's daughter, Rhoda Bickerdike.

5.3 × 5.2 cm. L of separate loops 4 and 4.1 cm   1992,12-3,1

Nelson Dawson first studied architecture and painting. He married Edith Robinson, also a painter, in 1893, by which time he had taken up metalwork, studying under the enameller Alexander Fisher. Nelson and Edith Dawson exhibited enamels regularly at the Arts and Crafts Exhibition Society from 1893. Together they played a significant role in the revival of enamelling in England at the end of the nineteenth century. In 1901, they founded the Artificers' Guild, in association with the jeweller Edward Spencer. According to a contemporary account, Edith Dawson did the enamels and Nelson Dawson designed the settings (*JSA* LVI, 1908, 289).

This buckle is exceptional in retaining its original oxidised silver surface; it is illustrated in C. Gere and M. Whiteway, *Nineteenth-Century Design from Pugin to Mackintosh*, London 1993, pl. 287. The price tag probably relates to the sale of the Dawsons' workshop after its closure in 1923. The buckle was not sold and remained in the possession of Rhoda Bickerdike, who made sketches of the workshop effects as a record prior to the sale. These sketches are now privately owned. This buckle, together with its two attachment loops, appears as item number 17 and is described as follows: 'buckle, silver, centre blue enamel, leaves dull purple, spots dull green.'(I owe this information to Charlotte Gere.)

Deck, Joseph-Théodore 1823-91

See Cat. 57. In addition to the bibliography already cited there is a useful contemporary account: R. Ménard, *L'Art en Alsace-Lorraine*, Paris 1876, 134-42.

380 Plate   [PLATE 145]

Tin-glazed earthenware, enamelled in relief in turquoise, red and various shades of blue with a bouquet of cornflowers and other blossoms within a border of lappets on a blue ground, in the Iznik manner.

MARKS Impressed on the reverse 'TH. DECK' and '1870', see mark for Cat. 57.

Designed and made in 1870 in the factory of Théodore Deck, Paris.

D 29.9 cm   1993,7-15,1

The decoration on this plate is very close to Iznik models. It is unusual in bearing a date stamp.

381 Vase   [PLATE 145]

Earthenware, in the form of a Chinese bronze *hu*, of rectangular shape with deep green glaze, beneath which is finely modelled relief decoration of fantastic birds, masks and geometric motifs, arranged in horizontal bands. In the original gilt-bronze mounts with feet.

MARKS Impressed on the base 'TH. DECK'; see mark for Cat. 57.

Designed and made in the factory of Théodore Deck, Paris, c.1880.

H 20.7 cm   1993,11-7,1

Deck's early ceramics of the 1860s and early 1870s were inspired by Iznik pottery, but from the late 1870s he turned to other sources. The shape of this vase copies Chinese bronze vases of the fourteenth century, which in turn were elongated versions of the ancient squat *hu* or wine vessel. The decoration, although a pastiche, is inspired by prototypes of the twelfth century BC. Chinese bronzes were much collected in Paris in the late 1870s and 1880s. For a similar Deck vase based on a Chinese bronze, see S. Kuthy, *Albert Anker, Fayencen in Zusammenarbeit mit Théodore Deck*, Zurich 1985, 14.

De Feure, Georges 1868-1953

See Cat. 58.

The following monograph has been published since the first edition of this catalogue: *Georges de Feure 1868-1943*, exhibition catalogue, Van Gogh Museum, Amsterdam, 1993.

382 Wine glass   [PLATE 146]

Clear glass, free-blown, the bowl with undulating profile, the stem decreasing down its length to an astonishingly thin section and then expanding again at the base.

Designed c.1901-2 for Siegfried Bing's Maison de l'Art Nouveau, Paris, and made by the Rheinische Glasshütten, Köln-Ehrenfeld, Germany.

H 17.2 cm   1993,10-12,1

An identical glass was given by Marcel Bing (Siegfried Bing's son) in 1908 to the Musée des Arts Décoratifs, Paris, with the information that it was designed by de Feure for the Maison de l'Art Nouveau (inv. no. 15267 B). It is one of three glasses given by Marcel Bing, of which two were described in the accession registers as by de Feure (15267 A and B) and the third by Colonna (15267 C). The two glasses by de Feure both bear on the base the manufacturer's original paper label, 'RG Ehrenfeld' in a circle. For an illustration of these three glasses, see L. Rosenthal, *La Verrerie française depuis 50 ans*, Paris 1927, pl. XV, where all three are described, apparently erroneously, as by de Feure.

De Feure designed a number of table glasses for Bing, many of which are illustrated in a special issue of *Deutsche Kunst und Dekoration* devoted to de Feure and his association with Bing. They all have undulating bowls and stems (*DK & D* 12, 1903, 322-3). The illustrations include the second of the de Feure glasses in the Musée des Arts Décoratifs (15267 A; *DK & D*, 1903, 322). There appears to be no contemporary illustration of the glass catalogued here. However, a group of glasses exhibited by the Rheinische Glasshütten at the Düsseldorf Exhibition of 1902 included a glass of virtually identical shape, but with applied trails on the bowl and foot (*Kunst und Kunsthandwerk*, V. Jahrgang, 1902, 526). Significantly, this group also included one of the de Feure glasses illustrated in *Deutsche Kunst und Dekoration*, but again with applied decoration, suggesting that the Rheinische Glasshütten made their own modified, and less elegant, versions of de Feure's designs for Bing. These glasses received special praise from the Viennese critic for their 'kräftigen Formen Behrens'scher Faktur' ('powerful shapes in the manner of Behrens', *KuKH*, 1902, 529).

I am grateful to Jean-Luc Olivié for the information about the glasses in the Musée des Arts Décoratifs and for the references in contemporary periodicals.

Doulton's Lambeth Pottery 1815-1956

There is a considerable body of literature on the various Doulton factories. A selection relevant to the Lambeth factory is listed below.

Eyles, D., *Doulton Lambeth Wares*, London 1975
Lambeth Art Pottery, exhibition catalogue, Richard Dennis, London 1975
'Art Pottery at Lambeth', *Leisure Hour*, 1885, 607-16
Sparkes, J., 'Lambeth stoneware', *JSA*, May 1874, 557-70 and 'Further developments at the Lambeth Pottery', March 1880, 344-57
Vallance, A., 'The Lambeth Pottery', *Magazine of Art* XXI, 1897, 221-4

383 Vase [PLATE 144]

Earthenware, with two handles, painted in black and blue on a cream ground with horizontal bands of decoration incorporating geometric patterns and stylised lotus, in the style of early Cypriot pottery.

MARKS Impressed on the base 'Doulton Lambeth Faience' with 'CYPRUS' and the date '1879'.

Made by Doulton's Lambeth Pottery, London, in 1879.

H 27cm   1993,10-10,1

Doulton was the first factory in England to establish an art pottery studio. In the late 1870s, they produced a range of ornamental earthenwares in Persian, Cypriot and other eastern or ancient styles.

'Cyprus' ware was inspired by early Cypriot pottery of c.650-550 BC. The British Museum was among the first to acquire material excavated on Cyprus: the first Cypriot pots entered the collections in 1869, from T.B. Sandwith, who was British Vice-Consul in Cyprus from 1865 to 1870 and who made the first serious attempt to classify Cypriot pottery. Further pots were acquired in 1873 from the pioneering excavations carried out in 1867 by R. Hamilton Lang, British Consul 1871-2. Then, in 1876, the Museum purchased parts of the celebrated collection of General Luigi Palma di Cesnola, American Consul in Cyprus 1865-76.

This Doulton vase is inspired by Cypriot egg-shaped amphorae with characteristic scale-pattern, geometric and lotus motifs. The closest parallel in the British Museum collections was acquired from Cesnola in 1876 (see H.B. Walters, *Catalogue of Cypriote, Italian and Etruscan Pottery*, 1912, no. C.841).

This vase is illustrated in Eyles 1975, col. pl. LV. No other examples of Doulton Cyprus ware have so far been recorded.

Dresser, Christopher 1843-1904

See Cat. 82-107.

384 Jardinière [PLATE 144]

Earthenware, of cylindrical form with three bun feet, decorated with transfer-printed pattern of flying cranes above waves in shades of blue on a white ground; Greek key-pattern borders. The transfer is applied in vertical sections and the joins are clearly visible. Small chips to rim.

MARKS Impressed on the base with the factory name 'MINTON', the Minton date code for 1880 and the shape number '1596'; printed in underglaze blue with Minton globe mark (see mark for Cat. 198) above a scroll bearing the pattern name 'JAPANESE CRANE' and design registration mark for 10 December 1872.

Both shape and pattern designed by Dresser, the shape in the late 1860s, the pattern in 1872. Made by Minton & Co., Stoke-on-Trent, in 1880.

H 21.2cm   1993,5-7,1

The Minton factory archive holds two pen and ink designs of flying cranes signed by Dresser. The pattern on this jardinière combines elements from both these designs. For an illustration of one of them, depicting three cranes with a moon and clouds above waves, see J. Jones, *Minton. The First Two Hundred Years of Design and Production*, London 1993, 180, dated to c.1870). The other shows three flying cranes with a Greek key-pattern border above and foliate scrolls below. Both designs were perhaps originally intended for a flat surface, and variants occur on tiles.

This pattern was widely used by Minton on a number of shapes not designed by Dresser. Significantly, the design registered by Minton in 1872, although based on Dresser's designs, was in the form of a circle, presumably for a plate (Public Record Office Register of Ornamental Designs, vol. BT 43/69, design no. 268725). A pair of plates with this circular design and corresponding design registration mark was sold at Phillips, London, 30 September 1993, lot 216A; both plates bore the Minton date code for 1879 and had traditional pierced basket-weave borders which did not suit the decoration. The shape of the jardinière, by contrast, is ideally suited to the design; no other example of the flying cranes pattern on this shape has been recorded.

385 Plate [PLATE 145]

Earthenware, of square shape with broad flat rims and angled corners; two circular depressions at each corner of the rim. Decorated with transfer-printed and hand-painted floral sprays, set asymmetrically, the enamel colours in shades of turquoise, pink, yellow and deep blue.

MARKS Printed underglaze in black on reverse with pattern name 'PERSIA'.

The design registered in 1884 and made by Old Hall Earthenware Company Ltd, Old Hall Pottery, Hanley, Staffordshire, before 1902, when the factory closed down.

W 22.8cm   1994,1-15,1

For discussion of the three patterns designed by Dresser for Old Hall, see Cat. 104, where this pattern is wrongly described as 'Persian'. On all the examples seen by the author, it is spelt 'Persia', and this would be more consistent with the other two names, 'Shanghai' and 'Hampden'.

Dümler, Peter 1860-1907

Höhr-Grenzhausen 1986, 32

386 Jug

Salt-glazed stoneware, grey body, cast, with relief decoration, cobalt blue and manganese glaze, flattened circular shape with raised foot and one handle. On the spout a grotesque Renaissance-style mask, and on each side medallions with coats of arms labelled 'Pfalz' and 'Trier', surrounded by a band of floral ornament.

MARKS Artist's initials 'PD' within the medallions on each side: on one side flanking the word 'Pfalz', and on the other, beneath the shield; impressed triangle for S.P. Gerz on the base, with incised number '776'.

Designed and modelled by Peter Dümler and made by the firm of S.P. Gerz, Höhr, c.1878-83.

H 28.3cm   1993,11-6,4

Dümler worked initially for the firm of Reinhold Hanke, which he joined at the age of fourteen in 1874 to train as a modeller. He also worked for S.P. Gerz before setting up his own firm, Dümler & Breiden, with his brother-in-law, Albert Breiden, in 1883. His work is characterised by the quality and detail of the modelling. This jug is made in the same way as the Merkelbach & Wick vase (Cat. 401), the flattened circle cast in two halves, the foot and neck also cast. For discussion of this technique, see Cat. 401. This and the following entry will be illustrated in D. Gaimster (ed.), *German Stoneware 1300-1900: A Handbook*, British Museum, forthcoming.

387 Pair of wall plaques

Salt-glazed stoneware, hand-thrown, grey body with high-relief applied decoration in cobalt blue, manganese and violet depicting profile heads of Ares and Minerva in the Renaissance style, their helmets and armour decorated with low-relief classical subjects: Minerva's helmet depicts Achilles dragging Hector round Troy, Priam begging for the body of Hector in Achilles' tent, and Achilles fighting Hector; the gorgette depicts the ransoming of Hector's corpse. Ares' helmet depicts the watch-towers of Troy and further scenes from Greek legend. The background to each head incised with foliate scrollwork, with 'MINERVA' on one plaque and 'ARES' on the other. The border of Minerva decorated in relief with pairs of confronted birds, an owl and an eagle, amidst foliage, the border of Ares with birds and animals. Both foot-rims pierced with holes for suspension. There are occasional firing faults on the Minerva plaque.

MARKS The artist's initials 'PD' are concealed within the decoration of the gorgettes on both plaques; on Minerva they appear on the left beneath a lock of hair and on Ares they appear in the shield held by the soldier on the far right. Impressed model number '14' on base of Minerva.

Designed by Peter Dümler and made by the firm of Dümler & Breiden, Höhr, Rhineland, c.1883.

D 35.2cm   1993,11-6,2-3

Unlike the jug discussed above, these plaques are made in the traditional way with relief decoration impressed in a mould in sections and then applied. Dümler was immensely proud of his ability to imitate sixteenth-century work, hence his idiosyncratic way of signing his pieces by disguising his initials amongst the decoration. These plaques are technical masterpieces and no comparable plaques with modelling of this quality and fine detail have been recorded. They were no doubt intended as a pair depicting the two gods of classical mythology, but one uses the Greek name, Ares (identified with Mars by the Romans), while the other uses the Roman name, Minerva (regularly identified with the Greek goddess Athena, hence the owls, symbol of Athens). For a later pair of plaques with similar heads of Minerva and Ares, executed by Dümler & Breiden in ivory-coloured stoneware, the ornament much altered and simplified, see *Renaissance der Renaissance*, exhibition catalogue, Schloss Brake, Lemgo, 1992, cat. no. 123. Dümler & Breiden gave up salt-glaze in the 1890s and produced only ivory body from then on. The firm is still in existence in Höhr.

Gerz, Simon Peter founded 1862, merged with R. Merkelbach in 1912

For brief details of this factory, see Bonn 1987, 44.

388 Pair of jugs

Salt-glazed stoneware, buff body, hand-thrown, decorated in the Japanese taste with three-dimensional applied dragons, their bodies forming handles and coiling round the neck and base of the jug; further applied decoration of floating lily leaves and tendrils. The dragons' bodies coil around opposite sides of the neck, suggesting that they were designed as a pair. The handles and applied work left uncoloured, the background in soft blue.

MARKS Impressed factory mark of S.P. Gerz on the base (see mark for Cat. 213 but without the tankard inside the triangle), together with 'GRES RHENANA' and model number '1125' impressed on the base of one jug and 'GRES NASSOVIA' with model number '1125' on the other; 'GES. GESCH.' (*gesetzlich geschützt*, registered) on both.

Made by S.P. Gerz, Höhr, Rhineland, c.1894.

H 24.2cm   1993,11-6,7-8

The use of a registered trademark incorporating the French word *grès* (stoneware) indicates an attempt to rival the French artist potters whose stonewares were much admired from the 1880s. It may also suggest that these jugs were made for export, hence the description as 'stoneware from the Rhineland' and 'stoneware from Nassau' (south of Höhr-Grenzhausen).

These jugs are exceptional in Westerwald production and demonstrate an attempt to emulate Japanese-style ceramics produced elsewhere in Europe and in America. They will be illustrated in D. Gaimster (ed.), *German Stoneware 1300-1900: A Handbook*, British Museum, forthcoming.

Gustavsberg AB founded 1825

Gustavsberg 150 år, exhibition catalogue, National Museum, Stockholm, 1975 (with English summary)
Lutteman, H. Dahlbäck, *Svensk 1900 tals keramik*, Västerås 1985
For brief accounts, see also London 1989b and M. Eidelberg (ed.), *Design 1935-1965. What Modern Was*, exhibition catalogue, Montreal and New York, 1991, 374-5.

389 Vase   [PLATE 146]

Porcellanous stoneware, with underglaze relief decoration applied in blue- and grey-coloured slips, comprising geometrically arranged stylised rose blossoms, leaves and branches; the blossoms incised in a square of blue within a thorny branch, the branches with incised leaves in grey, on a pale turquoise ground.

MARKS Painted in underglaze blue on the base 'Gustavsberg 1908' and artist's signature 'J. Ekberg'.

Designed by Josef Ekberg (d.1945) and made at the Gustavsberg porcelain factory, Stockholm, in 1908.

H 32.6cm   1993,10-12,2

Ekberg joined Gustavsberg in 1889 and worked there until his death in 1945. He became the factory's leading artist during the first decade of the century and developed his distinctive sgraffito decoration, of which this is a characteristic example. Gustavsberg's displays at the Stockholm exhibition of 1909 and the Malmö Exhibition of 1914 consisted almost entirely of designs by Ekberg, see Stockholm 1975, 26-7, with illustrations of the exhibition displays. For a covered jar with similar decoration of rose leaves and stems, also dated 1908, see Stockholm 1975, no. 140. For a wall-platter by Ekberg of 1911 with similar motifs see H. Makus, *Keramik aus Historismus und Jugendstil*, exhibition catalogue, Staatliche Kunstsammlungen, Kassel, 1981, no. 195.

Hansen, Karl Gustav born 1914

Hansen, B. and Møller, H. Sten, *Karl Gustav Hansen*, exhibition catalogue, Kunstindustrimuseet, Copenhagen, Aarhus 1988

390 Pair of candlesticks [PLATE 147]

Silver, cast and hand-raised, with two branches on an elongated oval base.

MARKS Stamped on the base 'Hans Hansen', 'DENMARK STERLING', and, in an oval, 'ANNO 1947'.

Designed in 1934 by Karl Gustav Hansen and made in 1947 by the firm of Hans Hansen, Kölding, Denmark.

H 7.6 cm, L 18.5 cm   1992,1-7,1-2

The firm of Hans Hansen, founded in 1906, is among a group of distinguished silversmiths' firms working at the same time as Jensen, such as A. Michelsen, Frantz Hingelberg, Just Andersen and Kaj Bøjesen (see J. Schwandt, 'Dänisches Silber des 20. Jahrhunderts, Teil II: Funkzionalismus, dreissiger und vierziger Jahre', *Weltkunst*, 1 December 1987, 3590-93). These candlesticks are an early design by Karl Gustav Hansen, son of Hans Hansen, dating from 1934, the year that his apprenticeship was completed. They exhibit many of the features of his apprenticeship test piece, a silver teapot and stand, for which he was awarded a silver medal (Hansen and Møller 1988, 8. I am grateful to Michael von Essen for this information).

Hoef, Christian Johannes van der 1875-1933

There is no monograph on van der Hoef. For biographical details see Gysling-Billeter 1975; Leeuwarden 1986; Leidelmeijer and van der Cingel 1983.

391 Vase [PLATE 146]

Earthenware, red body with buff inlay, glazed to yellow and brown, the inlay comprising a band of geometric ornament round the neck and a circular motif of four stylised butterflies in the centre of one side.

MARKS Incised on the base 'ontw CJ vd Hoef 23-1'.

Designed by C.J. van der Hoef c.1903-10 and made at the Fayencefabriek Amstelhoek, Omval, near Amsterdam, before 1910, when Amstelhoek closed.

H 29.4 cm   1992,6-10,1

Van der Hoef trained as a sculptor; he designed ceramics for a number of factories around 1900. From 1894 to 1910 he was director of the Amstelhoek factory, which had ceramic and metal workshops supplying interior design shops in Amsterdam such as Het Binnenhuis and De Woning. Van der Hoef's characteristic ceramics for Amstelhoek combined two-colour inlaid decoration derived from traditional Dutch peasant pottery with a sophisticated Art Nouveau line. They were first shown at the Turin Exhibition of 1902, where they were highly praised in contemporary accounts. For comparable pieces, see Leeuwarden

1986; Leidelmeijer and van der Cingel 1983, 75-7; Sotheby's, Amsterdam, 10 March 1986, lots 81-7, 91-9, 103-5 and 111.

Most Amstelhoek pieces bear the Amstelhoek factory mark and not the artist's signature. Frans Leidelmeijer has therefore suggested that this vase was made privately for van der Hoef at the factory. A vase of the same design with the same incised signature was purchased by the Kunstgewerbemuseum, Zurich, in 1908 (Gysling-Billeter 1975, no. 102). But the decoration on the Zurich example is not inlaid, suggesting that it is an experimental piece. No other vase of this design has been recorded.

392 Vase [PLATE 146]

Earthenware, buff body, elongated form with decoration in underglaze colours of blue and ochre on a cream ground comprising a central motif on one side of stylised addorsed deer, a band of geometric ornament round the neck and thin lines round the base.

MARKS Painted in black on the base 'AMPHORA HOLLAND ontw. C.J.v.d.Hoef 263-2'.

Designed c.1908-10 and made by the Tegel-en Fayencefabriek Amphora, Oegstgeest, near Leiden, Holland.

H 38.8 cm   1992,6-9,1

Van der Hoef worked for the newly founded firm of Amphora from about 1908 to 1910, designing both shapes and decoration. His designs won the firm a gold medal at the Brussels Exhibition of 1910. For comparable pieces, see Gysling-Billeter 1975, nos 95, 97-105 and 107; Leidelmeijer and van der Cingel 1983, 76-8; Sotheby's, Amsterdam, 10 March 1986, lots 116-27 (lot 125, with a motif of confronted stags similar to that on this vase, was acquired by the Rijksmuseum).

Huber, Patriz 1878-1902

Patriz Huber. Ein Mitglied der Darmstädter Künstlerkolonie, exhibition catalogue, Museum Künstlerkolonie, Darmstadt, 1992.

393 Waist-clasp

Silver, in two parts, hand-raised, with swirling motif in relief, the background textured, set with four green-stained chalcedony cabochon stones. The silver retains its original oxidised surface.

MARKS Stamped on the reverse with the designer's monogram 'PH', the manufacturer's monogram 'TF' for Theodor Fahrner (see mark for Cat. 342), the silver standard mark 950 and importer's monogram 'MBCo.Regd.' for Mürrle Bennett. The front stamped with London hallmarks and date-letter for 1902 and importer's marks of Mürrle Bennett & Company.

Designed c.1900-1901, made by the firm of Theodor Fahrner, Pforzheim, Germany, and imported for sale in London by the Anglo-German concern of Mürrle Bennett & Co.

H 4.3 cm   1991,5-2,1

Patriz Huber trained at the Kunstgewerbeschule in Mainz and then at the Kunstgewerbeschule in Munich. He was a member of the Darmstadt artists' colony from 1899 to 1902, when he spent a brief period working with van de Velde in Berlin before his suicide over an unhappy love affair in 1902. He is best known for his interior designs, furniture and small silver items.

The largest group of Huber's silverware is held by the Museum der Künstlerkolonie, Darmstadt (Ulmer 1990, nos 154-74), which acquired in 1991 an important archive of Huber designs made at the Darmstadt artists' colony (see exhibition catalogue noted above). This archive included three sheets of watercolour designs for jewellery, one of which contains the design for the British Museum clasp: see Darmstadt 1992, cat no. 157 for the sheet of designs and cat. no. XXVIIe for another example of this clasp in a private collection.

For further jewellery designed by Huber in various museums in Germany, see von Hase 1977, 232-7; see also Franzke 1987, no. 55; Heller 1982, nos 178-83; Rutherford and Beddoe 1986, no. 60 (in the Art Gallery and Museum at Brighton). For contemporary illustrations of the jewellery by Huber in the Darmstadt 1901 exhibition, see Koch 1902, 180-81.

Mürrle Bennett (Ernst Mürrle and J.B. Bennett) operated from Pforzheim and London from 1884 to 1916. Most of their goods were sold through Liberty's (see V. Becker, *Antique and 20th Century Jewellery*, London 1980, 255-7).

Kamp, Alfred 1882-1942

394 Punch bowl

Stoneware, with fluted body and lid, moulded relief decoration comprising bunches of grapes on the shoulders, the feet in the form of scrolls surmounted by lion masks, the handle in the form of a double lion mask. Covered all over with celadon-coloured glaze.

MARKS Impressed on the base of one of the feet with the monogram 'EEH' for the retailers (Eckhardt & Engler, Höhr) and the model number '269 D'.

Designed c.1925, made by the firm of J.P. Thewalt, Höhr, and retailed by Eckhardt & Engler, Höhr, Rhineland, Germany.

H 35.2 cm   1991,7-5,1

Alfred Kamp trained at the ceramics school in Höhr, moving to the Königliche Porzellan-Manufaktur in Berlin from about 1900 to 1910, where he worked as a modeller (see I. von Treskow, *Die Jugendstilporzellane der KPM, Bestandskatalog der Königlichen Porzellan-Manufaktur, Berlin 1894-1914*, Munich 1971, 257 and 280ff., illustrations from the factory shape book including several models by Kamp). He then returned to Höhr, where he became professor at the ceramics school and made several designs for stoneware for the firm of J.P. Thewalt. He is regarded as the most original modeller working in the Westerwald in the 1920s and 1930s.

This punch bowl, with its fluted body and celadon glaze, was an advanced design for the Westerwald at the time and represents an attempt to bring the Westerwald industry into line with current trends elsewhere in Europe. The celadon glaze departs from traditional Westerwald glazes of grey and blue, or brown and black; it was difficult to achieve and was produced only in the 1920s. (Much of the above information was supplied by Beate Dry-v. Zezschwitz and comes from an interview which she held with the late Herr Eckhardt, director of Eckhardt & Engler).

Karageorgevitch, Prince Bojidar 1861-1908

395 Waist-buckle

Gilded metal, cast and pierced, in the form of a sweet-pea branch with flowers, forming an asymmetrical oval, the surface of the flowers finely chased. Fitted with a hinged buckle plate.

MARKS Incised monogram 'BK' on the buckle plate.

Designed before 1908 by Prince Bojidar Karageorgevitch.

H 6.8 cm   1992,12-2,1

Little is known about the career of Prince Bojidar Karageorgevitch. A cousin of Peter I of Serbia, he worked in Paris as an author, painter and designer of decorative arts in the years around 1900, exhibiting at the Paris Salons in the early 1900s. At the Salon of 1908, he exhibited a range of buckles and other jewels, including a buckle of identical design, credited to 'Mme la Princesse Karageorgevitch', suggesting that he was working in partnership with his wife (*L'Art Décoratif aux Salons de 1908*, pl. 68). He wrote regularly on the Paris art scene for the *Magazine of Art* in the early 1900s (for example, in 1903-4 on Gallé and 1904 on the sculptor Pierre Roche).

Lie, Peder A. founded 1855

For a history of the firm of P.A. Lie, see W. Halén, *Drager. Gullsmedkunsten og drommen om det nasjonale*, Kunstindustrimuseet, Oslo, 1992, 33

396 Set of Viking-style jewellery

Silver, cast and chased, comprising a brooch and four buttons, the brooch with openwork design of human and animal masks and interlace, the buttons with interlace design. Contained in the original case labelled inside the lid: 'P.A. LIE JUVELEER CHRISTIANIA'. Two of the buttons have been converted for wear as earrings.

MARKS The brooch stamped on the reverse 'LIE', with silver standard mark '830 S' on an applied label. The buttons stamped 'LIE' and '830 S'.

Designed by Samuel Holm and made by the firm of P.A. Lie, Oslo, c.1890-1910.

D of brooch 6 cm, D of buttons 1.6 cm   1992,5-13,1-5

P.A. Lie established his shop in Oslo (formerly Christiania) in 1855; from the early 1870s he engaged the architect-designer Friedrich Wilhelm von Hanno who designed several pieces of silver in the 'Dragon style' as it was called in Norway. He was succeeded as chief designer by his student Samuel Holm during the 1880s. P.A. Lie was one of the largest silversmiths in Oslo in the late nineteenth century and a major exponent of the 'Dragon style' and the Scandinavian revival (Halén 1992, 33).

This set is a pastiche rather than a direct copy: the bearded human masks occur widely on Viking ornamental metalwork from Norway, from brooches to strap ends. The quatrefoil interlace motif on the buttons can be paralleled in earlier gold bracteates. The Kunstindustrimuseet in Oslo holds a similar brooch by David Andersen (information kindly supplied by Widar Halén).

Magnussen, Walter Claus 1869-1946

See Cat. 153.

397 Jug

Stoneware, with pewter lid, the body with moulded relief ornament of stylised plant forms; deep brownish-black lustrous matt glaze.

MARKS Impressed on the base with the artist's monogram, 'WM', and factory mark of the Kunsttöpferei Scharvogel, Munich, a bird incorporating the letters 'SKM'.

Designed before 1900 and made by the Kunsttöpferei J.J. Scharvogel, Munich.

H 35.6 cm (with lid)   1991,7-6,1

For discussion of Magnussen's designs for Scharvogel, see Cat. 153; for further examples, see Cologne 1978, cat. nos 544-6. This jug is illustrated in *Kunst und Handwerk*, 1900, 379, together with other Magnussen models; the glaze is described as 'dunkel graubraun, matt'. Richard Bormann also illustrated this jug in his influential book *Moderne Keramik* (n.d., c.1902, 58 and pl. opposite) and gave warm praise to Magnussen's designs for Scharvogel with their curvilinear relief modelling. The lustrous glaze is characteristic of Scharvogel's '*grès-flammé*' (flambé stoneware), first exhibited at the Munich Glaspalast exhibition in 1899. For Scharvogel, see Munich 1988, 149-51.

Margold, Emanuel Josef   1881-1962

See Cat. 156.

398 Biscuit tin

Base metal, printed with a stylised floral design in pink, white, blue, red, green, grey, black and gold on the lid; the sides with geometric motifs in white, black and gold.

MARKS Stamped on the base with the same mark as Cat. 156.

Designed in 1914-15 for the Keksfabrik Hermann Bahlsen, Hanover.

H 5.8 cm, W 12.2 cm, L 20.3 cm   1993,7-18,1   Given by Mrs Ilse Barker

For discussion of Margold's designs for Bahlsen's biscuit tins, see Cat. 156. For a biscuit tin with the same design as this one, illustrated in colour, see Ulmer 1990, cat. no. 221.

Merkelbach, Reinhold   founded 1845

Cologne 1978, 221-8
Dry-v. Zezschwitz 1981

399 Flask

Salt-glazed stoneware, hand-thrown, grey body with 'Cologne brown' glaze, applied relief decoration of a bearded mask on the neck and four medallions on the body, three with coats of arms, the central one with date 1596, flanked by two dated 1597, and the fourth, overlapping the base of the handle, with a profile male bust in armour bordered with an inscription identifying the bust as 'VITELLIUS GERMANICUS'. The handle with original pewter lid and thumb piece.

MARKS Impressed 'R. MERKELBACH GRENZHAUSEN', model number '7' and letter 'M' on the base; see mark for Cat. 137.

Made by the firm of R. Merkelbach, Grenzhausen, 1906-14.

H 32 cm   1993,11-6,6

This and the following flask belong to a series of direct copies of sixteenth-century originals in German museums, introduced by Merkelbach from 1906. This flask was advertised in plate 2 of Merkelbach's 1912 catalogue as 'after an original of 1596 in the Kunstgewerbemuseum, Cologne'; it held 8 litres and cost 20 marks. For the Frechen original, see G. Reineking v. Bock, *Kataloge des Kunstgewerbemuseums Köln. Band IV. Steinzeug*, 1976, cat. no. 323 and pl. 11, the central medallion with the arms of Bavaria and Pfalz, the flanking ones with the arms of

Jülich-Kleveberg, and cat. no. 868 for another Merkelbach copy given to the Cologne Museum by Merkelbach in 1909. The Merkelbach 1912 catalogue has not been reprinted, but the page with this copy is illustrated in G. v. Bock, 'Steinzeug — Nachahmung, Nachbildung oder Fälschung?' *Keramos* 49, 1970, 48.

These Merkelbach copies were never deceptive; their smooth 'Cologne brown' glazes are unmistakably early twentieth century. But they are made in traditional techniques, as distinct from the contemporary Jugendstil designs that were formed in the mould (see Cat. 332 and 401).

400 Liqueur flask

Salt-glazed stoneware, hand-thrown, grey body with 'Cologne brown' glaze, applied relief decoration of a bearded mask on the neck with long forked beard surrounded by rosettes and, on either side, two medallions with coats of arms incorporating the initials 'MC'. Twisted handle with original hinged pewter lid and thumb piece.

MARKS Impressed 'R. MERKELBACH GRENZHAUSEN' and model number '12' on the base, see mark for Cat. 137.

Made by the firm of R. Merkelbach, Grenzhausen, 1906-14.

H 20.6 cm   1993,11-6,5

This flask was advertised on page 1 of Merkelbach's 1912 catalogue (see v. Bock 1970, pl. 100) as 'after an original in the Suermondtmuseum, Aachen'. It held 0.75 litres and cost 7 marks. See also Lüthgen 1909, 8.

Merkelbach & Wick   associated from 1872

Dry-v. Zezschwitz 1989, 294-8

401 Vase

Salt-glazed stoneware, grey body, cast, with relief decoration in the Renaissance style, of flattened circular pilgrim-flask shape with two handles terminating in applied grotesque horned and bearded masks. On each side the same mock coat-of-arms with lions amidst foliage and the date 1565, the relief decoration in buff against manganese. Other mouldings highlighted in greenish-grey. The neck and foot are identical in form.

MARKS Impressed factory mark 'M&W' on the base.

Designed and made by the firm of Merkelbach & Wick, Grenzhausen, c.1873

H 37.3 cm   1993,11-6,1

The earliest historicist stonewares made in the Westerwald were direct copies of sixteenth-century models using traditional methods, that is, hand-thrown vessels with relief decoration that was impressed in a mould and then applied. Such pieces were first made by the firm of Reinhold Hanke in the late 1860s primarily in response to commissions from local nobles for replacement vessels to furnish their houses and castles in the revived 'altdeutsch' (old German) style.

However, at the Vienna Exhibition of 1873, Merkelbach & Wick exhibited to great acclaim their new technique of casting the vessel in a mould in order to create the relief decoration, see C. v. Lützow (ed.), *Kunst und Gewerbe auf der Wiener Weltausstellung 1873*, 1875, 54-5. The manufacture of relief-decorated vessels in plaster moulds had been introduced to the Westerwald by immigrant Bohemian manufacturers in the 1860s.

Merkelbach & Wick's contribution to the development of historicist stoneware was to adapt mould-making technology to the creation of original designs, as opposed to the copying of sixteenth-century models. This was achieved by forming whole vessels or parts of vessels in a mould previously carved in intaglio with the relief motif, so that the vessel came out of the mould already complete with the decoration in relief (see Cat. 332). For a full account of the techniques and development of historicist stoneware, see B. Dry-v. Zezschwitz, 'Westerwälder Steinzeug des 19. Jahrhunderts', in *Historismus. Angewandte Kunst im 19. Jahrhundert. Band 2*, Staatliche Kunstsammlungen, Kassel, 1989, 285-304. The use of the factory mark without a model number indicates an early production date. A contemporary review of the Gewerbeausstellung in Höhr in 1878 noted Merkelbach & Wick's revival of the manganese purple colour used by the potters of the Renaissance, together with their recent introduction of the greenish-grey colour, describing it as a 'grey turning to green, as beautiful as could be imagined' (*Mittheilungen für den Gewerbeverein des Herzogthums Nassau* 16, Wiesbaden 1878, 121, reference kindly supplied by G. Dry). For an illustration of this vase, see D. Gaimster (ed.), *German Stoneware 1300-1900: A Handbook*, British Museum, forthcoming.

Friedrich Wilhelm Merkelbach II (1840-96) and Georg Peter Wick (1837-1914) were officially associated in November 1873 although they had worked together from 1872. Wick trained as a sculptor; he studied at the Munich Academy from 1862 to 1865 and worked until 1872 in the Siderolith factory of Knödgen, Maxein & Cie in Höhr, where he learnt to make the plaster moulds. The factory became Wick-Werke AG in the early 1920s and closed in the early 1980s.

Minton & Co. founded 1793

See Cat. 196-8.

The following literature has been published since the first edition of this catalogue:

Bumpus, B., *Pâte-sur-pâte. The Art of Ceramic Relief Decoration 1849-1992*, London 1992

Jones, J., *Minton. The First Two Hundred Years of Design and Production*, London 1993

402 Pair of moon flasks [PLATE 144]

Parian porcelain, glazed dark brown, on one side *pâte-sur-pâte* decoration in white of profile heads in the classical style on a terracotta pink ground, each head contained within an elaborate cartouche. On one flask, a head of Medusa within Renaissance-style scrollwork, swags and grotesques; on the other, a head of the young Augustus within a hunting trophy with dogs chasing a stag. The neck of each vase glazed deep blue and decorated with gilded palmette ornament in the classical style, the handles gilded all over, with black outline decoration; the feet also glazed blue with gilded decoration. The gilding is worn.

MARKS Signed in *pâte-sur-pâte* beneath each cartouche with monogram 'TM'. Impressed on the base 'MINTONS'.

Made by Minton & Co., Stoke-on-Trent; decorated by Thomas Mellor in 1879.

H 26 cm   1993,10-11,1-2

These flasks are illustrated in Bumpus 1992, 121. Bernard Bumpus has kindly supplied the following information from the Minton archive: the flasks were entered in the Minton *pâte-sur-*

pâte estimate book on 20 May 1879. The shape (known as 'bottle, pilgrim') was number 1348, medium size. Mellor was given as the artist, and the description, which incorporates elements from both flasks, gives full details of the colours and gilding, including the 'Dark choc ground'. The cost of production was £4 11s. 10d., including Mellor's *pâte-sur-pâte* painting, which was assessed at £2 18s. 6d. The selling price appears to have been 8 guineas.

The heads are copied from celebrated engraved gems in the British Museum, both in the Strozzi collection in the eighteenth century and both acquired with the Blacas collection in 1867 and regarded then as masterpieces of classical gem-engraving but now thought to be post-classical in date. The *pâte-sur-pâte* Medusa head is after the 'Strozzi Medusa', a chalcedony intaglio found in Rome at the beginning of the eighteenth century, see H.B. Walters, *Catalogue of Engraved Gems . . . in the British Museum*, 1926, no. 1829. The Augustus head is after a sardonyx cameo (Walters 3578). Both gems have been considerably modified in the Minton versions and it may be that Mellor was working from illustrations, or from casts, or from one of the many neo-classical copies of these gems, for example, Gere et al. 1984, no. 898 (by Pistrucci and very close to the Minton Augustus).

Mellor was one of Marc Louis Solon's (see Cat. 273) most highly accomplished assistants and these flasks are among his best work. Mellor worked at Minton's from *c*.1869 to 1881, initially as a china painter and from 1874 as a surface modeller. He left Minton in 1881 for Wedgwood. The Chinese-style moon flask shape was a popular Minton shape and was often decorated with subjects that were not Chinese in inspiration.

Müller, Richard dates unknown

There is no monograph on Richard Müller; for biographical details, see K.H. Bröhan (ed.), *Kunst vom Jugendstil zur Moderne (1889-1939). Sammlung Karl H. Bröhan, Berlin, Band IV, Metallkunst*, Berlin 1990, 593.

403 Candlestick [PLATE 146]

Brass, cast and wrought, circular lobed base pierced in the centre from which rise three spiralling stems which join at the top where each stem bifurcates and joins again to form a calyx containing the candle holder. The tops of the stems are riveted to the candle holder. The stems appear to rise from the base as if in one piece, but they are in fact separate. Within the three stems at the base is attached a small spiral.

MARKS None.

Designed *c*.1900 and made by K.M. Seifert & Co., Dresden-Löbtau.

H 31.3 cm   1993,10-12,7

Richard Müller worked as an architect and designer in Dresden. From 1899, he designed a wide range of candlesticks and lamps for the lighting and metalwork firm of K.M. Seifert. He also made designs for glass, porcelain and furniture. Seifert executed the designs of a number of other artists, including Riemerschmid and Bruno Paul (see Cat. 406). A contemporary account of Seifert's lighting products gave particular praise to Müller's original designs (*Kunst und Handwerk* 53, 1902/3, 154ff., quoted in Bröhan 1990, 446). A candlestick of this design was included in Seifert's display at the Turin Exhibition of 1902, see *Kunstgewerbeblatt*, NF 14, 1903, 38.

Niemeyer, Adelbert 1867-1932

There is no monograph on Niemeyer. For a biography in English, with references to a number of articles in contemporary German publications, see Munich 1988, 76.

404 Vase [PLATE 146]

Hard-paste porcelain, with two handles, decorated with an overall pattern of intertwining tendrils and stylised flowers and leaves painted overglaze in purple on a white ground and gilded. The neck and handles left white with moulded relief decoration. The rim and foot with gilded edges.

MARKS Printed on the base in underglaze green with factory mark comprising a shield with 'Nymphenburg' below; three factory numbers painted overglaze in purple: '831', '783', '27'.

Designed c.1905 and made by the Königlich-Bayerische Porzellan-Manufaktur, Nymphenburg.

H 17.9 cm   1992,7-14,1

A painter by training and founder of the Munich Secession in 1892, Niemeyer became a leading artist-designer for the applied arts in Munich in the early 1900s. In 1902 he founded an interior decoration workshop in Munich, the Werkstätten für Wohnungseinrichtungen (which merged in 1907 with the Dresdner Werkstätten to become the Deutsche Werkstätten).

In 1906, the Nymphenburg porcelain manufactory set up a studio for Niemeyer, who had already been a designer for the factory for several years. This vase is one of his most successful early designs for Nymphenburg; it was made with several variations, see, for example, Munich 1988, cat. no. 52, which has a central band of leaves, and Franzke 1987, cat. no. 120 (with references to contemporary illustrations); see also G.C. Grosso, *Ceramiche del 'Modern Style'*, Museo Internazionale delle Ceramiche, Faenza, 1992, no. 44, which has only a simple pattern round the shoulders. The delicate all-over pattern is characteristic of the Munich style of the period.

Nienhuis, Bert 1873-1960

There is no monograph on Nienhuis. For biographical details, see Leidelmeijer and van der Cingel 1983, 78-80; Amsterdam 1985.

405 Jardinière [PLATE 146]

Earthenware, moulded, with matt glaze and in-glaze decoration of stylised butterflies in blue, yellow and green on a white ground. There is a small patch of restoration to the inside of the rim.

MARKS Printed factory mark of De Distel on the base.

Designed before 1905 and made by the Plateelbakkerij De Distel, Amsterdam, between 1904 and 1911.

H 15.4 cm, D 23 cm   1992,6-8,1

Nienhuis trained as a painter and was one of the four major designers for ceramics in Holland in the period 1895-1910, the others being W.C. Brouwer (see Cat. 28), C.J. van der Hoef (see Cat. 391-2) and T.C.A. Colenbrander. Nienhuis worked for De Distel from 1895, when the firm was founded, to 1911. He became head of the decorating department in 1901 and from 1903 began to develop his distinctive linear decoration in light colours on a matt-glazed ground, which won prizes at several international exhibitions, for example St Louis 1904, Milan 1906, Brussels 1910 and Turin 1911.

This jardinière is illustrated in a De Distel catalogue of 1904-11, p. 2, no. 29 and in *DK & D* XVI, 1905, 519.

Paul, Bruno 1874-1968

Popp, J., *Bruno Paul*, Munich 1916

Günther, S., *Interieurs um 1900: Bernhard Pankok, Bruno Paul und Richard Riemerschmid als Mitarbeiter der Vereinigten Werkstätten für Kunst im Handwerk*, Munich 1971

Günther, S., 'Das Werk des Karakaturisten, Möbelentwerfers und Architekten Bruno Paul (1874-1968)', *Stadt*, vol. 29 no. 10, October 1982, 18-45, 72

Bruno Paul: Deutsche Raumkunst und Architektur zwischen Jugendstil und Moderne, exhibition catalogue, Stadtmuseum Munich, 1992

For a biography in English, see Munich 1988

406 Candelabrum [FRONT COVER]

Brass, cast and wrought, with twelve arms and central shaft, making thirteen branches in all. The arms are constructed of six elements, each comprising a pair of branches, which swivel round the centre of the shaft, so that they can be arranged in the same plane, or at right angles to each other, forming a three-dimensional structure in the shape of a stylised tree.

MARKS None.

Designed in 1901 and made by K.M. Seifert & Co., Dresden-Löbtau, for the Vereinigte Werkstätten für Kunst im Handwerk, Munich.

H 41 cm, max W 71 cm   1993,10-12,5

Bruno Paul studied at the Kunstgewerbeschule in Dresden and from 1894 at the Munich Academy, supplying caricatures for the satirical magazine *Simplicissimus*. In 1897 he was a founder member of the Vereinigte Werkstätten, with whom he exhibited at the Paris 1900 Exhibition, at Turin in 1902 and St Louis in 1904.

This large candelabrum, with its ceremonial appearance, has been described as 'the most spectacular of all Jugendstil candelabras' (G. Dry in Munich 1988, cat. no. 77). It was until recently attributed to Pankok and was first published as by Paul by Graham Dry, with reference to its exhibition at the Munich Ausstellung für Kunst im Handwerk in 1901 (*Katalog*, 61, no. 145) and to an illustrated catalogue of the Vereinigte Werkstätten issued in 1912 which credits the candlestick to Paul ('Aspekte des floralen und linearen Stils: Münchener Jugendstilleuchter um 1900', *Weltkunst*, 1 August 1987, 2030-33). Dry also notes that it was sold in several sizes by the Vereinigte Werkstätten until at least 1914, though it appears to have been most popular between 1901 and 1907 when it forms a regular decorative feature in contemporary illustrations of rooms by the Vereinigte Werkstätten (for example, *Die Kunst* 12, 1905, 367). The use of bold forms with simple ribbed decoration marks a move away from the dependence on stylised plant forms that characterised early Munich Jugendstil work up to 1900 (see Cat. 403, candlestick by R. Müller).

Only two other versions of this candelabrum have been recorded, one in the Stadtmuseum, Munich (Munich 1988, cat. no. 77) and one in a private collection in Germany (Munich 1992, cat. no. 176). This third example has been in the same Munich family since it was bought in the early 1900s.

407 Candlestick [PLATE 147]

Brass, cast and wrought, with rectangular flat base, from which rises a flat rectangular slab, surmounted by a horizontal bar with downward curving ends, fitted with three candle holders.

MARKS None.

Designed in 1931 and made by the Deutsche Werkstätten, Dresden-Hellerau.

H 22.5 cm   1993,10-12,6

From 1907, Paul worked in Berlin, as director of the school attached to the Berlin Kunstgewerbemuseum, which was combined in 1924 with the Academische Hochschule für Bildende Künste to become the Vereinigte Staatschule für Freie und Angewandte Kunst, with Paul as its director until his resignation in 1933. He continued to work with the Deutsche Werkstätten; a candlestick of this design appears on the sideboard of a dining-room executed by the Deutsche Werkstätten in 1931 (Munich 1992, cat. no. 562). For a pair of similar candlesticks, see Munich 1992, cat. no. 202. This modernist candlestick is characteristic of Berlin metalwork of c.1930 and is close to the work of Albert Reimann (see Cat. 254).

Pellatt & Co. c.1790-1895

There is no monograph on Pellatt & Co. For an account of the different members of the Pellatt family and the Falcon Glass Works, see J. Rose, 'The Apsley Pellatts', *The Glass Circle* 3, 1979, 4-9. For Apsley Pellatt's publications, see *Memoir on the origin, process and improvement of Glass manufactures including an account of the patent Crystallo-Ceramie or Glass Incrustations*, London 1821, followed by a revised and enlarged edition, *Curiosities of Glass-Making*, 1849. See also Hajdamach 1991, 252-9.

408 Covered goblet [PLATE 146]

Glass, free-blown, ovoid body and cover, set on a tall knopped stem with raised foot, with wheel-engraved geometric decoration incorporating a band of interlaced leaf-shapes on both body and cover, and bands of vertical parallel lines.

MARKS Engraved 'Pellatt' surmounted by a crown, on the knop.

Made at Apsley Pellatt's Falcon Glass Works, Southwark, London, c.1862.

H 36.7 cm (with cover)   1992,7-11,1

This goblet is identical in form to a goblet shown by Pellatt at the International Exhibition in London in 1862 and illustrated in J.B. Waring's three-volume record of the exhibition (1863, vol. I, pl. 87). In preparation for the exhibition, Apsley Pellatt held a competition for designs for engraved glass, which had replaced cut glass in contemporary taste. The prize-winning designs were produced by his firm and at least some of them were shown at the exhibition (Rose 1979, 7). The goblet illustrated by Waring has decoration in the classical style and is described as 'designed by John H. Wood'. Whether this refers to the shape or the decoration, or both, is unclear. It may be that the goblet was a standard shape on which different designs were executed. In 1864, the firm presented a selection of the competition glasses to the Royal Museum of Scotland in Edinburgh (Rose 1979, pls 9-11) whence in 1967 a few models were transferred to the Victoria and Albert Museum (Rose, pls 7-8 and Morris 1978, pl. 43). See also Morris 1978, pl. 47 (private collection).

Pellatt pieces are rarely signed; the only other recorded pieces with this signature are a pair of oil-lamp bases in a private collection (Hajdamach 1991, 261, pl. 250). For an illustration of the British Museum goblet, see *Journal of Glass Studies* 35, 1993, 123.

The Falcon Glass Works, founded in the seventeenth century, were taken over by the Pellatt family about 1790. After a period as Pellatt & Green until the early 1830s, the firm traded under a number of names which appear to overlap: Apsley Pellatt, Apsley Pellatt & Co., Pellatt & Co. The publications listed above were written by Apsley Pellatt IV (1791-1863); under his direction, the factory became one of the pre-eminent London firms, making a wide range of decorative glass. From 1852 Apsley Pellatt's younger brother Frederick was in charge, until the latter's death in 1874, when the firm split into two parts which ceased trading in 1890 and 1895.

Powell, James & Sons, Whitefriars Glass Works, London 1834-1980

See Cat. 234-43 and 349.

Cat. 409-22 were acquired from Harry Powell's granddaughter, Dr Audrey Baker. They were Harry Powell's own table glasses, many of which he designed himself, and have remained in the family since his death in 1922. In common with most Powell glass, none of these pieces is marked, and so the provenance is of particular significance. I am grateful to Wendy Evans for information from the Museum of London Powell archive.

409 Decanter and stopper with two matching glasses for wine and sherry [PLATE 146]

Clear glass, free-blown, slightly ribbed. The decanter with ovoid body coming to a point at the base, ribbed foot and Powell's characteristic merese at join of body and foot. The stopper in the form of a flame. The glasses with gently undulating profile, the larger glass with ribbed foot.

Designed by Harry Powell before 1899.

409a Decanter: H 34.1 cm (with stopper)   1991,7-3,1
409b-c Glasses: H 12 cm and 11.2 cm   1991,7-3,13-14

A decanter of this shape, with matching glasses, all with a wheel-engraved pattern of stylised lotus blossoms, was made for the King of Siam in 1899 (Morris 1978, pl. 121). The service was made in both plain and engraved versions (see Shaw Sparrow 1904, pl. G18, and 1909, 253 and 259, plain, and *Studio Yearbook*, 1906, 245, patterned). According to his grand-daughter, Harry Powell regarded this as his most successful design for a decanter.

410 Tumbler

Clear glass, free-blown, extremely thin and lightweight, with four dented sides.

Designed probably by Harry Powell, c.1880.

H 8.3 cm   1991,7-3,15

Harry Powell records in his *Glassmaking in England*, 1923, 83, that decanters and vases with dents in the sides to provide a secure grip were produced by the firm from about 1880. This particular shape is copied directly from a characteristic type of Roman beaker. The Museum of London holds two miniature tumblers of this shape in coloured glass.

411 Two 'poppy-head' wine glasses

The larger glass green, the smaller glass clear; the bowls slightly ribbed, with dented sides; the feet also ribbed.

Designed by Harry Powell, c.1880-1900.

411a Green glass: H 14.5 cm   1991,7-3,6
411b Clear glass: H 13.2 cm   1991,7-3,7

Illustrated in Shaw Sparrow 1909, 252.

412 Two waisted tumblers

Clear glass, mould-blown and ribbed, with incurved sides.

Designed by Harry Powell, c.1880-1900.

412a H 11 cm   1991,7-3,3
412b H 6.6 cm   1991,7-3,4

A drawing of a glass of the same shape as the larger tumbler was shown in the Powell exhibition at the Museum of London in 1989; an annotation records that it was ordered by Walter Crane in 1910, but the design is thought to date from the late nineteenth century. Early versions were also made in opal glass. They were still being advertised in Powell's catalogues of the 1930s.

413 Wine glass and sherry glass

Clear glass, the bowls mould-blown with diagonal ribbing, ribbed feet.

Designed c.1880-1900.

413a Wine glass: H 12.8 cm   1991,7-3,8
413b Sherry glass H 11.4 cm   1991,7-3,9

This service appears in an undated archive photograph in a photographic album of about 1880-1900 in the Museum of London Powell archive (Ref. 80.547/3249), giving the model number of the wine glass as 918, selling at 14s. 6d. a dozen, and the sherry glass as model number 916, selling at 12s. 6d. a dozen. The service remained in production into the 1930s and appears in illustrations to the article on Whitefriars glass in *Commercial Art & Industry*, 1932 (see introduction to Cat. 234 etc.).

414 Water glass and wine glass

Clear glass, with cone-shaped bowls and short stems. The larger glass is ribbed, small chip to foot.

Designed c.1880-1900.

414a H 15.1 cm   1991,7-3,10
414b H 11.6 cm   1991,7-3,11

This service also appears in the photograph album in the Museum of London Powell archive (see Cat. 413). The photograph, which does not show the large water glass, is annotated with the model number 1464 only; the smaller glass sold for 8s. 6d. a dozen. This service was popular into the 1930s and appears in an article in *The Studio*, October 1931, 270, on 'Art and the table', in the article on Whitefriars glass in *Commercial Art & Industry*, 1932, and in the firm's catalogues throughout the 1930s.

415 Wine glass

Clear glass, mould-blown deep ribbed bowl, no stem, small knop only between bowl and foot.

Designed c.1880-1900.

H 9.6 cm   1991,7-3,12

This glass appears in the photograph album in the Museum of London Powell archive as model number 1404, selling at 15s. a dozen.

416-17 Two finger-bowls

Clear glass, free-blown, one (416) with frilly edge, the other (417) with the sides brought out to form four 'petals'.

Designed c.1880.

416 H 7.1 cm   1991,7-3,16
417 H 6.4 cm   1991,7-3,17

Finger-bowls were a common feature of late nineteenth-century place settings (see Mrs Loftie, *The Dining Room*, London 1878, 102-3). These wavy-edged bowls were used with or without matching plates and were also made in blue opal.

418-20 Finger-bowl, shallow bowl and a plate

Clear glass, the bowls slightly ribbed, the plate with flat rim and deep central depression.

Designed c.1900.

418 Finger-bowl: D 10.6 cm   1991,7-3,18
419 Shallow bowl: D 11.1 cm   1991,7-3,19
420 Plate: D 15.8 cm   1991,7-3,20

The finger-bowl appears in the Museum of London photograph album as model number 1245, selling at 16s. a dozen. It remained popular and appears in Whitefriars' catalogues of the late 1930s. A group of similar plates in green glass forms part of the group of Powell glass at Wightwick Manor, near Wolverhampton, but the acquisition date of this group is not recorded and it could be late nineteenth or early twentieth century (see J. Rudoe and H. Coutts, 'The table glass designs of Philip Webb and T.G. Jackson for James Powell & Sons, Whitefriars Glassworks', *Journal of the Decorative Arts Society* 16, 1992, 24-42).

421 Vase

Clear glass, squat, globular shape, mould-blown with diamond pattern.

Designed c.1900.

H 9.1 cm 1993,7-3,5

Powell & Sons were experimenting in the early 1900s with diamond-pattern moulding inspired by seventeenth-century prototypes. The shape, however, is derived rather from ancient glass.

422 Vase

Clear glass, free-blown, with two horizontal bands of honeycomb cutting divided by horizontal lines. The base is cracked in two places.

Designed c.1894.

H 10.4 cm   1991,7-3,2

This vase appears in a pattern book in the Museum of London archive, with model number 1150, annotated 'from a Roman cup in the Zurich Museum'. The archive also contains a volume of thumbnail sketches entitled 'Glasses with histories' made during Harry Powell's travels in Europe, with a page of sketches of Roman cut glass, one of which is annotated with the same model number and 'similar cup in Zurich Museum, different cutting'. The Musée Bellerive in Zurich acquired an identical vase from Powell & Sons in 1906, described by the firm itself as 'the Zurich cup' (Gysling-Billeter 1975, no. 360). Although it has not been possible to trace an exact prototype amongst the archaeological collections in Zurich, the Schweizerisches Landesmuseum holds a fragmentary beaker of this type from Vindonissa with a band of honeycomb cutting, which may have been in a more complete state at the end of the nineteenth century and may have served as the model for the Powell vase (I am indebted to Dr Sigrid Barten of the Musée Bellerive and to Dr Rudolf Degen of the Schweizerisches Landesmuseum for their help).

According to the archive volume, 'Glasses with histories', a Roman bowl from Leuna in the British Museum was 'copied at Whitefriars in Jany 1894'. A wine glass based on this bowl is illustrated in the *Art Journal*, 1896, 21. The use of shallow cutting to form a surface pattern that did not detract from the shape of the vessel was much praised at the time (see *JSA* 54, 16 March 1906, 502, and also 15 June, 776-81, for Harry Powell's paper on the subject of cut glass).

423 Decanter and stopper

Amber glass, mould-blown, with square body and ridged strap handle with a sharp angle to it, the stopper with flat top.

Designed c.1890-1900.

H 18.4 cm (with stopper) 1993,12-5,1 Given by Antony Griffiths and Judy Rudoe

This decanter is closely based on Roman glass bottles of the first or second century AD. Examples were in the collections of the British Museum by the 1870s. Given that Powell's were copying Roman cut glass in the last decade of the nineteenth century, it is likely that the introduction of these 'Roman' bottles dates from the same time. Harry Powell clearly admired Roman bottles of this kind; in his *Glassmaking in England*, 1923, he illustrates on the very first page, at the beginning of the chapter on Roman glass, a 'square jug, made in a mould, with strongly fixed handle'.

A similar, though smaller, bottle by Powell's is illustrated in the *Studio Yearbook*, 1911, 131. The shape continued in production and appears in the firm's catalogues of the 1930s as well as in a number of contemporary publications, e.g. H.G. Dowling, *A Survey of British Industrial Arts*, 1935, pl. XXII, and *The Studio*, 1931, 270.

Richardson, W.H., B. & J. 1829-1930

There is no monograph on this factory. For the most recent account, see Hajdamach 1991, 95-124.

424 Decanter [PLATE 146]

Glass, free-blown, both decanter and stopper in the form of a ring, the decanter with applied lion-head prunts round the outer edge and on each side, where they are placed within a band of acid-etched floral decoration. The interior of the ring is wheel-engraved to give an all-over matt surface. The neck has an applied rigaree. Neck, stopper and foot have simple bands of wheel-engraved decoration.

MARKS None.

Made by the firm of B. Richardson, Wordsley, Stourbridge, c.1878.

H 33.4 cm (with stopper) 1993,7-17,1

This decanter is closely related to an ewer shown by Richardson at the Paris Exhibition of 1878 and illustrated in an album made by the factory of all the exhibition pieces prior to their departure to Paris (the album is owned by Broadfield House Glass Museum). The Exhibition ewer was more elaborate, but was also ring-shaped and had similar applied lion-head prunts and acid-etched floral decoration. However, no example of the ewer is known, and this decanter is the only one so far recorded.

The 1878 Exhibition was the first time that the firm had taken part in an international exhibition since 1851, after which they had gone bankrupt, but they re-established themselves by 1853 and continued to introduce new styles and techniques, one of which was acid-etching, pioneered by Richardson's in the 1850s. This decanter, with its combination of acid-etched and applied decoration, and the use of wheel-engraving on the convex surface of the tyre, is a virtuoso piece of glassmaking.

The firm of Richardson was run initially by the three Richardson brothers, William Haden, Benjamin and Jonathan; it was known as B. Richardson from 1853 to 1864 and then traded under various partnerships until 1883, when it became H.G. Richardson. The firm was taken over by Thomas Webb in 1930.

Rörstrand Porslinsfabrik AB founded 1726

See Cat. 261.

Baeckstrom, A., *Rörstrand och dese tillverkninger, 1726-1926*, Stockholm 1930
Rörstrand under tre Århundraden 1726-1943, exhibition catalogue, National Museum, Stockholm, 1943
Three Centuries of Swedish Pottery, exhibition catalogue, Victoria and Albert Museum, London 1959
Lutteman, H. Dahlbäck. *Svenskt 1900 tals Keramik*, Västerås 1985
For recent brief factory histories in English, see London 1989b and M. Eidelberg (ed.), *Design 1935-1965. What Modern Was*, exhibition catalogue, Montreal and New York, 1991, 395-6.

425 Vase

Earthenware, with a band of moulded relief decoration on the neck of stylised flowers and leaves glazed in blue, green and red. The top of the neck and the body with incised spirals in green and yellow ochre on a white ground.

MARKS Printed in underglaze green on the base 'DESSIN ALF WALLANDER', with the Rörstrand factory mark 'Rörstrand' and three crowns, see mark for Cat. 261.

Designed by Alf Wallander c.1906-8 and made by the Rörstrand Porcelain Factory, Rörstrand, near Stockholm.

H 19 cm 1991,12-7,1

Alf Wallander (1862-1914) studied as a painter in Stockholm and Paris before joining Rörstrand in 1895. He became art director in 1900 and worked at the factory until 1910. He is best known for his delicately modelled Art Nouveau floral porcelains of about 1900, shown at the Paris 1900 Exhibition, for which the mark 'Dessin Alf Wallander' was introduced. This vase illustrates his later, more stylised designs for earthenware (see Lutteman 1985, 13, for a vase with similar incised spirals of c.1907 and Opie 1989, no. 331, for a vase of c.1906-8). The factory moved to Lidköping in 1932 (see Cat. 261).

St Petersburg, Imperial Porcelain Factory founded 1744

See Cat. 35.

426 Plate

Hard-paste porcelain, painted overglaze in bands of black, green and blue with interlaced gilded motifs incorporating a jewelled orb (*derzhava*), the double-headed eagle, the monogram of Alexander II, anchors, ships' chains and ropes.

MARKS Printed on the base with underglaze green crowned monogram of Alexander II (1855-81) and impressed cyrillic initials 'ML', presumably for the painter.

Designed by Hippolyte A. Monighetti between 1871 and 1873, as part of a service for the Imperial yacht *Derzhava*, and made by the Imperial Porcelain Factory, St Petersburg, before 1881.

D 24.5cm   1994,1-9,1

The name of the yacht, *Derzhava*, means 'orb' in Russian, hence the incorporation of imperial orbs amongst the nautical motifs in the decoration. Hippolyte Monighetti (1819-78) was an architect and Professor of the Academy of Arts in St Petersburg. The tradition of inviting professors from the St Petersburg Academy to make designs for the Imperial Porcelain Factory was begun in the late 1830s with the celebrated Kremlin service of 1837-8 (a plate from the Kremlin service decorated with a design based on a seventeenth-century Russian enamel dish in the Kremlin, was acquired in 1992, but its date is too early for inclusion in this catalogue). Monighetti designed most of the furnishings for the *Derzhava*. His designs for this porcelain service, which combine elements of the 'Old Russian' style with bold colours, are fully illustrated in E. Kirichenko and M. Anikst, *The Russian Style*, London 1991, pls 108-11.

The complete tea, coffee and dinner service comprised 930 pieces; for examples from the State Museum in Petrodvorets, see *An Imperial Fascination: Porcelain. Dining with the Czars*, Peterhof, exhibition catalogue, A La Vieille Russie, New York, 1991, cat. 291-7, pp. 127-9. Pieces from this service are also held by the Hillwood Museum, Washington, see K.V.H. Taylor, *Russian Art from Hillwood*, Washington 1988, 68, fig. 99.

Scheurich, Paul 1883-1945

There is no monograph on Scheurich. For biographical details, see Jedding 1981, 164-5.

427 Recumbent figure of Diana

Hard-paste porcelain, the figure reclining against a rock, set on an oval plinth. Glazed white all over.

MARKS Impressed on the edge of the plinth 'SCHEURICH', the underside with printed underglaze blue factory mark of a sceptre (see mark for Cat. 231), and impressed date-letter for 1922.

The model purchased from Scheurich by the Königliche Porzellan-Manufaktur, Berlin, in December 1917 and made by the KPM in 1922.

H 22.2cm, L 40.8cm   1993,11-10,1

Scheurich has been described as the 'most important porcelain modeller of the twentieth century' (Jedding 1981, 164). He trained at the Berlin Academy and his first models for porcelain were made for the Schwarzburger Werkstätten in 1910-11. This figure of Diana was one of three models purchased by the

KPM in 1917-18, the other two being standing figures of Apollo and Daphne. According to Jedding (1981, 164) and Beaucamp-Markowsky (1980, no. 33), the model of Diana dates from 1912 and those of the two standing figures from 1914. The three models gave a new impetus to the production of sculptural pieces at the KPM; the glazed white undecorated porcelain reflected the light and enhanced the modelling of the figures. The KPM paid Scheurich 1500 Marks for each of the three figures (Jarchow 1988, 243).

In the 1920s and 1930s Scheurich worked for Meissen, returning to KPM only in 1939, when Adolf Pfeiffer, who had directed the Meissen factory, became director at the KPM.

Schütz, Siegmund born 1906

Gollwitzer, G., *Form und Gestalt. Arbeiten aus der Werkstatt des Bildhauers und Formgebers Siegmund Schütz 1930-1972*, Schriftenreihe 'Die Münze', Band 17, Berlin 1972

Mundt, B., *40 Jahre Porzellan: Siegmund Schütz zum 80 Geburtstag*, Berlin 1986

See also Jarchow 1988, 214

428 Vase   [PLATE 147]

Hard-paste porcelain, of flared shape with two handles running from the rim to the foot.

MARKS Underglaze blue printed sceptre mark of the Staatliche Porzellan-Manufaktur; see mark for Cat. 231.

Designed in 1935 and made by the Staatliche Porzellan-Manufaktur, Berlin.

H 14cm   1993,2-4,1   Given by Keir McGuiness

Schütz, a sculptor and medallist, trained at the Dresden Academy from 1926 to 1931. From 1932 to 1936 he worked freelance for the Berlin porcelain manufactory, at the invitation of the Director, G. von Pechmann, who provided him with a studio, and then full-time until 1970. He specialised in small-scale cameo reliefs and vessels with low-relief decoration in plain white or celadon. The shape of this vase was known as 'Hölderlin-Becher' because it was also made with a relief portrait medallion of Hölderlin on one side. For an illustration of the vase with portrait, see Gollwitzer, pl. 29. See also Jarchow 1988, 285. The vase is still in production (information from B. Mundt).

Sèvres, Manufacture Nationale de founded 1756

See Cat. 80 and 269.

429 Plate   [PLATE 144]

Hard-paste porcelain, with painted and gilded decoration on a matt red ground. In the centre, a leaping panther above a Bacchic trophy of grapes, drinking horn, kylix, ribbon-tied thyrsus, lion's skin and laurel wreath within a basket, with a further classical vase to the left, all set on a rock-like base. The border is decorated with a frieze of palmettes and ivy leaves in white and matt gold with a burnished gold rim.

MARKS On the base printed green factory mark and date 's.54' in an oval and a special mark of an 'N' crowned for Prince Napoléon; the initials '.L.G.' for the gilder, L. Guyonnet, painted in black.

Commissioned by Prince Napoléon in April 1856 as part of a 114-piece dessert service with red ground and 'décor étrusque', probably for use by his mistress, the actress Mlle Rachel, in the Maison Pompéienne. The decoration executed by Guyonnet and other artists at the Manufacture Nationale de Sèvres in 1856.

D 24 cm   1992,7-9,1

The suggestion (by Bernard Dragesco) that Prince Napoléon had this elaborate service made for Mlle Rachel's use is based on an account of a visit to the actress in the Maison Pompéienne written by Arsène Houssaye, director of the Comédie Française and biographer of Mlle Rachel: 'we talked endlessly about the Etruscans, for it is well known that the actress's dining-room is painted like a dining-room at Herculaneum; Mlle Rachel even has a Sèvres service depicting all manner of subjects from the ancient wall-paintings' (A. Houssaye, *Les Confessions. Souvenirs d'un demi-siècle 1830-1880*, reprinted Geneva 1971, 333). The central trophy on this plate is a direct copy of a trophy published in *Le Antichità d'Ercolano*, Naples 1760, vol. III, 173, though without the grapes and the leaping panther, which seem to be additions of the artist. Eleven other plates from this service have so far come to light (in the possession of Bernard Dragesco in 1992) and they are all similarly decorated with trophies or landscapes with buildings derived from the vignettes in *Le Antichità d'Ercolano*.

Prince Napoléon (Napoléon Joseph-Charles Paul, called Jérôme, 1822-91), was the son of the Emperor Napoleon's brother Jérôme. In 1856, the year in which this service was commissioned, Prince Napoléon had begun the building of his celebrated 'Maison Pompéienne', a Graeco-Roman fantasy in the avenue Montaigne, Paris, designed by Hittorf, Normand and others. It was completed in 1860, sold in 1866 and demolished in 1891. Mlle Rachel (Rachel Félix, 1820-58) was largely responsible for the revival of the classical tragedies of Racine and Corneille.

The Sèvres factory archives (information kindly supplied by Bernard Dragesco and Tamara Préaud) contain full records of the order for this large service, the costings, the names of the decorators and the modeller, Dieterle. The plates were the most richly decorated part of the service: there were seventy-two at 76 F each, totalling 5472 F in all. For further details of the archive records and bibliographical references on the Maison Pompéienne, see A. Dawson, *French Porcelain. A Catalogue of the British Museum Collection*, 1994, cat. no. 189.

Summerson, Robert 1873-1953

430 Pot-pourri vase and cover

Copper, hand-raised, of ovoid form, with two ring handles, the lid ornamented with gadroons and pierced. The copper is patinated in two different tones: the handles are darker than the body. The vase is hand-raised from a single sheet of metal.

MARKS None.

Designed and made by Robert Summerson, London, in the 1920s.

H 15.6 cm   1991,5-3,1   Bequeathed by the artist to his son, Roy Summerson, who bequeathed it to the British Museum in accordance with his father's wishes

Robert Summerson was an engineer who worked in pewter and copper as a hobby. This is an accomplished piece in the Arts and Crafts tradition; the artist considered it his finest piece in view of the skill involved in hand-raising it from a single sheet of metal. The shape is of oriental inspiration.

Born in Sunderland, Summerson worked initially for his father's firm of gas engineers in that city. From 1910 to 1922 he worked for the Davis Gas Stove Company in Luton and from 1922 to 1935 for Sugg's Gas Appliance Manufacturers in London. He returned to the Davis company in Luton in 1936/7 until his retirement in 1952 (information kindly supplied by the artist's grandson, Stephen Summerson).

Van de Velde, Henry Clemens 1863-1957

See Cat. 290-95 and 354.

431 Vase

Salt-glazed stoneware, buff body, the body of globular form, with three handles emerging from the neck. The body made in two parts, the neck and handles made separately. There is a central ridge on the body, presumably to conceal the join. Covered all over with a bright blue glaze turning to lime-yellow at the top. An incised line emphasises the edge of the handles and rim.

MARKS Impressed on the base with the monogram of the artist (see mark for Cat. 293) and the factory model number '2055'.

Designed c.1902-3 and made by the firm of Reinhold Hanke, Höhr-Grenzhausen, Rhineland.

H 21.8 cm   1992,5-11,1

This vase belongs to the series commissioned from van de Velde in 1902 by the Westerwald district council through the Ministry of Trade in Berlin (see Cat. 293 for another vase from this series and full discussion of the commission). The series was noted for its experimental shapes and glazes; the blue colour on this vase is especially rare. This model was exhibited at the World's Fair in St Louis in 1904 (see *Die Kunst* 9, 1903-4, 325).

Other examples of this model with different glazes are to be found in the Badisches Landesmuseum, Karlsrühe (with *sang-de-boeuf* glaze, see Franzke 1987, no. 174) and in the Keramikmuseum, Westerwald, Höhr-Grenzhausen (mottled glaze, see Höhr-Grenzhausen 1986, no. 174).

Vieillard, J. & Cie 1845-95

J. Vieillard & Cie. Eclectisme et Japonisme, exhibition catalogue, ed. J. du Pasquier, Musée des Arts Décoratifs, Bordeaux, 1986

432 Plate   [PLATE 145]

Earthenware, decorated in relief enamelling with four overlapping panels in the Japanese manner on a geometric ground-pattern, also in coloured relief enamels. One panel, in the form of a fan, has a bird on a prunus branch with a 'cracked ice' ground; another, of rectangular shape, contains irises in red and orange with turquoise leaves on a gold ground. The other two panels are circular, one with Chinese *shou* characters in black amidst floral scrolls in grey and white, the other with lotus flowers in white, yellow, red and green. The chequered ground-pattern in royal blue, yellow and orange.

MARKS Impressed on the base 'J. VIEILLARD & CIE BORDEAUX', with model number 'D94' and '12' painted in black.

Designed probably by Amédée de Caranza and made by the firm of J. Vieillard & Cie, Bordeaux, c.1878-85.

D 34 cm   1992,12-1,1

The Bordeaux firm of Vieillard rivalled that of Théodore Deck in Paris and specialised in ceramics in the oriental taste, following the engagement of Amédée de Caranza as chef d'atelier between 1878 and 1882. Little is known of Caranza's early years, except that he was of Italian origin and born in Istanbul.

In 1867 he was working in Paris with Léon Parvillée, who specialised in Islamic-style ceramics, along with Théodore Deck and Eugène Collinot, who were both producing ceramics with relief enamelling. In 1885, Caranza fell out with the Vieillard brothers and left the factory; he devoted the rest of his career to making glass (Bordeaux 1986, 21-2).

Caranza is credited with introducing relief enamelling to the Vieillard factory and Vieillard's elaborate orientalist ceramics with relief enamels are generally attributed to him, see Bordeaux 1986, nos 87-8, 92-4. However, many of the pieces with Japanese-style decoration are attributed in the Bordeaux catalogue to the factory artist, Eugène Millet, who may have had a hand in the decoration of this plate.

Worcester Royal Porcelain Company Ltd
established 1862

See Cat. 313-15.

433 Covered dish

Bone china, of oval form, with elephant-head handles and four feet. The handle to the lid in the form of two dragons' heads and birds' feet. Decorated with overglaze painting in several colours (green, red, pink, grey, yellow, pale and dark blue, with black or blue outlines) of motifs in the oriental manner, set asymmetrically on a white ground. The motifs include overlapping circles, hexagons, leaves, a table with vases, a sword and lantern, scroll-paintings, etc. The handles and feet painted matt bronze in parts, with gilding.

MARKS Impressed on base and inside lid with factory mark and '2K' (lid) or '3K' (dish), together with printed black overglaze factory mark (see mark for Cat. 314) and date '75', and 'B/27' painted in red.

Made by the Worcester Royal Porcelain Company Ltd in 1875.

H 20.2 cm, L 35.6 cm   1993,12-6,1   Given by Judy Rudoe

This piece exhibits a combination of Chinese and Japanese motifs, characteristic of the Worcester factory, see Cat. 315.

Wright, Russel 1904-76

See Cat. 318-25.

434 Lemonade pitcher   [PLATE 147]

Spun aluminium, of flared form with slanting lip, circular handle with wood knop.

MARKS Stamped on the base 'RUSSEL WRIGHT'.

Designed c.1930 and made in Wright's own studio at 135 East 35th Street, New York City.

H 25.7 cm   1991,10-1,1   Given by Antony Griffiths

Unable to afford the machinery required to work pewter and chromium-plated steel, Wright turned to spun aluminium, which was cheaper and easier to work. Aluminium had until then been used for kitchen wares rather than tablewares, but Wright designed a line of informal serving accessories, exploiting the spinning process to create novel shapes such as this striking asymmetrical pitcher. The line was produced throughout the 1930s and included many newly created items to suit changing styles of entertaining — bun warmers, cheese boards, tid-bit trays, sandwich humidor, etc. (see Hennessey 1983, 20-24, Kerr 1985, 22-8, and a more recent publication, A. Kerr, *The Collector's Encyclopedia of Russel Wright Designs*, Paducah 1990, 30-40).

Wynand, Paul 1879-1956

See Cat. 330-32.

435 Beer tankard

Salt-glazed stoneware, grey-buff body with rich 'Cologne brown' glaze; relief decoration in the form of small bosses round the top and a band of ridges round the base. Fitted with the original pewter lid.

MARKS Impressed 'R. MERKELBACH GRENZHAUSEN' with model number '2118' on the base; see mark for Cat. 137.

Designed by Paul Wynand c.1909 and made by the firm of R. Merkelbach, Grenzhausen, c.1909-14.

H 14.3 cm   1993,11-5,2   Given by Graham Dry and Beate Dry-v. Zezschwitz

This tankard was advertised on plate 13 of Merkelbach's 1912 catalogue at 5 Marks. For a similar tankard, see Cologne 1978, cat. no. 453, and Bonn 1987, cat. no. 232.

Zeisel, Eva born 1906

See Cat. 333-5 and 358-61.

436-40 Fourteen pieces of tableware   [PLATE 147]

Earthenware; 436a-d: a teapot, sugar bowl and sweet dish glazed matt black all over, the teapot and sugar bowl with contrasting white lids, the sides of the sweet dish extended upwards to form an arched handle; 437a-e: a cup and saucer, two oval plates, oval fruit bowl and boat-shaped hors-d'oeuvre dish glazed white with overglaze printed linear motifs in black and gold resembling parabolas; 438: a cruet with transfer-printed floral motif on both sides in pinks, yellows and green; 439a-c: a ladle, four-sided bowl and oval lidded bowl glazed white; 440: a pair of candlesticks of the same continuous arched form as the sweet dish, glazed white with printed overglaze motifs in pink and black.

MARKS The black-glazed pieces unmarked, the rest mostly with printed blue and grey overglaze factory mark on the base, 'HALLCRAFT shape by Eva Zeisel' (the artist's name in the form of a facsimile signature) with monogram 'HC' and 'MADE IN USA BY HALL CHINA LTD'. The cup with printed gold pattern name 'FANTASY' and 'MADE IN U.S.A.', the cruet with printed gold pattern name 'BEAUX ARTS' and '2036'.

Designed c.1949-50 as part of the 'Tomorrow's Classic' dinner service and produced from 1952 by the Hall China Company, East Liverpool, Ohio.

436a Teapot: H 14.7 cm   1991,5-1,1
436b Milk jug: H 10.7 cm   1991,5-1,2
436c Sugar bowl: H 9.5 cm   1991,5-1,3
436d Sweet dish: H 15.5 cm   1991,5-1,4
437a Cup: H 6.1 cm, D of saucer 16 cm   1991,5-1,5 and 5a
437b Salad plate: L 21.8 cm 1991,5-1,6
437c Bread and butter plate: L 16.1 cm   1991,5-1,7
437d Fruit bowl: L 14.6 cm   1991,5-1,8
437e Hors-d'oeuvre dish: L 30.1 cm   1991,5-1,9
438 Cruet: H 19.2 cm   1992,7-15,3-6   Given by Dr Eva Zeisel
439a Ladle: L 13.5 cm   1992,7-15,4   Given by Dr Eva Zeisel
439b Four-sided bowl: L 15.3 cm   1992,7-15,5   Given by Dr Eva Zeisel
439c Oval lidded bowl: L 14.9 cm   1992,7-15,6   Given by Dr Eva Zeisel
440 Candlesticks: H 11.2 cm   1994,1-14,2 and 3

This was Zeisel's most popular service, without the eccentricities of her earlier 'Town & Country' service of 1946 (see Cat. 333-5 and 358-61), but retaining a flowing, organic line. 'Tomorrow's Classic' was designed by Zeisel without a pattern and was not immediately put into production. However, Charles Seliger of the Commercial Decal Company thought the forms would be ideally suited for decorated ware and he arranged for Hall China to produce it. The contract required Zeisel and her studio to provide nine patterns the first year and three each subsequent year. 'Fantasy' was inspired by the work of Naum Gabo and was designed by William Katavolos, Ross Littell and Douglas Kelley, students at the Pratt Institute in Brooklyn, where Zeisel had taught since 1939 (see Montreal 1984, 48 and figs 64-8). 'Beaux Arts' was designed by Zeisel's assistant, Irene Haas (Montreal 1984, fig. 67). Others were designed by Charles Seliger of Commercial Decal. For further discussion and history of Hall China Company, see M. Eidelberg (ed.), *Design 1935-1965. What Modern Was*, exhibition catalogue, Montreal and New York, 1991, 197-8 and 375.

441 Eight pieces of tableware [PLATE 147]

Earthenware, two serving bowls, two dinner plates, luncheon plate, bread and butter plate, cream jug and lidded oval sugar bowl, glazed white, the tear-shaped plates rising at one end to a wing or 'petal tip', as it was then called. The sugar bowl and the two nesting serving bowls rise at each side into petal-tip handles, those on the smaller oval bowl rising almost vertically. One of the dinner plates is decorated with a stencilled abstract pattern in red, pink, green and grey.

MARKS On base of luncheon plate, white dinner plate and cream jug, printed overglaze blue and grey factory mark as above, with the pattern name 'CENTURY'.

Designed c.1955 as part of the 'Century' dinner service, produced from mid-1956 by the Hall China Company, East Liverpool, Ohio.

441a Larger serving bowl: H 9.4 cm, L 27 cm   1992,7-15,7
441b Smaller serving bowl: H 12.5 cm, L 15.9 cm   1992,7-15,8
441c-d Dinner plates: L 29.1 cm   1992,7-15,9 and 12 (decorated)
441e Luncheon plate: L 24 cm   1992,7-15,10
441f Bread and butter plate: L 17.7 cm   1992,7-15,11
441g Cream jug: H 11.5 cm   1992,7-15,13
441h Sugar bowl: H 10.1 cm   1991,7-15,14
All given by Dr Eva Zeisel

Like 'Tomorrow's Classic', 'Century' was designed in white, but produced with a range of different patterns to meet the demand for decorated tableware. The pattern on the dinner plate was designed by Charles Seliger.

442 Two plastic dishes

Clear green plastic (plexiglas), one of double-lobed form, the other of trilobed form. The dish with two lobes has stress marks on the base; the dishes were modelled by air pressure and the stresses may have occurred during manufacture.

MARKS None.

Designed in 1947 as part of the 'Cloverware' series and made by the Clover Box and Manufacturing Company, Bronx, New York City.

442a Double-lobed dish: L 26 cm   1992,7-15,1
442b Trilobed dish: L 21.5 cm   1992,7-15,2
Given by Dr Eva Zeisel

These were among a number of experiments made by Zeisel at this time in designing for new media such as plastic. Zeisel designed only serving dishes in plexiglas because of its tendency to scratch. For further discussion and history of the Clover Box Company, see Eidelberg, op. cit. above, 111 and 368.

443 Four drinking glasses [PLATE 147]

Mould-blown, comprising two large tumblers in amber glass, one smaller tumbler in smoke and one squat coupe in smoke, all with undulating outlines and heavy bases.

MARKS None.

Designed c.1952 as part of the 'Silhouette' range and made by Bryce Brothers.

443a-c Tumblers: H 14.7, 13.7 and 11.1 cm   1992,7-15,19-21
443d Coupe: H 8.1 cm   1992,7-15,22
Given by Dr Eva Zeisel

The 'Silhouette' glass range was intended to complement 'Tomorrow's Classic' dinnerwares (see Montreal 1984, 58 and fig. 77). Zeisel designed glassware for a number of glass companies at this time.

444 Three drinking glasses [PLATE 147]

Clear glass, machine-made, with deep bases, the 'lo-ball' and cocktail with flared profile (444a-b), the fruit-juice glass taller with more vertical profile (444c).

MARKS None.

Designed c.1954 as part of the 'Prestige' range and made by the Federal Glass Company, Columbus, Ohio.

444a-b H 8.0 and 6.9 cm   1992,7-15,23-4
444c H 9.8 cm   1992,7-15,25
Given by Dr Eva Zeisel

For a contemporary illustration of these glasses, showing the reflective quality of the heavy bases, and a contemporary photograph of Zeisel in her studio with the glasses, working drawings, templates and turned plaster models, see Montreal 1984, 77, figs 98-9.

According to the designer, 'Many millions of them were produced by a huge automatic machine. I have found them in the airport in Zurich, at my cousin's in Paris, in the mountains of Venezuela and Jamaican markets. The Prestige glasses sold at 5 and 10¢ stores from (I believe) between 8¢ and 15¢ a piece. They look as if they had a thick bottom, with "silver" reflection. Yet the bottom is quite thin and in the center bulges out a bit, forming a sort of lens. They were also used to advertise Calvert whisky, and one could see them in huge ads on the street. Because they travel on the automatic machine in a hot, semi-molten stage, their profile has to be rather restrained, as they might collapse in that state. The profile of the Prestige glasses, though seemingly sharply dividing the foot from the body, is quite shallow' (letter from Dr Zeisel, 9 October 1992).

445-8 Coffee pot, cup and saucer, stemmed bowl and salt-shaker [PLATE 147]

Porcelain, glazed in yellow ochre, the cup with short stem on a wide, flat saucer, the salt-shaker in the form of a gourd, the coffee pot with elongated lid.

MARKS Each piece stamped on the base with raised letters and figures: coffee pot: 'z-13 U.S.A'; cup: 'z-31 U.S.A'; saucer: 'z-32 U.S.A'; bowl: 'z-12 U.S.A'; salt-shaker: 'z-25'.

Designed c.1963 and made by the Hyalyn Porcelain Company, Hickory, North Carolina.

445 Coffee pot: H 22.2 cm   1992,7-15,15
446 Cup: H 10.8 cm, D of saucer 15.7 cm   1992,7-15,16 and 16a
447 Bowl: H 15.4 cm   1992,7-15,17
448 Salt-shaker: H 20.4 cm   1992,7-15,18
All given by Dr Eva Zeisel

This service, with its rich glazes and elongated forms, was intended to give the effect of studio pottery although it was industrially produced (see Montreal 1984, 62 and fig. 84).

PLATE 144

Minton & Co., 1879 (Cat. 402); Sèvres, 1856 (Cat. 429);
W. T. Copeland & Sons Ltd, 1855, made 1881 (Cat. 375)

Doulton's Lambeth Pottery, 1879 (Cat. 383)

C. Dresser, Minton & Co., 1872, made 1880 (Cat. 384)

PLATE 145

W. Brownfield & Son, 1875 (Cat. 370); J.-T. Deck, c.1880 (Cat. 381); J. Vieillard
& Cie, c. 1878-85 (Cat. 432); F. Barbédienne, c. 1872-3 (Cat. 365)

J.-T. Deck, 1870 (Cat. 380); Figli di G. Cantagalli, c. 1880-1900 (Cat. 371);
C. Dresser, Old Hall Earthenware Co., 1884 (Cat. 385)

PLATE 146

Pellatt & Co., *c.* 1862 (Cat. 408); B. Richardson, *c.*1878 (Cat. 424); Cristalleries de Baccarat, 1878 (Cat. 363); P. Behrens, 1899 (Cat. 366); H. Christiansen, *c.* 1903 (Cat. 372); G. De Feure, *c.* 1901-2 (Cat. 382); J. Powell & Sons, before 1899 (Cat. 409)

Gustavsberg AB, 1908 (Cat. 389); A. Niemeyer, *c.* 1905 (Cat. 404); R. Müller, *c.* 1900 (Cat. 403); C. J. van der Hoef, *c.* 1908-10 (Cat. 392); B. Nienhuis, before 1905 (Cat. 405); C. J. van der Hoef, *c.* 1903-10 (Cat. 391)

PLATE 147

R. Wright, *c.* 1930 (Cat. 434); S. Schütz, 1935 (Cat. 428); J. E. Bang, 1936 (Cat. 364);
K. G. Hansen, 1934, made 1947 (Cat. 390); B. Paul, 1931 (Cat. 407)

E. Zeisel, five groups: ceramics, five on left, *c.* 1949-50 (Cat. 436-40), two nesting bowls front centre, *c.* 1955
(Cat. 441), three on right, *c.* 1963 (Cat. 445-8); glass, left, *c.* 1952 (Cat. 443), right, *c.* 1954 (Cat. 444)

Concordance of Register Numbers
and Catalogue Numbers

REGISTER NUMBER	CATALOGUE NUMBER	REGISTER NUMBER	CATALOGUE NUMBER	REGISTER NUMBER	CATALOGUE NUMBER
Old Acquisition 10710	33	1902,11-18,1	27	1978,7-4,9	183
Old Acquisition 10711	96	1903,4-10,1	30	1978,7-4,10	180
Slade 829 (bequeathed 1868)	40	1907,11-7,1	41	1978,7-4,11	175
Slade 955 (bequeathed 1868)	266	1907,11-7,2	42	1978,7-4,12	188
1878,4-13,1	59	1909,12-1,479	311	1978,7-4,13	186
1878,4-13,2	60	1920,3-18,16	273	1978,7-4,14	191
1878,4-13,3	62	1923,2-16,1	237	1978,7-4,15	168
1878,4-13,4	67	1923,2-16,2	240	1978,7-4,16	167
1878,4-13,5	61	1923,2-16,3	239	1978,7-4,17	169
1878,4-13,6	63	1923,2-16,4	238	1978,7-4,18	164
1878,4-13,7	68	1923,2-16,5	241	1978,7-4,19	165
1878,4-13,8	64	1923,2-16,6	234	1978,7-4,20	171
1878,4-13,9	69	1923,2-16,7	235a	1979,4-8,1	184
1878,4-13,10	70	1926,2-20,1	31	1979,10-5,1	313
1878,4-13,11	71	1928,7-25,1	78	1979,10-5,2	314
1878,4-13,12	72	1930,10-22,1	32	1979,11-2,1	26
1878,4-13,13	75	1945,2-4,2	163	1979,12-1,1	150a
1878,4-13,14	73	1945,2-4,3	176	1980,1-3,1 and 2	211
1878,4-13,15	74	1945,2-4,4	158	1980,1-4,1 to 3	147a to c
1878,4-13,16	66	1945,2-4,5	159	1980,2-2,1	87
1878,4-13,17	76b	1945,2-4,6	177a	1980,2-3,1	114
1878,4-13,18	76a	1945,2-4,8	189	1980,2-4,1	107
1878,4-13,19	65	1945,2-4,9	174	1980,2-5,1	92
1878,4-13,20	76d	1945,2-4,10	179	1980,3-1,1	315
1878,4-13,21	76e	1945,2-4,11 and 12	160a and b	1980,3-3,1	215
1878,4-13,22	76c	1945,2-4,13	181	1980,3-4,1 to 3	150b to d
1878,4-13,23	76f	1945,2-4,14	170	1980,3-5,1	228
1878,4-13,24	76g	1945,2-4,15	182	1980,3-6,1	97
1878,4-13,25	76h	1945,2-4,16	190	1980,5-3,1	93
1880,5-13,3	39	1945,2-4,18	177b	1980,5-4,1	100
1894,5-20,2	242	1945,2-4,20	192	1980,5-5,1 and 2	101b
1897 (Franks collection)	96	1976,9-3,1	127	1980,5-6,1	101a
1901,4-25,1	80	1977,5-3,1	205	1980,5-7,1	121
1902,7-21,1	199	1978,7-4,1	172	1980,5-8,1	299
1902,7-21,2	200	1978,7-4,2 and 3	173a and b	1980,5-9,1	22
1902,7-21,3	201	1978,7-4,4	166	1980,5-10,1	328
1902,7-21,4	202	1978,7-4,5	178	1980,5-11,1 to 5	134a to e
1902,7-21,5	203	1978,7-4,6	161	1980,5-12,1	232
1902,7-21,6	204	1978,7-4,7	185	1980,5-13,1	133
1902,9-14,1	25	1978,7-4,8	187	1980,5-16,1	226

REGISTER NUMBER	CATALOGUE NUMBER	REGISTER NUMBER	CATALOGUE NUMBER	REGISTER NUMBER	CATALOGUE NUMBER
1980,5-17,1	105	1981,6-5,1	123	1983,6-2,1	310
1980,5-18,1	84	1981,6-6,1	124a	1983,10-8,1 to 4	222a to d
1980,5-19,1	151	1981,6-6,2	124c	1983,10-8,5	24
1980,6-6,1	103	1981,6-7,1	4	1983,10-9,1	79
1980,6-7,1	106	1981,6-8,1	129	1983,10-10,1	82
1980,6-8,1	94	1981,6-9,1	213	1983,10-11,1	55
1980,6-9,1	218	1981,6-10,1	38	1983,11-4,2	309
1980,6-10,1	219	1981,6-11,1	306	1983,11-4,3	271
1980,6-12,1	216	1981,6-12,1	217	1983,11-5,1	329
1980,6-13,1	95	1981,7-11,1 to 24	296	1983,11-6,1	152
1980,6-14,1 and 2	275a and b	1981,7-12,1	286	1983,12-5,1	276
1980,6-15,1	290	1981,7-13,1	287	1983,12-5,2	277
1980,7-3,1	54	1981,7-14,1	209	1984,1-6,1	110
1980,7-7,1	5	1981,7-15,1	122	1984,2-7,1	139
1980,7-11,1	58	1981,7-16,1	247	1984,2-7,2	135
1980,10-7,1	250	1981,7-17,1	124d	1984,2-7,3	130
1980,10-7,2	252	1981,7-17,2	124b	1984,7-3,1	260
1980,10-7,3	249	1981,10-5,1	90	1984,7-3,2	289
1980,10-7,4	251	1981,11-4,1	246	1984,7-4,1	288
1980,10-7,5	282	1981,11-6,1	13	1984,10-10,1	317
1980,10-7,6	157	1981,12-3,1	154	1984,10-10,2	263
1980,10-11,1	20	1981,12-4,1 to 10	308	1984,11-7,1	221
1980,10-12,1	98	1981,12-5,1	208	1984,11-7,2	120
1980,10-13,1	99	1981,12-6,1	244	1984,11-8,1	272
1980,10-14,1	89	1981,12-7,1	270	1985,3-8,1	233
1980,10-15,1	140	1981,12-8,1	35	1985,3-8,2	43
1980,10-16,1 to 12	253	1981,12-8,2	18	1985,3-8,3	44
1980,10-17,1 to 7	112a to g	1981,12-9,1	295	1985,5-5,1	316
1980,11-7,1	111	1981,12-10,2	274	1985,10-16,1	261
1980,11-8,1	285	1982,1-7,1 to 3	125a to c	1986,3-2,1 and 2	128a and b
1980,11-9,1	284	1982,1-8,1	21	1986,3-3,1	48
1980,11-10,1	102	1982,1-8,2 and 3	19	1986,5-8,1	117
1980,11-11,1	85	1982,1-8,4	91	1986,6-8,1	230
1980,11-12,1 to 3	83a to c	1982,1-8,5 and 6	104a and b	1986,10-19,1	57
1980,11-13,1 to 6	132	1982,2-4,1	146	1986,11-2,1	293
1980,12-7,1	194	1982,2-5,1 to 4	301a to d	1987,1-9,1	47
1980,12-7,2	195	1982,3-1,1	297	1987,1-9,2	46
1980,12-7,3	193	1982,3-2,1	292	1987,1-10,1	109
1980,12-8,1 to 4	291a to d	1982,5-10,1 to 5	37a to e	1987,3-1,1	265
1980,12-9,1	303	1982,5-10,6 and 7	262a and b	1987,6-9,1	312
1980,12-10,1	212	1982,5-10,8	255	1987,6-11,1	28
1980,12-11,1	224	1982,5-12,1 and 2	298a and b	1987,7-10,1	3
1981,1-1,476	197	1982,5-12,3	245	1987,10-8,1	36
1981,1-1,477	196	1982,10-6,1 to 8	207a to h	1987,10-9,1	227
1981,1-1,478	198	1982,10-7,1	15	1987,10-10,1 and 2	264
1981,1-5,1	23	1982,11-2,1	88b	1987,10-11,1-1a and 2	145a to c
1981,1-8,1	11	1982,11-2,2	136	1987,11-2,1	269
1981,2-5,1	162	1982,11-4,1 and 2	302	1987,11-7,1 to 3	258a to c
1981,3-9,1 and 2	229	1982,12-3,1a to p	231a to p	1988,1-5,1	223
1981,3-10,1 and 2	304	1982,12-3,2	144	1988,1-6,1	6
1981,3-10,3	305	1982,12-3,3	307	1988,1-6,2	7
1981,3-10,4 to 12	119a to i	1982,12-3,4	16	1988,1-6,3	8
1981,3-10,13	256	1982,12-3,5a and b	108a and b	1988,1-6,4	9
1981,3-10,14	155	1982,12-3,6	210	1988,1-6,5	10
1981,3-11,1	283	1982,12-3,7	156	1988,1-7,1	267
1981,3-11,2 to 5	248a to d	1982,12-3,8	225	1988,1-8,1	113
1981,6-3,1	29	1982,12-4,1	86	1988,1-9,1a to d	318
1981,6-4,1	149	1982,12-5,1	1	1988,1-10,1	294
1981,6-4,2	148	1983,3-6,1	126	1988,1-11,1 to 4	14a to d

329

REGISTER NUMBER	CATALOGUE NUMBER	REGISTER NUMBER	CATALOGUE NUMBER	REGISTER NUMBER	CATALOGUE NUMBER
1988,1-12,1	131	1989,9-11,1	268	1992,5-11,1	431
1988,1-13,1	336	1989,11-3,1	56	1992,5-12,1	366
1988,1-14,1	243	1989,11-4,1	335	1992,5-13,1 to 5	396
1988,1-15,1	330	1989,11-5,1 and 1a	49	1992,6-8,1	405
1988,1-16,1	320	1990,1-8,1	17	1992,6-9,1	392
1988,1-17,1	319	1990,1-9,1	206	1992,6-10,1	391
1988,1-17,2	326	1990,4-6,1	346	1992,6-11,1	372
1988,1-18,1	321	1990,4-6,2	347	1992,6-12,1	364
1988,1-18,2a and b	322	1990,4-6,3	348	1992,6-13,1	374
1988,4-1,1	279	1990,4-7,1	338	1992,7-9,1	429
1988,4-1,2	280	1990,4-8,1 to 4	339	1992,7-11,1	408
1988,4-2,1	236	1990,5-6,1	337	1992,7-12,1	367
1988,4-3,1	118	1990,5-6,2	340	1992,7-14,1	404
1988,6-6,1	300	1990,5-6,3	343	1992,7-15,1 to 25	438 to 448
1988,6-7,1	235b	1990,5-6,4	345	1992,12-1,1	432
1988,6-8,1 to 4	281a to d	1990,5-6,5	352	1992,12-2,1	395
1988,6-8,5 to 7	220a to c	1990,5-6,6	341	1992,12-3,1	379
1988,6-9,1	278	1990,5-6,7	350	1993,2-4,1	428
1988,6-9,2	34	1990,5-6,8	353	1993,5-6,1 and 2	369
1988,7-3,1	331	1990,5-6,9	356	1993,5-7,1	384
1988,7-4,1	259	1990,5-6,10	357	1993,7-14,1	371
1988,7-5,1	262c	1990,6-7,1	2	1993,7-15,1	380
1988,7-6,1	52	1990,6-8,1	342	1993,7-17,1	424
1988,7-7,1 to 3	50	1990,7-11,1	354	1993,7-18,1	398
1988,7-8,1 and 2	51	1990,10-17,1	351	1993,10-10,1	383
1988,7-9,1	53	1990,10-18,1	153	1993,10-11,1 and 2	402
1988,7-10,1	77	1990,10-19,1 to 6	349a to f	1993,10-12,1	382
1988,7-11,1	141	1990,10-20,1	344	1993,10-12,2	389
1988,11-3,1	214	1990,12-2,1	358	1993,10-12,3 and 4	368
1989,1-2,1	12	1990,12-2,2	359	1993,10-12,5	406
1989,1-3,1	257	1990,12-2,3a and b	360	1993,10-12,6	407
1989,1-4,1	332	1990,12-2,4	361	1993,10-12,7	403
1989,1-5,1	138	1991,1-8,1	355	1993,11-5,2	435
1989,1-6,1	254	1991,5-1,1 to 9	442 to 443	1993,11-6,1	401
1989,1-7,1	333	1991,5-2,1	393	1993,11-6,2 and 3	387
1989,1-7,2 and 3	334	1991,5-3,1	430	1993,11-6,4	386
1989,1-8,1	325	1991,6-11,1	378	1993,11-6,5	400
1989,1-8,2 and 2a	324	1991,6-12,1	375	1993,11-6,6	399
1989,1-8,3	323	1991,6-13,1 to 2	370	1993,11-6,7 and 8	388
1989,5-8,1	45	1991,7-1,1	373	1993,11-7,1	381
1989,5-9,1	143	1991,7-2,1	363	1993,11-10,1	427
1989,5-10,1	142	1991,7-3,1 to 20	409 to 422	1993,12-5,1	423
1989,5-11,1	137	1991,7-5,1	394	1993,12-6,1	433
1989,5-12,1	81	1991,7-6,1	397	1994,1-9,1	426
1989,6-9,1	235c	1991,10-1,1	434	1994,1-10,1 and 2	365
1989,7-3,1	115	1991,12-5,1 to 8	362	1994,1-12,1	376
1989,7-3,2 and 3	116	1991,12-7,1	425	1994,1-12,2	377
1989,7-10,1	327	1992,1-7,1 to 2	390	1994,1-15,1	385

Index of Contemporary Exhibitions

This index lists only the major contemporary exhibitions in which objects described in this catalogue, or closely related items, were included. References are to catalogue numbers.

General Index